Health, Illness, and Health Care in Canada

Health, Illness, and Health Care in Canada

B. Singh Bolaria
Harley D. Dickinson

UNIVERSITY OF SASKATCHEWAN

Third Edition

NELSON

™

THOMSON LEARNING

Australia • Canada • Mexico • Singapore • Spain • United Kingdom • United States

NELSON

TM

THOMSON LEARNING

Health, Illness, and Health Care in Canada, Third Edition
Edited by B. Singh Bolaria and Harley D. Dickinson

Editorial Director and Publisher:
Evelyn Veitch

Acquisitions Editor:
Brad Lambertus

Marketing Manager:
Cara Yarzab

Developmental Editor:
Klaus G. Unger

Production Editor:
Emily Ferguson

Production Coordinators:
Jonathan Pressick,
Helen Jager Locsin

Copy Editor:
John Eerkes-Medrano

Creative Director:
Angela Cluer

Interior Design:
Sonya V. Thursby,
Opus House Incorporated

Cover Design:
Sonya V. Thursby,
Opus House Incorporated

Cover Art:
Ashes by Eric Field. Acrylic,
gouache, and crayon, 1999.
© Eric Field.

Compositor:
Janette Thompson, Jansom

Printer:
Transcontinental Printing Inc.

**Canadian Cataloguing
in Publication Data**

Main entry under title:

Health, illness, and health care
in Canada

3rd ed.
First ed. published under title:
Sociology of health care in Canada.
Includes bibliographical references
and index.
ISBN 0-7747-3657-7

1. Medical care – Canada.
I. Bolaria, B. Singh, 1936– .
II. Dickinson, Harley D., 1951– .

RA395.C3S62 2001   362.1'0971
C99-932015-7

Statistics Canada information is used with the permission of the Ministry of Industry, as minister responsible for Statistics Canada. Information on the availability of the wide range of data from Statistics Canada can be obtained from Statistics Canada's regional offices, its World Wide Web site at http://www.statcan.ca, and its toll-free access number 1-800-263-1136.

PREFACE

Health, illness, injury, and death, and the ways we as a society experience, understand, and respond to these realities of human existence affect us all. It is not surprising, therefore, that these issues are receiving an increasing amount of sociological attention in the form of new research, journals, books, and university courses. The publication of the third edition of *Health, Illness, and Health Care in Canada* serves in a small way to confirm the coming of age of both the sociology of health and illness and the sociology of medicine and health care in Canada.

In this revised third edition, we have tried to be responsive to the comments and observations of those who have used the book, both instructors and students, as well as those of reviewers. We hope we have succeeded.

Many of the chapters for this edition are new; others are revised and updated chapters from the second edition. All chapters are the result of original research and analysis written for this book by leading experts in the field. This edition also contains study questions, recommended annotated readings, and glossaries of important terms intended to facilitate its use as a textbook and to direct readers to key texts and articles in each area covered.

In the final organization of the content of this edition, we benefited from the feedback of our colleagues who have used the previous editions in their teaching and research and from the suggestions of anonymous reviewers. We hope that our colleagues find both the pedagogical material and organization of the text helpful and useful in their work, particularly in presentation of material for their courses.

With this third edition we hope that we have once again succeeded in bringing to instructors, students, and policymakers alike an accessible and timely examination of key issues facing Canadians in the areas of health, illness, and health care. We could not have done it alone. Bringing this book together depended on the kind cooperation and consideration of a multitude of people. Of course, the authors who contributed their expertise to this endeavour must be acknowledged for their hard work — we would like to thank them for their efforts. We are particularly grateful for their patience and perseverance throughout the long time frame it took to complete this project. We hope that they will be pleased with the final outcome. We would also like to thank the many instructors and students who have used the previous two editions and thereby made the third edition both possible and necessary. We wish to acknowledge the constructive comments and suggestions made by anonymous reviewers, which proved extremely helpful for the authors and editors of this book. We are certain that their comments and suggestions contributed to the overall quality of the content and analysis presented here.

We must thank several people at Harcourt Canada. This project has taken a long time to complete and required the efforts of many people. The professionalism, commitment, and patience shown by many people at Harcourt was a major component in the completion of this book. We are grateful to all those who started at the beginning of this project and to those who stuck with it to finalize the manuscript. First, we wish to mention Heather McWhinney, who provided guidance in the development of the content and organization of all the editions of this book. She was there from the very beginning, on the ground floor, so to speak, when we started with the first edition. Jutta Brendemühl, Camille Isaacs, and Martina Van de Velde ensured the progress of the project through to completion. The final responsibility as developmental editor, guiding the last stages of this work and seeing that the authors and editors incorporated the suggestions and comments of the reviewers in the final manuscript, fell on Klaus Unger. His hard and long hours of work producing summaries of reviewers' comments for each author and tactfully communicating this information to everyone was done remarkably well and successfully. We are especially grateful for his professionalism, enthusiasm, support, and above all, his patience. We must also thank the copy editor, John Eerkes-Medrano whose editorial work provided consistency and improved the quality of presentation. We are also thankful to Emily Ferguson, production editor, who brought the manuscript to publication.

Finally, we would like to thank our families yet again for their continued support. We all rejoice in this work's completion.

B. Singh Bolaria
Harley D. Dickinson
University of Saskatchewan

CONTENTS

PART 1

The Canadian Health Care System
and the Health Status of Canadians

Improving the health status of the population is *the* goal of a health policy. On this point, there is consensus. How a society should achieve that goal, however, is vigorously debated. The Canadian health care system in general, and medicare in particular, are the living legacies of efforts to find the best means to achieve health for all. Despite medicare's popularity, there is a growing consensus that this medically dominated, hospital-based health care system is no longer the best means to achieve better health for Canadians. Although everyone agrees that the health care system needs to be reformed, there is no agreement as to what those reforms should be. Nor do analysts agree on the effects of current initiatives to reform health care.

Dickinson and Bolaria provide an overview of the historical development of the Canadian health care system and an assessment of its current status in Chapter 2. They argue that medicare originated in the failure of the market to ensure that people received necessary medical care and hospital services. The introduction of medicare removed the financial barriers to medical care. In this regard, it is a resounding policy success, which is reflected in broad-based political support for medicare and its long status as the most popular government program.

Medicare, however, is not unflawed. The fee-for-service physician remuneration system guaranteed rapid inflation and a perpetual crisis of rising costs. The cost-sharing agreement between the federal and provincial governments discouraged experimentation with nonmedical and nonhospital forms of treatment. As a result, medicare has been undergoing reforms since its inception.

Currently these reforms entail efforts to shift the locus of treatment from institution to community, improve the integration and coordination of the full spectrum of health care services, increase stakeholder involvement in health care planning and service delivery, and improve the health status of the population. Regionalization of health services planning and service delivery is the principal means adopted to achieve these policy goals. The consequences of regionalization for the nature and organization of the health care system in general, and medicare in particular, remain to be seen. Whether regionalization improves health status also remains to be determined.

Dickinson and Kosteniuk pick up on the issue of population health status in Chapter 3. They provide an overview of several widely accepted indicators of population health status, including life expectancy at birth, mortality rates and causes of death, and various measures of self-reported health status. These, and other indicators, show that health status is unequally distributed within the population. In particular, inequalities based on income, gender, age, educational attainment, and race are reflected in differential life chances and health status.

Current research into the determinants of population health status shows that absolute deprivation is not the only indication of lower health status. There is a clear health gradient: every step up the socioeconomic ladder results in improved health status. Conversely, every step down the ladder decreases life chances and health status. In recent decades, imperatives for economic growth and development have resulted in both cutbacks to and the reform of income transfer and support programs and, more recently, tax cuts. These policies have unfortunately increased socioeconomic inequality in Canada. This fact poses immense challenges to health policymakers as they search for ways to improve the health status of Canadians.

1

Sociology, Medicine, Health, and Illness: An Overview

B. SINGH BOLARIA University of Saskatchewan

INTRODUCTION

Medical sociology covers a wide range of substantive areas and encompasses a diversity of issues pertaining to health and illness, medical institutions, the structure and organization of the health care sector, and the political, economic, and social determinants of the nature and composition of the health care delivery systems. Medical sociologists and others interested in this area approach and examine these essential topics and issues from various theoretical perspectives and paradigms and use varying levels of analyses and methodologies. Despite this diversity, certain paradigms and orientations still dominate the field of medical sociology. The purpose of this chapter is, by way of introduction, to outline these paradigms and discuss their policy implications. The following topics are examined: evolution and the dominant paradigm of scientific medicine, the definition and etiology of health and illness, and the focus and levels of analysis. In conclusion, the policy implications of dominant paradigms and levels of analyses are considered in the context of current fiscal constraints and the health care "crisis."

EVOLUTION AND THE DOMINANT PARADIGM OF SCIENTIFIC MEDICINE

The knowledge of modern scientific medicine is founded on the work of Koch, Pasteur, and other bacteriologists. The germ theory of disease, which gained prominence in the late nineteenth century, had a profound impact on the practice of medicine. As Waitzkin (1979, p. 684) states: "The isolation of specific bacteria as the etiologic agents in several infectious disease created a profound change in medicine's diagnostic and therapeutic assumptions. A unifactorial model of disease emerged. Medical scientists searched for organisms causing infections and single lesions in non-infectious disorders." Renaud (1977, p. 139) emphasizes the same point:

> Contemporary medical knowledge is rooted in the paradigm of the "specific etiology" of
> disease, that is, diseases are assumed to have a specific cause to be analyzed in the body's

cellular and biochemical systems. This paradigm developed out of the germ theory of disease of Pasteur and Koch.

While the germ theory helped to develop the prevention of infectious diseases and improved medical practice, this paradigm

> gave support to the idea of specific therapies, from which rose the essentially curative orientation of current medical technologies toward specific illness rather than the sick person as a whole, and the belief that people can be made healthy by means of technological fixes; i.e., the engineering approach. (Renaud, 1977, p. 139)

This paradigm basically adopted a "mechanistic model" of the human body. This approach has a long history. Philosophers like Descartes (1596–1650) established the philosophical base for a machine model of the human body; that is, that the human body is assumed to work in the same way as a machine. As McKeown (1965, p. 38) states:

> The approach to biology and medicine established during the seventeenth century was an engineering one, based on a physical model. Nature was perceived in mechanistic terms, which led in biology to the idea that a living organism could be regarded as a machine which might be taken apart and reassembled if its structure and function were fully understood. In medicine, the same concept led further to the belief that an understanding of disease processes and of the body's response to them would make it possible to intervene therapeutically, mainly by physical (surgery), chemical, or electrical methods.

Disease, then, is an alteration, a pathological change in the body machinery that must be "fixed" (Navarro, 1986, p. 166). Many diseases are viewed as mere technical defects; treatments are oriented toward restoring the "normal" functioning of the human machine. This approach basically ignores social causes of much ill health. The mechanistic–individualistic paradigm narrows and limits the medical task. As Doyal and Pennell (1979, p. 30) state:

> The adoption of a mechanistic paradigm of this kind did limit the nature and boundaries of what is conceived as the medical task. Thus, scientific medicine ultimately became curative, individualistic and interventionist, objectifying patients and denying their status as social beings.

This mechanistic conception brought about a shift from the consideration of illness as a breakdown of the total system to the notion that ill health could be caused by the malfunctioning of one particular part of the body machinery — in other words, localized pathology (Doyal & Pennell, 1979). This idea led to the medical fragmentation of the delivery of health care. Again, it is based on the premise that the human body is like a machine, and can, like any mechanical system, be broken down into different parts for repair (Rossdale, 1965). Many instruments were developed (thermometer, stethoscope) to examine the interior of the body machinery. This shift toward localized pathology had a profound impact on the division of labour (specialization) in medicine.

The specialization in medical knowledge and practice tends to focus on specific parts of the body machine, such as the nervous system, the cardio-vascular system, the gastro-intestinal system, and so forth (Navarro, 1986, p. 167).

The work of bacteriologists and other scientists undeniably had a positive impact on the control of infectious diseases and led to improvements in medical practice. However, several studies tend to cast doubt on the historical importance of these discoveries (Powles, 1973; Carlson, 1975). It is argued that the major decline in mortality and morbidity was due to better nutrition and sanitation and other environmental improvements, and that the decline in mortality and morbidity patterns, rather than following significant diagnostic and therapeutic discoveries, in fact preceded them (Waitzkin, 1979). Whatever the sequence of events, laboratory medicine with its emphasis on an individualistic, scientific, machine model of the human body achieved ascendancy. It should be noted that the dominant scientific paradigm is not mere linear evolution of scientific discoveries. As Navarro (1986, p. 167) and others have argued, the form and nature of medicine is determined by class and power relations in the society and not by scientific imperatives. The ascendancy of scientific laboratory-based medicine and the dominant position of **allopathic medicine** in North America in the beginning of this century is attributed by some writers to the publication of the Flexner Report (Brown, 1979; Berliner, 1977; Kunitz, 1974; Waitzkin, 1979; Kelman, 1977).

Abraham Flexner visited medical schools both in the United States and Canada in 1904–05. The Flexner Report (1910) was critical of the medical schools that did not have the facilities to teach laboratory-based scientific medicine. It called for the reorganization or, failing that, closure of such institutions (see also Chapter 4 of this book, pp. 55–81). Ninety-two medical schools were closed (mainly in the United States) or reorganized between 1904 and 1915 (Waitzkin, 1979). Some of these institutions taught alternative forms of healing, such as homeopathy, midwifery, and herbalism. This report was highly critical of these alternative practices and helped to relegate them to subordinate status vis-à-vis the allopathic practice of medicine (Kelman, 1977; Berliner, 1975; Kunitz, 1974). The norm for medical education and practice became laboratory-based scientific medicine. The Flexner Report was hailed "as the document that helped change modern medicine from quackery to responsible practice" (Waitzkin, 1979, p. 685).

Before the report's recommendations were implemented, the allopathic physicians had faced stiff competition, which affected their incomes, from practitioners trained in a variety of alternative healing traditions. The costs of delivering premedical education, as well as the necessity for expensive laboratory facilities, led to high tuition fees in medical schools, making medical education all but inaccessible to working-class students. As Waitzkin (1979, p. 686) notes:

> The American Medical Association strongly supported and subsequently helped enforce the Flexner Report's recommendations. The closure of many medical schools not based in laboratory science led to fundamental changes in the class composition of the profession, changes that went hand in hand with reduced competition and higher individual incomes for doctors.

In Canada, the rise and social legitimacy of scientific medicine was also bolstered by the Flexner Report. A focus on scientific education, the formation of medical associations, a tightening of licensing standards, and the marginalization of alternative forms of healing all helped to establish the monopoly of scientific medicine and change the social profile, prestige, and income of physicians (Macionis, Benoit, & Jansson, 1999, p. 343).

The Carnegie Foundation also helped support Flexner's tour and subsequent publication of the report. In addition, the General Education Board of the Rockefeller Foundation provided financial support to medical schools that implemented the report's recommendations (Nielsen, 1972). The philanthropic support of the Foundations was, according to Waitzkin (1979, pp. 686–687), based upon a number of considerations:

> The humanitarian image of this philanthropic work helped justify the exploitation of workers and the environment by which the parent industries accumulated high profits.... Secondly, the development of laboratory based medical science diverted attention away from the illness-generating condition of capitalist production and class structure.... A third reason for support of scientific medicine by the capitalist class was the need for a work force healthy enough to participate in the production process.

The Flexner Report, supported by the medical profession and by philanthropic foundations, helped to consolidate the dominance of the allopathic practitioners and to establish laboratory-based scientific medicine as the norm for medical education and practice. This mechanistic–individualistic conception is currently pervasive in medical practice and research. As Rodberg and Stevenson (1977, p. 113) point out: "Modern medicine operates according to an individualistic, scientistic, machine model. Humans receive medical treatment outside of, and abstracted from, their normal social and environmental context."

HEALTH AND ILLNESS

The mechanistic view of the human organism has dictated a similar vision of health and illness. For instance, the *Dorland Medical Dictionary* defines health as "a normal condition of body and mind, i.e., with all the parts functioning normally"; and disease is defined as "a definite morbid process having a characteristic strain of symptoms — it may affect the whole body or any of its parts, and its **etiology, pathology**, and prognosis may be known or unknown" (Inglefinger, 1982).

This mechanistic view of health and illness is of particular significance with regard to the etiology of health and illness as well as the treatment. As Doyal and Pennell (1979, p. 34) note: "Ill health is now defined primarily in terms of the malfunctioning of a mechanical system, and treatment consists of surgical, chemical or even electrical intervention to restore the machine to normal working order." Medical experts' advanced training permits them to recognize a "malfunction" and prescribe appropriate treatment to correct it and thus make the body "functional." In functional terms, health means "the state of optimum capacity of an individual for the effective performance of the roles and tasks for which he has been socialized" (Parsons, 1972, p. 117). In Parsons's definition, this "capacity to perform" appears to be the sole criterion of health. The experience of ill health in itself does not constitute illness.

Others have argued that health in capitalist society is tied to production and capital accumulation process. As Kelman (1977, p. 12) comments:

> At any point in time functional "health" is that organismic condition of the population most consistent with, or least disruptive of, the process of capital accumulation. At the individual level, this means the capacity to effectively do productive (contributing to accumulation) work.

Viewed in this way, health has important implications in terms of the level of health care services. Employers want to keep workers in good working order. As Rodberg and Stevenson (1977, p. 112) indicate: "From the point of view of capital, the health care system does not have to satisfy workers and it is not important that they feel well, as long as they are able to work hard." The definition of health and illness in relation to the accumulation process is an important aspect of the capitalist value system, which regards workers primarily as producers: "they are machines, one dimensional contributors to the accumulation process" (Rodberg & Stevenson, 1977, p. 112).

Viewed in this context, the investments to maintain healthy and productivity workers are considered in the same way as investments in other factors of production, and have to be balanced against returns. If workers are hard to replace or reproduction costs are high, employers are greatly concerned about the health of the workers and are interested in prolonging their productive life span. Conversely, if workers are easily replaceable, employers are less concerned about their health. Workers are kept healthy so long as the cost of health care is less than the cost of replacing them.

If workers are "owned" by the employers, such as occurs with slave labour, the employers are deeply interested in protecting their property. For instance, slaves in the United States had more systematic access to health care and enjoyed somewhat better health status than the freed slaves and poor whites (Postell, 1961; Stampp, 1956). However, health expenditures were tempered with return on this investment. Slaves were kept healthy so long as the cost of health care was less than the cost of replacing them (Kelman, 1977, pp. 16–17). In addition to this instrumental view of the health and fitness of the workers, "under capitalism, health is also defined in an individualistic way. It is always individuals who become sick, rather than social, economic or environmental factors which cause them to be so" (Doyal & Pennell, 1979, p. 35). This individualistic and functional definition of health provides the basis for the essentially curative focus of medicine itself, which has important social and economic significance (Doyal & Pennell, 1979). For instance, the expansion of technologically curative medicine provides the base for a profitable health care industry.

This type of analysis would suggest the termination of health resources to the elderly and infirm who no longer work and who contribute little to the accumulation process because investment in their health will produce few, if any, returns (Kelman, 1977; Rodberg & Stevenson, 1977; Dreitzel, 1971). To be sure, such policies, strictly speaking, have not been politically and culturally feasible. Even in the United States, where there is no universal health care program as in Canada, the elderly, chronically unemployed, and poor receive certain health services, however limited, under the medicare and medicaid programs. A strictly functional definition of health and sickness purely in terms of the worker's ability to perform cannot always be operationalized because of political and cultural considerations. It is of no less significance to note that nursing homes and other health care institutions that provide services to the aged also provide opportunities for capital investments and profits, particularly for nursing homes that are privately owned and operated but subsidized by public funds.

REDUCTIONISM IN MEDICINE

The mechanistic–individualistic conception of disease, which attributes disease to a "malfunctioning" of the human body, absolves the economic and political environment from responsibility for disease. Waitzkin (1979, p. 686) points out the reductionist tendencies of this understanding:

> Scientific medicine, fostered by the Flexner Report and the great philanthropies, tended toward reductionism. It shifted the focus of research and action from societal problems — a topic that implied potential threats to the organization of capitalist production and class structure — to pathophysiological disturbance at the level of the individual patient — much less threatening subject matter.

A similar reductionist approach emphasizes individual lifestyle. In Canada in 1974, the publication of Lalonde's paper "A New Perspective on the Health of Canadians," gave prominent attention to health risks associated with individual lifestyles and consumption patterns. Lifestyle was also one of the foci of another health policy, "Achieving Health For All: A Framework For Health Promotion" (Epp, 1986). While the clinical model attributes disease to the "malfunctioning" of the human body, the new reductionism introduces the idea that the causes of disease lie in individual lifestyles and behaviours. In the former case the normal functioning of the body can be restored through "technological fixes," while in the latter the solution lies primarily in changing individual behaviours and patterns of consumption. It is argued that since the major risk factors causing much of mortality are under the personal discretion of the individuals, there would be a considerable reduction in mortality if individuals would focus their attention on changing those aspects of their lifestyles that are injurious to their health. This focus on individual etiology and individual solutions is promoted also in other countries (Doyal & Pennell, 1979; Waitzkin, 1983). Both approaches obscure the social nature of disease and fail to recognize the important relationships between social and work environments and health and sickness.

Studies from the historical materialistic epidemiological perspective focus on illness-generating conditions.

SOCIAL PRODUCTION OF ILLNESS

Social medicine is primarily concerned with the conditions in the society that produce illness and death. While "traditional **epidemiology** has searched for causes of morbidity and mortality that are amenable to medical intervention, historical materialistic epidemiology [has] found causes of disease and death that derive from social conditions" (Waitzkin, 1983, p. 64). Social epidemiology and the environmental approach to health are in conflict with the biological and individual orientation of the predominant paradigm. The overarching theme of the social epidemiological approach is that health and illness cannot be understood by referring only to biological phenomena and medical knowledge. Rather, human health and illness are embedded in economic, social, and cultural contexts, and these factors play an important role in creating the social distribution of health and illness. Susser, Watson, and Hopper (1985) state: "Societies in part create the disease they experience and further, they materially shape the way in which diseases are to be experienced" (p. 17). Material and social conditions that produce illness and mortality include social class, economic cycles, socially produced stress, production processes, and working conditions (Waitzkin, 1983; Navarro, 1986).

The realization that social and material conditions produce illness and mortality and social variability in health and illness patterns is not new. There is a long history of research and analysis with focus on social and material conditions, most notably in the work of nineteenth-century scholars Friedrich Engels and Rudolf Virchow (Engels, 1973 [1845]; Virchow, 1957, 1958, 1960; cited in Waitzkin, 1983, pp. 65–75). Although their writings have received relatively little notice, their analysis is very relevant to the current debate. Engels's research was aimed at a broad description of working-class life as well as workers' health and safety. For Engels, the roots of illness and early mortality of working-class people was embedded in the process of industrial production and social environment. His analysis focused on the links between environmental toxins, poor housing conditions, poor nutrition, industrial production, working conditions in mining and the textile industry, and various infectious diseases, pulmonary disorders, black lung disease, eye disorders, and other occupational diseases and injuries. Virchow focused on the social and economic deprivations of working-class life and linked working-class people's higher morbidity and mortality to inadequate housing, poor nutrition, and inadequate clothing. These deprivations increased working-class susceptibility to disease and illness. While Engels focused his analysis mainly on structural contradictions of production and contradictions between profit and safety, Virchow focused on class inequalities in social distribution and the consumption of resources (Waitzkin, 1983).

The link between social and material conditions and illness and disease is increasingly recognized (Waitzkin, 1983; Navarro, 1986). For instance, cancer and other chronic diseases are substantially related to environmental factors and the workplace. There is also evidence linking incidence of illness to economic cycles and levels of employment. Disruption of stable community relations has consistently led to an increase in hypertension rates. Rather than focusing on individual lifestyle and its relation to stress, "historical materialist epidemiology shifts the level of analysis to stressful forms of social organization connected to capitalist production and industrialization" (Waitzkin, 1983, p. 63). Studies in the area of occupational health and safety produce persuasive evidence that links work environment and the labour process to illness and disease and points to basic contradictions between profit and safety. Social variability in mortality rates and life expectancy among individuals and groups is produced by structurally produced inequalities and the differing life and work experiences of individuals and groups.

Epidemiological data in Canada and elsewhere show a persistent and pervasive association between socioeconomic status and health status (Link & Phelan, 2000; Zong & Li, 1994; Hay, 1994; Mirowsky, Ross, & Reynolds, 2000; Syme & Yeu, 2000; Federal, Provincial and Territorial Advisory Committee on Population Health, 1999a, 1999b; Wilkinson, 1996; Evans, Barer, & Marmor, 1994; Marmot et al., 1984, 1991). Those who are advantaged with respect to socioeconomic status are also advantaged in health status. As Link and Phelan (2000, p. 43) remark: "People who are more advantaged with regard to resources of knowledge, money, power, prestige, and social connections enjoy a health advantage." Similar patterns of disease, illness, and mortality are prevalent for children (Canadian Institute of Child Health, 2000). Childhood disadvantages accumulate in later life. As Mirowsky, Ross, & Reynolds (2000, p. 60) state: "Relatively small social status differences in health established in childhood and adolescence accumulate and grow throughout most of adulthood." Socioeconomic inequalities are also linked to stress (Evans, Barer, & Marmor, 1994). Those of a lower socioeconomic status are not only subject to more stress but also have fewer resources to cope with it. The Whitehall Study of British Civil Servants (Marmot et al., 1984, 1991) provides strong and consistent evidence of differences in mortality and social hierarchy (levels) in the civil service.

Gender and racial inequalities produce social variability in the health status of men and women and racial groups. These health status differences are related to varying work experiences and social and material environments. Women's and men's life experiences are different and are shaped by socially structured gender roles. Different life circumstances and experiences in turn produce differences in health and illness patterns between men and women. Race and class intersect with gender to produce subgroup differences in health and illness patterns. Discrimination can affect the health status of racial minorities in a number of ways, including differential life chances, low socioeconomic status, and unequal access to health care.

TYPES OF ANALYSIS

A plethora of sociological and behavioural studies are devoted to analyzing the "medical behaviour" of individuals. These studies have produced a large body of theoretical and empirical literature. Much of this literature concerns the study of differential attitudes toward health and illness, differential health practices, variability of reactions to symptoms and illnesses, and variability in the use of health services.

Another kind of analysis focuses on the behaviour of the provider of services and health care institutions. The health sector, however, is integrally related to the larger society. It is therefore argued that to study the health care system without attention to its linkages to broad political, economic, and social forces is misleading. These studies try to transcend the individual level of analysis to find how these linkages determine the nature, composition, and function of the health care sector and the very definition of health and illness.

A significant portion of past research in medical sociology has been about the "medical behaviour" of consumers of health care services and the social processes that influence the decisions of individuals to use medical services (Albrecht & Higgins, 1979; Cockerham, 1978; Coe, 1970; Krause, 1977; Tuckett, 1976). A number of authors have identified sociopsychological, sociodemographic, and socioeconomic variables to account for variability in health behaviour and illness behaviour (Kasl & Cobb, 1966; King, 1962; Rosenstock, 1966; Zola, 1964; Suchman, 1965b; Mechanic, 1968; Andersen, 1968; Koos, 1967). These authors focus on psychological, social, ethnic, cultural, and class factors, with various degrees of emphasis (for details, see Bolaria, 1994, pp. 9–10).

The role of culture and ethnicity in patients' behaviour is described by other authors. Saunders (1954) notes the differences between Spanish-speaking Americans and Anglo-Americans in their attitudes and response to illness and in their use of health facilities. Anglo-Americans generally preferred modern medicine while Spanish-speaking people were more likely to use home remedies or folk medicine and family care. Similar observations have been made concerning other groups in various cultural contexts (Clark, 1959; Paul, 1955; Leighton & Leighton, 1945; Mead, 1953; Joseph, 1964; Stone, 1962; Rubel, 1960; Hartly, Straus, & Mead, 1961; Zborowski, 1952; Croog, 1961; Mechanic, 1963; Suchman, 1964, 1965b). These studies show considerable variations along cultural and ethnic lines.

The response to illness may also take the form of self-help or self-medication and consultation with relatives, friends, and neighbours (Phillips, 1965). Some writers also relate the delay in seeking medical help to particular medical orientations and to socio-economic factors (Polgar, 1959; King, 1962; Suchman, 1965a; Goldsen, 1957, 1963; MacGregor, 1961).

However, sociopsychological models, with their emphasis on the characteristics of individuals, their value systems, perceptions, health beliefs, and orientations, are of limited use because they tend to overlook the importance of class inequalities (except indirectly, as they affect perceptions and values), the availability of and accessibility to medical services, the organization and delivery of health care services, and other structural factors. These inequalities continue to exist even in Canada, where the principle of universality was a major impetus to the introduction of medical care in the 1960s (see, for example, Wilkins & Adams, 1983; Shah & Farkas, 1985). While a number of studies in this book attest to these inequalities, it is worth quoting at length from a statement by Jake Epp, minister of health and welfare, in a policy paper entitled "Achieving Health For All: A Framework For Health Promotion." Epp (1986, p. 398) states:

> The first challenge we face is to find ways of reducing inequities in the health of low- versus high-income groups in Canada.
>
> There is disturbing evidence which shows that despite Canada's superior system, people's health remains directly related to their economic status. For example, it has been reported that men in the upper income group live six years longer than men with a low income. The difference is a few years less for women. With respect to disabilities, the evidence is even more startling. Men in upper income groups can expect 14 more disability-free years than men with a low-income; in the case of women, the difference is eight years.
>
> Among low-income groups, people are more likely to die as a result of accidental falls, chronic respiratory disease, pneumonia, tuberculosis and cirrhosis of the liver. Also, certain conditions are more prevalent among Canadians in low-income groups; they include mental health disorders, high blood pressure and disorders of the joints and limbs.
>
> Within the low-income bracket, certain groups have a higher chance of experiencing poor health than others. Older people, the unemployed, welfare recipients, single women supporting children and minorities such as natives and immigrants all fall into this category. More than one million children in Canada are poor. Poverty affects over half of single-parent families, the overwhelming majority of them headed by women. These are the groups for whom "longer life but worsening health" is a stark reality.

Rather than studying the behaviour of the consumers, others have analyzed the behaviour of the providers of health services and the interaction among various interest groups within the health sector. Their focus is primarily on what "goes on" within the health sector without reference to the linkages between the health sector and the broader society. Studies in this area have focused on such topics as the organization and distribution of health care services, medical education, health care institutions (e.g., hospitals and nursing homes), the professional domination and medical division of labour, and racial inequality in the health sector (see, for example, Freidson, 1970a, 1970b; Fee, 1983).

Other analysts question the clinical effectiveness and technical claims of modern scientific medicine. Illich's work *Medical Nemesis* has received considerable attention in mass media and in professional circles. Illich (1976) provides considerable evidence of the ineffectiveness of modern medicine in reducing morbidity and mortality and in improving the health of the population. He portrays medicine as a coercive institution and has taken the view that current medical practices generally do more harm than good. Illich's analysis centres on three categories (clinical, social, and structural) of **iatrogenesis** (the causing or inducing of a disease by a physician or medical treatment). He feels that iatrogenesis is clinical when "pain, sickness, and death result from the provision of medical care"; social when "health policies reinforce an industrial organization which generates dependency and ill health"; and structural when "medically sponsored behaviour and delusions restrict the vital autonomy of people by undermining their competency in growing up, caring for each other and aging" (Illich, 1976, p. 165).

According to Illich, clinical iatrogenesis includes "all clinical entities for which remedies, physicians or hospitals are the pathogens or 'sickening' agents." Medical domination has led to loss of autonomy and creation of dependency for patients. The responsibility for health is expropriated from individuals by the medical profession.

Illich attributes these iatrogenic effects to the industrialization, bureaucratization, and monopoly power of the medical profession, as well as the overmedicalization of life, which perpetuates an addictive dependency on medicine and medical institutions. The solution, therefore, lies in debureaucratization, deindustrialization, and demonopolization. He proposes demedicalization and the return of more autonomy and responsibility to individuals for their health and self-care (for a critique, see Starr, 1981; Navarro, 1977, pp. 38–58; Waitzkin, 1976). He confines the solutions to the health care system itself, without reference to structural tendencies and political, social, economic, and class forces in the broader society that perpetuate this system. As Waitzkin (1983, p. 5) notes: "Without attention to these connections, the health system falsely takes on the appearance of an autonomous, free-floating entity, whose defects purportedly can be corrected by limited reforms in the medical sphere."

A considerable volume of literature does focus on the linkages between the political, economic, and social systems and the health care sector (see, for example, Navarro, 1986; Waitzkin, 1983; Doyal & Pennell, 1979). This approach is predicated on the fact that the contradictions in medicine reflect the contradictions in society; that is, the health sector is so integral to the broader society that the attempt to study the one without attention to the other will be misleading. As Waitzkin (1983, p. 5) comments: "Difficulties in health and medical care emerged from social contradictions and rarely can be separated from those contradictions." For instance, one of the contradictions in this society is between profit and safety. If it interferes with profits, an improvement in occupational health and safety is not very likely to be implemented. Gender and other inequalities in the health sector are reflections of these inequalities in society. While in the discussion of escalating health care costs the focus is generally on consumers and the health sector labour force, little attention is given to the corporate invasion of the medical sector, usually referred to as the "medical–industrial complex." A high-technology mentality has encouraged costly and expensive medicine.

Others have noted the role of the capitalist state, class contradictions, the ideology of medicine, medicalization, and illness related to the capitalist production process (for example, see Berliner, 1977; Fee, 1983; Salmon, 1977; Swartz, 1977; Walters, 1982;

Kelman, 1971, 1975, 1977; Navarro, 1976, 1977, 1986; Turshen, 1977; McKinlay, 1984; Waitzkin, 1983; Waitzkin & Waterman, 1974; Minkler, 1983; Crawford, 1980).

It is increasingly recognized that the sociopsychological models of consumer behaviour and studies that focus exclusively on the health sector and its contradictions do not provide an adequate and comprehensive analysis of the current health crisis, which is characterized by escalating costs and diminishing returns. By focusing on individuals and the health sector, these analyses tend to portray individuals and the health sector as though they existed in a vacuum. They tend to decontextualize the individuals and the health sector. The health care policies that flow from these analyses would further increase the disparities in health status and health care utilization in the populace. For instance, those who depend upon public-sponsored health services would be adversely affected by any rationing of services or promotion of self-care. It is argued that because of the close linkages between medicine and the social, economic, political, and class forces in the broader society, attempts to reform and transform medicine must be tied to wider strategies of change in the societal structure. The contradictions in medicine reflect contradictions of larger society, and they cannot be resolved by focusing on the health sector alone or on individual clinicians (Waitzkin, 1983, p. 8).

FROM HEALTH TO WELL-BEING AND HEALTH PROMOTION

The traditional definition of health as the absence of disease and sickness has come under increasing scrutiny. It is argued that this conceptualization of health individualizes the problem and hampers a broader consideration of the meaning of health and the societal causes of collective health and illness. A broader reconceptualization of the meaning of health encompasses a state of complete physical, mental, emotional, and social well-being — not merely the absence of disease (World Health Organization, 1946, p. 3). This extended concept places issues of health, illness, and health care in a broader social context and highlights conditions that need to be considered in any health policy initiatives.

Effective health promotion policy and practice need to consider the social determinants of health, such as the social, economic, and physical environment, health services, personal resources and coping, health knowledge, and lifestyle behaviours (Federal, Provincial and Territorial Advisory Committee on Population Health, 1999a). The health promotion framework proposes both strategies and mechanisms to eliminate barriers to achieving health for all. The strategies involve fostering public participation, strengthening community health services, and coordinating healthy public policy. The mechanisms to realize these strategies involve self-care, mutual aid, and a healthy environment (Dickinson, 1994). Thus, health education seems to be one of the central foci in achieving health for all.

Concomitant with these developments, there has been a shift in sociological inquiry away from the study of illness at the individual level to a macro-level that focuses on large-scale structural factors, including political and economic forces, the medical profession, and health-related institutions and agencies (Brown, 1996). Segall and Chappell (2000, pp. 2–20) characterize the shift in the scope and theme of sociological inquiry as a transformation of medical sociology into a sociology of health, which has a broader focus on health-related topics, including population health, health behaviour, and health promotion.

SUMMARY AND CONCLUSIONS

The mechanistic view of the human organism is still the prevalent and dominant paradigm in scientific medicine. This is significant with regard to the etiology as well as the treatment of health and illness. Ill health in this context means the breakdown and malfunctioning of the machine (the human body), and treatment consists of surgical or chemical interventions to restore normal functioning. In functional terms, the sole criterion of health is the capacity of the individual to perform as he or she has been socialized to perform. The experience of ill health in itself does not constitute illness.

Others have argued that health in capitalist society is tied to production and the capital accumulation process. Viewed in this way, health has important implications in terms of health services. Employers want to keep workers in good working order and "it is not important that they feel well as long as they are able to work hard." Viewed in this context, investments to maintain healthy and productive workers are considered the same way as investments in other factors of production, and they must be balanced against returns.

While the clinical model attributes disease to "malfunctioning" of the human body, the new reductionism introduces the idea that disease lies in individual lifestyle and behaviour. In the former case, the normal functioning of the body can be restored through "technological fixes," while in the latter, the solution lies primarily in changing individual behaviours and patterns of consumption. Both approaches obscure the social nature of disease, which is the subject matter of historical materialistic epidemiology, which identifies social conditions in society that produce illness, disease, and mortality. A number of recent studies underline the persistent association between socioeconomic status and health status.

This chapter also discussed the various sociopsychological, sociodemographic, and socioeconomic factors that influence the medical behaviour of consumers. Other studies have focused on the health sector and its contradictions, and a body of literature has emerged that focuses on the linkages between the political, economic, social, and class forces in the broader society and in the health care system. In a similar vein, the conventional definition of health as the absence of disease is increasingly replaced with a broader understanding of health as complete physical, mental, emotional, and social well-being.

The essays in this book examine the essential topics in medical sociology from a variety of theoretical perspectives and at various levels of analysis. Their common intention is to provide an understanding of medicine, health, illness, and the health care system.

GLOSSARY

allopathic medicine   The treatment of disease by conventional means; for example, by using drugs that have opposite effects to the symptoms.

epidemiology   The study of the incidence and distribution of diseases and of the control and prevention of diseases.

etiology The study of the causation of diseases and disorders, especially of a specific disease.

iatrogenesis The causing or inducing of a disease by a physician or by medical treatment.

pathology The science of bodily diseases; the symptoms of a disease.

REFERENCES

Albrecht, G.L., & Higgins, P.C., (Eds.). (1979). *Health, illness, and medicine.* Chicago: Rand McNally.

Anderson, R. (1968). *A behavioral model of families' use of health services.* Chicago: University of Chicago Press.

Berliner, H.S. (1975). A larger perspective on the Flexner Report. *International Journal of Health Services 5*, 573–592.

Berliner, H.S. (1977). Emerging ideologies in medicine. *Review of Radical Political Economics 9*(1), 116–124.

Bolaria, B.S. (1994). Sociology, medicine, health, and illness: An overview. In B.S. Bolaria & H.D. Dickinson (Eds.), *Health, illness, and health care in Canada* (2nd ed., pp. 1–18), Toronto: Harcourt Brace.

Bolaria, B.S., & Bolaria, R. (Eds.). (1994a). *Women, medicine and health.* Halifax and Saskatoon: Fernwood Publishing and Social Research Unit.

Bolaria, B.S., & Bolaria, R. (Eds.). (1994b). *Racial minorities and health.* Halifax and Saskatoon: Fernwood Publishing and Social Research Unit.

Brown, E.R. (1979). *Rockefeller medicine men: Medicine and capitalism in the progressive era.* Berkeley: University of California Press.

Brown, P. (Ed.). (1996). *Perspectives in medical sociology.* Prospect Heights, IL: Waveland Press.

Canadian Institute of Child Health (CICH). (2000). *The health of Canada's children.* Ottawa: Canadian Institute of Child Health.

Carlson, R. (1975). *The end of medicine.* New York: Wiley Interscience.

Clark, M. (1959). *Health in the Mexican–American culture.* Berkeley: University of California Press.

Cockerham, W.C. (1978). *Medical sociology.* Englewood Cliffs, NJ: Prentice-Hall.

Coe, M. (1970). *Sociology of medicine.* New York: McGraw-Hill.

Croog, S.H. (1961). Ethnic origins, educational level, and responses to a health questionnaire. *Human Organization, 20*, 65–69.

Crawford, R. (1980). Healthism and the medicalization of everyday life. *International Journal of Health Services, 10*(3), 365–388.

Dickinson, H.D. (1994). The changing health care system: Controlling costs and promoting health. In B.S. Bolaria & H.D. Dickinson (Eds.), *Health, illness, and health care in Canada* (2nd ed., pp. 106–129) Toronto: Harcourt Brace.

Doyal, L., & Pennell, I. (1979). *The political economy of health.* London: Pluto Press.

Dreitzel, H.P. (Ed.). (1971). *The social organization of health.* New York: Macmillan.

Engels, F. (1973 [1845]). *The conditions of the working class in England in 1844.* Moscow: Progress.

Epp, J. (1986, November-December). Achieving health for all: A framework for health promotion. *Canadian Journal of Public Health, 77*(6), 393–407.

Evans, R.G., Barer, M.L., & Marmor, T.R. (Eds.). (1994). *Why are some people healthy and others not? The determinants of the health of the population.* New York: Aldine DeGruyter.

Eyer, J. (1984). Capitalism, health, and illness. In J.B. McKinlay (Ed.), *Issues in the Political Economy of Health Care* (pp. 23–59). New York: Tavistock.

Federal, Provincial and Territorial Advisory Committee on Population Health. (1999a). *Statistical report on the health of Canadians.* Ottawa: Minister of Public Works and Government Services.

Federal, Provincial and Territorial Advisory Committee on Population Health. (1999b). *Toward a healthy future: Second report on the health of Canadians.* Ottawa: Minister of Public Works and Government Services.

Fee, E. (Ed.). (1983). *Women and health: The politics of sex in medicine.* Farmingdale, NY: Baywood.

Flexner, A. (1910). *Medical education in the United States and Canada.* New York: Carnegie Foundation.

Freidson, E. (1970a). *Professional dominance.* New York: Atherton Press.

Freidson, E. (1970b). *Profession of medicine.* New York: Dodd, Mead.

Goldsen, R. (1957). Some factors related to patient delay in seeking diagnosis for cancer symptoms. *Cancer, 10,* 1–7.

Goldsen, R. (1963). Patient delay in seeking cancer diagnosis: Behavioral aspects. *Journal of Chronic Diseases, 16,* 427–436.

Hartley, E., Straus, R., & Mead, M. (1961, October). Determinants of health beliefs and behavior. *American Journal of Public Health, 51,* 1541–1554.

Hay, D.I. (1994). Social status and health status. Does money buy health? In B.S. Bolaria & R. Bolaria (Eds.), *Racial minorities, medicine and health* (pp. 9–52). Halifax and Saskatoon: Fernwood Publishing and Social Research Unit.

Illich, I. (1976). *Medical nemesis: The expropriation of health.* New York: Pantheon.

Inglefinger, F.J. (Ed.). (1982). *Dorland medical dictionary.* New York: Holt, Rinehart and Winston.

Joseph, A. (1964, July–August–September). Physicians and patients: Some aspects of inter-personal relationships between physicians and patients with special regard to the relationship between white physicians and Indian patients. *Applied Anthropology, 1,* 1–6.

Kasl, V., & Cobb, S., (1966). Health behavior, illness behavior, and sick-role behavior. *Archives of Environmental Health, 12*(February), 246–266; and *12*(April), 531–541.

Kelman, S. (1971). Toward the political economy of medical care. *Inquiry, 8*(3), 30–38.

Kelman, S. (1975). The social nature of the definition problem in health. *International Journal of Health Services, 5*(4), 625–642.

Kelman, S. (1977). The social nature of the definition of health. In V. Navarro (Ed.), *Health and medical care in the U.S.: A critical analysis* (pp. 3–20). Farmingdale, NY: Baywood.

King, S.H. (1962). *Perceptions of illness and medical practice.* New York: Russell Sage.

Koos, E.L. (1967). *The health of Regionville.* New York: Hafner.

Krause, E.A. (1977). *Power and illness: The political sociology of health and medical care.* New York: Elsevier.

Kunitz, S.J. (1974). Professionalism and social control in the progressive era: The case of Flexner Report. *Social Problems, 22,* 16–27.

Lalonde, M. (1974). *A new perspective on the health of Canadians.* Ottawa: Information Canada.

Leighton, A., & Leighton, D. (1945). *The Navaho door.* Cambridge: Harvard University Press.

Link, B.G., & Phelan, J.C. (2000). Evaluating the fundamental cause explanation for social disparities in health. In C.E. Bird, P. Conrad, & A.M. Fremont (Eds.). *Handbook of medical sociology* (5th ed., pp. 33–46). Upper Saddle River, NJ: Prentice-Hall.

MacGregor, G. (1961, November). Social determinants of health practices. *American Journal of Public Health, 51,* 1709–1714.

Macionis, J.J., Benoit, C.M., & Jansson, S.M. (1999). *Society: The basics.* Scarborough, ON: Prentice-Hall/Allyn & Bacon.

Marmot, M.G., Shipley, M.J., & Rose, G. (1984). Inequalities in death-specific explanations of a general pattern. *Lancet, 83,* 1003–1006.

Marmot, M.G., Smith, G.D., Stanfeld, S., & Patel, C. (1991). Health inequalities among British civil servants: The Whitehall II study. *Lancet, 337,* 1387–1392.

McKeown, T. (1965). *Medicine in modern society.* London: Allen and Unwin.

McKinlay, J.B. (Ed.). (1984). *Issues in the political economy of health care.* London: Tavistock.

Mead, M. (1953). *Cultural patterns and technical change.* UNESCO, World Federation for Mental Health.

Mechanic, D. (1962, February). The concept of illness behavior. *Journal of Chronic Diseases, 15,* 189–194.

Mechanic, D. (1963). Religion, religiosity, and illness behavior: The special case of the Jews. *Human Organization, 22,* 202–208.

Mechanic, D. (1968). *Medical sociology.* New York: Free Press.

Minkler, M. (1983). Blaming the aged victim: The politics of scapegoating in times of fiscal conservatism. *International Journal of Health Services, 13*(1), 155–168.

Mirowsky, J., Ross, C.E., & Reynolds, J. (2000). Links between social status and health status. In C.E. Bird, P. Conrad, & A.M. Fremont (Eds.), *Handbook of medical sociology* (5th ed., pp. 47–67). Upper Saddle River, NJ: Prentice-Hall.

Navarro, V. (1976). *Medicine under capitalism.* New York: Prodist.

Navarro, V. (Ed.). (1977). *Health and medical care in the U.S.: A critical analysis.* Farmingdale, NY: Baywood.

Navarro, V. (1986). *Crisis, health, and medicine.* New York: Tavistock.

Nielsen, W.A. (1972). *The big foundations.* New York: Columbia University Press.

Parsons, T. (1972). Definitions of health and illness in the light of the American values and social structure. In E.G. Jaco (Ed.), *Patients, physicians, and illness* (2nd ed., pp. 107–127). New York: Free Press.

Paul, B. (Ed.). (1955). *Health, culture and community.* New York: Russell Sage.

Phillips, D.L. (1965, May). Self-reliance and the inclination to adopt the sick role. *Social Forces, 43,* 555–563.

Polgar, S. (1959, April). Health and human behavior. *Current Anthropology, 3,* 159–205.

Postell, W.D. (1961). *The health of slaves on southern plantations.* Baton Rouge: Louisiana State University Press.

Powles, J. (1973). On the limitation of modern medicine. In *Science, Medicine and Man* (Vol. 1, no. 1, 1–30). London: Pergamon.

Renaud, M. (1977). On the structural constraints to state intervention in health. In V. Navarro (Ed.), *Health and medical care in the U.S.: A critical analysis* (pp. 135–136). Farmingdale, NY: Baywood.

Rodberg, L., & Stevenson, C. (1977). The health care industry in advanced capitalism. *Review of Radical Political Economics, 9*(1), 104–115.

Rosenstock, I.M. (1966, July). Why people use health services. *Milbank Memorial Fund Quarterly, 44,* 94–127.

Rossdale, M. (1965, November-December). Health in a sick society. *New Left Review, 34,* 82–90.

Rubel, A.J. (1960, October). Concept of disease in Mexican–American culture. *American Anthropologist, 62,* 795–814.

Salmon, J. (1977). Monopoly capital and the reorganization of the health sector. *Review of Radical Political Economics, 9*(1), 125–133.

Saunders, L. (1954). *Cultural differences and medical care.* New York: Russell Sage.

Segall, A., & Chappell, N.L. (2000). *Health and health care in Canada.* Toronto: Prentice-Hall.

Shah, C.P., & Farkas, C.P. (1985). The health of Indians in Canadian cities: A challenge to the health care system. *Canadian Medical Association Journal, 133,* 859–863.

Stampp, K.M. (1956). *The peculiar institution.* New York: Knopf.

Starr, P. (1981). The politics of therapeutic nihilism. In P. Conrad & R. Kern (Eds.), *The sociology of health and illness: Critical perspectives* (pp. 434–448). New York: St. Martin's Press.

Stone, E. (1962). *Medicine among the American Indians.* New York: Hafner.

Suchman, E.A. (1964). Sociomedical variations among ethnic groups. *American Journal of Sociology, 70,* 319–331.

Suchman, E.A. (1965a, November). Health orientations and medical care. *American Journal of Public Health, 56,* 97–105.

Suchman, E.A. (1965b, Fall). Stages of illness and medical care. *Journal of Health and Human Behavior, 6,* 114–128.

Susser, M., Watson, W., & Hopper, K. (1985). *Sociology in medicine.* New York: Oxford University Press.

Swartz, D. (1977). The politics of reform: Conflict and accommodation in Canadian health policy. In L. Panitch (Ed.), *The Canadian state: Political economy and political power.* Toronto: University of Toronto Press.

Syme, S.L., & Yeu, I.H. (2000). Social epidemiology and medical sociology: Different approaches to the same problem. In C.E. Bird, P. Conrad, & A.M. Fremont (Eds.), *Handbook of medical sociology* (5th ed., pp. 365–376). Upper Saddle River, NJ: Prentice-Hall.

Tuckett, D. (Ed.). (1976). *An introduction to medical sociology.* New York: Tavistock.

Turshen, M. (1977). The political ecology of disease. *Review of Radical Political Economics, 9*(1), 45–60.

Virchow, R. (1957). *Werk und werkung.* Berlin: Rutten & Loeng.

Virchow, R. (1958). *Disease, life and man.* Translated by L.J. Rather. Stanford University Press.

Virchow, R. (1960). *Cellular pathology.* New York: DeWitt.

Waitzkin, H. (1976). Recent studies in medical sociology: The new reductionism. *Contemporary Sociology, 5,* 401–405.

Waitzkin, H. (1979). The Marxist paradigm in medicine. *International Journal of Health Services, 9*(4), 683–698.

Waitzkin, H. (1983). *The second sickness: Contradictions of capitalist health care* (Chapter 3, pp. 65–85). New York: Free Press.

Waitzkin, H., & Waterman, B. (1974). *The exploitation of illness in capitalist society.* Indianapolis: Bobbs-Merrill.

Walters, V. (1982). State, capital and labour: The introduction of federal–provincial insurance for physician care in Canada. *Canadian Review of Sociology and Anthropology, 19,* 157–172.

Wilkins, R., & Adams, O. (1983). *Healthfulness of life.* Montreal: Institute for Research on Public Policy.

Wilkinson, R.G. (1996). *Unhealthy societies: The afflictions of inequality.* London: Routledge.

World Health Organization (WHO). (1946). *Constitution of the World Health Organization.* New York: World Health Organization Interim Commission.

Zborowski, M. (1952). Cultural components in responses to pain. *Journal of Social Issues, 8,* 16–30.

Zola, I. (1964). Illness behavior of the working class: Implications and recommendations. In A. Shostak & W. Gomberg (Eds.), *Blue collar world: Studies of the American workers* (pp. 350–363). Englewood Cliffs, NJ: Prentice-Hall.

Zong, L., & Li, P.S. (1994). Different cultures or unequal life chances: A comparative analysis of race and health. In B.S. Bolaria & R. Bolaria (Eds.), *Racial minorities and health* (pp. 113–123). Halifax and Saskatoon: Fernwood Publishing and Social Research Unit.

2

The Canadian Health Care System: Evolution and Current Status[1]

HARLEY D. DICKINSON AND B. SINGH BOLARIA   University of Saskatchewan

INTRODUCTION

Health policy in Canada oscillates between preventative and curative approaches. In general, prevention and promotion are subordinate to treatment and cure, but the balance is historically variable. Policy shifts in one direction or the other are accompanied by shifts in the nature of control over, and the distribution of power within, the health care system.

The late nineteenth century, for example, witnessed the professionalization, scientization, and institutionalization of the cure-oriented, biomedical approach in health care (Foucault, 1980; Freidson, 1973). The last decades of the twentieth century saw a reassertion of the principles of Hygeia (the Greek goddess of health), or health promotion, and various other challenges to the dominance of the biomedical model and the medical profession.

This chapter outlines the key dimensions of the nature and organization of the Canadian health care system. It reviews the literature on the introduction of state hospitalization and medical care insurance programs (medicare). It then looks at current reform initiatives and argues that they are manifestations of the struggle both for, and against, **medical dominance**.

HEALTH CARE AND HEALTH CARE POLICY IN CANADA

Canada does not have a single health care system. Under the Canadian Constitution, health care is an area of provincial jurisdiction. As a result, Canada has ten provincial and three territorial health care systems. The main policy tools available to the federal government to influence health care policy and service delivery are rather blunt fiscal and budgetary mechanisms, which are combined with whatever influence the government exerts on public opinion and the public will.

The federal–provincial jurisdictional split has meant, historically, that health care reforms occur at the provincial or subprovincial levels of government. Examples include the Saskatchewan Municipal Doctor Plans, Union Hospital arrangements, regionalized forms of health policy planning and service delivery, and community clinics, as well as various hospital and medical care insurance plans (Douglas, 1946; Feather, 1991a, 1991b; Mombourquette, 1991; Mott, 1947; Roth & Defries, 1958; Wolfe, 1964).

Prior to 1940, health care insurance was an issue that was at various times on and off the national and provincial political agendas. By the 1940s, the failure of the market to ensure adequate access to necessary medical and hospital care, combined with the limitations of various locally developed collectivist solutions, had generated renewed interest in state medical care and hospitalization insurance. This was given added impetus by experiences with wartime military and industrial recruitment, when it was discovered that an alarmingly high number of recruits were too sickly for military or industrial service (Fuller, 1998, p. 27). This fact and other evidence demonstrating the poor health status of the Canadian population led to health insurance being firmly established as a key component in government plans for postwar reconstruction (Dominion–Provincial Conference, 1945).

Thus, in 1945, the federal government put forward a plan for a universal health care insurance program that would be cost-shared by the federal and provincial governments. The general rationale for state intervention in this area was the belief that improved access to hospital and physician services would result in improved health status. This, in turn, was understood to translate directly into increased productivity and national prosperity. A more particular motivation for proposing a state-financed universal and comprehensive health insurance program was concern that the proposed alternatives were inadequate (Taylor, 1978).

By the end of the war, a political consensus existed that health care could not be left to the market. Beyond that, however, there was little agreement. The medical profession favoured a hospital and medical care insurance system based on voluntary participation in physician-sponsored or commercial insurance plans (Fuller, 1998). Envisioned from this perspective, the state's role would be limited to providing coverage on a means-tested basis to those who could not afford to pay for it themselves. The private insurance industry was in favour of a similar arrangement. Business organizations, in general, as well as several provincial governments, also favoured such an arrangement because of concerns about "creeping socialism" (Fuller, 1998). Even the trade union movement was ambivalent about universal, compulsory state health insurance because it generally had negotiated collective agreements that provided health insurance coverage for its members through various voluntary private plans (Walters, 1982). Among the strongest supporters of state insurance were farmers' organizations, especially in Western Canada. Not surprisingly, the first compulsory, universal, state-financed, and state-administered hospitalization insurance plan was introduced in Saskatchewan by Premier Tommy Douglas and the newly elected, farmer-dominated Co-operative Commonwealth Federation (CCF) government (Dickinson, 1993).

The federal government was convinced of the necessity to introduce a similar plan on a national scale. Thus, in 1945, at the Federal–Provincial Conference on Reconstruction, draft legislation was introduced. Key features of this legislation were the establishment of health regions, patient registration with physicians, a capitation mode of payment, additional financial incentives for physicians who adopted preventative approaches, and the administration of the system by a commission of physicians and consumers (Taylor, 1978; Vayda & Deber, 1992, p. 126).

The proposed plan, however, was not implemented because of provincial government concerns about federal incursion into areas of provincial jurisdiction and a failure to reach agreement on taxation issues (Taylor, 1960). As federal–provincial discussions bogged down and the prospects of implementation receded into the future, a new consensus emerged around the adoption of an incremental approach to the introduction of state health insurance.

The first major step in this regard was taken at the provincial level by Saskatchewan's CCF government in 1946, when it introduced the country's first universal, comprehensive system of tax-financed hospitalization insurance. The federal government contented itself with introducing the National Health Grants program in 1948 (Vayda & Deber, 1992). This program was uncontentious from the perspective of the provinces and the organized medical profession because its main purpose was to increase hospital bed capacity across the country. The rationale was that increased and equalized hospital bed capacity would result in increased access to needed hospital services and, consequently, to equalized health status and increased productivity and economic prosperity. From a purely political perspective, the National Health Grants program also was seen as an important dimension of nation building.

The 1946 Saskatchewan hospitalization insurance program was designed to be eligible for federal cost-sharing once agreement was reached between the rest of the provinces and the federal government. Before that happened, however, four more provinces introduced hospitalization insurance plans. These five provinces increased pressure on the federal government to introduce the long-promised cost-sharing arrangements, which was done in 1956 with passage of the *Hospital Insurance and Diagnostic Services Act* (HIDS). By 1961, the remaining five provinces had introduced hospitalization insurance plans. The medical profession, although wary of this development, was not opposed to it, largely because it increased physicians' incomes and posed no real threat to professional autonomy.

Hospitalization insurance encouraged both physicians and patients to think of hospitalization as a treatment of first resort, which ensured high occupancy rates and rising costs. This inflationary feature of hospitalization insurance plans was reproduced and amplified in the medical care insurance plans that followed.

Although the introduction of state hospitalization was largely uncontentious, the introduction of medical care insurance was accompanied by bitter struggles. Analytical approaches to understanding the nature and consequences of those struggles vary (Badgley & Wolfe, 1967; Naylor, 1986; Taylor, 1978; Thompson, 1964; Tollefson, 1963), but a common theme is **medical autonomy** and dominance and their consequences for health care delivery (Blishen, 1969; Coburn, Torrance, & Kaufert, 1983; Swartz, 1977; Taylor, 1960; Touhy, 1994; Walters, 1982; White, 1984).

Walters (1982), for example, analyzes the introduction of medicare in terms of the state's contribution to capital accumulation and political legitimation. Relative to capital accumulation, she sees medicare as an attempt by the state to ensure the reproduction of a healthy and productive working class. Access to health care services, particularly hospital and physician services, is assumed to result in improved health status among the working population. The prevailing decentralized system of hospital and physician services was considered to be in need of rationalization and reform. Medical autonomy and the self-interest of the private insurance industry were seen as inadequate foundations for national health policy. From this perspective, medical autonomy and professional monopoly were seen as barriers both to the rationalization of the health care system and to improved population health status.

In contrast to Walters, Swartz (1977) argues that the introduction of medicare is best understood as a concession wrung from the capitalist class and its state through the struggles of a militant working class and its political allies. He maintains that medicare was part of an effort to appease the working class by increasing the social wage. Swartz's analysis draws attention to the ways in which the resistance of the medical profession resulted in modifications to the form and content of the original proposals for socialized medicine. These concessions had the effect of entrenching the interests and dominance of the medical profession (Naylor, 1986; Weller & Manga, 1983).

Coburn, Torrance, & Kaufert (1983) argue that the introduction of medicare is best understood as a response to working class agitation and an attempt to supply the capitalist class with adequate quantities of healthy labour. In contrast to Swartz (1977) and others, they argue that the introduction of medicare marked the beginning of the end of medical autonomy and dominance, not its entrenchment.

Thus, debate over whether medicare entrenched or undermined medical autonomy and dominance continues, and the evidence is contradictory. What is clear, however, is that the organized medical profession was afraid for its autonomy (Badgley & Wolfe, 1967). Although it was unable to thwart the introduction of medicare, the organized medical profession was able to force the governments of the day to make significant compromises.

The main compromises made by the government of Saskatchewan, which eventually came to characterize medical care insurance programs throughout all of Canada, were the retention of the **fee-for-service** system of remuneration and professional control over fee setting. From the perspective of the medical profession, fee-for-service, as opposed to the alternatives of a salaried physician service or a capitation scheme, was a bulwark against even greater erosion of its professional autonomy. It was well known that a consequence of this compromise would be increased medical care and hospital costs.

At the time, although there was an awareness of the fiscal effects of these decisions, this was not considered a serious problem, partly because fee-for-service remuneration was seen as a necessary compromise with the profession, and partly because it was still widely held that unrestricted access to physician and hospital services was the major factor in improving population health status. This assumption was soon challenged. At the same time, various cost-containment strategies were deployed.

MEDICARE AND COST CONTAINMENT

Following the lead of Saskatchewan and the recommendations of the 1964 Royal Commission on Health Services, the federal government introduced medicare in 1966. By 1972, all provinces and territories had opted into the program. The five principles upon which medicare was founded are universality of eligibility, comprehensiveness of coverage, portability between provinces, accessibility achieved by prepayment through taxation, and public administration on a nonprofit basis. Provinces that established medical care insurance programs in accordance with these principles were eligible for a 50–50 cost sharing (Soderstrom, 1978).

A core structural feature of the federal–provincial cost sharing agreement established in 1966 was that only services provided by physicians, either on an out- or in-patient basis, were included. This discouraged the provinces from developing alternatives to physician and hospital services, because they were not eligible for federal funds (Vayda & Deber, 1992). It did, however, encourage the provinces to try various cost control strategies (Dickinson, 1994).

In this regard, efforts were made to reduce the number and duration of contacts with the health care system during an episode of illness and to reduce the cost per contact. Even these efforts were discouraged, however, because each dollar in savings achieved by provincial governments resulted in a one-dollar reduction in federal government transfers. Not surprisingly, the provincial governments quickly came to be dissatisfied with this funding arrangement.

The federal government was also dissatisfied because its health care expenditures were determined directly by the level of provincial expenditures. Consequently, it had no control over the level of its expenditures. Thus, both federal and provincial governments were interested in changing the terms and conditions of the cost sharing arrangement (Soderstrom, 1978).

This was done in 1977 with enactment of the *Federal–Provincial Arrangements and Established Programs Financing Act* (EPF) by the federal government. The EPF had a number of effects:

- It provided a $20 per capita incentive for provinces to put more of their resources into community care.
- It reduced the federal government's share of the cost of medicare from approximately 50 percent to approximately 25 percent.
- It uncoupled federal costs from provincial expenditures.
- It limited the growth in direct federal government increases to the rate of growth of the gross national product (GNP).

Provincial health care expenditures above the rate of growth of GNP were ineligible for federal cost sharing (Crichton et al., 1997; Vayda, Evans, & Mindell, 1979). The motivation for the provinces to accept the terms of the EPF was the transfer of tax points from the federal to the provincial governments, in the form of an increased capacity to tax incomes as a means to offset reduced federal cash transfers.

The ascendancy of fiscal conservatism in the 1980s resulted in further federal cost cutting initiatives. In the mid-1980s, federal transfers to the provinces were reduced to 2 percent *below* the rate of growth in the GNP. In the early 1990s, further reductions in federal government transfers to the provinces were introduced. Under that formula, federal transfers were frozen for a period of two years at 1989–90 levels. In 1992–93, they were allowed to increase at a rate 3 percent *less* than the rate of increase in the GNP.

These changes resulted in decreased total health expenditures expressed as a proportion of gross domestic product (GDP). In 1994, for example, they were 9.7 percent of GDP, down from 10.1 percent in both 1992 and 1993. Despite this proportional decrease, total health spending increased to $72.5 billion in 1994, up from $71.8 billion the previous year. This represented a 1 percent rate of increase for 1994, down from 2.5 percent in 1993 and 5.6 percent in 1992 (Health Canada, 1996, p. 3).

Federal government reductions in **transfer payments** initiated a series of cost cutting measures at the provincial level. These included budget reductions, reductions in the number of hospital beds, efforts to control medical services fee increases, the deinsuring of some types of services, limits on the number of certain types of services for which physicians could bill, and increased monitoring and disciplinary powers for regulatory bodies (Advisory Committee on Population Health, 1999; Vayda, Evans, & Mindell, 1979, p. 226).

Government cost cutting efforts were also associated with changes in the types and location of health care services — a reduction in hospital services and an increase in various community-based and home care services — and an increased use of drug and alternative therapies. These developments corresponded to increased private expenditure on health care services (Health Canada, 1996).

Not surprisingly, physicians and other health care providers responded critically, and in some cases militantly, to these initiatives. There were, throughout the 1980s and into the 1990s, a number of nurses' and doctors' strikes, as well as increases in the use of **user fees** and **extra billing** to offset the effects of various cost control initiatives (Northcott, 1994).

Thus, cost control and various reforms were not popular with health care providers. Nor were they popular with the users. Reforms are generally claimed to have resulted in crowded hospital emergency rooms and longer waiting lists for diagnostic and therapeutic services. This has resulted in growing concerns that contemporary health reforms were really a strategy to dismantle medicare by stealth (Fuller, 1998). To counter these concerns, and to deflect the political consequences of being seen to violate a sacred political trust, politicians at all levels of government reasserted their commitment to the five principles of medicare.

The first retaking of vows came in the form of the *Canada Health Act* (CHA) in 1984. The CHA effectively banned extra billing by physicians by imposing dollar-for-dollar reductions in federal transfers to the provinces for each dollar in extra billing or user fees they allowed. One response of the organized medical profession and its political allies was to mobilize for the reprivatization of health care in Canada (Armstrong, 1997; Fuller, 1998; Stevenson, Williams, & Vayda, 1988; Weller & Manga, 1983).

In 1997, all levels of government again reaffirmed their commitment to the principles of medicare in the form of a joint statement. This was accompanied by a $1.5 billion increase (from $11 to $12.5 billion) in federal cash transfers to the provinces for health care. In 1999, the federal budget announced a further increase in health care funding through the Canada Health and Social Transfer (CHST). This amounted to an additional $11.5 billion, targeted specifically for health care to be distributed to the provinces and territories on an equal per capita basis over the next three years. In addition to the increased cash transfer, the 1999 federal budget announced increased tax point transfers to the provinces with the understanding that new revenues would be used for health care.

The contemporary health care system is much different from what it was when medicare was first introduced. Additionally, medicare is increasingly seen as an inadequate response to the health needs of Canadians.

THE DETERMINANTS OF HEALTH AND HEALTH PROMOTION

Not only have efforts been made to directly control costs in the health care system; health promotion has also become more prominent since the early 1970s. In particular, ideas about the relationship between enhanced access to hospital and medical services and improved population health status have changed dramatically. In the immediate post–World War II period, the primary goal of health policy was to optimize access to medical and hospital services — health policy was really health care policy narrowly conceived. There was, however, widespread optimism that this in itself would have a substantial impact on the health status of the population. By the early 1970s, this optimism had faded. The first official indication of this was the publication of a Green Paper by Marc Lalonde, the federal minister of national health and welfare, entitled *A New Perspective on the Health of Canadians*.

This document put forward the **health field concept**, which expressed the idea that health status is the result of several determinants, not simply, or even primarily, of access to medical and hospital services. The main determinants of population health were identified as human biology, self-imposed risks associated with individual lifestyle choices, environmental factors, and health care services. The Lalonde report noted that "there is little doubt that improvements in the level of health of Canadians lie mainly in improving the environment, moderating self-imposed risks and adding to our knowledge of human biology" (Lalonde, 1974, p. 18). There is no mention of increased access to medical services as a means to increase population health status.

The reaction to, and the assessment of, this initial statement of the determinants of health framework was mixed. Some, like Renaud (n.d., p. 230), saw it as only a few broad statements of little policy significance. Others saw the health field concept, particularly its emphasis on individual lifestyle choices, as a potentially harmful form of victim-blaming and a potential abandonment of the sick (Bolaria, 1988). Evans and Stoddart (1998, p. 561), on the other hand, suggested that the health field concept, or the determinants of health framework generally, resulted in a proliferation of outreach and screening programs in which increasing numbers of people are placed on continuing regimes of drug therapies and regular monitoring. Thus, the determinants of health policy framework, given its focus on individual lifestyle choices, was considered to perpetuate and expand the individually oriented, professionally dominated, clinical approach to health care and injury and illness prevention, not to accelerate its demise (Evans & Stoddart, 1998).

Others saw in the determinants of health–health promotion framework opportunities for empowering the marginalized and democratizing a wide array of social institutions (Dickinson, 1996; VanderPlaat, 1998). This optimism was tempered by a healthy dose of realism. Simply because a potential exists for health promotion to contribute to a greater equality of health status through democratic empowerment does not guarantee that potential will be realized. Powerful vested interests actively and passively resist the sweeping changes in power associated with health promotion; the history of health care reform is replete with such struggles.

At about the same time that the determinants of health–health promotion framework was being articulated, others were arguing that modern, scientific medicine had a direct negative impact on health (Illich, 1976). The notion of **iatrogenic illness** was quite influential in critical social science circles. This notion was given increased credence with the publication of empirical studies showing that some physicians' services — from drug prescriptions to surgical procedures — were medically unjustified (Swartz, 1987).

Concerns about the iatrogenic effects of medicine and mounting evidence showing that many health care services were unnecessary motivated an assessment of the effectiveness of clinical interventions known as evidence-based medicine (EBM) (Sackett et al., 1998; Gray, 1997; National Forum on Health, 1998; Dickinson, 1998). The EBM movement can be understood as having two contradictory origins. On the one hand, it is part of an effort to rationalize medical and hospital care. As such, it is part of contemporary efforts to micro-manage the practice of medicine and to erode medical autonomy and dominance in determining the form and content of the health care system (Grahame-Smith, 1995; Naylor, 1993). On the other hand, it is part of the response of the organized medical profession, particularly university-based researchers, to bolster claims that the clinical practice of medicine is more science than art (Sackett et al., 1998). These contradictory origins of EBM are reflected in practising physicians' contradictory responses to it (Dickinson, 1998).

In their analysis of the health field concept, Vayda, Evans, and Mindell (1979, p. 226) noted that if medical and hospital services contributed only a small and decreasing amount toward increased population health status, there was no justification for continually increasing health care expenditures. Given this, several analysts saw the determinants of health policy framework as the first serious effort to dismantle medicare (Armstrong, 1997; Swartz, 1987).

Proponents of the determinants of health framework responded to criticisms by refining and refocusing the health field concept (Advisory Committee on Population Health, 1994; Epp, 1986; Evans, Barer, & Marmor, 1994; Evans & Stoddart, 1998; Hamilton & Bhatti, 1996; Mustard & Frank, 1991; Report on the Round Table, 1996). To allay these fears and clarify the concept of health promotion, an influential federal government policy paper stated that the concept was "an approach that complements and strengthens the existing system of health care" (Epp, 1986, p. 2).

Despite the controversy over the effects it has had for medicare, the determinants of health–health promotion policy framework has focused attention on a number of important issues. First, it highlights the fact that access to medical and hospital services has not eliminated inequalities in health status. Disadvantaged groups continue to have lower life expectancy, poorer health status, and a higher prevalence of disability than others (Advisory Committee on Population Health, 1999; Bolaria, 1994; D'Arcy, 1998; Epp, 1986; Frideres, 1994; Wilkins & Sherman, 1998). This health effect is on a gradient within all socioeconomic groups (Hertzman, Frank, & Evans, 1994; Marmot et al., 1978; Dickinson & Kosteniuk, this volume).

Second, the injury- and illness-prevention dimension of health promotion has focused attention on a wide array of preventable injuries and illnesses that differentially characterize social groups. These include, *inter alia*, youth suicide, disease associated with tobacco use, sexually transmitted diseases, and injuries associated with impaired driving.

Third, the health care needs of the population are changing. It used to be the case that the main sources of morbidity and mortality were infectious diseases, but now chronic conditions and disabilities predominate. This change has been referred to as the "epidemiological shift." It has significant implications for the nature of health care needs and, consequently, for the nature and organization of health care services.

Many chronic conditions are not currently amenable to medical or hospital treatment. Modern medicine has no cures for chronic conditions like arthritis, diabetes, heart disease, and mental illness. The aging of the Canadian population has added urgency to efforts to find appropriate and affordable means to deal with a wide range of chronic

conditions that are often associated with the elderly. What is required is long-term support in the management of these conditions. Although medicine often has a role to play
in managing many chronic conditions, it need not always play a dominant role.

The adoption of the determinants of health–health promotion policy framework,
along with various cost control strategies, has resulted in numerous changes to the
nature and organization of health care services. Not since the introduction of medicare
itself has such dramatic change occurred.

REGIONALIZATION: FROM INSTITUTIONAL TO COMMUNITY CARE

The most recent and dramatic reform of the health care system has been regionalization. The most recent regionalization efforts emerged in the late 1980s and early 1990s.
As a policy instrument, regionalization is designed to accomplish several health policy
objectives. These include cost control, improved health outcomes, increased respon-
siveness to health care needs, flexibility in care delivery, better integration and coordination of services, and greater citizen awareness of, and participation in, health care
planning and service delivery (Angus, 1991; Angus et al., 1995; Crichton et al., 1997;
Dorland & Davis, 1996; Lomas, 1996; Lomas, Woods, & Veenstra, 1997; Lewis, 1997;
Mhatre & Deber, 1998).

How are we to understand these changes and their consequences? It is generally
agreed that regionalization marks an important shift in the model of health care governance and service delivery. The main direction of the change is away from collegial control and medical domination of health policymaking and service delivery, toward some
form of either communal or corporatist control.

Blishen (1991, p. 145), for example, sees regionalization as a system of control in
which "a community, or a community organization such as a consumer's group, rather
than an occupational group, such as physicians, or a third party such as the government, seeks to define the needs of members and the manner in which they are satisfied." He is cautious in his early assessment of regionalization. Although he recognizes
that it has redefined the relations between the state, the medical profession, and consumers in the direction of increased consumer control, he feels there is no evidence to
show that it is a more effective way to organize and deliver health care.

Crichton et al. (1997) also see regionalization as a shift in the nature and organization
of health care planning and service delivery. Unlike Blishen, however, they see it as a manifestation of neocorporatism, which, following Pleiger (1990), they see as an element of an
emerging welfare society. The key features of the welfare society are the decentralization
of decision making and the involvement of various stakeholders in partnerships as a
means of reaching policy consensus. This is distinct from the centralized, bureaucratic,
and professionally dominated mode of decision making associated with the welfare state.
As Crichton et al. (1997, p. 40) observe, in a welfare society, "the former power holders
have to share their power with other groups of corporate decision makers."

Enthusiasm for a corporatist model of policymaking emerged from a 1980 OECD
conference. At that conference, it was argued that a corporatist model of policymaking
was more likely to enable policymakers "to contain the bargaining power of physicians
and other provider groups and thereby move the system towards real health outputs"
(Wilensky, 1981, p. 194). Britain, Canada, and the United States were identified as

countries that were least likely to accomplish this because of the nature of their policy-making processes. The Canadian federal government did, however, in the 1980s, adopt more of a corporatist approach to policymaking (Crichton et al., 1997).

Picking up on this theme, Lomas et al. (1997) see regionalization in general, and the new regional health authorities (RHAs) in particular, as both allies and "fall guys" for provincial governments in their struggle for control of the health care system. As allies, the RHAs are intended to increase community participation and empowerment relative to policymaking and health system governance. The putative goal is to generate the critical mass of political power needed to break the "medicare pact" — the structural features of medicare that entrenched medical dominance, inflationary cost increases, and a curative approach to health problems. As fall guys, the new RHAs are intended to deflect criticism from provincial governments as budgets are cut and the health care system is rationalized.

At this time, it seems unlikely that regional health authorities are designed to break the medicare pact. No provincial government has given the RHAs control over medical care or pharmaceutical budgets. Without such control, RHAs have no capacity to adopt a "command and control strategy" relative to nonhospital medical care services. The exclusion of control over medical care and pharmaceutical budgets is not an oversight. Medical resistance to any organizational reform considered a threat to professional autonomy and collegial control is fierce. Indeed, the organized profession effectively scuttled earlier attempts at regionalization because of the threat to medical autonomy (Taylor, 1978).

As with earlier health reform initiatives, provincial governments have taken an incrementalist approach. The first step is the rationalization of institutional, particularly hospital, services; the second is the vertical and horizontal coordination and integration of institutional and community services. The provinces have differential priorities in this regard. Some, like Saskatchewan and New Brunswick, rationalized hospital services before regionalization. In Saskatchewan, for example, this entailed closing or converting 53 small rural hospitals to community health centres. Other provincial governments left this task to the newly created RHAs.

The consequences of these differing strategies relative to the goal of creating new political allies remains to be seen. In part it will depend both on how various interest groups respond to the RHAs and on how the RHAs themselves respond to the provincial governments. If local citizenry perceive the RHAs as empowering them and giving them effective control over the best way to satisfy local health needs, particularly their health care needs, then the regionalization might be considered a successful experiment in democratic corporatism.

On the other hand, if RHAs join forces with disgruntled citizens and health care providers against provincial government cutbacks, then it might also be seen as a successful experiment in community empowerment but a failure as a means to wrest control over health policy and health care service delivery from service providers. Aware of this possibility, some provinces have prohibited health care providers from serving on RHAs. Others that had announced intentions to institute elected boards have backed away from that commitment.

If this second scenario comes to pass, it will likely herald the end of the regionalization experiment and the beginning of a search for a new way to break the medicare pact.

The coalition for the privatization of health care is ever ready to extol the virtues of the market and modern management techniques as a panacea for all that ails a public health care system like medicare.

Despite repeated assurances to the contrary, concerns remain that current health reforms are simply paving the way for the reprivatization of health care (Armstrong, 1997; Fuller, 1998; O'Neill, 1998; Tsalikis, 1989). In one sense, as we have just seen, this is the case. Government is trying to limit medical autonomy and dominance relative both to health policy and health care services. In itself, however, reduced medical autonomy and dominance is not a threat to medicare.

There is, however, a more serious threat to medicare, related to its structure. Currently, medical and hospital-based services are covered by medicare. Other services, in general, are not. As the system shifts the locus of treatment from hospital to community, and as service providers other than medically trained physicians come to play a larger role in health care delivery, a *de facto* privatization of health care is also occurring.

Pressures are also mounting for the privatization of the medical and hospital care sector of the health care system. Leading the charge in this regard are the medical profession, private sector health care corporations (many of which are U.S.-based), and provincial governments ideologically committed to the market as a social policy tool. Pressure to adopt market solutions to social policy problems is given added impetus through various trade liberalization agreements and organizations.

CONCLUSION

This chapter has examined the changing goals of health policy and their relationship to the changing nature and organization of the health care system. A central theme in analyses of health care in Canada is the nature and locus of control. More specifically, health care policy and service delivery has been greatly influenced, if not dominated, by the organized medical profession. Current reform initiatives, including the adoption of the determinants of health policy framework and the regionalization of health care decision making and service delivery, are the most recent manifestation of the struggle to control the health care sector and improve population health status.

The chapter has also shown that the outcome of these efforts is currently unknown. It is not certain what the future holds. There is a potential for a more needs-based, publicly funded, and democratically controlled health care system to emerge. There is also, however, the potential for an increasingly privatized, corporate-controlled health care system to develop. There is, perhaps, even more evidence to suggest that this is the future of health care in Canada.

STUDY QUESTIONS

1. *Some have argued that the development of health policy in general and the introduction of medicare in particular can be understood in terms of broad-based class interests. Outline and discuss these arguments.*
2. *A debate exists over the effect of medicare on the position and power of the medical profession. Outline and discuss this debate.*

3. *The health promotion policy framework constitutes a significant threat to medicare. Discuss.*
4. *The regionalization of health care planning and service delivery is seen by some as a means to democratize health care decision making and to increase community control. Others maintain that it is a threat to our publicly funded health care system and another step toward a corporate controlled, for-profit, American-style health care system. Discuss.*
5. *The movement to introduce evidence-based medicine (EBM) has been argued to be both a means to entrench medical dominance and a means to erode it. Outline and discuss.*

GLOSSARY

extra billing The practice of billing patients directly a sum over and above the agreed fee set by medicare; in the current Canadian health care system, this practice is disallowed.

fee-for-service A remuneration system in which service providers are paid an agreed-upon fee for each eligible service they provide.

health field concept A conceptual framework for analyzing the principal subcomponents of the determinants of health, namely, human biology, environment, lifestyle, and health care organization; this concept was developed in the 1974 Lalonde Paper.

iatrogenic illness Illnesses or injuries resulting from medical interventions.

medical autonomy The medical profession's independence relative to the organization and content of medical work, and the control and supervision of others. This is generally justified by the following three claims: medical work is based on an esoteric body of knowledge inaccessible to the lay public; it is based on the best current science; and it requires practitioners to be schooled in this knowledge through a common education process.

medical dominance The medical profession's control both over other occupations in the health care division of labour, and over patients. Medical dominance is reflected in the medical profession's historical commitment to market-based, fee-for-service, solo practices, which it maintains results in the best quality of medicine.

transfer payments In the context of the Canadian health care system, cash transfers from the federal to provincial governments to help pay for health care services.

user fees Fees charged to health care service users; in the current Canadian health care system, they are disallowed.

RECOMMENDED READINGS

Dorland, J.L., & Davis, S.M. (Eds.). (1996). *How many roads...? Regionalization and decentralization in health care.* Kingston: Queen's University School of Policy Studies. The proceedings of a conference, providing both analytical and descriptive papers on the implications of the regionalization of health care from national, provincial, and local perspectives.

Evans, R.G., Barer, M.L., & Marmor, T.R. (Eds.). (1994). *Why are some people healthy and others not? The determinants of health of populations.* New York: Aldine DeGruyter. The culmination of a 5-year research program into the determinants of the health of populations, undertaken by the Canadian Institute for Advanced Research. It explores the linkages between a wide range of health determinants, including social inequalities and other macro- and micro-environmental factors.

Hamilton, N., & Bhatti, T. (1996). *Population health promotion: An integrated model of population health and health promotion.* Ottawa: Health Canada. The first and clearest effort to synthesize the health promotion and the population health policy frameworks.

Hamowy, R. (1984). *Canadian medicine: A study in restricted entry.* Vancouver: Fraser Institute. A detailed historical study of the development of the Canadian medical profession and the ways in which it has secured professional autonomy and dominance. The author argues that the efficiency and effectiveness of medical care can be improved through market competition.

Organisation for Economic Co-operation and Development (Ed.). (1981). *The welfare state in crisis: An account of the conference on social policies in the 1980s.* Paris: Author. An important book, presenting international perspectives on the welfare state and the causes, consequences, and possible cures for its intensifying crisis.

REFERENCES

Advisory Committee on Population Health (ACPH). (1994). *Strategies for population health: Investing in the health of Canadians.* Ottawa: Health Canada.

Advisory Committee on Population Health (ACPH). (1999). *Toward a healthy future: Second report on the health of Canadians.* Ottawa: Health Canada.

Angus, D.E. (1991). *Review of significant health care commissions and task forces in Canada since 1983–84.* Ottawa: Canadian Hospital Association/Canadian Medical Association/Canadian Nurses' Association.

Angus, D.E., Auer, L., Cloutier, J.E., & Albert, T. (1995). *Sustainable health care for Canada.* Ottawa: University of Ottawa Press.

Armstrong, P. (1997). Privatizing care. In P. Armstrong, H. Armstrong, J. Choiniere, E. Mykhalovskiy, & J.P. White (Eds.), *Medical alert: New work organizations in health care* (pp. 11–30). Toronto: Garamond Press.

Badgley, R.F., & Wolfe, S. (1967). *Doctors' strike: Medical care and conflict in Saskatchewan.* Toronto: MacMillan of Canada.

Blishen, B. (1969). *Doctors and doctrines: The ideology of medical care in Canada.* Toronto: University of Toronto Press.

Blishen, B. (1991). *Doctors in Canada: The changing world of medical practice.* Toronto: University of Toronto Press in association with Statistics Canada.

Bolaria, B.S. (1988). The politics and ideology of self-care and lifestyles. In B.S. Bolaria & H.D. Dickinson (Eds.), *Sociology of health care in Canada* (pp. 537–549). Toronto: Harcourt Brace Jovanovich.

Bolaria, B.S. (1994). Income inequality: Food banks and health. In B.S. Bolaria & H.D. Dickinson (Eds.), *Health, illness, and health care in Canada* (2nd ed., pp. 245–254). Toronto: W.B. Saunders.

Coburn, D. (1998). State authority, medical dominance, and trends in the regulation of health professions: The Ontario case. In D. Coburn, C. D'Arcy, & G.M. Torrance (Eds.), *Health and Canadian society: Critical perspectives* (3rd ed., pp. 332–346). Toronto: University of Toronto Press.

Coburn, D., Torrance, G.M., & Kaufert, J.M. (1983). Medical dominance in Canadian historical perspective: The rise and fall of medicine? *International Journal of Health Services, 13*(3), 407–432.

Crichton, A., Robertson, A., Gordon, C., & Farrant, W. (1997). *Health care a community concern? Developments in the organization of Canadian health services.* Calgary: University of Calgary Press.

D'Arcy, C. (1998). Social distribution of health among Canadians. In D. Coburn, C. D'Arcy, & G. Torrance (Eds.), *Health and Canadian society: Critical perspectives* (3rd ed., pp. 73–101). Toronto: University of Toronto Press.

Dickinson, H.D. (1993). The struggle for state health insurance: Reconsidering the role of Saskatchewan farmers. *Studies in Political Economy, 41,* 133–156.

Dickinson, H.D. (1994). The changing health care system: Controlling costs and promoting health. In B.S. Bolaria & H.D. Dickinson (Eds.), *Health, illness, and health care in Canada* (2nd ed., pp. 106–129). Toronto: W.B. Saunders.

Dickinson, H.D. (1996). Health reforms, empowerment and the democratization of society. In M. Stingl & D. Wilson (Eds.), *Efficiency vs. equality: Heath reform in Canada* (pp. 179–190). Halifax: Fernwood.

Dickinson, H.D. (1998). Evidence-based decision-making: An argumentative approach. *International Journal of Medical Informatics, 51,* 71–81.

Dickinson, H.D., & Kosteniuk, J.G. (2002). Health status in Canada. In B.S. Bolaria & H.D. Dickinson (Eds.), *Health, illness, and health care in Canada* (3rd ed., pp. 37–52). Toronto: Nelson Thomson Learning.

Dominion–Provincial Conference on Reconstruction. (1945). *Health welfare and labour: Reference book for dominion–provincial conference on reconstruction.*

Dorland, J.L., & Davis, S.M. (1996). Regionalization as health care reform. In J.L. Dorland & S.M. Davis (Eds.), *How many roads...? Regionalization and decentralization in health care* (pp. 3–7). Kingston: Queen's University School of Policy Studies.

Douglas, T.C. (1946, December). Saskatchewan plans for health. *Health,* 1–3.

Epp, J. (1986). *Achieving health for all: A framework for health promotion.* Ottawa: Health and Welfare Canada.

Evans, R.G., Barer, M.L., & Marmor, T.R. (Eds.). (1994). *Why are some people healthy and others not? The determinants of population health.* New York: Aldine DeGruyter.

Evans, R.G., & Stoddart, G.L. (1998). Producing health, consuming health care. In D. Coburn, C. D'Arcy, & G.M. Torrance (Eds.), *Health and Canadian society: Critical perspectives* (3rd ed., pp. 549–579). Toronto: University of Toronto Press.

Feather, J. (1991a). From concept to reality: Formation of the Swift Current health region. *Prairie Forum, 16*(2), 59–80.

Feather, J. (1991b). Impact of the Swift Current health model: Experiment or model? *Prairie Forum, 16*(4), 225–248.

Foucault, M. (1980). The politics of health in the eighteenth century. In C. Gordon (Ed.), *Power/knowledge: Selected interviews & other writings, 1972–1977* (pp. 166–182). New York: Pantheon.

Freidson, E. (1973). *Profession of medicine: A study of the sociology of applied knowledge.* New York: Dodd, Mead.

Frideres, J.S. (1994). Racism and health: The case of the native people. In B.S. Bolaria & H.D. Dickinson (Eds.), *Health, illness, and health care in Canada* (2nd ed., pp. 202–210). Toronto: W.B. Saunders.

Fuller, C. (1998). *Caring for profit: How corporations are taking over Canada's health care system.* Vancouver/Ottawa: New Star Books/Canadian Centre for Policy Alternatives.

Grahame-Smith, D. (1995). Evidence-based medicine: Socratic dissent. *British Medical Journal, 310*, 1126–1127.

Gray, J.A.M. (1997). *Evidence-based health care: How to make health policy and management decisions.* Edinburgh: Churchill Livingstone.

Hamilton, N., & Bhatti, T. (1996). *Population health promotion: An integrated model of population health and health promotion.* Ottawa: Health Canada.

Health, Welfare and Labour. (1944). Reference book for dominion–provincial conference on reconstruction (Ottawa: Author).

Health Canada. (1996). *National health expenditures in Canada, 1975–1994: Summary report.* Ottawa: Author.

Hertzman, C., Frank, J., & Evans, R.G. (1994). Heterogeneities in health status and the determinants of population health. In R.G. Evans, M.L. Barer, & T.R. Marmor (Eds.), *Why are some people healthy and others not? The determinants of health of populations* (pp. 67–92). New York: Aldine DeGruyter.

Illich, I. (1976). *Limits to medicine, medical nemesis: The expropriation of health.* Toronto & London: McClelland & Stewart, in association with Marion Boyars.

Lalonde, M. (1974). *A new perspective on the health of Canadians: A working document.* Ottawa: National Health and Welfare.

Lewis, S. (1997). *Regionalization and devolution: Transforming health, reshaping politics?* HEALNet Regional Health Planning Theme, Occasional Paper No. 2. Saskatoon.

Lomas, J. (1996). Devolved authorities in Canada: The new site of health-care system conflict. In J.L. Dorland & S.M. Davis (Eds.), *How many roads…? Regionalization and decentralization in health care* (pp. 26–34). Kingston: Queen's University School of Policy Studies.

Lomas, J. (1997). Devolving authority for health care in Canada's provinces: 4. Emerging issues and prospects. *Canadian Medical Association Journal, 156*(6), 817–823.

Lomas, J., Woods, J., & Veenstra, G. (1997). Devolving authority for health care in Canada's provinces: 1. An introduction to the issues. *Canadian Medical Association Journal, 156*(3), 371–377.

Marmot, M.G., Rose, G., Shipley, M.J., & Hamilton, P.J.S. (1978). Employment grade and coronary heart disease in British civil servants. *Journal of Epidemiology and Community Health, 32*, 244–249.

Mhatre, S.L., & Deber, R.B. (1998). From equal access to health care to equitable access to health: A review of Canadian health commissions and reports. In D. Coburn, C. D'Arcy, & G. Torrance (Eds.), *Health and Canadian society: Critical perspectives* (3rd ed., pp. 459–484). Toronto: University of Toronto Press.

Mombourquette, D. (1991). 'An inalienable right': The CCF and rapid health care reform. *Saskatchewan History, 43*(3), 101–116.

Mott, F.D. (1947). Hospital relations: Hospital services in Saskatchewan. *American Journal of Public Health, 37*, 1539–1544.

Mustard, F., & Frank, J. (1991). *The determinants of health.* CIAR Publication No. 5. Toronto: Canadian Institute for Advanced Research.

National Forum on Health. (1998). *Evidence and information: Making decisions (Vol. 5).* Sainte-Foy, QC: Editions MultiMondes.

Naylor, C.D. (1986). *Private practice, public payment: Canadian medicine and the politics of health insurance, 1911–1966.* Montreal & Kingston: McGill–Queen's University Press.

Naylor, C.D. (1993). The Canadian health care system: A model for America to emulate? In A. King, T. Hyclack, R. Thornton, & S. McMahon (Eds.), *North American health care policy in the 1990s* (pp. 25–66). Chichester: John Wiley & Sons.

Northcott, H.A. (1994). Threats to medicare: The financing, allocation, and utilization of health care in Canada. In B.S. Bolaria & H.D. Dickinson (Eds.), *Health, illness, and health care in Canada* (2nd ed., pp. 65–82). Toronto: W.B. Saunders.

O'Neill, M. (1998). Community participation in Quebec's health system. In D. Coburn, C. D'Arcy, & G. Torrance (Eds.), *Health and Canadian society: Critical perspectives* (3rd ed., pp. 517–530). Toronto: University of Toronto Press.

Pleiger, D. (1990). Policy networks and the decentralization of policy making. *Bulletin European Social Security, 55–56,* 37–39.

Renaud, M. (n.d.). Social sciences and medicine: Hygeia vs. Panakeia. *Health and Canadian Society, 1*(1), 229–247.

Report on the Round Table. (1996). *Report of the round table on population health and health promotion.* Ottawa: Health Canada.

Roth, F.B., & Defries, R.D. (1958). The Saskatchewan Department of Public Health. *Canadian Journal of Public Health, 49*(5), 276–285.

Sackett, D.L., Rosenberg, W.M.C., Muir Gray, J.A., Haynes, R.B., & Richardson, W.S. (1998). Evidence-based medicine: What it is and what it isn't. Centre for Evidence-Based Medicine. http://cebm.jr2.ox.ac.uk/ebmisisnt.html.

Soderstrom, L. (1978). *The Canadian health system.* London: Croom Helm.

Stevenson, M., Williams, A.P., & Vayda, E. (1988). Medical politics and Canadian medicare: Professional response to the Canada Health Act. *Millbank Quarterly, 66*(1), 65–104.

Swartz, D. (1977). The politics of reform: Conflict and accommodation in Canadian health policy. In L. Panitch (Ed.), *The Canadian state: Political economy and political power* (pp. 311–343). Toronto: University of Toronto Press.

Swartz, D. (1987). The limits of health insurance. In A. Moscovitch & J. Albert (Eds.), *The benevolent state: The growth of welfare in Canada* (pp. 255–270). Toronto: Garamond Press.

Taylor, M.G. (1960). The role of the medical profession in the formation and execution of public policy. *Canadian Journal of Economics and Political Studies, 25*(1), 108–127.

Taylor, M.G. (1978). *Health insurance and Canadian public policy: The seven decisions that created the Canadian health insurance system.* Montreal & Kingston: McGill–Queen's University Press.

Thompson, W.P. (1964). *Medical care: Programs and issues.* Toronto: Clarke, Irwin.

Tollefson, E.A. (1963). *Bitter medicine: The Saskatchewan medicare feud.* Saskatoon: Modern Press.

Touhy, C. (1994). Health policy and fiscal federalism. In K.G. Banting (Ed.), *The future of fiscal federalism* (pp. 189–212). Kingston: Queen's University School of Policy Studies.

Tsalikis, G. (1989). The political economy of decentralization of health and social services in Canada. *International Journal of Health Planning and Management, 4*(4), 293–309.

VanderPlaat, M. (1998). Empowerment, emancipation and health promotion policy. *Canadian Journal of Sociology, 23*(1), 71–90.

Vayda, E., & Deber, R.B. (1992). The Canadian health care system: A developmental overview. In C.D. Naylor (Ed.), *Canadian health care and the state: A century of evolution* (pp. 125–140). Montreal & Kingston: McGill–Queen's University Press.

Vayda, E., Evans, R.G., & Mindell, W.R. (1979). Universal health insurance in Canada: History, problems, trends. *Journal of Community Health, 4*(3), 217–231.

Walters, V. (1982). State, capital and labour: The introduction of federal–provincial insurance for physician care in Canada. *Canadian Review of Sociology and Anthropology, 19*(2), 157–172.

Weller, G.R., & Manga, P. (1983). The push for reprivatization of health care services in Canada, Britain and the United States. *Journal of Health Politics and Law, 8*(3), 495–518.

White, R.F. (1984). The professions and collective action: Responses to state control and public criticism. In A. Wipper (Ed.), *The sociology of work: Papers in honour of Oswald Hall* (pp. 469–486). Ottawa: Carleton University Press.

Wilensky, H.L. (1981). Democratic corporatism, consensus, and social policy: Reflections on changing values and the "crisis" of the welfare state. In OECD (Ed.), *The welfare state in crisis: An account of the conference on social policies in the 1980s* (pp. 185–195). OECD: Paris.

Wilkins, R., & Sherman, G. (1998). Low income and child health in Canada. In D. Coburn, C. D'Arcy, & G. Torrance (Eds.), *Health and Canadian society: Critical perspectives* (3rd ed., pp. 102–109). Toronto: University of Toronto Press.

Wolfe, S. (1964). Saskatchewan's community clinics. *Canadian Medical Association Journal, 91*, 225–229.

NOTE

1. A version of this paper was originally published under the title "The Evolution of Health Care in Canada: Towards Community or Corporate Control?" in William C. Cockerham (Ed.), *Blackwell Companion to Medical Sociology* (Oxford: Blackwell, 2001). Reprinted with permission.

3

Health Status in Canada

HARLEY D. DICKINSON AND JULIE G. KOSTENIUK   University of Saskatchewan

INTRODUCTION

The sociology of health and illness is concerned with the relationship between health, illness, injury, and death, on the one hand, and the nature and organization of society, on the other. It has long been known that morbidity (injury and illness) and mortality (death) are related to the nature and organization of society in at least four ways: (1) social conditions may cause illness or death; (2) they may create predispositions among particular groups of individuals to certain illnesses; (3) they may facilitate the transmission of the causes of illnesses; and (4) they may influence the course and outcome of illnesses (Rosen, 1963, p. 44). Because different categories of people occupy different positions in the social structure, these four processes act upon them in different ways. Thus, one would expect to find a differential distribution of health and illness between groups. This is precisely what is found.

For many decades policymakers in Canada and elsewhere thought that the best way to address inequalities and improve the health status of all segments of the population was to eliminate barriers, particularly financial barriers, to necessary medical and hospital services. Medicare, in part, was the result of this thinking.

As important as the elimination of financial barriers to medical care was to improving the health of individuals, it came to be recognized that the health care system and access to it was not the only determinant of health status. By the early 1970s, **population health** status was acknowledged to be the result of the interaction of several factors, including the health care system, the social and physical environments, individual lifestyles, and human biology. This idea is termed the "health field concept" (Lalonde, 1974).

The health field concept, despite criticisms and changing socioeconomic conditions (McKay, 2000), has become a basis for health policy in Canada and elsewhere. Within this policy framework, the primary focus of health policy has shifted from accessibility to the health care system as the means of improving population health to more broadly based efforts to promote health through intervention into the domains of all the determinants of health (Mustard & Frank, 1991; Evans, Barer, & Marmor, 1994).

Under the old policy paradigm, health was largely understood as the absence of illness or injury. Under the new policy paradigm, health is understood to be the capacity of individuals and social groups to interact with their environments "in ways that promote subjective well-being, the optimum development and use of mental [and physical] abilities… [and] the achievement of individual and collective goals consistent with justice and the attainment and preservation of conditions of fundamental equality" (Epp, 1986, p. 7). Clearly, access to medical and hospital services, in itself, is inadequate in promoting health understood in this way. This definition of health also gives rise to a need to develop multidimensional measures of health and health status to enable an assessment of the degree to which **health promotion** policies and practices are successful.

Researchers most often rely upon measures of physical and mental ill health to assess the health of populations. Physical ill health measures include, but are not limited to, **life expectancy**, rates of disease and health care utilization, measures of physical inactivity, functional capacity, and the prevalence of disability and activity restriction. The prevalence of health complaints, symptoms of nervous conditions, and self-rated functional health status are a few of the more subjective measures used to gauge physical health. Mental ill health indicators comprise rates of depression, psychiatric complaints, and nervous conditions. The new definition of health (Stewart-Brown, 1998) corresponds to an increased reliance upon self-reported health measures.

Research shows that self-reported health not only correlates well with clinical diagnoses, but is also a valid predictor of disease, sickness, and mortality (Grayson, 1993; Kennedy et al., 1999; Macran et al., 1994). Despite this, concern exists that an exclusive reliance upon self-reported health measures may result in an inaccurate picture of population health status. These concerns are grounded in the fact that people's self-perceptions may be affected by such things as personality differences and the various ways in which they adopt a "sick role" (Madge & Marmot, 1987, p. 116).

In this chapter, a number of key indicators of the health status of different social groups in Canada are presented, particularly trends in life expectancy at birth and **mortality rates** for the primary causes of death. This presentation is followed by some international comparisons and a brief conclusion.

SELECTED INDICATORS OF HEALTH STATUS

Life Expectancy

A key indicator of population health status is life expectancy at birth. Canada, like other advanced capitalist societies in the past several decades, has experienced increased life expectancies at birth and increased average age at death. These general trends hold for both males and females. A traditional female advantage in terms of life expectancy persists, despite a closing of the gap in recent years. Table 1 shows that the average life expectancy at birth for females in Canada in 1931 was 62.1 years; for males it was 60.0 years, for a difference, at birth, of 2.1 additional years of life for women compared with men. By 1996, the average life expectancy for females had increased to 81.4 years, and for males it had increased to 75.7 years. This represented a difference of 5.7 additional years of life expected for females compared with males. The gap between females and males has been declining since 1981, when it reached a high of 7.1 additional years of

TABLE 3.1 *Average Life Expectancy at Birth, Canada, by Sex, Selected Years, 1931–1996*

Year	Female	Gain	Male	Gain	Female–Male Difference in Life Expectancy
1931	62.1	—	60.0	—	2.1
1941	66.3	4.2	63.0	3.0	3.3
1951	70.8	4.5	66.3	3.3	4.5
1961	74.2	3.4	68.3	2.0	5.9
1971	76.4	2.2	69.3	1.0	7.1
1981	79.0	2.6	71.9	2.6	7.1
1996	81.4	2.4	75.7	3.8	5.7

Source: Statistics Canada (1978a, pp. 3–4; 1988b, p. 12); ACPH (1999, p. 26).

life. Since that time, although both females and males have continued to achieve gains in life expectancy, the gains for males have exceeded those for females.

Mortality Rates and Causes of Death

Part of the reason for the increased life expectancy at birth is the dramatic decline in **infant mortality** rates. The greatest decline in infant mortality, for both males and females, occurred between 1931 and 1951. The main reason for the decline was decreased mortality from infectious diseases such as whooping cough, influenza, bronchitis, pneumonia, enteritis, and diarrhea (Dominion Bureau of Statistics, 1967, p. 9). In 1995, about 99 percent of all deaths for infants in the **neonatal period** were caused by **congenital anomalies** (33 percent) and other causes specific to the perinatal period, such as respiratory distress, prematurity, and low birth weight (66 percent) (Advisory Committee on Population Health [ACPH], 1999, p. 75).

The infant mortality rate has declined steadily since 1951. Recently, however, the rate of decrease has slowed because of the above-mentioned shift in the primary causes of death among that age group. Even so, the infant mortality rate decreased to 5.6 per 1000 live births in 1996 from about 42 per 1000 in 1950 (Statistics Canada, 1988a, p. 9, figure III; ACPH, 1999, p. 305). This marks the first time that the rate has fallen below 6 per 1000.

Infant mortality rates, however, vary markedly between income groups in Canada ranging from a low of 4.5 infant deaths per 1000 live births for the highest-income group to a high of 7.5 deaths per 1000 live births for infants in the lowest income group (ACPH, 1999, p. 75). The inequality in infant mortality rates is even more striking for First Nations peoples. Despite a drop in infant mortality rates from 28 per 1000 live births in 1979 to 12 per 1000 live births in 1994, the rate remains twice as high as for the Canadian population in general (ACPH, 1999, p. 76).

The percentage of all deaths accounted for by those less than 1 year of age and those 65 years and older has changed dramatically, as can be seen in Table 2. Deaths in the

TABLE 3.2 *Number and Percentage of All Deaths by Age Groups, Both Sexes, Canada, Selected Years, 1951–1995*

	1951		1961		1971		1981		1991		1995	
	Number	Percent	Number	Percent	Number	Percent	Number	Percent	Number	Percent	Number	Percent
Under 1 year	14.7	11.7	13.0	9.2	6.3	4.0	3.6	2.1	2.5	1.3	2.3	1.1
1–24 years	7.2	5.7	6.3	4.5	7.7	4.9	6.5	3.8	4.1	2.1	3.8	1.8
25–44 years	8.8	7.0	8.2	5.8	9.1	5.8	9.4	5.5	10.8	5.5	11.4	5.3
45–64 years	27.7	22.0	30.3	21.5	36.2	23.0	36.9	21.6	33.6	17.2	33.9	16.1
65+ years	67.4	53.6	83.2	59.0	98.0	62.3	114.6	67.0	144.6	73.9	159.5	75.7
Total deaths	125.8	100.0	141.0	100.0	157.3	100.0	171.0	100.0	195.6	100.0	210.9	100.0

Sources: Statistics Canada (1978b, pp. 32–33; 1982, pp. 16–17; 1997, pp. 14–15).

under 1 year age group dropped from 11.7 percent of all deaths in Canada in 1951 to 1.1 percent in 1995. Though not as dramatic, there has been a general downward trend for all age groups except those 65 years and older. For that age group, the percentage of all deaths increased from 53.6 to 75.7 between 1951 and 1995. The increased proportion of deaths among those aged 65 years and over is the result of several factors, including decreased mortality in all other age groups and the fact that the Canadian population is getting older.

Part of the reason for this demographic shift is the reduction of infectious diseases as causes of death. Consequently, individuals generally live longer. Various chronic diseases have become the leading causes of morbidity and mortality in Canada. Since at least 1950, for example, the leading causes of death have been diseases of the circulatory system, cancer, accidents, and respiratory diseases.

Circulatory diseases, both heart diseases and stroke, were the leading cause of death for both males and females from 1950 to 1993. Despite this, there have been substantial decreases in both male and female age-standardized mortality rates (ASMRs) for circulatory diseases, as shown in Table 3. Explanations of the observed decline include the following factors:

- reductions in risk-producing behaviours and characteristics, such as cigarette smoking, obesity, high cholesterol diets, and high blood pressure;
- increased preventative behaviours, such as higher levels of physical activity;
- reduced severity of diseases; and
- improved treatments (Statistics Canada, 1988a, p. 9).

Deaths due to cardiovascular diseases are not evenly distributed across Canada. Death rates from cardiovascular diseases are higher in the Maritime provinces than in the Western provinces. Not surprisingly, provincial rates for cardiovascular diseases parallel prevalence rates for smoking, high blood pressure, and obesity (ACPH, 1999, p. 21).

The second leading cause of death in Canada, for both men and women, is cancer. Table 3 shows that for men the age-standardized mortality rate (ASMR) from all types of

TABLE 3.3 *Age-Standardized Mortality Rates (ASMR) for Leading Causes of Death, Canada, 1950 and 1993*

| | 1950 | | | 1993 | | | Percentage Change in ASMR, 1950–1993 | |
| | ASMR per 100 000 | | Male Excess | ASMR per 100 000 | | Male Excess | | |
Causes of Death	Males	Females	%	Males	Females	%	Males	Females
Circulatory diseases	708	567	25	340	204	67	−52	−64
Cancer	179	165	8	241	154	56	+35	−7
Respiratory diseases	84	62	35	88	43	105	+5	−31
External causes	104	46	126	67	27	148	−36	−41
All other causes	294	244	20	154	106	45	−48	−57

Source: Wilkins (1995, p. 40).

cancer increased by 35 percent between 1950 and 1993. For females, over that time period, it decreased by 7 percent.

Among males, lung cancer death rates levelled off after 1984 after decades of increases. Reduced lung cancer death rates among men in Canada, as well as a number of other countries, are related, at least in part, to decreased cigarette smoking among men. There is also evidence that filter and lower-tar cigarettes may contribute to reduced risk of lung cancer (Statistics Canada, 1988b, p. 1). Among women, lung cancer death rates are still rising, particularly for those over 65 years of age. Increased female death rates from lung cancer follow increased cigarette smoking, after a lag of at least 20 years (Statistics Canada, 1988b, p. 10). Breast cancer rates are also still rising among women and, like lung cancer death rates, have been doing so since the 1970s. Breast cancer was estimated to be the most common newly diagnosed cancer in 1998 (ACPH, 1999, p. 22).

Again, provincial differences in cancer incidence and death rates are rather striking: Nova Scotia has the highest age-standardized incidence and death rates for men. This is mostly the result of higher lung cancer rates. For women, the highest incidence rates for lung cancer are also in Nova Scotia, while the highest death rates are in Prince Edward Island (ACPH, 1999, p. 22).

Death by accident, which includes all external causes of injury and poisoning, was the third leading cause of death, both for males and females in 1996 (ACPH, 1999, p. 23). In the case of accident-related deaths, there has been a decrease in the age-adjusted rates since the mid-1970s, with a levelling off in the mid-1980s. Motor vehicle death rates continued a steady downward trend that has been attributed to the reduced speed limits established in 1976–77, the introduction of mandatory seat belt use in most provinces between 1976 and 1986, and reductions in the incidence of impaired driving (ACPH, 1999, p. 23).

Although these figures on the rates and causes of death reveal important information, they also obscure some significant facts about age-specific death rates and causes of death. For example, among Canadian infants less than 1 year old, the two leading causes of death are diseases specific to the perinatal period and congenital anomalies.

Table 4 shows that for those aged 1 to 24 years, the two leading causes of death for both males and females were accidents and cancer. For males, accidents accounted for almost 70 percent of all deaths, while cancer, the second leading cause, represented 6.9 percent of male deaths. Fifty-one percent of all female deaths were caused by accidents, and 12.4 percent were caused by cancers.

A similar pattern exists among 25–44-year-olds. In 1995, 44.8 percent of deaths among males were the result of accidents. Interestingly, the second leading cause of death for men in this age group was infectious and parasitic diseases, accounting for 15.6 percent of all male deaths. An additional 11.9 percent of all male deaths were caused by diseases of the circulatory system and 12.1 percent were the result of cancers. For females 25–44 years of age, 27.3 percent of deaths were the result of accidents and adverse effects; 36.4 percent were caused by cancers, and 11 percent were the result of diseases of the circulatory system.

The pattern remains the same for the next age group. For those between the ages of 45 and 64 years, the three leading causes of death were cancer, diseases of the circulatory system, and accidents, corresponding to 43.5, 27.4, and 7.8 percent respectively of all deaths, regardless of gender. There were also significant gender differences in that age group. The leading cause of death for males was cancer, at 37.9 percent, followed by diseases of the circulatory system at 31.4 percent, with accidents coming third at 9.1 percent

TABLE 3.4 *Leading Causes of Death, Various Age Groups, Canada, 1995*

Causes of Death	Male Number	Male Percent	Female Number	Female Percent	Total Number	Total Percent
Under 1 year old						
• Certain perinatal causes (excluding stillbirths)	566	43.4	424	41.6	990	42.6
• Congenital anomalies	372	28.5	312	30.6	684	29.5
• Respiratory diseases	35	2.7	18	1.8	53	2.3
• Diseases of the nervous system and sense organs	23	1.8	28	2.8	51	2.2
• All other causes	307	23.6	236	23.2	543	23.4
All causes	1 303	100	1 018	100	2 321	100
1 to 24 years old						
• Accidents and adverse effects	1 778	69.8	593	51.0	2 371	63.9
• Malignant neoplasms	177	6.9	144	12.4	321	8.7
• Diseases of the nervous system and sense organs	102	4.0	61	5.3	163	4.4
• All other causes	491	19.3	364	31.3	855	23.0
All causes	2 548	100	1 162	100	3 710	100
25 to 44 years old						
• Accidents and adverse effects	3 517	44.8	951	27.3	4 468	39.5
• Infectious and parasitic diseases	1 226	15.6	121	3.5	1 347	11.9
• Malignant neoplasms	945	12.1	1 267	36.4	2 212	19.5
• Diseases of circulatory system	933	11.9	382	11.0	1 315	11.6
• All other causes	1 221	15.6	760	21.8	1 981	17.5
All causes	7 842	100	3 481	100	11 323	100
Ages 45 to 64 years						
• Malignant neoplasms	8 037	37.9	6 722	53.1	14 759	43.5
• Diseases of circulatory system	6 671	31.4	2 602	20.5	9 273	27.4
• Accidents and adverse effects	1 933	9.1	703	5.6	2 636	7.8
• All other causes	4 577	21.6	2 629	20.8	7 206	21.3
All causes	21 218	100	12 656	100	33 874	100
65 years and over						
• Diseases of circulatory system	32 387	41.3	35 964	44.4	68 351	42.9
• Malignant neoplasms	22 168	28.3	18 340	22.6	40 508	25.4
• Respiratory diseases	9 208	11.7	7 930	9.8	17 138	10.7
• All other causes	14 705	18.7	18 776	23.2	33 481	21.0
All causes	78 468	100	81 016	100	159 478	100
All ages						
• Diseases of circulatory system	40 091	36.0	39 025	39.3	79 116	37.5
• Malignant neoplasms	31 332	28.1	26 478	26.7	57 810	27.4
• Respiratory diseases	10 210	9.2	8 678	8.7	18 888	9.0
• All other causes	29 763	26.7	25 156	25.3	54 919	26.1
All causes	111 396	100	99 337	100	210 733	100

Source: Statistics Canada (1997, pp. 14–15).

of all male deaths in 1995. The leading cause of death for females was cancers, which accounted for 53.1 percent of all deaths. Diseases of the circulatory system were the second leading cause of death, at 20.5 percent.

The three leading causes of death for both males and females 65 years and older were diseases of the circulatory system, cancers, and respiratory diseases. Diseases of the circulatory system accounted for 41.3 and 44.4 percent of male and female deaths respectively in the 65 years and older age group. Twenty-eight percent of male deaths and 22.6 percent of female deaths in this group were caused by cancers, while 11.7 and 9.8 percent of male and female deaths respectively were the result of respiratory diseases.

Age and gender are not the only sources of variation in morbidity and mortality rates. Indeed, it is probably the case that age and gender differences in mortality rates and causes of death are influenced by the different socioeconomic statuses and social positions of men and women, of the young and the old. Support for this notion is provided when one examines the distribution of morbidity and mortality by income. Table 5 shows that in the late 1970s, the lowest 20 percent of male income earners in Canada, at birth, could expect 9.5 fewer years of life compared with women in the same income bracket.

Comparing high-income-earning men to low-income-earning men reveals a similar pattern (Wolfson, Rowe, & Gentleman, 1990). In the late 1970s, men in the top 20 percent of income earners could expect 73.4 years of life at birth, compared with the 67.1 years expected for men among the lowest 20 percent of income earners. Thus, high-income men could expect 6.3 more years of life than low-income men. In addition to having a greater life expectancy, high-income men could expect about 14 more years of disability-free life than could men with low incomes. For women, the difference was 8 years (Epp, 1986, p. 4).

Income level is also directly related to life expectancy at birth for women, although, as shown in Table 5, differences between low-income women and high-income women are not as great as for men. High-income women, however, could expect 79.4 years of life at birth, compared with 73.4 years for men, for a difference of 6 additional years of life for high-income women compared with high-income men. The difference in life expectancy at birth for high-income women compared with low-income men is the most dramatic — 12.3 additional years of life.

TABLE 3.5 *Income Level by Quintiles and Life Expectancy at Birth, by Sex, Canada, Late 1970s*

	Life Expectancy at Birth	
Income Quintiles	**Female**	**Male**
First	76.6	67.1
Second	77.6	70.1
Third	78.5	70.9
Fourth	79.0	72.0
Fifth	79.4	73.4
Total	78.3	70.8

Source: Hay (1988, p. 30); adapted from Wilkins and Adams (1983, p. 1078, Table 3).

Life expectancy at birth increased for both males and females during most of the twentieth century. Associated with this increase is an increased average age at death and a transition in the major causes of mortality away from infectious diseases and toward chronic and degenerative diseases.

INTERNATIONAL COMPARISONS

Life expectancy at birth in Canada compares very well with that of the member nations of the Organisation for Economic Co-operation and Development (OECD). Canada ranks third, behind only Switzerland and Japan. On mortality rates overall, Canada again does well, coming behind only South Korea, Japan, Iceland, and Switzerland (ACPH, 1999, p. 28).

When Canadians are compared with others in countries where the populations have rated their own health status, again, they fare well. Canada comes in second, tied with the United States, with 90 percent of the population reporting good or better health. Only Norway surpassed Canada, with 92 percent. Sweden comes next at 77 percent, followed by Spain at 72 percent, Finland at 69, Germany at 46, and South Korea at 44 (ACPH, 1999, p. 28).

United Nations Measures of Human Development

Several efforts have been made to develop composite indices of health status that enable international comparisons over time. Probably the best known of these is a series of United Nations Measures of Human Development. This series, created in 1990, is an attempt to provide a view of human development as a multifaceted process. It is an important indicator of population health that measures development in terms of life expectancy, education, and standard of living. Canada has been ranked first of more than 170 countries on this measure in the last two United Nations reports. The other top ten ranked countries, in descending order, were France, Norway, the United States, Iceland, Finland, Netherlands, Japan, New Zealand, and Sweden (ACPH, 1999, p. 30).

When gender differences in longevity, literacy and school enrollments, and standard of living are included, Canada again is ranked first of 102 countries. In descending order, the top ten countries on this measure, introduced in 1998, were Norway, Sweden, Iceland, Finland, the United States, France, New Zealand, Austria, and Denmark (ACPH, 1999, p. 30). Canada's ranking slips to seventh of more than 170 countries on the Gender Empowerment Measure (GEM), following Sweden, Norway, Denmark, New Zealand, Finland, and Iceland. The eighth, ninth, and tenth positions were occupied by Germany, Netherlands, and Austria respectively (ACPH, 1999, p. 30). The GEM measures women's earned income share as a percentage of men's, and women's participation in politics and decision making positions. The fact that Canada drops in rankings when this measure is used indicates that there is still room for improvement in the area of gender equity.

On these three measures of population health, Canada does very well. But when the United Nations Human Poverty Index–2 (HPI–2) is applied, Canada slips to tenth place out of seventeen industrialized countries. The HPI-2 measures four variables:

1. longevity — the percentage of people not expected to live past age 60;
2. knowledge, indicated by the functional illiteracy rate;

3. standard of living, measured in terms of the percentage of people living below the income poverty line — the percentage of people who earn less than 50 percent of the mean disposable income of their society; and
4. participation, measured by unemployment for 12 or more months.

The top nine countries ahead of Canada on this measure are Sweden, Netherlands, Germany, Norway, Italy, Finland, France, Japan, and Denmark (ACPH, 1999, p. 30).

The Human Poverty Index-2 attempts to capture the notion that human poverty is not merely an economic measure and that it cannot be adequately measured by average (mean) national income. The United States, which has the highest mean national income of all seventeen industrialized countries, had the lowest poverty ranking on this measure. Sweden, on the other hand, was ranked thirteenth in terms of average national income and first on the HPI-2. In its most recent report on the health status of Canadians, the Advisory Committee on Population Health indicated that two lessons could be learned from this: first, " 'poverty' is not just about income — it is also about reduced opportunities in employment, education, and political life. Second, development progress is closely tied to the degree of inequity in income distribution in any given country" (ACPH, 1999, p. 31).

The United Nations indices are important measures of population health. It is clear that there is much work to be done in terms of developing indicators of population health that adequately capture and summarize the aspects of human social life that have measurable consequences for health status. It is also clear that despite Canada's good showing on these measures, there is still room for improvement.

INEQUALITY AND THE HEALTH GRADIENT

Since the 1970s, a major goal of the Canadian government's health policy has been to reduce inequities in the health status of the Canadian population (Lalonde, 1974; Epp, 1986). Accomplishing this goal requires more than equal access to medical and hospital care. A growing body of research shows that Canadians with low income and education levels are more likely to have poor health status, regardless of the health measure employed. Additionally, they have higher mortality rates for every cause of death (ACPH, 1999).

It is not just absolute economic deprivation that is related to poorer health status. Studies employing these health measures in analyses of socioeconomic status typically conclude that a socioeconomic gradient exists regardless of the health measure used.

There are hidden health hazards in society that fall more upon those at the lower rungs of the social ladder. It is not simply a case of the poor experiencing more illnesses and dying at higher rates than the well-off. It is also the case that *within* socioeconomic groups, those at every higher social position have increasingly better health. This is the case regardless of whether education, occupation, or income is used as the measure of socioeconomic status.

Primary social **determinants of health** include the categories of social status and demographic indicators. In the former category are status markers such as education, occupation, income, and employment status. Gender and age are the key demographic indicators. These status markers and demographic factors in turn affect the secondary determinants of health. The life course perspective contends that one's health both reflects the advantages of past social position and predisposes one to the advantages of future social position (Blane, 1999).

Secondary health determinants include behavioural factors such as cigarette and alcohol consumption, physical environment issues of working and living conditions, and psychosocial mechanisms such as stress, personal control, social support, and social involvement. As one might imagine, the pathways interweaving the primary and secondary determinants of health, as well as the biological or genetic determinants of health, are extremely complex.

Few Canadian studies have tested the theory that the socioeconomic gradient in health has its roots in the pathways between the primary and secondary determinants of health. It seems likely that the social circumstances that reflect and determine individuals' standing in the social hierarchy also determine gradients of health status through the myriad of secondary determinants mentioned above. For instance, income translates into the buying power to improve one's health in a multitude of direct and indirect ways. It also lessens the burden of social comparison that may lead to illness-causing stress and broadens and secures one's circle of friends. Education may be equated with higher social status since it typically leads to higher-paying occupations. Yet, education also provides the capacity for extending opportunities for acquaintances and knowledge. Occupational standing denotes social status via control over one's workplace and work pace, again broadening one's social network to provide functional support, increasing self-esteem, and leading to higher income and better benefits.

Of the secondary health determinants mentioned above, psychosocial mechanisms such as social support and stress are prominent within the current debate on health. Evidence points to the indirect benefit of social support as a buffer of the negative influences of stress upon health. Social support may partly prevent a person from being exposed to harmful stress in the first place (Madge & Marmot, 1987), and it may directly affect health by steering individuals away from negative health behaviours, promoting physician visits, and supporting healthy lifestyles (Stansfeld, 1999). Positive social support meets social needs via instrumental assistance such as financial aid, as well as informational support, social companionship, and emotional comfort (Tijhuis et al., 1995).

Williams and Collins (1995) note that given similar stressful events, the health of lower-social-status groups is affected more negatively than that of higher-status groups. Stress is the result of at least two types of stressors: life events such as bereavement, retirement, and job loss, and chronic stressors such as ongoing demands at work and home (Kessler & Wortman, 1989). The social isolation, anxiety, low self-esteem, and low levels of control induced by such stressors manifest as physical and mental health problems (Brunner & Marmot, 1999).

An analysis of the National Population Health Survey of Canada supports the existence of a social gradient in health. Five percent of Canadians within the highest income quintile rated their health as fair or poor, as compared with 10 percent of middle-income earners and 21 percent of lowest-income earners. Furthermore, 73 percent of the highest-income Canadians ranked their health as very good or excellent, compared with 61 percent of middle-income earners and 21 percent of lowest-income earners.

Of the factors mentioned, income receives the greatest attention as the most meaningful determinant of health within many countries. With respect to health, income as a marker of people's relative position within society takes precedence over income as a tool to improve absolute living standards. Evidence shows that median income within societies is less important than equality of income distribution in terms of health status indicators such as infant mortality rates (Waldmann, 1999), life expectancy rates (Wilkinson, 1999b), and self-rated health (Kennedy et al., 1999).

Each segment of our society suffers greater ill health than the segment above it in the social hierarchy, with the exception of those at the very top of such a ladder. How should such inequalities in health be addressed? This question points to the implications of confronting the issue of the social gradient in health versus the relative income hypothesis of income distribution and health.

For individuals in developed countries, the social gradient in health means that their social status leads to a certain health outcome, via direct and indirect pathways, compared with that of every other person in the society. Thus, improved health is the likely outcome for every individual if a society's entire social hierarchy is shifted upward. Whether the health of those individuals at the bottom half of the hierarchy improves to a greater extent than those in the upper half as a result of such a shift is debatable (Judge et al., 1998).

For those same individuals, the relative income hypothesis means that their standing as members of a particular social status group is an important health determinant. Regardless of their country's mean income, their life expectancies are greater in comparison to that of their counterparts in another country if their country's income distribution is more equitable. A comparison of countries with varying types of income distribution points to the health benefits of narrow income differentials for the entire population (Kawachi et al., 1999). Additional and related possible outcomes of smaller income gaps include an improved public education system, greater productivity and economic growth, decreased stress and violence levels, lower mortality rates, increased social cohesion, and stronger democracies (Kawachi & Kennedy, 1999; Wilkinson, 1999a).

CONCLUSION

This chapter has explored selected aspects of the relationship between the nature and organization of society and differential patterns of mortality and morbidity. It introduced the notion that health is a resource, and not just the absence of disease, as the foundation of the "population health promotion policy" framework. The "health as resource" perspective emerged from the health field concept introduced in the mid-1970s and subsequently developed as the determinants of health framework.

A presentation of selected health status indicators demonstrated that socioeconomic and power inequalities are inversely related to health status. Furthermore, the notion of a health gradient was introduced. This research-based finding indicates that it is not just absolute deprivation that is detrimental to health but that every step down the socio-economic ladder is associated with negative health consequences.

Using United Nations–developed indicators of human development, Canada's relative ranking in terms of population health status was summarized. Although Canada ranked high on all indicators, there is clearly room for improvement in terms of the more equitable distribution of wealth and power.

The "determinants of health–population health policy" framework clearly shifts the gaze of policymakers away from an exclusive focus on the health care system. By broadening our understanding of the factors involved in determining health status, it directs policymakers' attention toward the identification and coordination of the range of areas known to have a direct bearing on health. This range includes income security, employment, education, housing, business, agriculture, transportation, justice, and technology (Epp, 1986, p. 10).

Historically, policymakers in these areas did not have health promotion as a primary policy objective. Getting health onto the policy agenda in such a broad and diverse field of policymaking is a tremendous challenge. The challenge goes well beyond sensitizing and educating policymakers in these fields to the health consequences of their policy domains; in some policy domains, such as environment and economic development, health considerations can be seen as inimical to other policy objectives. Thus, the achievement of improved population health status through the reduction of inequities, although a desirable and achievable goal, is a process fraught with contradictions and conflicts.

ACKNOWLEDGEMENT

Parts of this chapter were previously published in H.D. Dickinson, Health and health care in Canada. In M. Kanwar & D. Swenson (Eds.), *Canadian sociology* (pp. 271–304). Dubuque, IA: Kendall/Hunt, 1999.

STUDY QUESTIONS

1. *Using the categories of the health field concept, discuss the observed patterns in mortality rates due to circulatory diseases, accidents, and lung cancer.*
2. *Using a determinants of health framework, outline and discuss some of the factors involved in gender differences in life expectancy.*
3. *What are some of the impediments to developing policies directed toward reducing the health gradient?*
4. *Would increased spending on the health care system result in improvements in population health status in Canada? Why?*

GLOSSARY

congenital anomalies Various inherited illnesses and conditions that are present at birth.

determinants of health A wide array of socioeconomic, political, cultural, psychological, genetic, and environmental forces and factors that determine health status.

health promotion The process for enabling people to take control over and improve their health.

infant mortality The death of a live-born infant within the first year of life.

life expectancy A statistical estimate of the number of years of life that members of a society can expect at birth; widely accepted as a primary indicator of population health.

mortality rates A measure of the rate of death within a population, expressed as a ratio.

neonatal period The first seven days of an infant's life.

population health An approach that addresses the entire range of factors that determine health.

RECOMMENDED READINGS

Advisory Committee on Population Health. (1999). *Toward a healthy future: Second report on the health of Canadians*. Ottawa: Health Canada. The second version of a comprehensive government report on the health status of the Canadian population; essential reading for anyone interested in health and health policy in Canada.

Epp, J. (1986). *Achieving health for all: A framework for health promotion*. Ottawa: Health and Welfare Canada. A policy document elaborating on the health promotion policy framework, particularly useful for understanding the goals of health promotion policy, the main challenges it has to address, the mechanisms of health promotion, and implementation strategies.

Evans, R.G., Barer, M.L., & Marmor, T.R. (1994). *Why are some people healthy and others not? The determinants of health of populations*. New York: Aldine DeGruyter. This important book is one of the first to bring together key research findings from within the determinants of health analytical framework.

Lalonde, M. (1974). *A new perspective on the health of Canadians: A working document*. Ottawa: Health and Welfare Canada. An important and highly readable policy document that lays out the key concepts for the population health–health promotion policy framework.

REFERENCES

Advisory Committee on Population Health (ACPH). (1999). *Toward a healthy future: Second report on the health of Canadians*. Ottawa: Health Canada.

Blane, D. (1999). The life course, the social gradient, and health. In M. Marmot & R. Wilkinson (Eds.), *Social determinants of health* (pp. 64–80). New York: Oxford University Press.

Brunner, E., & Marmot, M. (1999). Social organization, stress, and health. In M. Marmot & R. Wilkinson (Eds.), *Social determinants of health* (pp. 17–43). New York: Oxford University Press.

Dominion Bureau of Statistics. (1967). *Life expectancy trends 1930–1932 to 1960–1962*. Ottawa: Minister of Trade and Commerce.

Epp, J. (1986). *Achieving health for all: A framework for health promotion*. Ottawa: Health and Welfare Canada.

Epp, J. (1988). *Mental health for Canadians: Striking a balance*. Ottawa: Health Canada.

Evans, R.G., Barer, M.L., & Marmor, T.R. (1994). *Why are some people healthy and others not? The determinants of health of populations*. New York: Aldine DeGruyter.

Grayson, J.P. (1993). Health, physical activity level, and employment status in Canada. *International Journal of Health Services, 23*(4), 743–761.

Hay, D.A. (1988). Mortality and health status trends in Canada. In B.S. Bolaria & H.D. Dickinson (Eds.), *Sociology of health care in Canada* (pp. 18–37). Toronto: Harcourt Brace Jovanovich.

Judge, K., Mulligan, J., & Benzeval, M. (1998). Income inequality and population health. *Social Science and Medicine, 46*(4–5), 567–579.

Kawachi, I., Wilkinson, R., & Kennedy, B. (1999). Introduction. In I. Kawachi, B. Kennedy, & R. Wilkinson (Eds.), *The society and population health reader: Income inequality and health* (pp. xi–xxxiv). New York: New Press.

Kawachi, I., & Kennedy, B. (1999). Health and social cohesion. In I. Kawachi, B. Kennedy, & R. Wilkinson (Eds.), *The society and population health reader: Income inequality and health* (pp. 195–201). New York: New Press.

Kennedy, B., Kawachi, I., Glass, R., & Prothrow-Stith, D. (1999). Income distribution, socioeconomic status, and self-rated health. In I. Kawachi, B. Kennedy, & R. Wilkinson (Eds.), *The society and population health reader: Income inequality and health* (pp. 137–147). New York: New Press.

Kessler, R.C., & Wortman, C.B. (1989). Social and psychological factors in health and illness. In H.E. Freeman & S. Levine (Eds.), *Handbook of medical sociology* (pp. 69–86). Englewood Cliffs, NJ: Prentice-Hall.

Lalonde, M. (1974). A new perspective on the health of Canadians: A working document. Ottawa: National Health and Welfare.

Macran, S., Clarke, L., Sloggett, A., & Bethune, A. (1994). Women's socioeconomic status and self-assessed health: Identifying some disadvantaged groups. *Sociology of Health and Illness, 16*(2), 182–208.

Madge, N., & Marmot, M. (1987). Psychosocial factors and health. *Quarterly Journal of Social Affairs, 3*(2), 81–134.

McKay, L. (2000). Making the Lalonde Report. Towards a new perspective on health project. Health Network, Canadian Policy Research Networks, Background Paper. CPRN. www.cprn.com.

Mustard, F., & Frank, J. (1991). *The determinants of health.* Toronto: Canadian Institute for Advanced Research.

Rosen, G. (1963). The evolution of social medicine. In H.E. Freeman, S. Levine, & L.G. Reeder (Eds.), *Handbook of medical sociology* (pp. 17–61). Englewood Cliffs, NJ: Prentice-Hall.

Stansfeld, S. (1999). Social support and social cohesion. In M. Marmot & R. Wilkinson (Eds.), *Social determinants of health* (pp. 155–178). New York: Oxford University Press.

Statistics Canada. (1978a). Life expectancy (years) at selected ages for each sex and province, 1931, 1941, 1951, 1956, 1961, 1966, and 1971. In *Vital statistics,* vol. III, *Deaths.* Ottawa: Minister of Supply and Services (cat. no. 84-206).

Statistics Canada. (1978b). Death rate by sex and age, Canada, 1921–1975. In *Vital statistics,* vol. III, *Deaths.* Ottawa: Minister of Supply and Services (cat. no. 84-206).

Statistics Canada. (1982). *Causes of death, vital statistics,* vol. IV, *1981.* Ottawa: Minister of Supply and Services Canada (cat. no. 84-203).

Statistics Canada. (1988a). *Mortality, summary list of causes, vital statistics,* vol. III, *1986.* Ottawa: Minister of Supply and Services (cat. no. 84-203).

Statistics Canada. (1988b). *Causes of death, vital statistics,* vol. IV, *1986.* Ottawa: Minister of Supply and Services Canada (cat. no. 84-203).

Statistics Canada. (1997). *Mortality, summary list of causes, 1995.* Ottawa: Minister Responsible for Statistics Canada (cat. no. 84F0209XPB).

Stewart-Brown, S. (1998). Emotional wellbeing and its relation to health. *British Medical Journal, 317,* 1608–1609.

Tijhuis, M.A., Flap, H.D., Foets, M., & Groenewegen, P.P. (1995). Social support and stressful events in two dimensions: Life events and illness as an event. *Social Science and Medicine, 40*(11), 1513–1526.

Waldmann, R. (1999). Income distribution and infant mortality. In I. Kawachi, B. Kennedy, & R. Wilkinson (Eds.), *The society and population health reader: Income inequality and health* (pp. 14–27). New York: New Press.

Wilkins, K. (1995). Causes of death: How the sexes differ. *Health Reports, 7*(2), 33–43 (cat. no. 82-003).

Wilkins, R., & Adams, O.B. (1983). Health expectancy in Canada, late 1970s: Demographic, regional, and social dimensions. *American Journal of Public Health, 73*(98), 1073–1080.

Wilkinson, R. (1999a). The culture of inequality. In I. Kawachi, B. Kennedy, & R. Wilkinson (Eds.), *The society and population health reader: Income inequality and health* (pp. 492–498). New York: New Press.

Wilkinson, R. (1999b). Putting the picture together: Prosperity, redistribution, health, and welfare. In M. Marmot & R. Wilkinson (Eds.), *Social determinants of health* (pp. 256–274). New York: Oxford University Press.

Williams, D.R., & Collins, C. (1995). U.S. socioeconomic and racial differences in health: Patterns and explanations. *Annual Review of Sociology, 21*, 349–386.

Wolfson, M., Rowe, G., & Gentleman, J.F. (1990). Earnings and death effects over a quarter century. Research Papers Series, No. 30, Social and Economic Studies Division, Analytical Studies Branch. Ottawa: Statistics Canada.

NOTE

1. This information was provided with the cooperation of Statistics Canada. Readers wishing further information may obtain copies of related publications by mail from Publications Sales, Statistics Canada, Ottawa, Ontario KIA 0T6 or by phone at 1-613-951-7277 or national toll-free 1-800-267-6677. They may also facsimile their orders by dialling 1-613-951-1584.

PART 2

The Health Sector Workforce and the Delivery of Health Care

The basis of care in the health care system is the service provider. The three chapters in this section examine an array of factors that affect the nature, organization, and conditions of work for doctors and nurses and the consequences of these factors for service providers and recipients. These chapters focus on the two principal occupations in the health care system: doctors and nurses.

Soma Hewa argues in Chapter 4 that the development of the medical profession is usefully understood as an example of the rationalization of modern societies. Hewa describes rationalization as a process of grounding action in calculable, concrete, scientific evidence. With its roots in the Enlightenment, modern medicine came to be the dominant profession in the health care hierarchy, and the biomedical model has become the predominant one. Although still a powerful model and mode of practice, modern medicine increasingly is being criticized for reducing our understanding and treatment of illness to the realm of biology, and for failing to adequately consider the psychological, social, and environmental determinants of health and illness.

Hewa elucidates the main dimensions of the biopsychosocial model of health and illness and draws out some of its main implications for the social roles and functions of both patients and doctors. He maintains that the newly emerging model, if institutionalized in a reformed health care system, will result in a loss of medical dominance vis-à-vis other health care providers and consumers. He concludes with the suggestion that the biopsychosocial model heralds the arrival of postmodern society.

Wotherspoon, in Chapter 5, focuses on the development of nursing education and its relationship to the development of nursing as an occupation. He argues that contradictions inherent in the provision and utility of nurses in Canada have limited nurses' position in the health care division of labour and ensured their subordination to the medical profession and hospital management. He argues further that medical dominance was partly facilitated and secured by the subordination of nursing.

Wotherspoon analyzes the nature and organization of contemporary nursing education and the contradictory consequences it has for the power and autonomy of nurses. Current educational and professionalization strategies are contributing to a significant fragmentation and differentiation of nursing work. The implications of this trend for professional development strategies are explored.

Varcoe and Rodney, in Chapter 6, focus on the nature and consequences of health care reforms, particularly hospital reforms, for nurses and patients. They argue that these reforms are a reflection of a corporate ideology that stresses the need to do more with less in the face of perpetual scarcity. The ideology of scarcity, combined with the biomedical model of health and illness, has given rise to a form of work organization in which only a limited range of health care needs are recognized as legitimate. As a result, only a few health care services are valued, while others are considered to be dispensable. Thus nurses increasingly are discouraged, if not prohibited, from providing the emotional care required by many patients and their families.

The consequences of health care reforms and these management regimes for patients are a reduced quality and quantity of care. For nurses, the consequences are high levels of personal stress, distress, and disease. Many nurses respond to the distress by donating their private time to the job so that they can perform the essential functions of care that current corporate management regimes disallow. Some nurses have developed strategies of resistance to corporate imperatives and sabotage of management regimes in their attempts to provide care for patients and their families. Varcoe and Rodney conclude their chapter with the observation that an informed critique of current reforms is a prerequisite for real health care reform.

4

Physicians, the Medical Profession, and Medical Practice

SOMA HEWA Research in Philanthropy and Social Development

INTRODUCTION

When was the last time you saw your family doctor? Most likely, you were sick and needed treatment. When we think of health and medicine, we usually think of the doctor. There is a very good reason for that: one cannot buy a prescription drug without the recommendation of a doctor, and one cannot be admitted to a hospital, consult a specialist, or have a test done without first seeing a physician. This is why doctors are usually regarded as the "gatekeepers" of our health care system. Furthermore, people tend to seek the physician's assistance when they are most vulnerable both physically and emotionally. Thus, it is natural that people develop a strong confidence and trust in the physician's role as a provider of medical care. Traditionally, the physician has been society's premier representative of the ultimate value of health.

Medicine and medical practice in modern society are intimately related. They both evolved in response to a particular value system that transformed Western civilization. This transformation, which began in the sixteenth and seventeenth centuries, has been described by Max Weber in terms of a process of **rationalization**, which encouraged individuals to seek calculable, concrete evidence based on empirical observation, instead of relying on metaphysical speculation about the world. For instance, rather than assuming that supernatural forces caused certain illnesses, individuals began to focus on empirical investigation. This process of rationalization continues, in that modern medicine is inclined to explain illness in terms of measurable biological parameters and to treat the patient as a biological organism. This feature of medicine has since come to be called the **biomedical model**. In recent years, the tendency of this approach to neglect social and psychological factors has been criticized. Indeed, many now argue that the current approach to health and illness, wherein life events and biological disorders are "medicalized," is simply inadequate. They suggest that health and illness must be understood in terms of a new medical model that includes not only biological parameters but also social, psychological, and environmental factors.

This chapter has two objectives. The first is to examine the historical contexts in which the biomedical model emerged, as well as the model's implications for the development of the medical profession and the practice of medicine in modern society. Here, we will emphasize that by its determined adoption of scientific and technological advances, medical practice in modern society has overlooked the socioeconomic conditions of the person. Second, with a view to the specific limitations of the biomedical model, this chapter discusses the structural parameters and components of the proposed **biopsychosocial model** and its potential for medical practice. In particular, it will examine the extent to which this new model has gained support in Canadian society during the past few years. Although the discussion is largely based on general interpretations of medical practice and the development of the medical profession within the framework of the biomedical model, this chapter will draw attention to specific Canadian studies.

THE PROCESS OF RATIONALIZATION

In his well-known book *The Protestant Ethic and the Spirit of Capitalism*, Max Weber observed that he was interested in ascertaining "those psychological sanctions which, originating in religious belief and the practice of religion, gave a direction to practical conduct and held the individual to it" (Weber, [1920] 1958, p. 97). Weber's aim was to show how Protestantism had given new impetus and new meanings to the rational pursuit of social and economic activity. According to Weber, the anxious search by Protestant Christians for the certainty of eternal salvation resulted in a fundamental change in the individual's interpretation of the world during the Reformation. For Weber, the change was away from mysticism and traditional ways of thinking and doing things. It was the beginning of the process of rationalization in the West — the capacity of the individual to think logically and rationally. Weber called it "instrumental rational action," which he defined in terms of predictability and calculability. That is, the goal and the means are methodically and rationally linked: "Action is instrumentally rational," argued Weber, "when the end, the means, and the results are all rationally taken into account and weighed" (Weber, [1922] 1978, p. 26). Rationalization emphasized calculability and predictability as the basis for social actions and rejected metaphysical speculations.

Weber suggested that the process of rationalization has penetrated almost every aspect of life — medicine, science, arts, music, commerce, and public administration, to mention a few — and has produced unparalleled development in the West. The liberation of the individual from traditional ways of thinking and the emphasis on empirical observations opened up a wide range of technological developments and scientific discoveries. For example, the invention of the printing press facilitated communication among nations, and the development of the mariner's compass removed traditional obstacles to reaching distant lands by sea. Renaissance advancements in measurement and the understanding of perspective (a popular theme in painting) indicate a general refinement of people's inquiry into the empirical world, a refinement also evident in medical developments during this time. The discovery of the circulation of blood (*De motu Cordis*) in 1628 by William Harvey (1578–1657) revolutionized the understanding of the human body. Harvey described this circulation by comparing the human body to a large mechanical system. His conclusions, based on direct observation rather than speculation, not only eliminated the existing metaphysical explanations but also laid the foundation for the mechanistic view of the human body.

Harvey's discovery was reinforced by René Descartes (1596–1650). In his *Treatise of Man*, published in 1664, Descartes clearly separated the human body from the mind. In so doing, he subscribed to what was known during his time as the "analytical method." That is, entities to be investigated are resolved into separable causal units. The whole could be understood, both materially and conceptually, by reconstituting the parts. The Cartesian mind–body dualism expanded Harvey's mechanical analogy of the human body by insisting that the body is composed of separate but independent parts, directed by a rational soul located in the pineal gland. As Descartes described it: "I must describe to you first the body by itself...I assume the body is nothing else than a statue or machine...indeed, the nerves of the machine I am describing to you may very well be compared to the pipes of the machinery of fountains, its muscles and its tendons to various other engines and devices which serve to move them...its heart is the spring" (Descartes, [1664] 1927, pp. 350–354). This mechanical model of the body was compatible with the technological and scientific developments following the Renaissance.

Although this new scientific and rational thinking led to many economic and social benefits for the individual, it undermined traditional social values. The dominant social values in modern society tend to alienate the individual from his or her social environment. For Weber, the irony here is that the rationalization that occurred as a response to religious beliefs eventually created its own antithesis: that the rational individual no longer gives credit to human social values. This is the price that modern society has paid for its pursuit of empirical truth. Weber described this paradox in his closing remarks of *The Protestant Ethic*: "For the last stage of this cultural development, it might well be truly said: specialist without spirit, sensualist without heart." The rational scientific paradigm, Weber contended, has "trapped" humankind forever in an "iron cage" (Weber, [1920] 1958, p. 182).

THE BIOMEDICAL MODEL

The foundation of modern Western medicine is generally described as the biomedical model. It assumes that diseases are the results of deviations in the normal functioning of biological (somatic) variables. Further, it distinguishes between the body and the mind, and asserts that disease can be treated separately from the mind. As diseases represent some form of departure from the normal order of biological variables, they can be cured by medicine, which restores the normal functioning of the body. The body is thus like a machine, and any breakdown of it — a disease — can be repaired. Since medicine assumes the mechanical metaphor, it presumes that the doctor is a mechanic who undertakes the task of repairing the dysfunctional body. As the whole biomedical model — the body, disease, medicine, and doctor — has been understood in terms of a mechanical metaphor, it is described as the "mechanistic biomedical model" (Engel, 1977; Hewa, 1994a; Hewa & Hetherington, 1995; Nettleton, 1995). This particular approach to the human body tends to overestimate the role of medicine as a technological imperative. Furthermore, the mechanistic view of the body increases with the fragmentation of knowledge about the human body, which is a result of medical specialization and the development of medical technologies. Consequently, it leaves no room within its framework for the social, environmental, behavioural, and psychological dimensions of health and illness (Nettleton, 1995). The biomedical model not only requires that the disease be dealt with as an entity independent of social and behavioural factors, it also advocates that behavioural disorders themselves are caused by biochemical or neuropsychological deficiencies. Subjective interpretations of health and illness are deemed irrelevant.

Clearly, biomedicine takes a reductionist approach to disease. The complex phenomenon of disease is reduced to a single primary principle of cause and effect. Here, the primary causal factor is physical, which can be explained in terms of the language of chemistry and physics. The philosophical foundation of the mechanistic biomedical model was reinforced in the nineteenth century by the development of the **germ theory of disease**, which postulated that every disease was caused by a specific, identifiable agent (such as a bacterium or virus). Cures were sought that were understood to destroy the infecting agent within the biological realm. In a series of empirical studies between 1861 and 1880, Louis Pasteur demonstrated that injection of *cholera vibrio* into chickens produced this (and no other) disease. In 1882, Robert Koch discovered the *tubercle bacillus*, which was pronounced as the cause of tuberculosis. These two important discoveries contributed to the doctrine of "specific etiology" and the concept of a "magic bullet" (chemical agents that destroy the organisms). Researchers aimed to find single, specific causes of disease and then to destroy them with "magic bullets," leaving other organisms unharmed (Jones & Moon, 1987). Although the germ theory was a major breakthrough in the development of medicine, it also convinced scientists to focus exclusively on laboratory procedures. Instead of making the reasonable judgement that bacteria and viruses are the prime causative agents of disease (their pathogenic effects being mediated by socioenvironmental conditions), supporters of the germ theory totally dismissed the importance of nonbiological factors. Thus, the practice of medicine in the twentieth century came to rest solidly on the following premises:

1. Disease is a process accounted for by deviations from the norm of measurable biological parameters.
2. Disease is best understood by means of a science like pathophysiology, where principles are formulated in terms of molecular biology, biochemistry, and physics.
3. The human patient is a biological organism ("whole body") such that, in Descartes' phrase, "were there no mind in it at all, it [the body] would not cease to have the same functions."
4. Each part of the body is thus a field for specialized knowledge.
5. The cure for disease is typically achieved physically (e.g., reducing or neutralizing the pathogenic agent).
6. Medicine is an applied science developed through laboratory research (Foss & Rothenberg, 1987, pp. 29–35; Engel, 1977, pp. 131–132).

The relationship among these specific components of the biomedical model — physician (the observer), medical technology (means of observation, or diagnosis), patient (the observed), and medicine (the "magic bullet") — can be illustrated in a simple model, as in Figure 1. It shows that, consistent with the mind–body dualism, the physician is a detached observer — a vital requirement to ensure scientific objectivity in the biomedical model. Thus, medical technology stands between the patient and physician. It is through the lens of technology (various laboratory tests and physical examinations) that illness is diagnosed and an appropriate therapy — the "magic bullet" —

determined. This entire process is unaffected by the patient's socioeconomic and psychological conditions.

THE PHYSICIAN AND THE PRACTICE OF MEDICINE

Being imbued with the mechanical metaphor of the biomedical model, modern physicians require an objective stance when dealing with an illness. Their self-image reflects the view of medicine as a discipline that has adopted not only the rationality of the scientific method, but also the accompanying values of science, such as objectivity. Although physicians themselves are aware of the difference between scientists who undertake pure laboratory research and medical practitioners who are trying to alleviate pain and suffering, the medical profession continues to give privilege to the work of scientists. One of the dominant assumptions that has evolved from the biomedical model is that the physician as a practitioner is guided primarily by a set of objective and scientific rules (Mishler, 1989). Thus, no formal attention need be given to the patient's subjective interpretation, which would only undermine the due process of diagnosis and the selection of appropriate treatment. Medical students are taught to be emotionally detached from their patients; they must learn to separate emotions, feelings, values, and other normative circumstances when exercising their judgement regarding an illness. These were the perceived attributes of a "great physician" in the earlier part of the century (Shryock, 1979), and they continue to be so in our day (Pietroni, 1991).

The emphasis on separating physician from patient increased over time with the development of diagnostic technology. For instance, the history of medicine can be seen primarily in terms of technological advancement. A prominent medical doctor writes:

FIGURE 4.1
The Biomedical Model of Health and Illness

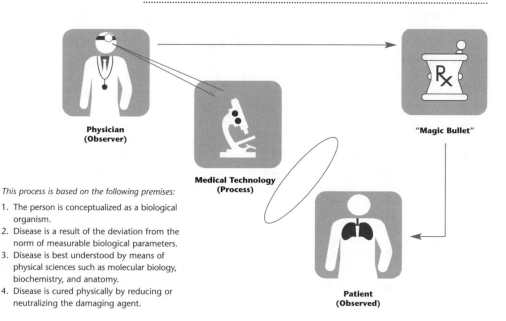

Physician
(Observer)

Medical Technology
(Process)

"Magic Bullet"

Patient
(Observed)

This process is based on the following premises:

1. The person is conceptualized as a biological organism.
2. Disease is a result of the deviation from the norm of measurable biological parameters.
3. Disease is best understood by means of physical sciences such as molecular biology, biochemistry, and anatomy.
4. Disease is cured physically by reducing or neutralizing the damaging agent.

"The identifying of disease sites became gradually more specific as diagnostic tools, such as the stethoscope, were invented. With the aid of improved technology in the making of lens systems, it came to be appreciated that organs sicken because the microscopic cells within them sicken" (Nuland, 1988, p. xviii). While the importance of such tools is not being questioned here, it is also true that the power they are given has tended to come at the expense of the patient, who has become an increasingly passive and less reliable source of information for diagnosing illness. While technology and laboratory charts have slowly gained credibility as part of the physician's routine examinations, the consideration of nontechnical information has gradually diminished (Engel, 1977). According to Reiser (1993), the diagnosis of illness by the physician has evolved in three stages:

1. *The patient's statements describing the illness and symptoms.* Also known as the "clinical dialogue," the patient's statement was partly guided by the physician's careful questioning about the history and symptoms of the illness. Although the patient's narrative of the illness and its symptoms was based on lay knowledge, skilled clinicians produced valuable descriptions of diseases prior to the development of advanced laboratory procedures and medical technologies. More importantly, the physician was not an entirely detached observer.
2. *The physician's observation of symptoms and the patient's behaviour.* This method was somewhat different from the previous one, in that the physician observed the external symptoms of the patient's body, skin colour, tongue, facial expressions, breathing order, blood, urine, and stools. These observations were often supplemented by the comments pertaining to the patient's behaviour. The physician sensed specific symptoms. For example, by touching the patient, the physician was able to measure the regularity and quality of the pulse, as well as the body temperature.
3. *The modern development of laboratory tests and visual technology.* The development of visual technology and laboratory tests provides a security blanket for both patients and physicians. For patients, it means precise and accurate diagnosis of their illness, a vital requirement for effective treatment. For the physician, the technology helps to reduce substantially the personal effort required to properly diagnose the illness. It also reduces the amount of time that physicians must spend to evaluate the case history of each patient. Furthermore, in contemporary medical practice it reduces the burden of lawsuits; the battery of tests eventually verify that the physician has done everything he or she could do to treat the patient. Studies have shown that many laboratory tests and X-rays ordered by physicians yield very little information that is new or useful for the diagnosis. Such tests have been described as "defensive medicine" — the use of technologies as diagnostic procedures to avoid litigation (Hersey, 1972; Reiser, 1993, pp. 170–171). Also, third-party payment systems, like the publicly insured medical program in Canada, offer an incentive for doctors to order such procedures (Rachlis & Kushner, 1989).

The persistent demand for machine-produced evidence in the late twentieth century stems from the belief that science and technology can produce accurate and reliable information. Further, it is based on the assumption that the scientific spirit entered clinical practice through technology. The physician who utilizes laboratory procedures to diagnose illness views himself or herself as a "scientist." Thus, contemporary physicians tend to attach a hierarchical value to medical evidence in terms of their relevance: facts obtained through complex scientific procedures are believed to be more accurate and relevant to diagnosis than are facts physicians detect with their own senses, which, in turn, are treated as being of more value than facts disclosed by the patients themselves. Therefore, the medical practice of a physician who employs laboratory procedures may be regarded as superior to that of the physician who relies solely on his or her clinical observations. This is particularly true when assessing prose clinical records, in contrast to laboratory evidence delineated into precise medical "facts" by numbers and graphs. In this way, the progress of medical knowledge is represented by the fact that qualitative observations have been replaced by quantitative observations. Thus, some physicians find it uncomfortable to use terms such as "a little bit," or "a good deal" in clinical reports, and have more confidence in expressing themselves in terms of grams, degrees, and seconds. Such quantitative expressions reduce the level of "anxiety" among physicians, particularly in uncertain situations (Reiser, 1993, p. 162).

The ready acceptance of laboratory tests as part of the clinical diagnosis has also contributed to physicians' distrust of their own observations of illness. They have largely abandoned their own judgements in the face of technological and laboratory advances. This process has diminished individual doctors' ability to examine patients thoroughly; if physicians believe they can get all the answers in a report from the laboratory, they will often stop their own search for the clinical evidence of disease (Engel, 1976). This also gives physicians time to see more patients and spend less time in clinical examinations. Thus, a critically ill patient might "get a dozen people around the clock, all busily preoccupied with his heart rate, pulse, electrocardiogram or pulmonary functions, his secretions or excretions but not with him as a human being" (Kubler-Ross, 1970, p. 9). It is also true that medical technology provides a powerful shield for those within the profession to defend themselves from the perception that medicine is of only limited use to a critically ill patient. If the patient dies, the physician is able to demonstrate that *everything* was done and, therefore, that the death was not preventable.

The emphasis on objectivity and empirical observation that became an important aspect of the biomedical model has effectively removed the physician from treating the "whole person." The process of separating the body from the whole person was accentuated by the development of medical specialization in the early twentieth century, which enabled physicians to further narrow their concentration and acquire a greater precision in this knowledge. The increasing reliance upon medical technology has become a symbol of objectivity in medical practice. Any diagnostic failure is attributed to the current lack of medical knowledge or appropriate technical tests. In this way, medicine has become increasingly technologically based, abstract knowledge that, as we shall now see, has contributed to the professionalization of medicine.

THE PROFESSIONALIZATION OF MEDICINE, OR THE RATIONALIZATION OF "VOCATION"

As noted earlier, Weber suggested that the process of rationalization has penetrated into every aspect of modern society. He described rationality in terms of a wide range of concepts in different social and historical contexts (Albrow, 1990). For example, in rationality as calculation, Weber illustrated the importance of calculability in economic life. Calculability became the defining feature of rational commerce and the development of modern Western capitalism. In rationality as logic, Weber discussed the role of precise and abstract concepts in natural sciences, philosophy, and, more importantly, in law. Formal rationality in these disciplines, according to Weber, guarantees clarity, consistency, certainty, coherence, and system, which are all attributes of reason (Weber, [1922]1978, pp. 880–882). It is in rationality as science that Weber developed his ideas about the development of professions. For Weber, scientific knowledge, both natural and social, has removed humans from irrational foundations (myth and magic). The empirical sciences represent the mastery of a seemingly complex world by rational knowledge: "Science today," argued Weber, "is a 'vocation' organized in special disciplines in the service of self clarification and knowledge of interrelated facts. It is not the gift of grace of seers and prophets dispensing sacred values and revelations, nor does it partake of the contemplation of sages and philosophers about the meaning of the universe. This, to be sure, is the inescapable condition of our historical situation" (Weber, [1922] 1946, p. 152). Weber contended that technical competence and the knowledge of minute details of the materials involved in work are the key to both autonomy and power among professions. Although he developed these observations specifically in connection with professional bureaucrats in modern organizations, "knowledge" and "technical competence" immediately suggest professional experts like physicians today. Furthermore, the bureaucratic structure is as important a part of medical practice in modern society as in any other profession (Weber, [1922] 1947, p. 339, also n. 59).

Weber's ideal types of the power and authority of modern professions have been further elaborated in recent years by a number of sociologists (e.g., Goode, 1957; Greenwood, 1957; Freidson, 1970; Berlant, 1975). The characteristics of a profession identified by these studies are relevant to understanding the current medical profession:

- prolonged training in a body of specialized and abstract knowledge;
- emphasis on the notion of providing a service;
- rights to set educational standards and entry requirements;
- the power to regulate professional conduct, review complaints against the members, and recommend disciplinary actions; and
- members who are strongly identified with their profession.

Sociologists often consider medicine the ideal type of profession and compare other occupations, implicitly or explicitly, against it. The medical profession has achieved almost unparalleled professional power, autonomy, prestige, and income. Most other occupations that seek to professionalize have taken the medical profession as their model. How did the medical profession achieve such dramatic progress? Medical sociologists address this question by reviewing the history of medical education and the rise of professional organizations within the medical profession (Cockerham, 1992). To understand the development of this profession in Canada requires a quick review of the history of medical practice and medical education in this country.

PROFESSIONALIZATION OF MEDICINE IN CANADA

The medical profession is largely responsible for the organization and the distribution of medical care in society. It controls medical knowledge by deciding who qualifies to be a member of the profession and how that person should practise. However, this wasn't the case when medical knowledge was still primitive. A brief review of nineteenth-century medical practice in Canada shows that irregular medical practice and the lack of professional standards were widespread. The limitations in medical knowledge meant a more diverse role for the physician as a medical care provider: "In his role as a general practitioner he practiced the skills of the surgeon, obstetrician, paediatrician, psychiatrist, and pharmacist, and he mastered all the knowledge medical science had to offer" (Canada, 1964, p. 229). The situation was further complicated by the continuing disputes between "regular" and "irregular" doctors over the legitimacy of credentials. Between 1815 and 1865, a series of statutes were enacted "to restrict the practice of medicine to those whom the recognized profession considered qualified" (Blishen, 1991, p. 9). However, in the absence of consensus among physicians about proper standards of practice, the law did very little to stop irregular practice. The level of medical knowledge was so limited that almost anyone could become a doctor after a short period of apprenticeship to a practitioner: "physicians learned their limited skills from their predecessors, who they served as apprentices. Practitioners tended to locate in the urban centers, leaving the inhabitants of rural areas to fend for themselves as best they could" (Blishen, 1991, p. 9). Although legislation failed to eradicate the problem of unqualified doctors practising medicine, it contributed to a growing trend to regulate medical practice in Canada. It also confirms that external regulations have a limited effect in controlling knowledge-based professions (Freidson, 1970). Regulatory mechanisms must evolve within the profession itself.

One of the key factors contributing to the professionalization of medicine was medical education. This being said, medical education was both backward and poorly organized in North America at the turn of the century. In Canada, there were about eleven medical schools, many of which were corporations without any controls. Even of those owned by universities, the faculty was partly or altogether comprised of independent practitioners who were trying to make ends meet. They had little or no time to conduct research or to supervise the clinical work of their students. After spending a year or two learning basic materials in core medical courses, the ambitious and the well-to-do students generally went to Europe for further studies and training. Universities normally defended the right of their students to license without further examinations before the medical boards, which had the authority to regulate medical education (Osler, [1885] 1982).

The condition of medical education in Canada and the United States at the beginning of the twentieth century was best described by Abraham Flexner, the author of the famous Flexner Report (1910) on medical education in these two countries (see also Chapter 1 of this book, pp. 5–6). Flexner found considerable variation among the curriculums, examinations, and entrance requirements of Canadian medical schools:

> In the matter of medical schools, Canada reproduces the United States on a greatly reduced scale. Western University (London, Ontario) is as bad as anything to be found on this side of the line. Laval (Quebec) and Halifax Medical Colleges (Dalhousie) are feeble; Winnipeg and Kingston represent distinct effort towards high levels; McGill and Toronto are excellent. (Flexner, 1910, p. 325)

In addition to being highly critical of the existing conditions of medical education in these two nations, the report had a profound impact on reorganizing medical education on a scientific basis. It took medical education away from the medical practitioners and placed it within the university educational system, so that the quality of this education could be maintained. The Flexner Report was comprehensive enough that its recommendations included nearly every aspect of medical education. Some of the key recommendations included:

1. Medical schools were to adopt a 4-year medical curriculum.
2. The laboratory teaching exercises and the quality of instruction were to be improved by creating a full-time faculty.
3. The clinical teachings were to be improved by introducing clinical advisers.
4. Medical schools were to become fully integrated into the university system.
5. Medical research was to be incorporated into teaching programs (Flexner, 1910, pp. 72, 101, 102, 105, 154).

In the United States, the immediate result of the report's release was that more than half of the 155 existing medical schools disappeared within a few years (Starr, 1982). In Canada, a number of steps were taken to reorganize medical education: "The good schools continued to move ahead, the intermediate schools moved to overcome the criticisms, and the poor schools made prodigious efforts to meet the standards outlined in the report. In the end, no Canadian medical school closed" (McPhedran, 1993, p. 1533). The quality of instruction was vastly improved by creating full-time faculty positions and better laboratory facilities for medical students. Also, the number of areas available for specialization and research was increased with access to hospital patients. However, general practice continued to remain the main focus of the education until the mid-1950s. The educational reforms that followed the Flexner Report placed medical education in North America within the parameters of the biomedical model and accelerated the professionalization of medicine.

Modern medical education, which is in large part a continuation of Flexner's recommendations, includes three levels: premedical, professional, and graduate studies. At the premedical level, students are provided with a basic knowledge in medical sciences and, to some extent, in behavioural sciences. At the end of the premedical program, students earn a bachelor's degree in arts or science or some other undergraduate degree. The professional level consists of 4 years of study leading to the M.D. degree. In the first 2 years, students are provided with instruction in preclinical subjects such as anatomy, histology, biochemistry, physiology, pathology, bacteriology, and pharmacology. In the last 2 years, they are introduced to the clinical sciences, and this is followed by a period of internship. The overwhelming representation of natural scientific disciplines in the core curriculum reveals the prevailing assumption that knowledge of the theories and methods of natural science will help the practitioner to learn the causes and cures of disease (Blishen, 1991, p. 79). A clear absence of social or behavioural sciences in the professional and graduate levels of medical education shows that knowledge in these disciplines is perceived to be irrelevant to medical practice.

Along with educational reforms, there emerged a more systematic organizational structure to evaluate and regulate educational standards. The Association of Canadian Medical Colleges (ACMC), established in 1943, is the only body that coordinates medical education in Canada. It has official relationships with the Canadian Medical Association (CMA), the Royal College of Physicians and Surgeons of Canada, the

Medical Council of Canada, the Association of American Colleges, and the American Medical Association. Established in 1953, the College of General Practice of Canada is solely concerned with the creation and maintenance of high standards in general practice. Its specific role is described as that of "an academic body with broad educational aims; to arrange for research in general practice, and for publication of original articles by general practitioners; to arrange for staff appointments for G.P.s, and suitable recognition for members in the field of general practice; to do all things necessary to maintain a high standard in general practice" (MacDermot, 1967, p. 138). The Royal College of Physicians and Surgeons of Canada, created in 1929, has the power to admit applicants for specialty practice, following a period of postgraduate training and passing the examinations of the Royal College (Grove, 1969, p. 152).

General practitioners have a limited knowledge in a broad field. Through specialization, they gain more competence and skills. As the field of expertise is narrowly defined, they can better master the learning materials and exercise a greater authority in their judgements. A broad range of such specializations has emerged in response to the development of medical technology and the growth of scientific knowledge. Specialization also brings more economic and political power for practitioners, along with prestige among their colleagues — a powerful incentive to become a specialist.

MEDICAL PRACTICE IN CANADA

After World War II, one of the main concerns of the Canadian Medical Association was to meet the increased demand for physicians in Canada. The baby boom in the 1950s and the influx of immigrants arriving in Canada after the war increased the demand for physicians. A number of key factors determine the demand for health care. The most critical factors are demographic variables such as death and birth rates, net migration, patterns of illness, and the age composition of the population. In addition to these demographic variables, changes in technology and consumer preferences can trigger some significant fluctuations in the demand for health care services.

The prediction of the future demand for medical manpower is a difficult task. Health care planning often fails to meet the demand, thus causing either a surplus or a serious shortage of trained personnel and facilities. In 1961, the Royal Commission on Health Service in Canada predicted a sharp increase in the Canadian population in the 1980s, which led to the expansion of existing medical schools and the creation of four new ones. However, the population did not increase as much as demographers predicted. To exacerbate the situation, the number of immigrant doctors arriving in Canada increased, while very few left the country during the same period. This has led to a sharp increase in the number of physicians in Canada since the 1960s. For example, in 1961, the physician–population ratio was 1:857. By 1975, the ratio had declined to 1:585; 10 years later, it had come down to 1:506. The ratios ranged from 1:476 in Quebec and 1:485 in Ontario and British Columbia to lows of 1:765 in New Brunswick and 1:803 in Prince Edward Island (Taylor, 1990, pp. 26–27).

Currently, in Canada, there are about 29 000 general practitioners, 19 000 specialists, and 7500 surgeons. General practitioners play a critical role in the Canadian health care system by providing medical care and making referrals to specialists (Ministry of Industry, 1997a, p. 118; 1997b, pp. 21–23). According to Table 1, on the average, there was

TABLE 4.1 *Population per Physician and Distance to Nearest Physician, by Province, Canada, 1993*

Country/Province	Population	Physicians	Population per Physician	Mean Distance to Nearest Physician (km)	Percentage of Population by Distance (km) to Nearest Physician					
					less than 5	5–24	25–49	50–99	100–149	150+
Canada	27 296 859	57 291	476	3.1	86.8	11.5	1.2	0.3	0.1	0.1
Newfoundland	568 474	1 139	499	6.7	72.4	24.0	2.5	0.1	0.3	0.8
Prince Edward Island	129 765	180	721	4.4	64.3	35.7	—	—	—	—
Nova Scotia	899 942	2 048	439	4.0	69.6	29.3	1.1	—	—	—
New Brunswick	723 900	1 090	664	5.1	62.8	35.5	1.7	—	—	—
Quebec	6 895 963	15 435	447	2.0	91.2	8.2	0.3	0.1	0.1	—
Ontario	10 084 885	20 760	486	1.8	90.7	8.9	0.3	0.1	—	—
Manitoba	1 091 942	2 239	488	6.2	78.4	16.8	2.5	1.2	0.2	0.7
Saskatchewan	988 928	1 547	639	8.3	67.9	20.5	10.0	1.3	0.1	0.2
Alberta	2 545 553	4 641	548	3.9	82.9	13.5	2.9	0.5	0.1	—
British Columbia	3 282 061	8 118	404	2.3	91.2	7.2	1.1	0.3	0.1	—
Yukon	27 797	40	695	23.6	68.4	13.6	4.6	4.0	4.3	5.0
Northwest Territories	57 649	54	1 068	155.2	57.3	0.7	0.2	3.9	6.5	31.4

Source: *1993 Canadian Medical Association Physician Master File*; 1991 Census. Adapted from Ministry of Industry (1997b, p. 29).

one physician for every 476 Canadians in 1993. In terms of accessibility, about 87 percent of the population lived less than 5 kilometres from the nearest physician. However, there was a remarkable imbalance in the distribution of physicians between urban centres and less developed rural and northern territories of the country. For example, in the Northwest Territories, the physician–population ratio was 1:1068 and the average distance to the nearest physician was more than 150 kilometres. Yet, according to some experts, Canada has too many doctors. They point out that since the 1970s, the population has been growing at a rate about 1.1 percent a year while the number of doctors has been growing at an average of 3.4 percent. Furthermore, they argue that Canadian medical schools annually produce about 1800 doctors. These doctors are joined each year by approximately 350 immigrant doctors. In the meantime, about 900 doctors leave practice annually due to retirement, death, career changes, or other reasons. To maintain the current physician–population ratio, which is already too high, critics recommend an immediate reduction of at least 500 doctors each year (Rachlis & Kushner, 1989, p. 139).

Although it is difficult to reach consensus about an ideal ratio of physicians to population, the World Health Organization (WHO) and the United Nations (UN) have developed an optimum physician–population ratio of 1:650 (Taylor, 1990, p. 198). This has given some strength to those who demand a sharp reduction in the number of doctors in Canada. The Health Manpower Advisory Committee, created in 1982, proposed that the number of general practitioners be reduced by encouraging trainees to pursue certain specialties, such as surgical and laboratory procedures, which need to be strengthened. The committee recommended a further reduction of postgraduate training of general practitioners by 125 per year. With all these adjustments, the committee anticipated a continuing surplus of doctors by the year 2000.

Any attempt to reduce the number of doctors is a politically unpopular measure. It means a reduction of opportunities for Canadians to pursue a career in medical practice. The alternative is equally unpopular with the Canadian taxpayers. Each physician adds $150,000 to $250,000 a year to the provincial medical care bill for income, overhead, diagnostic tests, prescriptions, hospital admissions, and so on. In recent years, concerned with maintaining limits on public spending and the need to address the rural shortage of physicians, provincial governments have been negotiating with the provincial medical associations to limit the number of doctors practising in urban centres and to provide more incentives for young recruits to set up practice in northern and rural communities (Taylor, 1990, p. 199).

TYPES OF MEDICAL PRACTICE IN CANADA

There are four types of medical practice in Canada: 1. self-employed solo practice; 2. partnership practice; 3. group practice; and 4. practitioners employed by government agencies, universities, private companies, and hospitals.

Self-employed solo practice is the most common type of medical practice. Solo practitioners have their own office, hire their own clerical staff, and refer patients to their colleagues. Most of them are general practitioners.

The second most common type of practice is the partnership practice among two or more physicians. Generally, these practitioners are in the same specialty. They share the same physical facilities, expenses, and revenue.

Group practice is different from partnership practice in a number of ways. It is a more formally organized medical enterprise among a number of physicians who may or may not be in the same specialty. They share expenses and income and employ nurses and clerical staff. Group practices often have their own medical laboratories, which provide a comprehensive service to their patients.

The last category is also described as bureaucratic practice because physicians in this type of medical practice are also subjected to the bureaucratic regulations of the organization or private agency that has employed them. Doctors employed by the Canadian Armed Forces, universities, or large business organizations are examples of this type of medical practitioner.

The first three categories of physicians are normally considered "private practitioners," the largest group of medical practitioners in Canada. All private practitioners earn income through "fee for service." Fee scheduling establishes a price for each medical service or procedure covered by the Canadian health care plan. The provincial medical associations and provincial governments negotiate the fee schedule. However, the medical associations themselves decide how the money should be allocated to the different specialties and services (Blishen, 1991, pp. 59–60).

PHYSICIAN–PATIENT RELATIONSHIPS

The preceding sections discussed the philosophical and theoretical basis of the biomedical model, and how, within that particular framework, the physician's role has come to be seen as that of a natural scientist. Viewed strictly from this perspective, the physician's role is drained of much of its actual meaning and life, and the physician tends to become an abstraction. But in reality, the essence of being a doctor lies in treating sick people. The task of treating the sick does not take place in a social vacuum; it involves a set of rules, norms, and expectations concerning the conduct of the physician and patient. Therefore, sociologists consider the physician–patient relationship a social system. Parties involved in this system are moved by sentiments and interests, as well as the formal status of their roles. Taking Weber's analysis of instrumental rational action as the general framework, Talcott Parsons's functionalist approach to society postulates that social relations are systems that exist in an equilibrium. What makes social life possible, according to the functionalist approach, is the expectation that people will comply with or function according to the norms and values common to their particular social system when they interact with each other. That is, even in highly emotionally charged and unpredictable situations, like illness, interactions are governed by harmonious and shared values. Parsons's conceptualization of the **sick role** as an integral part of the social system was one of the earliest attempts to define health and illness within a general theory of social action (1951, pp. 428–479). Although the theory has been subjected to much criticism over the years, it paved the way for the development of several alternative theoretical perspectives. The following section briefly examines Parsons's theory and some criticisms of it.

THE SICK ROLE CONCEPT

Parsons's functionalist perspective of the sick role is based on a number of assumptions concerning physician–patient relationships. There are four basic aspects of his model:

1. The individual is not responsible for his or her condition.
2. The sick individual is exempted from normal task and role obligations.
3. Being sick is undesirable, and one should want to get well.
4. The patient must seek competent professional help.

The sick role concept is based on the assumption that illness is a temporary state. The individual in that particular state is granted certain rights and privileges. Further, the sick individual is not responsible for the condition, and thus he or she is exempted from all personal responsibilities. The incapacity to perform one's social roles becomes the basis for the legitimate social exemption from such responsibilities. However, the presence of illness must be sanctioned by the medical profession. Although the sick individual is released from normal social roles, he or she must follow a therapeutic (curative) process to get well. Here, Parsons distinguishes between the biological basis of illness and its social context. Illness is, both biologically and socially, an altered state, but the extent to which a sick person is accommodated depends upon the norms and values of the given culture. Also, whether the sick individual is exempted from normal duties is determined by the severity of the illness. The more severe the illness, the greater the exemption; the less severe the illness, the less the exemption. Furthermore, in most illnesses beyond those that are relatively minor, spontaneous recovery is highly unlikely. Therefore, there is an obligation on the part of the sick individual and the family to seek out competent help and to cooperate in a concerted effort to restore health.

From a theoretical standpoint, it is unimportant whether recovery is spontaneous and a natural remission or is aided by a physician and drugs. What is important is that personal desire, the motivation of the sick individual alone, is not enough to get well. The sick individual must submit to a competent authority to gain recovery. The competent authority in Western society is the physician. Parsons believed that the sick role, if properly observed, becomes the social control mechanism necessary for the maintenance of the social system (Wolinsky, 1988, p. 105).

The sick role theory has been criticized by sociologists from a wide range of perspectives. Some critics have pointed out that Parsons's analysis may be applied only to acute physiological illness. Most acute physiological illnesses are readily noticed by the individual and brought to the physician's attention. Such illnesses are often cured and pose no threat of stigmatization for the sick individual who seeks professional help. In contrast, chronic conditions such as heart disease and cancer are not readily recognized by the sufferer, nor are they easily cured by medical treatment. Thus, in a chronic illness, like cancer, diagnosing the illness may take longer due to the initial delay in contacting a physician. This may pose a serious threat to life or cause irreparable damage to vital organs. Therefore, chronic illness, by its nature, is difficult if not impossible for the physician to treat in a way that would return the sick individual to health. Kassebaum and Baumann (1965, pp. 16–27) identified a number of factors that distinguish the sick roles of the chronically ill from those of the acutely ill. The chronically ill:

1. often find it difficult to resume normal role performance at a pre-illness level;
2. are generally confined to a permanent condition of disability, instead of a temporary condition;

3. are forced to accept current levels of role performance and autonomy, rather than attempting to regain the levels of performance and autonomy that existed at the onset of their illness; and
4. are more likely to experience a deterioration of their socioeconomic status.

These factors, particularly in a culture that emphasizes independence and self-reliance, can have devastating consequences for the sufferers' self-esteem. They can result in a fundamental breakdown in social interaction even within close circles such as family in Western society, where interactions are for the most part based on the notion of reciprocity: the chronically ill person who expects too much or makes too many demands is likely to be rejected by others (Freidson, 1970, p. 235).

The sick role theory has also been criticized from the perspective of physician–patient relationships. According to Gallagher (1976), Parsons's model is based on the traditional one-on-one therapeutic relationship occurring in the office of the private physician. For Parsons, this was unproblematic because he viewed this relationship as a reciprocal one: the doctor needs the patient, and the patient needs the doctor. Although it may be reciprocal, this relationship is not equal. In Parsons's formulation, the basis for control by the physician is vested in the necessity to provide therapeutic care to the sick patient. According to the sick role theory, this is straightforward in the case of curative medicine, especially when the patient wants to get out of the sick role. However, Gallagher and others have questioned whether this asymmetrical physician–patient relationship has any benefit to the patient. For example, the patient may have more knowledge about the conditions of the illness than does the physician. People often have an accumulated knowledge about their bodies, and they rely on that knowledge to maintain health and prevent illness (MacIntyre & Oldman, 1985). Further, when receiving preventative medical care, the patient is not in the sick role, and he or she is not obligated to comply with the physician's recommendations. Thus, critics argue that when the emphasis is on the prevention of illness rather than on a cure, the patient's own understanding of the problem (e.g., the impact of smoking on health) and participation in deciding on a particular treatment (how to quit the habit) contribute to a positive result.

Among many critics of the sick role concept, Freidson (1970) has drawn attention to the problem of transforming the identity of the person who suffers from an illness. This is especially serious at a time when there is a growing category of illnesses identified as "lifestyle" related problems:

> To be sick in today's society has ceased to designate a purely biological state and come to define a status, or even a group identity. It is becoming more and more evident that we perceive the reality of illness in these terms, for we tend to identify our neighbor as a "diabetic," almost in the same manner as we identify him as a "professor," or a "mason." To be sick henceforth constitutes one of the central categories of social perception. (Herzlich & Pierret, 1987, p. 53)

Illness may create a new identity for the person, who may never be able to get away from it. If the illness is considered to be serious and life threatening, people will react more seriously than they would in a situation of minor illness. On the basis of society's reaction to an illness, Freidson has elaborated Parsons's sick role concept by incorporating it with the **labelling theory** to make it more relevant to contemporary society. He examines three types of legitimacy that determine the extent to which the sick person is likely to be granted the rights and privileges of the sick role:

1. conditional legitimacy, in which the illness is curable and thus the sick person can get well easily — the legitimacy of the person's access to the sick role is conditional;
2. unconditional legitimacy, in which the illness is not curable and thus the sick person cannot do anything to get well — the person's access to the sick role is unconditionally legitimate; and
3. illegitimacy, in which the illness results in a stigma — the person's access to the sick role may be treated as illegitimate, and thus the rights and privileges of the sick role are unlikely to be granted.

Although Freidson's observations were strictly theoretical, they have some significant relevance to most real cases of illness. For instance, his observations on illegitimacy have been confirmed empirically by Segall (1976), who found a definite problem in the sick role concept when applied to mental illness. Segall argues that there is a fundamental difference in society's attitude toward physiological illness and psychiatric illness in North America. In physiological illness, argued Segall, the individual is expected to seek professional help and is not subjected to stigmatization. By contrast, seeking professional help for psychiatric illness often results in the stigmatization of the individual. The common assumption is, according to Segall, that psychiatric illness is inherently evil and that the sufferer is partly responsible for the condition. People who are known to have a history of mental illness often have difficulty in finding jobs and in getting along with other people without being rejected. Thus, mentally ill patients tend to stay in institutions even after they recover from the illness (Cockerham, 1989).

In an attempt to reconstruct the sick role concept, Freidson examines the process of the social construction of illness. He argues that the reality of illness that we perceive is often socially constructed rather than being real in the biological or physical sense. That is, our perceptions about "reality" are based on the way we see things and interpret them, not on actual physical evidence. Medicine, as a form of knowledge, has the power and the authority to "label" one individual as being ill and another as well, without actually having to investigate the conditions in which they live. According to Freidson, this means that medicine *creates* illness as a particular "state" that individuals may assume. For example, in some societies individuals are labelled as sick, whereas in others individuals with the same physical condition are not sick. Thus, Freidson argues that medicine's official social role is to create illness.

Unlike Parsons, who suggested that the physician legitimizes the sick role, Freidson argues that the physician is merely accessory to it by simply providing the social possibility of acting sick (Freidson, 1970, p. 206). This happens in two stages: the first step is to determine what specific qualities or attributes entail a state of health, or what represents the state of ill health; the second step is to study illness according to these defined conditions of health or the attributes of ill health. Freidson compares this process to the sociological study of deviance, in which sociologists first define the nature of deviance and then identify such individuals or groups according to the defined variables. Once a particular condition is identified as an illness, it is subjectively organized and transformed into a particular social role, which in turn is used to assign a new status. This leads to certain reactions on the part of society, which further help the individual to internalize the new status. This process of defining and identifying illness has transformed a wide range of conditions or "life events" into illnesses on the basis of subjective understanding rather than the objective reality of the situation.

THE PROBLEM OF MEDICALIZATION

According to some critics, medicine's monopoly in defining illness and wellness is not a neutral activity (Hewa & Hetherington, 1993). An increasing number of human behaviours are being defined as pathological. Conditions from attention deficit disorder (ADD) to alcoholism and being overweight are now considered to require experts. It is important to recognize that the tendency to define certain behaviours and conditions as pathological is intimately connected to the structure of power and its capacity to "depoliticize" the masses (Freidson, 1970; Zola, 1972; Riessman, 1983). This is possible insofar as people do not understand how their bodies function, what causes illnesses, and how to prevent them. These issues are considered highly technical matters that need to be explained by a physician. In this way, scientific expertise has generally usurped people's understanding of their own bodies, rendering the public passive, or depoliticized, in the face of medicine's technical authority. For instance, according to feminist critics of the medical profession, the medicalization of women's lives is a part of the larger attempt to maintain male dominance in society (Liddle, 1989). To act as a competent practitioner, the physician should be able to control the relationship with the patient. Thus, social control has become an important aspect of physician–patient relationships.

The impact of power is effective to the extent that doctor and patient share the concerns and assumptions that facilitate a relatively conflict-free interaction facilitated by patient compliance (Hardesty, 1988). For example, the threat of breast cancer makes it necessary for every woman to visit her doctor for regular checkups to ensure that she is cancer-free. In the course of these visits, the physician gradually gains the confidence of the patient and thereby becomes the real authority on the person's health. On the other hand, the person tends to develop a strong trust in the physician's assurances and may lose her own ability to cope with even minor ailments without consulting the physician. Thus, a person's natural ability to cope with life events is replaced by a dependency on expertise that is little understood (Illich, 1976; Hewa, 1994b).

Medical intervention to control the health status of individuals during the last few decades has resulted in a reconstruction of normal life events in terms of medical definitions. Death, birth, and illness are, for example, normal life events that are defined and acknowledged by society (Sudnow, 1967; Rothman, 1978). The medicalization of these socially defined life events legitimizes the medical control of life. According to Sudnow (1967), death is clearly a physical event that is socially defined, to the extent that two persons in a similar physical condition may be distinguished as dead or not. The same physical conditions may appear in both death and near death, depending upon what happens next. People who survive a life-threatening event are not dead and those who do not survive are dead. Physicians control the definition and diagnosis of death. For instance, those who are dead, within the institution of a hospital, are "pronounced" dead by physicians. The pronouncement of death, in turn, acknowledges death. In this manner, it has become a medical event rather than a social one. Similarly, birth is a socially defined, normal life event. Childbirth under normal conditions, with the assistance of a midwife or relatives, is basically a nonmedical event. But the medical presence is now viewed as a necessary condition for its safe conduct. Rothman (1978) has argued that since the beginning of the nineteenth century, medical intervention in the process of birth has redefined childbirth as a medical event and has discredited all the family and religious values attached to it.

Critical responses to the process of medicalization, as described, draw our attention to a host of important concerns; we turn now to a model for reconceiving medicine and medical practice along more holistic grounds, an approach urged by such critiques.

A NEW APPROACH TO HEALTH AND ILLNESS: BEYOND THE BIOMEDICAL MODEL

In his famous essay "Science as a Vocation," Weber made a sweeping generalization about the future of modern society: "The fate of our times is characterized by rationalization and intellectualization and, above all, by the disenchantment of the world" (Weber, [1922] 1946, p. 155). This was a reiteration of his earlier remarks in *The Protestant Ethic and the Spirit of Capitalism* ([1920] 1958, p. 183) that modern society is dominated by specialists and experts, whose attempts to find precise and calculable facts in all social actions through scientific methods have drained the human spirit; human society is lost in the midst of technical and practical reasoning. Weber's prediction about the domination of instrumental rational action in modern society is evident in modern medicine. Much of the mystery of the human body has disappeared in the past century as a result of the growth of laboratory science and the convincing victory of its mechanistic paradigm. Rationalization in the West has resulted in what Weber called the "intellectualization" of life and the displacement of human social values, and has given rise to the belief that everything can potentially be measured and understood by science.

There is no doubt that scientific and technological developments in medicine have vastly expanded the knowledge of diseases and the means of controlling them. Notwithstanding these achievements, the mechanistic paradigm in medicine has undermined our ability to understand the whole picture of the human existence. It individualizes illness and fails to take into consideration the social factors that produce illness (Doyal & Pennell, 1979). This reductionist approach of modern medicine is inadequate to deal with contemporary health problems. Moreover, as MacKeowan (1979) has pointed out, improvements in health such as the eradication of infectious disease owe much less to scientific medicine than to improved sanitary services, the supply of nutritious food, and education. MacKeowan suggests, as a result, that medicine is mistaken in its concentration on internal intervention and should pay greater attention to external influences and personal behaviours, which he considers the major determinants of illness. In this sense, medicine is a net that catches the victims of social, political, and economic ills, rather than a system that fosters and enhances health. Medicine and medical practice have been given credit for improving health when other social institutions have actually done more, and they have likewise been blamed for not alleviating health problems that are the responsibility of these other institutions (Duhl, 1986).

In light of these limitations of the biomedical model and the current practice of medicine, sociologists and some members of the medical profession have proposed a new approach to health and illness (Engel, 1980; Duhl, 1986; Foss & Rothenberg, 1987; Hewa & Hetherington, 1995). Although it is called a new approach, it does not suggest that the biomedical model be abandoned. Rather, it proposes to combine the biomedical aspects with the social, psychological, and environmental aspects of health and illness. Thus, it represents a wide range of concerns that influence health and illness. This new model is described as a biopsychosocial model of health and illness. According to this model, three fundamental systems collectively determine health and illness:

1. *Physiological System:* This pertains to the biological structure and includes all the subsystems, such as the circulatory system, respiratory system, immune system, nervous system, and digestive system. Organs in the system have their own components, such as tissues, cells, and molecules, which form the human body.
2. *Psychological System:* This includes emotions, aggression, and cognitive perspective. These elements fluctuate during normal life events; if the person is able to maintain a mental balance during periods of emotional stress, that person is considered to be mentally healthy. However, the loss of employment, family breakdown, or the death of a loved one can trigger a serious disorder in the psychological system (Liem, 1981). The psychological reactions to such events include depression, anxiety, and schizophrenia. They may also include a weakening of the body's immune system.
3. *Socioeconomic System:* Urbanization, industrialization, the environment, lifestyle, values, nutrition, and working conditions are included here. Such conditions change continuously, and their effects can be far-reaching. For example, urbanization, industrialization, the crisis in values, and automation in the workplace have been identified as the causes of health disorders aptly known as "problems in living" (Cockerham, 1992, p. 6).

As shown in Figure 2, within this biopsychosocial model, each system is a component of a larger system. For example, the individual is a psychological and physiological (psychosomatic) person interacting with the socioeconomic environment. On a larger scale, each person is a component of the family, and the family is a component of the community. Further, each system, subsystem, and component exists in equilibrium within and between systems. Therefore, it is incorrect to understand them simply as a collection of constituent parts. Accordingly, the diagnosis of illness on the basis of specific biochemical factors is incomplete because the manifestation of illness is a long and complex process that eventually appears as a biochemical deviation. In order to determine the cause of an illness, it is necessary to establish a relationship between the biochemical processes and the sociopsychological variables of illness. Thus, the physician's first source of information is the patient himself or herself or some other informed person. The clinical study is a dialogue between two "persons" (Engel, 1980, p. 538).

It is unrealistic to expect a well-developed biopsychosocial model to become fully integrated with medical practice in a short period of time. It may take several decades to create necessary public health policies, educational programs, and instruments that identify specific components and interactions among different systems. It is an ongoing effort by various professional groups, social activists, and policymakers to articulate this perspective. The growing recognition of this model in Canadian society is increasingly evident in health care policies and certain educational measures undertaken by the medical profession. The following section briefly examines such policy perspectives and their implications for the biopsychosocial model.

The **Ottawa Charter for Health Promotion** (1997) is an international policy statement sponsored by the World Health Organization (WHO), which worked with other organizations to convince all nations to adopt the charter as the guiding formula for their national health policies by the year 2000. It defines health as "a resource for everyday life, not the objective of living. Health is a positive concept emphasizing social and personal resources, as well as physical capacities. Therefore health promotion is not just the responsibility of the health sector, but goes beyond healthy lifestyles to well-being." It identifies a wide range of social, political, and environmental factors that influence health: "The fundamental conditions and resources for health are peace, shelter, education, food, income, a stable ecosystem, sustainable resources, social justice and equity. Improvement in health requires a secure foundation in these basic prerequisites" (WHO, 1997, p. 1). By means of this charter, health promotion is no longer a subject of rhetoric but one of public policy in Canada. Following the WHO initiative, a policy statement of Health and Welfare Canada, entitled *Achieving Health for All*, recognized

FIGURE 4.2

Biopsychosocial Model of Health and Illness

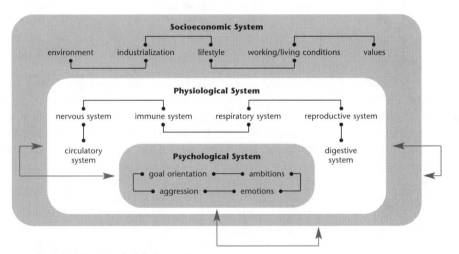

The systemic relationship is based on the following premises:

1. The individual is a psychological and physiological (psychosomatic) person interacting with the socioeconomic environment.
2. The primary determinants of health and illness are mutually interrelated psychological, physiological, and socioeconomic factors.
3. Disease is a result of systemic biopsychosocial disorder.
4. Appropriate treatment for disease includes psychological, physiological, and socioeconomic "counteractants" applied synergistically.

three major areas to be strengthened within the Canadian health care system: the reduction of socioeconomic inequalities; the promotion of healthy lifestyles; and the development of adequate facilities to cope with chronic conditions, disabilities, and mental health problems (Epp, 1986).

In view of these new policy perspectives, social scientists and public health experts have developed specific measures of health and illness that incorporate social and psychological factors and thus extend the traditional biomedical approach. These include subjective assessments by patients. For example, the Health Attitudes and Behaviour Survey of Canada (1986) identified a number of interactional issues affecting the health attitudes and behaviour of Canadians (Health and Welfare Canada, 1986). People's perception of illness and health is often complicated by psychosocial interactions. Studies have shown that all social classes experience stress in their working and living environments, which influence their emotional stability and health (Dohrenwend, 1975; Kessler, 1979). The survey reveals that emotional condition is a crucial variable for determining when people perceive themselves as ill and when they begin to act ill. Sometimes individuals perceive themselves as ill, although there is nothing biologically wrong. Their self-perception of illness may result from emotional distress caused by life events and their working and/or living conditions. This discrepancy between the self-perception of illness and the actual development of biochemical disorders needs to be taken into consideration when determining an individual's health. The survey also found that those who are strong and fit have the resources or reserves of health to effectively cope with illness.

Another integrated measure of health and illness is the **Activities of Daily Living (ADL) Index**, an active directory of health assessments that compiles data on the social, psychological, economic, and health status of people. It provides information about the individual's ability to perform daily living activities such as shopping, preparing food, taking medication, and handling finances. The ADL Index is a useful guide for evaluating the health conditions of the person (Kovar, 1995).

Numerous studies have demonstrated a clear link between poverty and ill health. Specifically, child poverty has been identified as a major factor contributing to learning disabilities, dropping out of school, and other behavioural problems. These findings have given a powerful voice to those who demand that the government should do more to eradicate poverty, unemployment, and homelessness in Canada. The current level of social spending, including the GST credit, the Child Tax Benefit, and Employment Insurance, is not adequate to deal with poverty effectively (Campaign 2000).

In the biopsychosocial model, the physician considers all the information pertaining to various system levels and their possible usefulness for understanding illness and care. As such, the physician–patient relationship does not begin at the onset of an illness. The practice of medicine requires the physician to be an activist in promoting healthy economic and social policies, environmental practices, lifestyles, and working and living conditions. Physicians for Smoke-Free Canada is one such project, dedicated to eradicating smoking. It lobbies provincial and federal governments to adopt tough legislation against the advertising and sale of tobacco products and organizes conferences to educate the public (Sullivan, 1993). Similarly, physicians often work with community groups to promote health education. For example, the Vancouver Women's Health Collective provides women with information about the functioning of their bodies to make them aware of alternatives to drugs and surgery (Health and Welfare Canada, 1984).

In 1994, with an objective to expand the activities of physicians and nurses beyond their traditional roles, Health Canada initiated a program entitled the Self-Care Project. The specific aim of the project is "to stimulate and support people's self care efforts by virtue of their knowledge, experience and accessibility, especially in primary care." The project has identified a number of interacting components whereby physicians can lend support for self-care. These include sharing knowledge, facilitating learning and personal development, and helping people build support networks (Health and Welfare Canada, 1999, pp. 1–2). These new developments, both in health care policies and in the role of health care providers, indicate a significant departure from the philosophy of the biomedical model toward the development of a more comprehensive approach to health and illness in Canada.

CONCLUSION

This chapter has examined the development of the biomedical model, the role of the physician, and the professionalization of medicine in terms of Max Weber's theory of rationalization. Western medicine and medical practice are intimately related, in that they both have evolved in response to the call for calculable and predictable social actions, a trend that became the dominant theme of Western civilization. The process of rationalization eliminated speculative and metaphysical interpretations of the human body. It also contributed to the development of scientific medicine, technological and laboratory procedures for diagnosing illness, and professional experts with objective knowledge. As a result, the practice of medicine became predominantly concerned with measurable physical symptoms as a deviation from the norm of biological parameters, rather than the more systemic causes of illness. In recent years, there has been a growing disenchantment with the biomedical model.

In view of these limitations in the biomedical model, this chapter examined the potential of the proposed new biopsychosocial model for medical practice. According to this new model, physiological, psychological, and socioenvironmental factors are interdependent systems that collectively determine health and illness. Some critics argue that the rise of consumerism and the growth of alternative forms of consumption and health are part of a broader cultural transformation — a move from modernism to postmodernism. In this view, the biomedical model was fundamentally a modernist project, in that it was based on the scientific orthodoxy, claimed a superior knowledge, and thereby secured a monopoly in the field of health (Bakx, 1991). At the present time, this monopoly of scientific medicine is gradually being dismantled in favour of alternative forms of care. Thus, there is an ongoing transformation, or "revolution," in Western medicine, which conceives a new role for health professionals as health strategists and gives greater responsibility to individuals and communities to actively engage in all levels of systems to promote health and avoid illness. In this new model, the physician–patient relation is an interactive process that shapes healthy social and economic policies, lifestyles, and environmental practices. Evidence suggests that the new model is gaining wider recognition in Canada.

STUDY QUESTIONS

1. *Critically discuss the key assumptions of the biomedical model and how these assumptions have shaped the nature of medical practice in modern society. Provide examples to elaborate your arguments.*
2. *In view of the current distribution of physicians in Canada, how would you propose to deal with the shortage of doctors in northern and rural Canada?*
3. *Critically examine the various components of the biopsychosocial model. What specific roles would you assign to individuals, families, and communities to maintain health and avoid illness? Provide examples to support your arguments.*

GLOSSARY

Activities of Daily Living (ADL) Index An active directory of health assessments that compiles data on people's social, psychological, economic, and health status.

biomedical model The foundation of modern Western medicine, which recognizes diseases as the result of deviations of the normal functioning of biological variables that can be cured by medicine.

biopsychosocial model A new medical model that incorporates biological parameters with psychological, socioeconomic, and environmental factors that collectively determine a person's health and illness.

germ theory of disease The doctrine of specific etiology that postulates that every disease is caused by a specific identifiable agent, such as a bacterium or virus; it seeks to find cures within the biological realm.

labelling theory The process by which people classify and characterize social behaviours and other individuals.

Ottawa Charter for Health Promotion Developed by the World Health Organization (WHO) and introduced at a conference in Ottawa, this document defines health as a broad perspective of everyday life that includes physical capacities, personal resources, and a wide range of social, political, and environmental factors that influence health and illness.

rationalization The political, social, and economic changes that followed the Reformation in the 16th and the 17th centuries; the key characteristic of the process is its emphasis on the predictability and calculability of human social conduct.

sick role The characteristic behaviours that a sick person adopts in accordance with the normative demands of the situation.

RECOMMENDED READINGS

Blishen, B. (1991). *Doctors in Canada*. Toronto: University of Toronto Press. A fairly comprehensive analysis of the development of the medical profession in Canada. Both historical and contemporary changes in the profession are discussed in broad social and political contexts.

Freidson, E. (1970). *Profession of medicine: A study in the sociology of applied knowledge*. New York: Harper and Row. One of the best interpretations of the development of the medical profession. By identifying the key characteristics of a profession, Freidson analyzes how the medical profession has become one of the most powerful occupational groups in modern society.

Nettleton, S. (1995). *The sociology of health and illness.* Cambridge: Polity Press. A well-written medical sociology textbook that neatly integrates social scientific perspectives into issues and problems of medicine and medical practice; the materials covered are thorough and extensive.

Rachlis, M., & Kushner, C. (1989). *Second opinion: What's wrong with Canada's health-care system and how to fix it.* Toronto: Collins. Two of the most vocal critics of the Canadian health care system, Rachlis and Kushner provide an interesting analysis of the current crisis in the distribution of services and the allocation of resources in simple and understandable language. However, this is not a sociological text.

Wolinsky, F.D. (1988). *The sociology of health: Principles, practitioners, and issues.* Belmont: Wadsworth. One of the best American textbooks in medical sociology; reviews an extensive array of secondary literature on a wide range of topics and is extremely useful for all levels of students in this field.

REFERENCES

Albrow, M. (1990). *Max Weber's construction of social theory.* London: Macmillan.

Bakx, K. (1991). The "eclipse" of folk medicine in western society. *Sociology of Health and Illness, 13*, 20–38.

Berlant, J.L. (1975). *Profession and monopoly: A study of medicine in the United States and Great Britain.* Berkeley: University of California Press.

Blishen, B. (1991). *Doctors in Canada.* Toronto: University of Toronto Press.

Campaign 2000, Report Card on Child Poverty in Canada. www.campaign2000.ca.

Canada. (1964). *Report of the Royal Commission on Health Services*, vol. I. Ottawa: Queen's Printer.

Cockerham, W.C. (1989). *Sociology of mental disorder.* Englewood Cliffs, NJ: Prentice-Hall.

Cockerham, W.C. (1992). *Medical sociology.* Englewood Cliffs, NJ: Prentice-Hall.

Descartes, R. ([1664] 1927). Treatise on man. In R.M. Eaton (Ed.), *Descartes selections.* New York: Charles Scribner's Sons.

Dohrenwend, B.P. (1975). Sociocultural and social-psychological factors in the genesis of mental disorders. *Journal of Health and Social Behaviour, 16*, 365–392.

Doyal, L., & Pennell, I. (1979). *The political economy of health.* London: Pluto Press.

Duhl, L.J. (1986). *Health planning and social change.* New York: Human Sciences Press.

Engel, G.L. (1976). Are medical schools neglecting clinical skills? *Journal of American Medical Association, 236*, 861–863.

Engel, G.L. (1977). The need for a new medical model: A challenge for biomedicine. *Science, 196*, 129–136.

Engel, G.L. (1980). The clinical application of the biopsychosocial model. *American Journal of Psychiatry, 137*, 535–544.

Epp, J. (1986). *Achieving health for all: A framework for health promotion.* Ottawa: Health and Welfare Canada.

Flexner, A. (1910). *Medical education in the United States and Canada.* New York: Carnegie Foundation for the Advancement of Teaching.

Foss, L., & Rothenberg, K. (1987). *The second medical revolution: From biomedicine to infomedicine.* Boston: New Science Library.

Freidson, E. (1970). *Profession of medicine: A study in the sociology of applied knowledge.* New York: Harper and Row.

Gallagher, E.B. (1976). Lines of reconstruction and extension in the Parsonian sociology of illness. *Social Science and Medicine, 10,* 207–218.

Goode, W.J. (1957). Community within a community. *American Sociological Review, 22,* 194–200.

Greenwood, E. (1957). Attributes of a profession. *Social Work, 2,* 45–55.

Grove, J.W. (1969). *Organized medicine in Ontario.* Toronto: Queen's Printer.

Hardesty, M.J. (1988). Information tactics and the maintenance of asymmetry in physician–patient relationships. In D.R. Maines & C.J. Couch (Eds.), *Communication and social structure.* Springfield, IL: Charles Thomas.

Health and Welfare Canada. (1984). Women and self care. *Health Education, 2,* 22.

Health and Welfare Canada. (1986). Health attitude and behaviour survey. *Health Promotion, 24,* 18–36.

Health and Welfare Canada. (1999). Self-care: Health care network. www.hc-sc.gc.ca/hppb/healthcare.

Hersey, N. (1972). The defensive practice of medicine. *Milbank Memorial Fund Quarterly, 50,* 69–97.

Herzlich, C., & Pierret, J. (1987). *Illness and self in society.* Baltimore: Johns Hopkins University Press.

Hewa, S. (1994a). The coming revolution in western medicine: A biopsychosocial model for medical practice. *International Review of Modern Sociology, 24,* 117–125.

Hewa, S. (1994b). Medical technology: A Pandora's box? *Journal of Medical Humanities, 15,* 171–181.

Hewa, S., & Hetherington, R.W. (1993). The rationalization of illness and the illness of rationalization. *International Journal of Contemporary Sociology, 30,* 143–153.

Hewa, S., & Hetherington, R.W. (1995). Specialists without spirit: Limitations of the mechanistic biomedical model. *Theoretical Medicine, 16,* 129–139.

Illich, I. (1976). *Limits to medicine.* Toronto: McClelland & Stewart.

Jones, K., & Moon, G. (1987). *Health, disease and society.* London: Routledge and Kegan Paul.

Kassebaum, G.C., & Baumann, B.O. (1965). Dimensions of the sick role in chronic illness. *Journal of Health and Human Behaviour, 6,* 16–27.

Kessler, R.A. (1979). Stress, social status, and psychological distress. *Journal of Health and Social Behaviour, 20,* 259–272.

Kovar, M.G. (1995). Health assessment. In G.L. Maddox (Ed.), *The encyclopedia of aging.* New York: Springer.

Kubler-Ross, E. (1970). *On death and dying.* New York: Macmillan.

Liddle, M.A. (1989). Feminist contributions to an understanding of violence against women — three steps forward, two steps back! *Canadian Review of Sociology and Anthropology, 26,* 759–775.

Liem, R. (1981). Economic change and unemployment: Contexts of illness. In E.G. Mishler et al. (Eds.), *Social contexts of health, illness and patient care.* New York: Cambridge University Press.

MacDermot, H.E. (1967). *One hundred years of medicine in Canada.* Toronto: McClelland & Stewart.

MacIntyre, S., & Oldman, D. (1985). Coping with migraine. In N. Black et al. (Eds.), *Health and Disease: A reader.* Milton Keynes: Open University Press.

MacKeowan, T. (1979). *The role of medicine: Dream, mirage, or nemesis?* Princeton, NJ: Princeton University Press.

McPhedran, T.M. (1993). Canadian medical schools before ACMC. *Canadian Medical Association Journal, 148*, 1533–1537.

Ministry of Industry. (1997a). *Canada year book.* Ottawa: Author.

Ministry of Industry. (1997b). *Health reports, 8*(4) (cat. no. 82-003).

Ministry of Public Works and Government Services Canada. (1997). *Health promotion in Canada: A case study.* Ottawa: Author.

Mishler, E.G. (1989). Critical perspectives on the biomedical model. In E.G. Mishler et al. (Eds.), *Social contexts of health, illness and patient care.* New York: Cambridge University Press.

Nettleton, S. (1995). *The sociology of health and illness.* Cambridge: Polity Press.

Nuland, S.B. (1988). *Doctors: The biography of medicine.* New York: Alfred A. Knopf.

Osler, W. ([1885] 1982). The growth of a profession. In C.G. Roland (Ed.), *Sir William Osler 1849–1919: A selection for medical students.* Toronto: Hannah Institute for the History of Medicine.

Parsons, T. (1951). *The social system.* Glencoe, IL: Free Press.

Pietroni, P. (1991). *The greening of medicine.* London: Victor Gollancz.

Rachlis, M., & Kushner, C. (1989). *Second opinion: What's wrong with Canada's health-care system and how to fix it.* Toronto: Collins.

Reiser, S.J. (1993). *Medicine and the reign of technology.* Cambridge: Cambridge University Press.

Riessman, C.K. (1983). Women and medicalization: A new perspective. *Social Policy, 14*, 3–18.

Rothman, B.K. (1978). Childbirth as negotiated reality. *Symbolic Interaction, 2*, 124–137.

Segall, A. (1976). The sick role concept: Understanding social behaviour. *Journal of Health and Social Behaviour, 17*, 163–170.

Shryock, R.H. (1979). *The development of modern medicine.* Madison, WI: University of Wisconsin.

Starr, P. (1982). *The social transformation of American medicine: The rise of a sovereign profession and the making of a vast industry.* New York: Basic Books.

Sudnow, D. (1967). *Passing on: The social organization of dying.* Englewood Cliffs, NJ: Prentice-Hall.

Sullivan, P. (1993). Doctors need to be more vocal in opposing smoking, AMA representative tells Canadian MDs. *Canadian Medical Association Journal, 148*, 249–253.

Taylor, M.G. (1990). *Insuring national health care: The Canadian experience.* Chapel Hill, NC: University of North Carolina Press.

Weber, M. ([1920] 1958). *The protestant ethic and the spirit of capitalism.* New York: Charles Scribner's Sons.

Weber, M. ([1922] 1978). *Economy and society.* G. Roth & C. Wittich (Eds.). Berkeley: University of California Press.

Weber, M. ([1922] 1946). *From Max Weber: Essays in sociology.* H.H. Gerth & C.W. Mills (Eds.). New York: Oxford University Press.

Weber, M. ([1922] 1947). *The theory of social and economic organization.* T. Parsons (Ed.). New York: Free Press.

Wolinsky, F.D. (1988). *The sociology of health: Principles, practitioners, and issues.* Belmont: Wadsworth.

WHO, Regional Office For European Policy For Health for All. (1997). Ottawa Charter for Health Promotion, First International Conference on Health Promotion, Ottawa, Canada, November 17–21, 1986. www.who.dk/policy/ottawa.

Zola, I.K. (1972). Medicine as an institution of social control. *Sociological Review Monographs, 20*, 487–504.

5

Nursing Education: Professionalism and Control

TERRY WOTHERSPOON University of Saskatchewan

INTRODUCTION

The first Canadian training school for nurses opened in St. Catharines, Ontario, in 1874. According to "The First Annual Report of The St. Catharines Training School and Nurses' Home, July 1, 1875":

> the skilled nurse, by minutely watching the temperature, conditions of skin, pulse, respiration, and the various functions of all the organs, and reporting faithfully to the attending physician, must increase the chances of recovery two-fold. (cited in Gibbon & Mathewson, 1947, p. 145)

Clearly, "nursing skill" meant "service" in a dual way, with both the patient and the physician being served. The emergence of the hospital system within the context of burgeoning industrial capitalism set the tone for a nursing force characterized by a unique blend of Christian dedication, Victorian femininity, medical faith, and labour discipline. In this context, nurse training was oriented to produce a cheap, subservient, readily available work force armed with a basic knowledge of hospital and sanitary procedures.

By the beginning of the twenty-first century, discourses emphasizing faithful service have been supplanted by those that stress professionalism, technical knowledge, and health care advocacy. Nurse training, and even much nursing work, has moved out of the hospital system. Nursing education is now concentrated in universities and colleges, augmented with symposia on credentialing, specialization, nursing research, and advanced medical technology. Nurses have promoted their occupation, sometimes through militant action, as a profession with distinct skills and privileges based on their claims to a unique body of nursing knowledge.

This chapter is concerned with the development of nursing education in Canada. The transformation that has just been described is interpreted in conjunction with the observation that Davies (1980, 1995) makes that nursing education in Britain and the United States emerged as a compromise arising from inadequate resources, struggles for control, and the nature of nursing as women's work. In particular, this chapter emphasizes the ways in which contradictions in the provision and utility of the education of nurses in Canada have served to limit nurses' position in the Canadian health care system. Since the nineteenth century, with the emergence of the well-known "Nightingale system," prescient nurses and nursing supervisors have recognized the potential value of training for the establishment of a distinct sphere of nursing activity within the overall health care system. However, the nature of that training and role has been subject to varying, often conflicting, conceptions of groups within nursing and interests outside of nursing. Ultimately, then, the development of nursing and nurse training must be understood as part of a wider network of social, political, and economic relations.

NURSES AND PROFESSIONALISM

Professionalism is the key concept in most recent analyses of nursing. Nurses are regarded either as constituting a profession, with their traditional low status a relic of the past, or as falling short in their drive to professionalism, in which case the reasons for their failure become the focus of analysis.

A typical expression of the first view is the statement that nursing has been involved in a "progressive development toward professionalism" (Elliott, 1977, p. 69; Schwirian, 1998, pp. 12–13). Three interrelated factors are commonly cited to highlight this apparent evolutionary progress: the specialization and bureaucratization of health care, increasingly sophisticated medical technology, and the growth of nurses' own professional awareness (Innis, 1970; Kelly, 1985). As health care has become a more comprehensive, sophisticated enterprise, new medical knowledge and health care functions have become unequally distributed among participants in the health care system. This has afforded nurses the opportunity to organize and push for increased status and responsibility; they have willingly emulated the medical profession with the assumption that full professionalism is an inevitable outcome. In this evolutionary mode, the role of education is clear — education is the vehicle for professional status. More education for more nurses, built around a distinct scientific core of nursing knowledge, would allow nurses simultaneously to adapt to a changing world and to occupy a position of enhanced importance in the division of labour in health care (Canadian Nurses' Association, 1997; Rogers, 1978).

As desirable as this image is from a nursing perspective, it fails to analyze adequately the wider context within which nursing operates, and it ignores many of the major constrains that continue to act upon nursing. Arising from the blend of optimism and frustration that has marked nurses' ongoing struggles for status, this viewpoint has interpreted the substantive gains that nurses have made against a backdrop of influential individuals and interest groups which seem to have no enduring connection to other aspects of social structure. The real historical barriers to nursing status seemingly can be dissipated merely through hard work and upgrading of skills on the part of nurses.

The second viewpoint paints a less flattering image of nurses. It takes as its starting point the obstacles that nurses face in their quest for status, and concludes that nurses are at best a semi- or para-profession, most likely doomed to an eternal inferiority to the medical profession (Cockerham, 1986; Wolinsky, 1980). Probably the clearest manifestation of this perspective is the fact that nursing is virtually ignored or given only passing consideration in much of the literature on the sociology of medicine. Against the visible unity and autonomy of the (predominantly male) medical profession, the service orientation of the internally divided (predominantly female) nursing ranks seems highly appropriate. This patronizing and accusatory view is expressed clearly by Hall (1970, p. 12), to whom

> it seems clear that, to date, nurses have not tried to focus their work efforts in a scientific mould. While medical care has been specializing along new types of diagnosis and treatment at a bizarre speed, nursing has shown no such trend.

We are left with the impression that no matter how strongly nurses struggled in the past to establish their occupational status, they have not worked hard enough. Ironically, this view fits nicely with the first position on nurses' professionalism, differing primarily in the assessment of the likelihood of nurses' success in achieving professionalism.

Unfortunately, the debate over whether or not nursing is a profession tends to divert attention from questions of greater significance. Professionalism is assumed to be a desirable attribute, without any critical appraisal of the conditions within which professionalization occurs or of the strategic importance of professionalism as an ideological position (see Johnson [1972] for an extended critique of this approach). Instead, the circumstances under which the health care system and the role of nursing within it have developed are attributed to grand, amorphous tendencies such as "progress," "technological change," and "interest-group politics" without any sustained analysis of social relations in which these processes are grounded. Therefore, occupational roles and training are treated as neutral phenomena, given shape by the whims and visions of individuals acting as part of a seemingly natural evolution of social forces.

An alternative explanation of the development of nursing and nurse education focuses on the social relations that give shape to and are influenced by nursing. Nurses are recognized as dependent wage earners who pose problems of cost and control to their employers (Armstrong, Choiniere, & Day, 1993; Cannings & Lazonick, 1975; Rafferty, 1996; White, 1990). Nursing emerges from and acts upon distinct social structures and practices that are characterized by regular, often contradictory, patterns. Consequently, issues concerning the training and welfare of nurses, although important in their own right, are viewed as meaningful only when interpreted in the context of wider trends associated with health care organization, policy, and finance.

NURSES AS SALARIED EMPLOYEES

One clear indication of the status of nurses is expressed by the relative incomes of nurses and other health care workers. As the data in Table 1 indicate, the incomes of nurses have increased steadily both in absolute terms and in comparison with the average income of the Canadian work force as a whole. Of the three tabulated health occupational categories, nurses have made the greatest relative gains. However, nurses' salaries still remain, on average, just below the national average for all occupations and less than one third of the average for physicians and surgeons.

The most common justification for the latter trend is that medical training is more arduous and is of much longer duration than nurse training. Therefore, in accordance with a functionalist analysis of stratification, the higher salaries of doctors are seen to represent a "payoff" for the years of training and sacrifice undertaken by the individual in order to fill the important medical positions (Davis & Moore, 1945). This correlation

TABLE 5.1 *Employment Income for Selected Health Occupations:*
Average and Ratio to Average Canadian Occupational Income, 1931–1991

| | Health Occupations | | | | | | All Canadian Occupations | |
| | Physicians and Surgeons | | Nurses | | Nursing Aides, Assistants, and Orderlies | | | |
Census Year	Average Employment Income ($)	Ratio to Canadian Average	Average Employment Income ($)	Ratio to Canadian Average	Average Employment Income ($)	Ratio to Canadian Average	Average Employment Income ($)	Ratio to Canadian Average
1931	3 095*	3.65*	580	0.68	524	0.62	848	1.00
1941	2 693*	3.10*	596	0.69	486	0.56	868	1.00
1951	2 936*	1.59*	1 107	0.60	1 074	0.58	1 851	1.00
1961	13 836	4.34	2 421	0.76	1 847	0.58	3 191	1.00
1971	25 308	4.69	4 344	0.81	3 572	0.66	5 391	1.00
1981	52 839	3.87	13 036	0.96	9 301	0.68	13 635	1.00
1986	85 023	3.17	26 123	0.98	18 430	0.69	26 781	1.00
1991	102 370	3.04	33 510	0.99	22 684	0.67	33 714	1.00

* Figures for 1931 to 1951 do not include income for self-employed physicians and surgeons, and hence are likely to underrepresent actual physician and surgeon income for those years. 1986–1991 figures are for full-year, full-time workers.

Source: Statistics Canada (1993 and other years).

between years of training and occupational income is borne out, in broad terms, by general surveys of the labour force that reveal that workers with higher levels of education are likely to be found in higher income categories (see, for example, the monthly reports issued by Labour Canada under the title of *The Labour Force*). As such, it serves as a rallying point for nursing advocates who argue that more and better education is necessary for higher status. There are, though, some problems in this analysis. The income–education linkage is more likely to be a product of initial privilege, class power, and other social dynamics than an indicator of true market value (Livingstone, 1998). Moreover, the whole question of what constitutes recognized training must be considered. Historically, as will be discussed below, nurses have been trained on the job, providing cheap hospital labour in a prolonged apprenticeship period that is not regarded in the same way as is, for example, medical-ward experience and internship. At the same time, the fiscal returns and inducements for nurse training are not nearly as significant as a "reward for education" argument would have us believe.

A second argument for the relatively low wages that nurses receive is that nurses are much more poorly organized and less assertive than is the medical profession. Certainly doctors have benefited tremendously from the strength and ability of organizations like the Canadian and American Medical Associations to promote their own interests. In contrast, nursing leaders have chronically lamented the seeming inability of nurses to mobilize into a cohesive, powerful force. Unfortunately, advocates of these arguments tend to regard nurses and doctors as two independent rather than interdependent groups, and to confuse cause and consequence. While the medical and nursing professions each have their unique histories, the picture is incomplete without an analysis of how the medical profession has been able to advance in large part at the expense of nursing, through the subordination and guided development of nursing by doctors, health care policymakers and managers, and the structure of health care systems.

This suggests the need for a relational analysis that can account for contradictions and constraints in nursing development. We can illustrate this type of analysis by returning to Table 1 and taking note of the third category of health occupations, after doctors and nurses. The wage levels of nursing aides, assistants, and orderlies have remained relatively constant, at between 56 and 69 percent of average occupational earnings. This implies that nursing, as an intermediate health occupation, can both exert pressure on and be subject to pressure from at least two levels — doctors and managers from above and auxiliary health care workers from below. Therefore, by way of example, health care administrators make decisions influenced by the fact that individual nurses are less costly than physicians but more costly than auxiliary health care workers. At the same time, nurses have reason to fear that they are potentially more dispensable to the health care system than are other health care workers under present circumstances. Nurses, for example, are excluded from legislation that enables physicians and surgeons to prescribe medication or perform surgery. These relations are intensified with the introduction of new medical technology and health care treatment models that serve to redefine the place and role of various health care workers. If the diagnosis of a cancer, for example, can be made by a laboratory technician with the aid of a sophisticated instrument, and if cancer can be treated with drugs prescribed by a physician, where does the nurse fit in? At another level, a greater integration of the health care system with other social educational services could provide opportunities for nurses to enhance their role in health care, or it could have the effect of making nursing a redundant occupation, as social workers, auxiliaries, nursing assistants, or other new occupations begin to provide nursing services.

So far, there is mixed evidence with regard to the future of nursing. There is a general tendency for licensed health care personnel, including **registered nurses**, to be replaced by unlicensed health care providers, but there are considerable variations among provinces in this regard (Saskatchewan Union of Nurses, 1998). As health care is restructured, full-time nurses are increasingly being replaced by part-time nurses, nursing is gradually shifting to noninstitutional settings relative to hospitals and other long-term health care sites, and nurses are subject to new forms of surveillance and **intensification** of their work (Armstrong, Choiniere, & Day, 1993, p. 46; Armstrong & Armstrong, 1996).

Viewed in this context, nursing education is a significant variable in the development of the health care system. Education acts as a conduit for nursing knowledge, status, and credentials, but it also serves to stamp into place particular conceptions of nursing. More precisely, while the provision of educational opportunities is generally associated with the advancement of nursing, it is also a factor in the historical subordination of nurses.

WORK AND EDUCATION IN THE CANADIAN CONTEXT

Nursing education, like other forms of vocational training, began outside the formal system of public education in Canada. Mass public schooling emerged through the attempts by nineteenth-century school reformers to ensure the transformation of individuals into morally disciplined political subjects within a sphere of state rule (Corrigan, Curtis, & Lanning, 1987; Wotherspoon, 1998). Vocational training was more strictly concerned with imbuing persons in specific jobs with the competencies and discipline that would make them productive workers. Once established in the throes of industrial development, however, the state public school system was subject to conscription by private capitalist interests concerned with obtaining at public expense a cheap, compliant, and differentiated labour force; schooling thus became penetrated by the logic of vocationalism (Bowles & Gintis, 1976; Schecter, 1977). However, a contradictory dynamic was generated by subordinate social groups that saw in public schooling a vehicle for upward social mobility and participation in hitherto closed political channels (Carnoy & Levin, 1985). A major consequence of the struggles that ensued over the nature and content of state schooling was the emergence in the twentieth century of the education system as the primary channel of individual access to the job market.

The developing linkage between school and work provided a focal point for the energies of competing social interests. The educational credential provided a screening mechanism for employers, a "meal ticket" for individuals, and an instrument to guarantee status for certain prestigious occupational groups such as medical doctors. Little overt challenge was presented to the tacit consensus that formal schooling was a legitimate educational and selective enterprise. Instead, conflict centred on the amounts and content of formal education appropriate to particular occupations or positions in the labour force. As debate arose concerning how much and what kinds of education a person needed to enter, certain jobs began to dominate educational discourse; wider questions about the structures of education and work were no longer issues. The ground rules for work and schooling solidified, and only the details were open to contention (Wotherspoon, 1998).

Nurse training, which began in Canada within the hospital system, was absorbed into the state education system only through a protracted series of developments. The interconnection of such factors as the rising cost to hospitals of providing nurse training, corporate and state intervention in the health care system, and the organized efforts of nurses accompanied a transformation in nursing work away from a strictly supervised feminine servitude to a bureaucratically organized wage-labour force. The following sections outline the development of nurse training in Canada and discuss the nature of the Canadian nursing labour force.

THE DEVELOPMENT OF NURSING EDUCATION IN CANADA

The formal training of nurses in Canada began in the 1870s for the purpose of producing hospital personnel who could adequately carry out doctors' order (Mussallem, 1965, pp. 5–6). In the mid-nineteenth century, nursing was nearly unique as an occupation legitimately open to women. Nursing was established from the outset of the development of medical science as an auxiliary occupation, concerned primarily with "caring" rather than "curing," or hygiene rather than medical treatment (Gamarnikow, 1978; Corea, 1985; Rafferty, 1996). The medical division of labour, reproducing the patriarchal structure of the bourgeois home and workplace, was clear — men were doctors and women were nurses.

Nursing, nonetheless, did present opportunities, however limited, for the career advancement of a select group of women. Early nursing promoters, such as Florence Nightingale in Britain and Isabel A. Hampton in North America, saw that an inexpensive, regimented nursing force could provide the necessary foothold to establish nursing in the health care process. The advantage of this strategy to solidify nursing status through the promotion of its ethos of service was that nursing could develop as a relatively autonomous enterprise, hierarchically organized around hygienic ideals under the supervision of women (Carpenter, 1977, pp. 166–167). However, the development of this autonomy was highly constrained.

Hospital administrators quickly came to appreciate the value of nurses for developing a clientele and providing inexpensive labour. With a nursing force at hand, public hospitals could shift their image and emphasis from providing a repository for the terminally ill to serving as a centre for treatment and recovery. The possibility that patients could be ministered back to health was crucial for an emerging industrial nation that required a continuous supply of able-bodied workers. Hospitals, in becoming important centres of health care, simultaneously began to train and contain nurses. Thus, generally following the pattern of industrialization in Canada, the number of hospital schools of nursing increased from one in 1874 (in St. Catharines) to 20 in 1900, 170 in 1909, and approximately 220 in 1930 (Canadian Nurses' Association [CNA], 1968, p. 33; Duncanson, 1970, p. 112).

In this context, nurse training accomplished several contradictory functions. Extending over a 2–3-year period, training programs ensured that a supply of nurses was continually available for hospital service. The exploitation of the nurse trainee prevailed over educational aims so that lecture and study time was a "privilege" granted only in the interstices of up to 15 hours of daily ward duty (Duncanson, 1970, pp. 112–113; Mussallem, 1965, p. 6). Nurse training programs dampened the hostilities of doctors, who scorned nurses as unskilled and uneducated. At the same time, doctors who were suspicious that they might some day be displaced by trained nurses found that they could advance their own interests by their involvement in the nurse training program as lecturers and moral guardians. Discipline over nurse trainees was further maintained by a highly regimented supervisory structure, constant surveillance facilitated by the establishment of dormitories, inculcation of the virtues of obedience and commitment, and the absence for most trainees of any occupational alternatives.

The advantages in terms of costs and services that nurses offered to the hospital system were also used by nursing leaders in the early part of the twentieth century as levers for gaining certain concessions, including reductions in the workday, specified educational time allocations, formalized instruction, and more standardized curricula (Duncanson, 1970, p. 113; Mussallem, 1965, p. 7). Trained nurses, working to enhance their own status in contrast with untrained nursing personnel, organized local, national, and international associations to provide a body for political lobbying. Nursing, as promoted by nursing administrators, was to be of service because it brought to the health care sector a cultivated worker who conformed to high standards of female gentility and passivity (Coburn, 1987, p. 448). In 1893, the American Society of Superintendents of Training Schools for Nurses of the United States and Canada was formed by 40 nursing-school superintendents in order to push for better-quality and more uniform nursing educational standards. This society laid the groundwork for a dominion-wide nursing organization, the Canadian National Association of Trained Nurses, established in 1908, which in 1924, with 52 affiliated member organizations, became the Canadian Nurses' Association, or the CNA (CNA, 1968, pp. 36–38). These organizations focused the profession's energies on a drive for the establishment of registries of trained nurses, which received some degree of legislative recognition in all nine provinces between 1910 and 1922 (CNA, 1968, p. 38). They also began, especially with the aid of a 1914 Special Committee report on education, a lengthy campaign to have nursing education incorporated into the state education system (King, 1970, p. 69).

In the midst of these developments, the fundamental contradiction between state and private demands for low-cost but widespread health care services on the one hand, and nurses' demand for adequate training and remuneration on the other, intensified. In the early decades of the twentieth century, health care services were becoming instituted as a regular social provision, in conjunction with the rise of a stable national workforce. Exacerbating this trend was the success of the medical profession in acquiring greater influence with the health care system. In this, the medical associations were aided by the large corporate foundations, especially the Carnegie Foundation, which sponsored the influential Flexner Report of 1910. In the wake of the report, major recommendations to reduce the number of North American medical schools and the supply of medical graduates, and to tighten control over medical education standards were quickly adopted (MacFarlane, 1965, pp. 19–21).

The data in Table 2 reveal the impact of these events on the medical and nursing labour forces. The supply of physicians was greatly moderated, especially in the period from 1911 to 1921, when the population per physicians ratio actually increased, meaning that there were fewer physicians per capita in 1921 than in 1911. However, medical care was at that time highly labour-intensive so that, with fewer doctors, either patients received less medical attention, doctors worked harder, or other health care personnel filled the void. The rapid increase in the nursing labour force prior to the end of the 1980s (after which the number of nurses declined) suggests the importance of the latter

TABLE 5.2 *Number of Physicians and Nurses, and Population per Physician and Nurse in Canada, 1901–1998*

Year	Physicians		Nurses	
	Number	Population per Physician*	Number†	Population per Nurse*
1901	5 441	978	280	19 014
1911	7 411	970	5 600	1 284
1921	8 706	1 008	21 385	410
1931	10 020	1 034	20 462	506
1941	11 873	968	25 826	441
1951	14 325	976	41 088	325
1961	21 290	857	70 647	258
1971	32 942	659	148 767	146
1981	45 542	538	206 184	119
1986	53 207	495	237 181	107
1991	60 559	467	230 940	122
1996	54 958	548	227 830	131
1997	55 243	546	229 813	131
1998	56 203	541	227 651	134

*Based on census data.

†Registered nurses for 1941 to 1971; census figures for 1931 (graduate nurses) and earlier years (nurses). Excludes Newfoundland prior to 1961; excludes Yukon and Northwest Territories prior to 1941. The 1921 figure includes nurses-in-training. Figures for 1981 and later include only nurses registered during the first four months (three in Quebec) of the registration period and registered in the same province in which they work or reside.

Source: For 1901 to 1971, Statistics Canada (1983). For 1981 and 1986, Health Canada (1995). For the 1990s, Canadian Institute for Health Information, *Health Personnel Database Reports.*

possibility. The number of nurses increased by nearly four times between 1911 and 1921 and maintained an annual rate of increase of 55.1 percent, compared with a rate of 8.2 percent for doctors, between 1911 and 1986. Lower-cost nurses, trained for dedicated service and disciplined by social and labour market conditions, served, in effect, to subsidize the greater occupational rewards that doctors were in a position to enjoy.

With an expanded and diversified health care role, though, nurses were also able to assert more strongly their monetary and educational demands. However, as with doctors, nurses' progress in this regard was highly dependent on the intervention of external agencies. A university **degree program** in nursing, the first in Canada, was established at the University of British Columbia in 1919, and, with the efforts and financial assistance of the Canadian Red Cross Society, public health nursing programs were developed in six universities by 1920–21 (King, 1970, p. 70). However, as King indicates, there were serious inadequacies in the early university nursing programs in terms of both upgrading nursing skill and raising nursing status relative to other university-educated occupational groups: "In the teaching of nursing great emphasis was placed on technical skill, following orders, and adhering to established practice; the intellectual component was subservient to the daily round" (1970, pp. 71–72).

There is evidence, too, of a strong occupational split in nursing between nursing supervisors and instructors, who had been trained in and had advanced through the hospital service system, and nurses who saw the need to develop the profession through university education and research (King, 1970, pp. 73–75). The latter group was given support by George Weir in the 1932 report *Survey of Nursing Education in Canada*, cosponsored by the CNA and the Canadian Medical Association. The report's primary recommendation was that nursing schools be removed from hospital control and placed under the auspices of the provincial education systems.

With the onset of the international economic crisis in the 1930s, the fate of this recommendation was suspended between conflicting interests. In the early part of the decade, expenditures on health services declined (Statistics Canada, 1983), placing increased pressure on the health care system and its labour force to operate more efficiently. At the same time, these conditions provoked intensified efforts from several quarters for an overall upgrading of the health care system. Potentially militant trade unions and the unemployed, subject to severe social and economic dislocation, posed a worrisome threat to state and corporate interests. A series of social reform measures, including health insurance schemes, were introduced by provincial and federal legislatures as part of an attempt to pacify the working class and stabilize economic conditions (Swartz, 1977).

Corporate interests also played a more direct role, primarily through their charitable foundations, which provided financial assistance and funded research for selected health, education, and welfare projects, in order to secure social harmony, develop a stable work force, and promote a favourable investment climate. In the field of health care, the W.K. Kellogg Foundation has a history of prominence, having contributed over $263.5 million to various health care programs, mostly in the United States, Canada, and Latin America, between 1930 and 1980 (Kellogg, 1979, p. 112). Of that total, $822 000 was spent between 1944 and 1952 to provide staff, consultative services, and curricular and instructional resources for twelve university nursing schools (ten in the United States and two in Canada), and a grant of over $165 000 served to establish an experimental undergraduate nursing program, grounded in basic science training, at the University of Saskatchewan, beginning in 1952 (Kellogg, 1955, pp. 143–148).

At the same time, other pressures were mounting to push the training of nurses out of the hospitals. Nurses, who in the 1930s often accepted board and lodging from their hospital employers in lieu of full salary payment, began in the 1940s to return to the community and, simultaneously, to demand higher wages (CNA, 1968, p. 34). A similar situation developed for nurses in training who exchanged fees and labour in return for training and services. The Department of National Health and Welfare estimates that by 1960, the average direct annual cost to the hospital per student was $1000 (Mussallem, 1965, p. 40). Because hospitals compensated for this cost by extracting unpaid or underpaid labour from nursing students and by underpaying nursing instructors, a generally unsatisfactory situation prevailed. Moreover, low wages and low levels of government educational assistance made it economically unviable for most nurses and nursing teachers to extend their education beyond the minimal time period required for graduation from basic training, especially when the training program was prolonged excessively by the priority of work over training in the hospital system. Consequently, it is not surprising that Mussallem (1965), in a study prepared in the early 1960s for the Royal Commission on Health Services in Canada, indicts the nursing education system of the time as haphazard, outdated, educationally unsound, and inadequate for the needs of nurses and the health care system.

The Royal Commission's report itself recommended a reduction in the time span of the diploma program from three to two years and a separation of nurse training from hospital demands for nursing service, and stressed that the increasing need for qualified nurses required the coordinated development of nursing education programs integrated into the general system of higher education in Canada and the provinces (Duncanson, 1970, pp. 122–123). While the Royal Commission inquiry was being conducted, nurses' organizations, educational institutions, and the Ontario government cooperated in an initiative that led to the establishment in 1964 of a nursing diploma program at the Ryerson Polytechnical Institute. By 1968, in the wake of this precedent, 26 nursing diploma programs were offered in institutions other than hospital schools of nursing across Canada; by 1977, full-time enrollment in community college nursing diploma programs was 17 789, compared with 5136 in hospital programs (CNA, 1981, p. 2; Statistics Canada, 1977). A similar expansion was underway in university degree nursing programs, with more programs, greater number of students, and the establishment of graduate degree programs.

RECENT TRENDS IN NURSING EDUCATION AND THE NURSING LABOUR FORCE

The move away from hospital-based nurse training has been associated with a general improvement in the overall status of nurses, but it has not solved several fundamental problems associated with training and maintaining a nursing labour force. There are currently two main educational streams for entry into nursing practice: university degree programs of 3 to 5 years in length, and nursing **diploma programs**, offered mainly through the community college system, of 1 to 3 years in length. In 1994, there were 109 initial diploma programs and 26 basic and 32 post-R.N. baccalaureate programs in nursing in Canada (Statistics Canada, 1995, pp. 47–48), compared with 170 hospital schools and 16 university baccalaureate programs in 1963 (Mussallem, 1965, p. 11). However, despite a recent trend to emphasize the importance of the degree qualification in nursing, about two thirds of nursing graduates continue to receive their initial training in diploma programs (see Table 3).

The provision of nursing education through the public education system has ensured that certain levels of funding, facilities, and standards will be maintained for nurse training, sheltered from the vagaries of hospital administration. At the same time, though, new sets of constraints emerge as nursing education is forced to compete for resources with other educational and state priorities. Insofar as the educational credentials of teachers, a major cost factor in postsecondary educational institutions, are linked to promotion and salary scales, nursing education is relatively inexpensive. In 1994, for example, only 27.7 percent of full-time university nursing teachers had completed doctorates, compared with an overall Canadian university teacher average of over 70 percent (Lortie, 1994, p. 32; Statistics Canada, 1995, p. 53). In addition, such low cost highly specific programs as computer-assisted instruction and self-directed learning modules are becoming prominent features of some university nurse education programs (Crawford, 1978; Hannah, 1978). These programs, besides reducing the costs of education relative to more open-ended discovery and analysis-based courses, prepare the student for work roles that are highly structured and involve few opportunities for the worker to exercise discretion on the job.

But despite the potentially lower cost of nursing education programs, there are indications that governments have made only limited commitments to support nurse

TABLE 5.3 *Numbers of Nursing Graduates from Initial Diploma and Basic Baccalaureate Programs in Canada, and Number of Immigrant Graduate Nurses Entering Canada, 1962–1995*

Year	Number of Nurses Graduating from Canadian Programs			Number of Immigrant Graduate Nurses*
	Initial Diploma Programs	Basic Baccalaureate Programs†	Total	
1962	6 246	148	6 394	1 621
1963	6 764	171	6 935	1 879
1964	7 107	154	7 261	1 967
1965	7 154	206	7 360	2 829
1966	7 167	220	7 387	3 732
1967	7 249	273	7 522	4 262
1968	7 591	300	7 891	3 375
1969	7 978	381	8 359	3 248
1970	8 212	413	8 625	2 274
1971	9 543	515	10 058	989
1972	9 596	487	10 083	892
1973	8 985	609	9 594	1 418
1974	9 205	694	9 899	1 702
1975	8 933	845	9 778	1 839
1976	9 087	954	10 041	1 130
1977	6 203	977	7 180	607
1978	7 403	1 455	8 858	405
1979	6 680	1 330	8 010	467
1980	6 685	1 453	8 138	653
1981	6 478	1 425	7 903	977
1982	6 621	1 590	8 211	999
1983	6 761	1 686	8 447	358
1984	6 871	1 729	8 600	300
1985	7 218	1 957	9 175	283
1986	6 762	2 037	8 799	387
1987	7 054	2 221	9 275	730
1988	6 981	2 265	9 246	1 044
1989	7 636	2 313	9 430	1 185
1990	7 005	2 552	9 557	1 263
1991	7 022	2 363	9 385	1 405
1992	7 061	2 562	9 623	1 008
1993	7 231	2 975	10 206	870
1994	6 963	2 824	9 787	823
1995	6 152	3 133	9 285	627

*Immigrants who indicated that nursing is their intended occupation.
†Figures from 1978 and later include graduates of post-R.N. baccalaureate programs.

Source: Health and Welfare Canada (annual series, 1969, 1976, 1985). Mussallem, H.K. (1965). Health Canada (1995). Ryten, E. (1997). Citizenship and Immigration Canada (annual series).

training programs, particularly at the university level. Table 3 indicates that immigration has provided Canada with a major source of trained nurses, especially in the late 1960s and early 1970s during the transfer of nursing education out of hospitals. By importing trained labourers (although not all workers will necessarily become employed in their intended occupations), Canada is able to transfer the cost of educating a substantial pool of workers to the countries of origin and gain in the process a cheap, often docile work force (Bolaria, 1987). Depending upon where the workers are placed in job situations, this will either ensure that lower-paid positions are constantly filled (as opposed to increasing wage levels), or reduce the overall costs of maintaining a trained work force.

The lack of government support for nursing education, especially at the university level, is also revealed in the problems that nurses face in upgrading their basic training. Nurses often discover that they are left out of decisions to introduce, and shut out from training to operate, new medical technology (Wallis, 1978). Absence of credit courses for upgrading training at work, lack of time off to attend classes that are offered, and lack of financial assistance are common problems for nurses working in Canadian hospitals and health care institutions; nurses in at least one institution have even held bake sales and auctions to raise money for a tuition-assistance fund (Allen, 1985, p. 12). Significantly, according to 1995 data, only 43 083 (or 18.5 percent) of the 232 869 registered nurses employed in nursing in Canada have an academic degree (calculated from Statistics Canada, 1996, p. 16). Moreover, as some of the trends noted above suggest, even the attainment of a university degree does not guarantee that nurses will be prepared to step into decisive, autonomous health care positions. There does not appear to be a significant change from the days of hospital service for nurse trainees. Nonetheless, there is evidence that the state has channelled funds into specific vocational streams, such as psychiatric nursing and dental nursing, since the 1960s in response to political, economic, and employment relation factors (Dickinson, 1987; Statistics Canada, 1977).

A potential consequence of these trends is the fragmentation of nursing. In accordance with the degree/diploma distinction, two streams are emerging — one more highly skilled and educated and the other service-oriented and less educated — reminiscent of the separation of trained nurses from untrained nursing personnel in the early part of the twentieth century. This is consistent with the demands of nursing organizations in the 1960s for an increased recognition of the dual educational credential system (CNA, 1968, p. 4) but contains implications for the organization of nursing that may well undermine the very cause nurses are championing.

Hospitals remain the major workplace for Canadian nurses, but there is a shift in the direction of greater community-based health care. Between 1992 and 1998, among registered nurses working in nursing, the proportion who worked in hospitals declined from 66.3 to 62.4 percent, while those who worked in community health settings increased from 7.1 to 11.5 percent (Canadian Institute for Health Information, 1998, p. 2; 1999, p. 2). Educational credentials have a bearing on the kinds of places and positions nurses are employed in. As the data in Table 4 indicate, registered nurses with basic diploma training are overrepresented in general staff nursing positions in hospital, community health, and office settings, or they occupy intermediate and lower-level supervisory positions. By contrast, those with a university degree are more likely to be employed in settings with greater discretion or decision making authority.

A second related aspect of segmentation in nursing appears in the gender structure of the occupation. Nursing remains an overwhelmingly **feminized occupation**.

TABLE 5.4 *Registered Nurses Employed in Nursing in Canada by Position and Highest Level of Education in Nursing, 1995*

Position	Total Number	Highest Level of Education, Expressed as Percentage of Nurses Within Each Position			
		Registered Nurse Diploma	Baccalaureate	Master's	Doctorate
Chief Nursing Officer/Director	3 578	60.0	32.0	7.8	0.2
Assistant/Associate Director	896	50.3	38.8	10.3	0.6
Supervisor/Coordinator	9 314	68.5	29.1	2.4	0.1
Clinical Nurse Specialist	1 481	42.8	30.6	26.5	0.1
Head Nurse	8 178	72.7	25.5	1.8	<0.1
Staff/Community Heath Nurse	169 646	85.2	14.4	0.4	<0.1
Office/Industrial Nurse	3 249	88.3	11.5	0.2	<0.1
Instructor/Professor	5 538	27.6	57.2	13.8	1.4
Researcher	874	61.0	30.9	7.3	0.8
Consultant	2 182	51.0	39.7	9.1	0.3
Not Stated*	16 668	73.8	24.0	2.1	0.1
TOTAL					
— percent	100	83.0	15.9	1.1	0.5
— number	221 604*	178 521	39 785	3 124	174

*Totals do not include 11 265 cases where level of education was not specified.

Source: Calculated from Statistics Canada (1996).

Although the number and proportion of male nurses is gradually increasing, in 1995, men constituted only 3.8 percent of the registered nursing force in Canada, compared with 2.4 percent a decade earlier. Female nurses were slightly more likely than male nurses to have university degrees in nursing, but male nurses were more likely to be employed in administrative and supervisory positions (Trudeau, 1996, pp. 23–24). Moreover, according to census data, in 1990, male nurses who worked on a full-time, full-year basis earned an average of $35 964, which was about $2600 more than their female counterparts (Statistics Canada, 1993, pp. 12–13).

Consequent to the growth of the health care system have been increasingly sustained legislative and managerial efforts to make the operation of the system more efficient and accountable. Initiatives such as community health centres, prescription drug assistance programs, and the closure or consolidation of hospital systems, regardless of their possible medical merits, have the clear effect of increasing the output of hospital workers while shifting some health care services from hospitals to less expensive and less labour-intensive in-home and community alternatives (Salmon, 1984). At the same time, institutional health care is being reorganized primarily through innovations in the supervision patterns of hospital and nursing-home employees in order to increase centralized managerial control and maximize employee productivity (Armstrong & Armstrong, 1996; Carpenter, 1977). Nursing, as the largest single category of health care workers, remains central to the politics and structure of health care in Canada.

The observed tendencies toward **bifurcation** in nursing suggest that any benefits from a restructured organization of health care services will be distributed in a highly asymmetrical fashion. Within nursing, males and nurses with degrees, especially post-graduate degrees, are moving into positions likely to serve as bases for further consolidation of authority and resources. While the resources that go into nursing education, as well as nursing initiatives in the direction of credentialling, the development of nursing knowledge, and specialization may serve to upgrade the status of nursing as a whole, they are more likely to be channelled toward the minority of nurses who can use credentials and authority positions to their advantage. If these initiatives do enable nurses on the whole to legitimize their claims to greater proportions of health care resources, nursing administrators are liable to rely less upon nurses and more upon lower-paid auxiliaries to provide health care services. The upper stream of credentialled nurses, with the assistance of agencies such as the Kellogg Foundation, which has recently funded major projects in nursing research, accreditation, and doctoral studies (CNA, 1983, pp. 29–30), may be able to insulate itself from the erosion of the profession as a whole by strengthening its own claims to essential health care skills and knowledge that it alone possesses.

The trend toward greater professional recognition of nursing is represented especially in the CNA focus, reinforced through complementary positions advanced by several provincial nursing associations, on "entry into practice," which called for a minimum requirement of a complete baccalaureate degree as the standard for entry into nursing practice by the year 2000 (CNA, 1982, p. 1; Registered Nurses' Association of British Columbia, 1983). As the CNA itself admitted, such a goal seemed difficult to attain, given the slow rate of increase in the proportion of student admissions to degree nursing programs relative to diploma programs and the continuing lack of funds to expand degree nursing programs (1986, p. 5). Instead, support given to degree programs and nursing research may be channelled into specialized programs supporting the small proportion of nursing practitioners who, on the basis of the degree credential, may stake sole claim to the title of "nurse." In 1995–96, more than 20 000 students nationally were enrolled in diploma programs in nursing, compared with just under 9400 in the longer degree programs (Statistics Canada, 1998, pp. 60, 68). At the same time, fiscal and administrative support previously given to nursing diploma programs is likely to be directed to promoting the expanded production of auxiliary health care workers. Projections that Canada will face a severe shortage of registered nurses in the next 15 years (induced in part by work pressures that motivate nurses to leave, or refuse to enter, the profession), will also influence the future of nursing and nurse training (CNA, 1997, pp. 14, 18; Ryten, 1997, pp. 43–44). Paradoxically, then, by advancing credentialling and research policies in the interest of the profession as a whole, nurses may be contributing to their own division into a highly skilled and educated nursing elite and a mass of undertrained, low-paid support workers.

Nurses are increasingly cognizant of their uncertain status within a changing health care sector. In many cases they have been able to use the realities of chronic shortages of health care workers to their advantage, gaining concessions in wages and improved professional working conditions from their employers. At the same time, however, they have had to rely upon collective action to make substantive gains or even to hold their ground against reductions in health care services and expenditures. As an indication of mounting tensions within the health care sector, nurses across Canada have not been hesitant to engage in strikes and other militant actions over the past decade (Hibbert,

1992; White, 1990). In 1999, striking nurses in Saskatchewan even defied provincial back-to-work legislation. In the process, nurses have been forced to rethink their status as workers and as professionals. While the service ethic remains an important component of nurse training and work, nurses have shown through their struggles that the nature of that service can no longer be bound within restricted terms of docility.

CONCLUSION

This chapter has emphasized how the transformation of nursing from a subordinate service occupation into a more specialized and sophisticated profession has been rendered more apparent than real in many key respects through a series of external and internal constraining factors. Education has been a crucial channel for the occupational development of nursing, serving both to advance and to suppress its status. The pattern of nursing and nursing education in Canada has followed the interplay of nurses' organized efforts to establish their occupation with the development of a Canadian labour force in general and a health care labour force in particular. The frequent success of corporate, state, and medical interests in guiding the development of nursing has had a significant impact on the present status of nursing as a wage labour force divided by education and gender. Nurses, though, have come to recognize that their status as the largest single health care occupation is a potential power base (Armstrong, Choiniere, & Day, 1993; Kerr, 1996; Lerner, 1985; Mussallem, 1977). By promoting their ability to serve client needs and health care priorities rather than economic or systemic requisites, while simultaneously avoiding the trap of accepting a professional ideology as substitute for actual resources, nurses may yet succeed in their quest for status. To this end, nurses are beginning to align themselves with other groups of workers, including teachers and public services employees, who face similar threats and challenges. The consequences of nurses' development of a political strategy are significant, for without a clear analysis of their occupational situation, nurses are likely to suffer, as will the quality of the health services that they are able to provide.

STUDY QUESTIONS

1. *Which factors have facilitated the emergence of nursing as a prominent health care occupation? Which factors have served to constrain the development of nursing in Canada?*
2. *Discuss the relationship between nursing and the development of the medical profession.*
3. *What implications have changes in medical technology and in the organization of health care services had for the development of nursing?*
4. *Discuss the ways in which the state education system is subject to pressures from various social interests, as illustrated by the example of nursing.*
5. *How does the development of nursing compare with trends in other related occupations such as teaching and social work? Should nurses have the right to strike?*

GLOSSARY

bifurcation The division of a body or object into two parts; in the case of nursing, a trend is evident in which different segments of the nursing force, with varying credentials and expertise, are engaged in diverse working situations reflected in unequal workloads, pay, and working conditions.

degree program An education program, normally consisting of 3 to 5 years of formal education in an accredited university, leading to a degree.

diploma program An education program, normally consisting of 2 to 3 years of formal education in an accredited community college, leading to a diploma.

feminized occupation An occupation in which the majority, or increasing proportions, of workers are female; such work tends to be more highly structured and hierarchically organized, and less well paid, than other forms of work.

intensification A process in which workers are required to perform an increasing number of duties or tasks in a job; normally associated with increased external control over the work by people in managerial, administrative, or ownership positions.

professionalism An ideology that emphasizes the attainment of high levels of knowledge, skill, status, and control within a particular occupation.

registered nurse A nurse licensed to practise nursing by a professional certification body within Canadian jurisdictions on the basis of credentials received through accredited nursing diploma or degree programs.

RECOMMENDED READINGS

Armstrong, P., & Armstrong, H. (1996). *Wasting away: The undermining of Canadian health care*. Toronto: Oxford University Press. An overview of the factors leading to recent reforms in the health care system. The authors emphasize how political choices have affected both the quality of health care and the nature of nursing and other health care work.

Armstrong, P., Choiniere, J., & Day, E. (1993). *Vital signs: Nursing in transition*. Toronto: Garamond Press. A concise analysis of the impact of key changes to the health care system on nursing work. The organization of nursing, and nurses' efforts to shape their work, are understood through power struggles over the introduction of new technologies, cutbacks in state spending, managerial control strategies, and gender relations.

Davies, C. (1980). *Rewriting nursing history*. London: Croom Helm. A collection of articles offering a unique approach to the analysis of nursing history, concentrating on the United States and United Kingdom. Nursing is understood as a multifaceted form of work (and predominantly women's work) that has emerged through struggles over work organization, professionalism, and control.

Davies, C. (1995). *Gender and the professional predicament in nursing*. Bristol, PA: Open University Press. An expansion upon central themes identified in the collection the author edited in 1980 (see above), and a compelling argument that nursing needs to be understood as an occupation shaped by notions of femininity and women's work. While nurses are seen to be valued socially for their work as caregivers and health care providers, nursing as work is devalued. Nurses therefore experience increasing frustration and discontent over barriers to their desires for professional advancement and efforts to shape nursing and health care.

Kerr, J.R., & MacPhail, J. (1996). *Canadian nursing: Issues and perspectives* (3rd ed.). St. Louis: Mosby-Year Book. An introduction to general issues related to nursing and nurse professionalism from a nursing perspective, although there is little analysis of these issues. Key areas of concern include the development of nursing and nurse organizations, changing forms of nursing work and practice, and challenges facing nurses.

REFERENCES

Allen, M. (1985, May). Baccalaureate education remains an enigma for many nurses. *Canadian Nurse, 81*(5), 12.

Armstrong, P., & Armstrong, H. (1996). *Wasting away: The undermining of Canadian health care*. Toronto: Oxford University Press.

Armstrong, P., Choiniere, J., & Day, E. (1993). *Vital signs: Nursing in transition*. Toronto: Garamond Press.

Bolaria, B.S. (1987). The brain drain to Canada: The externalization of the cost of education. In T. Wotherspoon (Ed.), *The political economy of Canadian schooling* (pp. 301–322). Toronto: Methuen.

Bowles, S., & Gintis, H. (1976). *Schooling in capitalist America*. New York: Basic Books.

Canadian Hospital Directory. (1984). *Canadian hospital directory statistical compendium*.

Canadian Institute for Health Information. (1998). *More registered nurses working part-time and in community-based health care: 1997 figures*. Ottawa. http://www.cihi.ca/facts/canhr.htm.

Canadian Institute for Health Information. (1999). *Canada's nursing workforce aging, more nurses working part-time*. Ottawa. http://www.cihi.ca/medrls/10may99.htm.

Canadian Nurses' Association. (1968). *The leaf and the lamp*. Ottawa: Author.

Canadian Nurses' Association. (1981). *The seventh decade 1969–1980*. Ottawa: Author.

Canadian Nurses' Association. (1982). *Entry to the practice of nursing: A background paper*. Ottawa: Author.

Canadian Nurses' Association. (1983). *Nursing in Canada 1983*. Ottawa: Statistics Canada and Canadian Nurses' Association.

Canadian Nurses' Association. (1986, October). Collaboration between nurse educators in the use of nursing education resources. *Entry to Practice Newsletter, 2*(5).

Canadian Nurses' Association. (1997). *The future supply of registered nurses in Canada: A discussion paper*. Ottawa: Canadian Nurses' Association.

Cannings, K., & Lazonick, W. (1975). The development of the nursing labor force in the United States: A basic analysis. *International Journal of Health Services, 5*(2), 185–216.

Carnoy, M., & Levin, H.M. (1985). *Schooling and work in the democratic state*. California: Stanford University Press.

Carpenter, M. (1977). The new managerialism and professionalism in nursing. In M. Stacey, M. Reid, C. Heath, & R. Dingwall (Eds.), *Health and the division of labour* (pp. 165–193). London: Croom Helm.

Citizenship and Immigration Canada. (annual series). *Immigration Statistics*. Ottawa: Minister of Public Works and Government Services Canada.

Coburn, J. (1987). I see and am silent: A short history of nursing in Ontario, 1850–1930. In D. Coburn, C. D'Arcy, G.M. Torrance, & P.K. New (Eds.), *Health and Canadian society: Canadian perspectives* (pp. 441–462). Markham: Fitzhenry & Whiteside.

Cockerham, W.C. (1986). *Medical sociology* (3rd ed.). Englewood Cliffs: Prentice-Hall.

Corea, G. (1985). *The hidden malpractice: How American medicine mistreats women*. New York: Harper & Row.

Corrigan, P., Curtis, B., & Lanning, R. (1987). The political space of schooling. In T. Wotherspoon (Ed.), *The political economy of Canadian schooling* (pp. 21–43). Toronto: Methuen.

Crawford, M.E. (1978, February). The curriculum revision process — experienced at the college of nursing, the University of Saskatchewan. In *Perspectives: Nursing education, practice and research* (pp. 1–16). Proceedings of the 1978 Annual Meeting of the Western Region — Canadian Association of University Schools of Nursing. Calgary: University of Calgary.

Davies, C. (1980). A constant casualty: Nurse education in Britain and the USA to 1939. In C. Davis (Ed.), *Rewriting nursing history* (pp. 102–122). London: Croom Helm.

Davies, C. (1995). *Gender and the professional predicament in nursing*. Bristol, PA: Open University Press.

Davis, K., & Moore, W.E. (1945). Some principles of stratification. *American Sociological Review, 10,* 242–249.

Dickinson, H.D. (1987). Vocational education and the control of work: The case of psychiatric nursing in Saskatchewan. In T. Wotherspoon (Ed.), *The political economy of Canadian schooling* (pp. 231–251). Toronto: Methuen.

Duncanson, B. (1970). The development of nursing education at the diploma level. In M.Q. Innis (Ed.), *Nursing education in a changing society* (pp. 109–129). Toronto: University of Toronto Press.

Elliott, M.R. (1977). Nursing and interdisciplinary practice. In B. LaSor & M.R. Elliott (Eds.), *Issues in Canadian nursing* (pp. 43–72). Scarborough: Prentice-Hall.

Gamarnikow, E. (1978). Sexual division of labour: The case of nursing. In A. Kuhn & M. Wolpe (Eds.), *Feminism and materialism — Women and modes of production* (pp. 96–123). London: Routledge & Kegan Paul.

Gibbon, J.M., & Mathewson, M.S. (1947). *Three centuries of Canadian nursing.* Toronto: Macmillan of Canada.

Hall, O. (1970). Social change, specialization, and science: Where does nursing stand? In M.Q. Innis (Ed.), *Nursing education in a changing society* (pp. 3–15). Toronto: University of Toronto Press.

Hannah, K.J. (1978, February). Overview of computer-assisted learning in nursing education at the University of Calgary. In *Perspectives: Nursing education, practice and research* (pp. 43–56). Proceedings of the 1978 Annual Meeting of the Western Region — Canadian Association of University Schools of Nursing. Calgary: University of Calgary.

Health Canada. (1995). *Health Personnel in Canada 1992.* Ottawa: Minister of Supply and Services Canada.

Health and Welfare Canada. (1985). *Canada health manpower inventory 1985.* Ottawa: Minister of National Health and Welfare.

Hibbert, J.M. (1992). Strikes by nurses. In A.J. Baumgart & J. Larsen (Eds.), *Canadian nursing faces the future* (pp. 575–595). St. Louis: Mosby-Year Book.

Innis, M.Q. (Ed.). (1970). *Nursing education in a changing society.* Toronto: University of Toronto Press.

Johnson, T. (1972). *Professions and power.* London: Macmillan.

Kellogg, W.K., Foundation. (1955). *The first twenty-five years: The story of a foundation.* Battle Creek: Author.

Kellogg, W.K., Foundation. (1979). *The first half-century 1930–1980: Private approaches to public needs.* Battle Creek: Author.

Kelly, L.Y. (1985). *Dimensions of professional nursing* (5th ed.). New York: Macmillan.

Kerr, J.R. (1996). Political awareness in nursing. In J.R. Kerr & J. MacPhail (Eds.), *Canadian nursing: Issues and perspectives* (3rd ed., pp. 208–215). St. Louis: Mosby-Year Book.

King, M.K. (1970). The development of university nursing education. In M.Q. Innis (Ed.), *Nursing education in a changing society* (pp. 67–85). Toronto: University of Toronto Press.

Lerner, H.M. (1985). Educating nurses for power. In R.R. Wieczorek (Ed.), *Power, politics, and policy of nursing* (pp. 90–95). New York: Springer.

Livingstone, D.W. (1998). *The education–jobs gap: Underemployment or economic democracy.* Boulder, CO: Westview Press.

Lortie, R. (1994, Fall). Part-time university teachers: A growing group. *Education Quarterly Review, 1*(3), 30–34.

MacFarlane, J.A. (1965). *Medical education in Canada.* Royal Commission on Health Services Special Study No. 13. Ottawa: Queen's Printer.

Mussallem, H.K. (1965). *Nursing education in Canada.* Royal Commission on Health Services Special Study No. 16. Ottawa: Queen's Printer.

Mussallem, H.K. (1977). Nurses and political action. In B. LaSor & M.R. Elliott (Eds.), *Issues in Canadian nursing* (pp. 154–181). Scarborough: Prentice-Hall.

Rafferty, A.M. (1996). *The politics of nursing knowledge.* London: Routledge.

Registered Nurses' Association of British Columbia. (1983). *Entry into the practice of nursing in the year 2000: Position statement of the registered nurses' association of British Columbia.* Vancouver: Author.

Rogers, M.E. (1978). Emerging patterns in nursing education. In J.A. Williamson (Ed.), *Current perspectives in nursing education: The changing scene, Vol. 2* (pp. 1–8). St. Louis: C.V. Mosby.

Ryten, E. (1997). *A statistical picture of the past, present and future of registered nurses in Canada.* Ottawa: Canadian Nurses' Association.

Salmon, J.W. (1984). Organizing medical care for profit. In J.B. McKinlay (Ed.), *Issues in the political economy of health care* (pp. 143–186). New York: Tavistock.

Saskatchewan Union of Nurses. (1998, January). How rationalization of health services is effecting [sic] nursing in Saskatchewan/What's happening to nurses elsewhere? A look at the provinces. *Spectrum,* 5–20.

Schecter, S. (1977). Capitalism, class, and educational reform in Canada. In L. Panitch (Ed.), *The Canadian state: Political economy and political power* (pp. 373–416). Toronto: University of Toronto Press.

Schwirian, P.M. (1998). *Professionalization of nursing: Current issues and trends* (3rd ed.). Philadelphia: Lippincott.

Statistics Canada. (1977). *Survey of vocational education and training 1976–77.* Ottawa: Minister of Supply and Services Canada.

Statistics Canada. (1983). *Historical statistics of Canada* (2nd ed.). Ottawa: Minister of Supply and Services Canada.

Statistics Canada. (1993). *Employment incomes by occupation. Census of Canada. The nation.* Ottawa: Minister of Industry, Science and Technology (cat. no. 93-332).

Statistics Canada. (1995). *Nursing in Canada and nursing education programs, 1994.* Ottawa: Minister of Industry (cat. no. 83-243).

Statistics Canada. (1996). *Nursing in Canada, 1995. Registered nurses.* Ottawa: Minister of Industry (cat. no. 83-243).

Statistics Canada. (1998). *Education in Canada, 1997.* Ottawa: Minister of Industry (cat. no. 81-229).

Swartz, D. (1977). The politics of reform: Conflict and accommodation in Canadian health policy. In L. Panitch (Ed.), *The Canadian state: Political economy and political power* (pp. 311–343). Toronto: University of Toronto Press.

Trudeau, R. (1996, Autumn). Male registered nurses, 1995. *Health reports, 8*(2), 21–27.

Wallis, M. (1978, February). The technological society — its implications for nursing. In *Perspectives: Nursing education, practice and research* (pp. 81–91). Proceedings of the 1978 Annual Meeting of the Western Region — Canadian Association of University Schools of Nursing. Calgary: University of Calgary.

Weir, G.M. (1932). *Survey of nursing education in Canada.* Toronto: University of Toronto Press.

White, J. (1990). *Hospital strike: Women, unions, and public sector conflict.* Toronto: Thompson Educational Publications.

Wolinsky, F.D. (1980). *The sociology of health: Principles, professions, and issues.* Toronto: Little, Brown.

Wotherspoon, T. (1998). *The sociology of education in Canada: Critical perspectives.* Toronto: Oxford University Press.

6

Constrained Agency:
The Social Structure of Nurses' Work

COLLEEN VARCOE AND PATRICIA RODNEY University of Victoria

INTRODUCTION

The upheaval and change characteristic of Canadian health care at the end of the twentieth century shape the conditions of nurses' work and challenge the viability of that work. Perhaps unintentionally, health care reform agendas and their implementation have paradoxically worsened the conditions of nurses' work and thus the care nurses are able to provide. This chapter outlines key elements of the present sociopolitical context of health care and explores the consequences for nurses' work of the shift in the **culture** of health care to a corporate ideology.[1]

This chapter will examine how corporate ideology operates in the everyday work of nurses and other health care providers, and in particular how the ideology of scarcity (Varcoe, 1997) — the pervasive assumption that resources are too scarce to provide adequate care — works with management technology in the control of work. We will consider how nurses' work is organized within scarcity and how nurses participate in corporate ideology. Patterns of practice foster a certain kind of "efficiency" by limiting and devaluing the body care and **emotional labour** of nursing. Nurses then donate unpaid time to limit the moral distress[2] they experience while working under such conditions. This chapter will consider both the moral distress and the health risks faced by nurses working in these conditions and will examine their impact on patients.

This critical analysis of the culture of health care[3] is offered in the spirit of building on the strengths of the current system. Thus it will conclude by exploring how individuals and groups might develop a critical awareness of the culture of health care and the social structure of work and how a greater nursing "voice" in policy might benefit all.

This chapter builds on the authors' two ethnographic studies of the contemporary culture of health care and draws on the empirical work of other scholars, particularly Campbell (1987, 1994), Stelling (1994a), and Yyelland (1994). The authors' two studies are:

1. A study of nurses' enactment of their moral agency, conducted in two acute medical units in two hospitals. The study included over 200 hours of participant

observation and 22 interviews with eleven nurses from acute care and three from home care (Rodney, 1997).

2. A study of nurses' practice in relation to violence against women, conducted in the emergency units of two hospitals and their communities. The study involved over 200 hours of participant observation, and interviews with 45 participants, including nurses, social workers, physicians, clerks, and patients (Varcoe, 1997).

Both studies used feminist and critical perspectives and drew on the work of theorists such as Collins (1986, 1989, 1993), Smith (1987, 1990, 1992), Foucault (1978, 1980), Geertz (1973), Sherwin (1992), and Taylor (1992, 1995). Following completion of these studies, the authors of this chapter drew on the work of Noblit and Hare (1988) to combine the findings. Thus, this chapter draws on each study as well as on secondary analysis of the combined data.

THE CORPORATE CONTEXT OF CONTEMPORARY HEALTH CARE

The Canadian health care system increasingly exists in a context of **globalization**,[4] in which capital flows around the world to serve the interests of an economically dominant elite (Laxer, 1996, 1998). While the espoused intent of the health care reforms occurring in Canada and other Western countries is to improve the quality and accessibility of health care, the implementation of the reforms is fuelled by a powerful and covert **corporate ideology**. Canadian health care reforms are being enacted in an era when there are escalating inequities in the distribution of human resources — and a corresponding acceptance that actions to save money in health care or other social services are inherently justifiable (Anderson & Reimer-Kirkham, 1998; Bolaria, 1994; Carniol, 1995; Laxer, 1996, 1998; McQuaig, 1993, 1998; Saul, 1995, 1997; Stephenson, 1999). This has resulted in a mechanistic, reductionist approach to health services that threatens the Canadian commitment to universal and equitable health care (Anderson, Dyck, & Lynam, 1997; Armstrong & Armstrong, 1996; Blue, Keyserlingk, Rodney, & Starzomski, 1999; Brown, 1996; Burgess, 1996; Cassidy, Lord, & Mandell, 1995; Dickinson, 1994; Fuller, 1998; Northcott, 1994; Picard, 2000; Rachlis & Kushner, 1994; Sherwin, 1992; Storch, 1996; Thorne, 1993). Cost constraint has, to a significant extent, trumped the quality and accessibility of health care.

Economic trends in Canada, including budget deficits and restrictions in the role of the federal government in maintaining the principles of medicare, put tremendous pressure on provincial and territorial governments to economize on health spending (Storch & Meilicke, 1994). Consequently, Canada has experienced "a climate for change in the organization and management of health services that transcend[s] anything since the foundation for the current system was completed in 1968" (Storch & Meilicke, p. 32). This climate has generated extensive cost constraint measures within health care, including **capping** (setting a predetermined level or number of activities to be done within a specific program, e.g., limiting the number of specific surgeries to be done over a year); **downsizing** (bed closures, staff layoffs, and redesign of the remaining activities, e.g., reducing the length of hospital stay); and consolidation of activities (e.g., merging hospital boards and executive management, which often includes a downgrading of the status and role of medicine and nursing in the new organizational structure). The measures further include restructuring and work redesign strategies such as reducing the levels of management, "cross training techniques" that allow staff to be moved between patient care areas, and changing the staff "mix," often by replacing registered nurse staff with practical nurses and/or care aides (Dick & Bruce, 1994, pp. 99–101).

Thus, over the past 10 years, hospital units and entire hospitals have been closed, community services have been shuffled, and health care staff have been moved around or dismissed at an unprecedented rate and scope. Alarmingly, there is little systematic Canadian research to evaluate the impact of these changes. The data from the United States, however, illustrate a serious erosion of the quality of care associated with similar cost constraint measures, particularly as workloads have increased for nurses and poorly qualified personnel have been used to replace nurses (Aiken, Clarke, & Sloane, 2000; Barry-Walker, 2000; Mohr, 1997; Mohr & Mahon, 1996; Phillips & Benner, 1994; Scanlon, 1996–1997; Shindul-Rothschild, Berry, & Long-Middleton, 1996; Wolf, 1994). Canadian data also portray increasing nursing workloads, with reductions in the quality of care and problems with trust, commitment, and morale (Canadian Nurses' Association, 1998; Ferguson-Paré, 1997; Freeman & O'Brien-Pallas, 1998; Keddy et al., 1999; Laschinger et al., 2000; Oberle & Grant, 1994; Sibbald, 1997; Woodward et al., 1998). For example, nurses in long-term care reported that staffing was reduced so drastically that elderly, debilitated residents were not adequately fed (Oberle & Grant, 1994).

Why has a corporate ideology, with its aforementioned problems, taken such hold in Canada? An **ideology** is a set of ideas and images; "a shared set of fundamental beliefs, attitudes, and assumptions about the world that justify 'what is'" (Thomas, 1993, p. 8). Ideologies are usually taken for granted because they are unconscious. They provide the conceptual machinery for questions, for the data gathered or ignored, and for the chosen interpretations (Thomas, p. 8). A corporate ideology has taken hold in Canada and is largely taken for granted. Noted Canadian cultural critic John Ralston Saul (1995, 1997) claims that the nation operates on myths (such as ideas that "we spend too much on social services," "current levels of care are no longer affordable") rather than memory and that it has lost sight of its commitment to the "**common good**"[5] that characterized the development of Canada as a nation. Operating on myth provides opportunities for unexamined ideas to exert their powerful influence. In health care Canada has allowed its commitment to the common good to be replaced by corporatism.

This chapter will therefore attempt to unmask what has been taken for granted. It will explore the consequences of corporate ideology for the everyday work of nurses and other health care providers, as well as for patients and their families. What has been taken for granted must be made visible if the nation is to move toward the more equitable health care system that most Canadians desire.

CORPORATISM AT THE LEVEL OF PATIENT CARE

Both the ideologies and the practices of the corporate culture of health care are played out at the level of direct patient care. The research cited above indicates that each cost constraint measure has a direct impact on nursing practice, creating more work, more uncertainty, and less control over how nursing time is spent. Perhaps most importantly, "redesign" strategies, such as those aimed at reducing the length of hospital stay, have resulted in an increase in patient acuteness and turnover, which in turn directly affects nursing workload. Nurses find themselves caring for more acute patients and processing more patients more quickly. Downsizing activities such as bed closures require nurses to organize those closures, move to new practice areas, and organize the reopening of beds and work areas. The consolidation of hospital boards and executive management, staff layoffs, and eliminating levels of management (and often the managers) create a climate of instability and uncertainty. Further, with less contact between direct care providers and management, nurses generally have less impact on decision making. Moving nurses to unfamiliar patient care areas and replacing registered nurses with practical nurses and/or care aides dilutes levels of skill, placing heavier responsibilities on the remaining staff.

An Ideology of Scarcity

Our research indicates that nurses must adjust their work to this evolving corporate context and make sense of the changing conditions of work. Nurses participate in the corporate ideology and organize their work to maximize a certain kind of efficiency. One of the most profound ways that the ideas and images of corporatism are enacted at this level is through an **ideology of scarcity**. Ideas and images of resources as scarce and unattainable abound in the day-to-day world of nursing practice. And these ideas and images in turn drive practices that emphasize certain kinds of streamlining and efficiencies.

Corporate rhetoric and ideas dominate thinking both within the health care system and in the wider social context. Nurses receive messages about the state of the economy and health care from many sources, ranging from media messages, including local and health care specific media, to managers and coworkers. In the settings studied by the authors, messages about scarcity predominated. National newspapers emphasized constraint, local media focused on downsizing, and health care agency publications stressed budgets. Many managers (at all levels) promoted ideologies that resonated with the ideas of efficiency in a time of scarcity. In the words of a hospital manager, "To do the best job with the resources that you have, that is what exemplary is."

Within nursing work in these settings, this ideology of scarcity was primarily expressed in talk about time and enacted in nurses' work in the form of certain "efficiencies." Nurses' talk revealed an acceptance of scarcity as the driving force in health care and as the driving force that organizes nursing practice. In the words of one nurse, "It's money, it's management, it's things I can't really argue with." Another said:

> You'd like more staff and you'd like more participation but in reality there isn't the money, you aren't going to get the staff, so don't spend the time whining and sniveling, it's not going to be there. Just do the best you can with what you have.

Despite the sense of acceptance of the new "fiscal realities," nurses' talk also conveyed a profound awareness of the discrepancies between the care they valued and the care they were able to provide. Most of this talk was couched in terms of time: time that nurses did not have to provide the care that their patients required. Time was described as "lacking," "inadequate," and "nonexistent," and the predominant impact of this scarcity was seen as inadequate attention to nonphysical care.

Nurses identified their attention to the nonphysical needs of patients as the aspect of care that suffered most, both during the provision of routine care and when patients experienced significant emotional crises. Nurses talked about the ways they routinely curtailed their conversation and attention to the emotional needs of patients, and the authors observed nurses letting patients know that they were busy so that patients did not expect to engage in conversation. Nurses routinely mentioned that they did not have time for "the psychosocial," meaning attention to patients' nonphysical needs. One nurse said that when patients request extra attention, "you think 'just don't bother me anymore, I want to do my work and get out of there.'"

Even during devastating events, nurses felt they were unable to afford the time required for emotional care. Most who were interviewed told at least one story that exemplified such situations. Each nurse told a story about a patient who had experienced a profound loss, such as the death of a child or partner, or a terminal diagnosis, for whom the nurse was unable to provide the support the patient needed.

> [I]t is really hard for a nurse to just sit there and *do nothing* at a bedside when she's got a gazillion things to do, but with some people that is almost what you need to do, just sit there for five minutes and not say anything, just be there and that builds the trust. Anyway that's a dream, we don't have the time to do that any more. [emphasis added]

Note that this nurse refers to her emotional care as doing "nothing." Based on her analysis of nurses' talk about time in two studies, Stelling (1994a) concluded:

> This talk about time is not really about time at all....When nurses say they do not have time for interactional work with patients, the real problem is that they are unable to maintain its high priority when confronted with the demands and expectations of others. Thus time can be seen as a metaphor for autonomy and control; the emphasis on the shortage of time reflects the importance and pervasiveness of the lack of autonomy and control. (p. 210)

Consistent with Stelling's findings, the emphasis on corporate efficiency and physical "treatment" was seen by nurses in our two studies to be valued by other health care providers, especially those who have the most powerful influence on nursing practice — managers and physicians. Relationships between nurses and managers within the units were often characterized by a continuous struggle over resources, and nurses often saw physicians as supportive of the corporate ideology.[6] One nurse said:

> The Emerg Physicians are there to make money, they are there to see the maximum number of patients in the minimum amount of time and they are somewhat reluctant to deal with patients that are psychosocial or emotional because it takes longer and there is always that feeling of being inadequate when dealing with it, whether due to a lack of experience or lack of resources.

Ideas of scarcity in health care are dominant in public spheres, at all levels of government, and among health care providers at various levels within the system. Nurses accepted these ideas to a large extent and shaped their practice to conform to corporate ideology and imperatives. Time, nurses' most valuable resource, was viewed as a scarce commodity and was often spent in the service of corporate goals rather than nursing or patient priorities. Thus, these ideas of scarcity supported cost constraint measures, and both the ideas and constraints structured nurses' work. As a result of corporate streamlining, nurses' work became structured as "efficient" practice.

CORPORATE STREAMLINING AND "EFFICIENT" PRACTICES

In response to cost constraint measures and messages about the inevitability of scarcity in health care, and with at least a partial acceptance of those messages, nurses' work is organized to maximize their "efficiency." This efficiency is organized by what Smith (1987, 1990) calls "the relations of ruling" — structures, institutions, and regulations — that create understandings taken up by the nurses themselves. The relations of ruling between management and nurses are mediated by various management technologies that organize nurses' efforts to efficiently process patients.

Nursing work is organized by a series of management technologies. The relationship between restraint and nursing labour has been accomplished through the introduction of management technology to manage nurses' labour (Campbell, 1994). Based on her study of nurses' work, Campbell described how the introduction of patient classification and workload measurement systems in the 1970s and 1980s fundamentally altered control of nursing staffing decisions. The introduction of these technologies began the shift of decision making about patient "needs" and staffing from the site of "production" (i.e., where the work is done) to management.

These technologies, designed to improve the "efficiency" of nurses' labour, created "objective data" about patient "needs" and matched this data with the amount of nursing work required, thus transferring dominance from the professional judgement of nurses to that of managers who can claim to "know" based on data. Unfortunately, these formulas do not account for what Campbell (1994) calls "indeterminate work"; they calculate staffing based on minimized and standardized estimates of patient needs that do not account for individual or "real" patients.[7] Of course, a major component of nurses' "indeterminate work" is their emotional labour in support of patients. The consequences of these moves to manage nurses' labour include cutting the time allowed to complete care, speeding up of the pace of work, and adding more paper work. Campbell (1987) concluded:

> Recommended as a rational method of improving nurse productivity, I argue that objective needs assessment and staffing procedures result in decisions that are neither as rational as they seem nor more trustworthy than those made on nurses' judgement alone. The objective decisions do, however, mean that nursing-care time can be limited and nurses' work intensified. Such outcomes add stress to nurses' working conditions that, combined with reductions in the scope and level of services able to be offered under new time constraints, threaten the quality of care for hospital patients. (p. 463)

Today, with the introduction of sophisticated computerized information systems (at great expense to the health care system), management technologies have become less visible. When a nurse orders a laboratory test, sends a request to the pharmacy, or calls a porter to transport a patient, these acts are automatically counted and recorded and ultimately used in decision making about workload and staffing patterns. Printouts of varying levels of activity at different times of day are available. The problem of failing to capture the "indeterminate work" of nursing persists, but the data collection and decision making is invisible to nurses. Thus they participate unknowingly and are unable to contribute to a critical analysis of decision making. Whereas in the 1980s nurses critiqued patient classification and workload measurement systems as they filled in paper forms, as the technologies become more pervasive and less visible, such critique becomes impossible. There are no opportunities to object, "But that doesn't capture what we do!"

Over the past several decades, then, staffing patterns have been adjusted by using various management technologies to the point that the indeterminate work of nursing has been squeezed almost out of existence. Because only certain practices are "counted," because physiological care and medical treatment are valued over other forms of care, and because scarcity has been accepted, patterns of practice have developed to accommodate these values. Thus, the form of "efficiency" that has evolved is one that provides physiological care and medical treatment as quickly and as cheaply as possible.

In the units studied by the authors, the patterns of practice reflected this sort of "efficiency." In the emergency units, the predominant practice pattern was one of "efficient processing." In this pattern of practice, patients were: 1. "stripped down" (literally and figuratively), to 2. identify a manageable problem (such as a chest pain, laceration, or fever), and 3. processed according to this manageable problem in order, to 4. empty the stretcher. Various strategies were used to keep patients "on track." Assessments were routinized and circumscribed and patients were encouraged to give only the information needed to identify the problem. Such strategies began with opening questions at triage such as, "What brings you to emergency today?" and continued with checklists and flow sheets tailored to identify physiological problems. These strategies were facilitated by behaviours that let patients know how busy the staff were and discouraged them from making demands for attention beyond what the nurse could meet.

Similarly, in the medical units, the actual running of departments was often seen to have priority over the needs of patients, including both physical and nonphysical needs. Patient needs were subordinated to the needs of departments, so, for example, an unstable patient might be transported without adequate personnel and equipment (such as oxygen, a stretcher, and a nurse, rather than a wheelchair and a porter) in order to prevent delays in the X-ray department; home care patients with disabilities might be admitted to hospital and anesthetized repeatedly for small procedures because those procedures could not be coordinated.

In the various settings studied, nurses not only developed patterns of practice to maximize their own "efficiency" but also devised systems of working within the constraints of others. Nurses spent a good deal of effort accommodating the efficiencies of other health care providers and departments. In the emergency units, nurses' first priority was usually to prepare patients for the physician's assessment; they would process the physician's orders immediately following the assessment and would immediately cease their own work to allow others to complete theirs. For example, upon the arrival of any physician, technician, or porter, nurses would interrupt their work. Further, nurses devised other ways of facilitating the efficiency of others. For example, because physicians had limited time to spend on each patient and because nurses were often too busy to "catch" the physician, nurses devised systems to alert physicians. In both one medical and one emergency unit, brightly coloured pieces of paper were attached to the front of charts to highlight particular problems.

One of the major ways in which these "efficient"[8] practices were maintained by nurses was the use of workplace sanctions. Nurses let one another know what was expected, rewarded one another for maintaining "efficiency," and penalized each other for not maintaining expectations. Nurses expressed regard for those who were "efficient" in terms of providing physical care and "getting the tasks done," and expressed derision for those who were "slow," were "bleeding hearts," spent "too much time talking," and so on.

There are a few [nurses] in particular who deal with the emotional aspect first, unless of course [patients] are bleeding out or whatever. They meet the wrath of some of the other staff members quite significantly. "She's not pulling her load, she's doing that PR crap."

Paradoxically, accommodating the efficiencies of other health care providers and departments sometimes threatened already thin nursing resources. One nurse manager revealed how "capping" (in which some departments close, to keep their quota of activities down) created problems with the budget in her acute medical unit:

One of the things that frustrates...to no end is the capping days because that's to save money supposedly, except you have the same work going on with half the resources and therefore [it] adds to the length of stay...for example...patients come in with abdominal pain.... And if it's a capping day there's nobody doing ultrasounds so that means that if that patient needed an ultrasound they could go home if they had [it].... Or, you need to have a test done but they've closed the department for the capping day, so the patient has to go [farther away]...but there's only two porters on and it might take them an hour to go to there as opposed to twenty minutes.

This excerpt reflects the cost constraint measures listed earlier. That list (capping, downsizing, consolidation of activities, restructuring, and work redesign strategies) made it seem that each measure is isolated and has a predictable effect — a reduction in overall hospital costs. However, as the above illustrates, the effects are complex, interrelated, unpredictable, and often undesirable. In this example, capping days implemented by other departments actually increased the patient length of stay. Clearly, this is not the type of efficiency intended by a cost–benefit analysis that has health as the intended outcome.

Sanctions enacted by staff nurses were also evident at administrative levels. Administrators applied sanctions for "inefficiencies" such as an increased length of stay. The manager cited above explained:

[M]y unit is expected to have a length of stay of seven days and my last year the length of stay was eleven days.... I mean reality is...patients going through chemotherapy [cancer treatment] or stuff like that...[often have a length of stay of] twenty days and then you have all the [patients with endocarditis] that have just all of a sudden appeared in the population...[because of illicit intravenous] drugs.... I mean they've got an average length of stay of thirty days so you just change the population...the "seven days" comes from the literature...other medical units [that] have been able to get their length of stays down. However, there's been no comparison of [our population to theirs].

She went on to explain how the failure to comply with corporate edicts resulted in consequences that in turn created more problems.

[T]here's no money so we ended up closing. Summer time last year we closed twelve beds to try and reap in the money so the outcome was nursing lay off...if you can't shut down any more beds then what we're going to do is [use] aides, not nurses.

Failure to meet corporate goals, such as in this case the increased length of stay, often carried the risk of sanctions for managers, units, and staff, including staff layoffs, and/or the replacement of registered nurses with less prepared staff. This also demonstrates that cost constraint measures are not completely rational, as Campbell (1987) warned over 10 years ago. Units that are different in terms of patient population and patient needs are grouped together and expected to hold to the same standards in terms of markers such as length of stay, per capita costs, and so on. Thus, administrative sanctions work with sanctions applied by nurses to enforce practice in congruence with corporate goals.

CORPORATE CASUALTIES[9]

Thus far, this chapter has argued that the corporate culture of health care is made manifest in an ideology of scarcity. It further argued that corporate streamlining and efficient processing shape direct patient care. But what is the impact on nurses as individuals and for nursing as a profession? What are the consequences for the patients, families, and communities that nurses serve? Overall, the social organization of "cost efficiency" exacts both a professional and personal toll when nurses are expected to accept responsibility for delivering a safe and sufficient level of care under conditions that become less and less capable of sustaining this work. The consequences are serious, not just because of the human costs to nurses, but because of the impact on the quality of care received by patients, families, and communities.

Disposable Nurses

Nurses providing direct care are treated as if they are disposable in at least four ways. Their intellectual and emotional labour, and their personal time and well-being, are too often sacrificed for the efficiency of the system. For example:

> [W]hen it gets busy, when it gets so busy you're so busy coping sometimes with just the actual immediate physical needs and their meds getting out and stuff like that that you often don't have the time to really think through the assessments...when I go home afterwards I think, "Wow, what about such and such?"...and you know, you hit yourself.... There's things that I forget too, like I go home and I think, "Now I wonder if..."

First, let us look at the nurse's intellectual labour. This experienced medical nurse took pride in her ability to assess her patients and was acknowledged as a clinical resource by her colleagues. Yet in the interview cited above, she went on to tell a story of how she had missed picking up bladder distention on a patient who was showing many of the classic signs. Indeed, this nurse was what Benner and her colleagues would have recognized as an expert at clinical judgement. She knew "the particular patient, his typical pattern of responses, his story and the way in which illness has constituted his story. [She knew this] through advanced clinical knowledge...gained from experience with many persons in similar situations" (Benner, Tanner, & Chesla, 1996, p. 1). Yet she had little opportunity to employ that judgement in her work. In this sense, her intellectual labour was not valued.

Second, being busy with "just the actual immediate physical needs" means that nurses' emotional labour — the labour of dealing with emotional needs — is compromised (Varcoe, 1997; Yyelland, 1994).[10] For example, a nurse working in an emergency department said:

> There was a young fellow…diagnosed with leukemia down there, first thing in the morning they wheeled him in and told him what he had and he didn't want me to leave. Of course you are torn because you've got a lot of other things to do and in many respects he is a priority but the way we worked down there is ABC, life-threatening, limb-threatening and he is neither of those…. I waited for awhile and then I said, "Do you want to be alone or do you still want me to stay until your family comes…or can I get you a Social Worker or something?" I'm trying everything to get another body in there so I can get out and that's wrong, but what do you do?

And, as noted, nurses sometimes demeaned one another for attending to patients' emotional needs.

Thus, both intellectual and emotional labour are devalued by the way work is organized and by nurses themselves. Nurses in the two authors' studies cited at the beginning of this chapter did not have time to "think through" their care. Nor did they have time to "talk about it." Such concerns about excessive workloads — workloads that get in the way of nurses meeting the professional standards of their practice — are by no means new. At least four decades of empirical work in diverse studies from various practice contexts echo this concern (Rodney & Starzomski, 1993). What is new is the escalation of workloads and the concomitant reduction of professional resources (Aiken, Clarke, & Sloane, 2000; Canadian Nurses' Association, 1998; Mohr & Mahon, 1996; Nagle, 1999; Oberle & Grant, 1994; Shindul-Rothschild, Berry, & Long-Middleton, 1996; Sibbald, 1997). Nurses in the two authors' studies conveyed their distress, and sometimes resignation, about this. For instance, the following is an excerpt from field notes made at the beginning of a night in Emergency:

> I joined Dorothy who said, "We're short already," looking with consternation at the white board on which staff assignments (and patient names and bed numbers) are written. Later, Lenore growled, "We don't have time to do anything but the tasks, the workload is ridiculous." She tells me that in the 11 years she has worked in Emergency, she has never seen it so bad (referring to the workload). She says she is very frustrated and that she writes notes daily to the Head Nurse, but the Head Nurse's "hands are tied." (Field Notes, Varcoe, 1997, p. 123)

Third, nurses' personal time was often treated as disposable. Not surprisingly, in order to complete their tasks, nurses routinely stayed past the end of their designated work shift but did not usually claim overtime pay. In other words, they "donated" time to the health care system.[11] Nurses' "donations" often jeopardized their personal time. This was particularly apparent for nurses who faced concurrent child care demands. For example, one nurse spoke of staying late on the medical unit to care for a critically ill patient about to be transferred to intensive care. Because she stayed to care for the patient, her husband was unable to attend an important meeting at work because she would not be home in time to look after their child.

Again, nurses' donation of time is not a new empirical finding. It has appeared in a number of other studies of nurses' work (e.g., Corley & Mauksch, 1988; Stelling, 1994a, 1994b; Walters, 1994; Yyelland, 1994). For example, Stelling found that nurses often stayed past the end of their shifts but would only "claim" the overtime if it was a recognized medical emergency. She says:

> There is an irony here. Women are supposed to give first priority to their families, and are consequently assumed or expected to have a lesser commitment to their careers. Somehow nurses' commitment to their patients, which is manifest in the way they talk about nursing and their work, in the overtime they work, and in their willingness to "pick up the slack," seems to be equated to women's "natural" commitment to their families and thereby deemed irrelevant to their professional commitment. Thus it becomes invisible and doesn't count as commitment. (1994a, p. 623)

Nurses' commitment to their patients and their own families, and their difficulty in meeting these commitments, exacts significant personal costs. Therefore, the fourth "disposable" to be explored is nurses' well-being. Campbell (1994) noted that nurses working under excessive workloads suffer frustration, anxiety, and self-blame about the care they are able to give (p. 594). Nurses in the two authors' studies often experienced profound guilt and fatigue. As the experienced medical nurse cited above said, "You know, you hit yourself." An emergency nurse was embarrassed and apologetic about her work environment. After several hours of dashing from patient to patient, providing only urgent care and using techniques to forestall patient demands, she turned to one of the authors, nearly in tears. "I'm sorry," she said, gesturing back to the unit, which was crowded, noisy, crawling with people pushing various pieces of equipment about. "You should see it the way it should be, not like this."

The nurses on both medical and emergency units spoke of how tired they felt at the end of most shifts. The physical demands of providing basic nursing care to elderly and/or dependent patients were substantial, and there was almost always a sense that nurses were racing against the clock to complete the required tasks. Confounding the physical demands was the fatigue generated both by shift work and by the "second shift" that many nurses experienced in caring for their families. This finding has been well documented in previous studies: decades of research have explored the impact of nurses' work, the effects of shift work, and the impact on the quality of life for people (particularly women) in a variety of occupations who must balance responsibilities in the home and in the workplace (e.g., Doyal, 1994; Long & Kahn, 1993; Lynn & Todoroff, 1995; Swanson-Kauffman, 1987).

As well as the guilt and fatigue that nurses in the authors' studies experienced, there was an ever-present (but not often discussed) level of personal risk, both physical and psychological. The physical risk was multidimensional. One nurse manager warned:

> The other thing that we've got going on now is a lot more infectious diseases. You know with the AIDS patients, they're coming in with chicken pox and stuff.... We're having a lot more dangerous [exposure to illnesses]...HIV, TB [tuberculosis], we've had a meningitis outbreak and...it's a personal threat to ourselves also....violence in patients.... I think it contributes to the fatigue.... And threat of injury.

During the authors' fieldwork, they were told that a significant amount of "sick time" was taken by staff due to events such as back injuries, which had escalated with the increased acuteness and heavy care requirements of patients. In the emergency units nurses told of often taking "mental health days" informally and through stress leave programs.

Clearly, nurses do not practise in environments that are conducive to their well-being (Attridge & Callahan, 1987; Curran & Miller, 1990; Growe, 1991; Keddy et al.,

1999; Kramer, 1974; McClure, Poulin, Sovie, & Wandelt, 1983; O'Brien-Pallas, Baumann, & Villeneuve, 1994; Picard, 2000; Walters, 1994). Nor are such environments conducive to the care of patients, families, or communities (Aiken, Clarke, & Sloane, 2000; Laschinger et al., 2000).

Overlooked Patients

In the corporate culture of health care today, nurses are all too often treated as disposable, while the well-being of patients, families, and communities is all too often overlooked.[12] In the authors' two studies, for instance, they observed situations in which elderly patients did not receive the basic physical care they required, patients with substance use problems who were not treated appropriately for their withdrawal, women who had experienced violence and who did not receive the counselling or referral they required, and family members of dying patients who were not adequately supported.

Such situations arose at least partly because nurses and other members of the health care team (including physicians) were working under almost impossible structural constraints. The administrators with whom the authors spoke also felt powerless to challenge or reverse these constraints. One nurse manager whose unit chronically functioned at 110 percent of the workload index (itself a poor estimate that under-measured nursing work) found that despite staff working "flat out," they were routinely unable to meet basic patient needs. Another manager noted that unless staff came to work with "100 percent energy, a clear mind, and an open heart," the demands of the workplace were impossible to meet.

What is often lost in today's era of cost constraint is nurses' and other health care providers' ability to work together to respond to complex health care needs. Indeed, even basic physical needs are not well addressed, particularly for the elderly. The "body care" inherent in nursing work — the work that addresses people's experiences of their embodied existence, especially when their bodies fail to function normally (Lawler, 1993, p. vi) — is overlooked. One of the nurses in the authors' research provided this illustration:

> [A] lady…was in with neck pain, back pain and knee pain and they thought she possibly had some collagen disease [an autoimmune disorder], [she was] very stiff and all this kind of stuff. She had an IV [intravenous], she wanted to go on the [bed]pan constantly, she was on a slipper [small] pan because she couldn't get on a bigger one — she was too stiff — constantly it [the urine] would back flow and get on the pad or she'd squirt over the front or something you know, and…I didn't really think about it, I just thought "It's the IV that's going," so the second night I capped [stopped] the IV, she was still going…something was going on in my mind you know, like she's not going [voiding] that much [quantity]…so I did an in and out catheter post void, eleven seventy-five [millilitres] I got, so it was all overflow [her bladder was overdistended]…. But I didn't pick up on that the first night…. I was just trying to…get everything together you know and…we had a couple of [patient] transfers in, a couple of admissions and things like that so you don't always pick up on those things.

The woman of whom the nurse spoke had a serious and debilitating medical condition, yet it was extraordinarily difficult for the nurse — who was an expert — to assess even her basic physiological functions. In another situation, an elderly woman immobilized with serious rheumatoid arthritis was to be discharged into the care of her daughter and son-in-law. The daughter was ill with cancer, and the son-in-law was in his sixties. Yet the body care involved in toileting the elderly woman, feeding her, washing her, and so on was not recognized or planned for in "the system." Nor was there the opportunity to devise a comprehensive interdisciplinary plan to help her with her pain and mobility. And there was certainly not the time to help her adjust to her altered level of independence or to listen to the concerns she might have for her daughter. Further, the needs of her family were not taken into account. In fact, the authors' observations indicate that it is patients and family members in these kinds of situations who are at risk of deteriorating rapidly in the community and returning to the emergency department in full-blown crisis. Although the intent of health care reform has been to limit the costs of *treatment*, it has been *care* that has been limited.

The Western health care system has a long history of unresponsiveness to the needs of patients, families, and communities, particularly the needs of those marginalized because of age, race, gender, chronic illness, disability, and so forth (see, for example, Anderson, 2000; Anderson, Blue, & Lau, 1991; O'Neil, 1987; Rachlis & Kushner, 1989; Sherwin, 1992; Stephenson, 1999; Thorne, 1993; Varcoe, 2001). As was mentioned above, recent cost constraint measures have only made this unresponsiveness worse, especially for those who are marginalized (Anderson, Dyck, & Lynam, 1997; Blue et al., 1999; Cassidy, Lord, & Mandell, 1995; Mohr & Mahon, 1996; Watson, 1994). Although nurses in the authors' studies primarily rationed their most valuable resource — their time — based on patient acuteness, social judgements based on class, ethnicity, substance use, and so on figured in their allocation of resources.

Community care is also suffering. The three community nurses interviewed by the authors described their difficulty in organizing appropriate care for patients with complex illnesses and disabilities. Recent studies in Alberta echoed these concerns and profiled the anguish that nurses experience when they try to support "high risk" families who are having difficulties with parenting (MacPhail, 1996; Oberle & Tenove, 2000; see also Duncan, 1992).

CONSTRAINED AGENCY

Clearly the well-being of nurses, patients, families, and communities is threatened in the corporate culture of health care. In closing this portrait of the social structure of nurses' work, it is worth considering some of the moral implications for nurses and what they mean for nurses as moral agents.[13] Nurses' enactment of their moral agency can be understood in terms of how they fulfill their moral responsibility and accountability and how they deal with ethical problems in their practice (Rodney, 1997).

Moral Distress

Nurses are often in situations in which they cannot fulfill their moral responsibility and accountability, and they are overwhelmed by ethical problems. And they experience a great **moral distress** because of this. The ethical problems they face are sometimes dramatic questions of life and death decision making — for instance, how to help a family decide whether or not to initiate tube feeding for a person who has suffered a stroke.

More often, the ethical problems that nurses face are everyday questions, such as whether to restrain or "tie down" a confused patient. These questions are ethical because they revolve around "the good" in practice (Rodney, 1997).[14]

Significantly, the ethical problems faced by nurses in the authors' studies frequently emerged as a result of constraints and cutbacks in the workplace. For example, the need to physically restrain confused patients or to rapidly force-feed dependent elders was increased by inadequate staffing levels that precluded alternative approaches to care. Thus, the ethical problems that nurses dealt with were embedded in everyday practice in an era of health reform — problems that, as Liaschenko (1993a) has warned, are frequently "discounted or trivialized or sentimentalized" in biomedical ethics (p. 9). Nurses felt badly about the abrogation of their professional responsibility and accountability, and about the difficulties they experienced in trying to deal with ethical problems in their practice. The emergency nurse cited above was frustrated and tearful when she said, "You should see the way it should be, not like this." The nurse manager cited earlier was "frustrated to no end" with "capping days." And so on. Almost every nurse encountered during the authors' fieldwork expressed this kind of distress, and, of course, it was echoed by physicians, social workers, physiotherapists, patients, family members, and others involved (directly and indirectly) in patient care.

The nurses' distress was not just fatigue. Their distress reflected the anguish and powerlessness inherent in moral distress. That is, nurses made moral choices (e.g., to set up support for an elder whose caregiver was physically abusive), but situational constraints made it difficult to translate moral choices into moral actions (Jameton, 1984; Rodney & Starzomski, 1993; Wilkinson, 1985). The moral distress that nurses experience is a reflection of their difficulty enacting their moral agency (Erlen & Frost, 1991; Ketefian & Ormond, 1988; Liaschenko, 1993b; Millette, 1994; Munhall, 1990; Rodney, 1997; Rodney & Starzomski, 1993; Storch, 1992; Wilkinson, 1989; Yarling & McElmurray, 1986; Yeo & Ford, 1996). As the enactment of moral agency is prerequisite to professional practice, the social structure of nurses' work threatens the foundation of professional practice as well as the well-being of nurses as people.

Moral Resistance

Nurses in the authors' studies did not passively acquiesce to the constraints inherent in the social structure of their work. They resisted in various overt and covert ways. Despite the constraints, nurses made efforts to "get to know" their patients, to work with others as a team, and to negotiate better care, particularly when they faced ethical problems. To illustrate, the nurse who spoke of the elderly woman immobilized with serious rheumatoid arthritis explained how she (at least partially) resolved the problem of premature discharge of her elderly patient:

> So I said to her doctor, "Well, what are the plans for this lady?"... You've got to find out these things, and I was saying, "You know, it was taking two [people to get her up]," so he went in there and he says, "Okay, we want you up more," he got physio involved...and then we can now say to her, "Okay, the doctor says that he wants...he thinks you can probably go home in three or four days, we've got to get you up and moving."

This nurse worked to know the patient and her family, and the physician listened to her with respect. Moreover, she actively negotiated to bring various players together to create a better discharge plan.

Nurses also attempted to enact their moral agency by bending the rules. In other words, they went outside of what was officially sanctioned in their attempts to provide good care. For instance, a nurse in a medical unit where there were no regular venues for communication with physicians (such as patient care rounds) explained how she requisitioned blood tests without waiting for a physician's order when worried about a patient's electrolyte status. She explained, "You always have to work a way around the system to make it work." Similarly, nurses in emergency bent the rules, for example, by giving patients unordered pain medications to take home.

Interestingly, the authors' observations are congruent with the findings from a large qualitative field study by Hutchinson (1990). During this study of nurses' unprofessional behaviour, Hutchinson reported that nurses described a variety of rule-bending behaviours — for personal or private reasons, for increased efficiency, and for the sake of the patient. Hutchinson named the latter "responsible subversion," claiming that nurses' behaviour was responsible "because they used their best nursing judgement to decide what rule to bend, and when and how to do it," but also subversive "in that they violated rules made by hospital and nursing administrators or physicians" (p. 7). Hutchinson explained:

> Unlike administrators and physicians, who can essentially create rules, nurses do the work of patient care within a context of rules imposed by others. Many times the web of institutional and medical rules conflict with the nurse's own internal "rules" or beliefs about patient care. Responsible subversion occurs only in response to a conflict between systems and/or people. A conflict exists when the accepted rules in a given situation prohibit nurses from doing what they believe is in the patient's best interest. (p. 7)

The nurses observed by the authors were usually motivated by what they saw as the best interests of the patients they were caring for, and they were certainly caught in conflicts between institutional and medical rules (e.g., to monitor electrolytes only on a physician's order) and their own beliefs about what patients needed (e.g., to have electrolytes monitored during replacement therapy). Importantly, at least some responsible subversion was a result of trying to "make up for" workplace constraints (e.g., the lack of patient care rounds and workloads that limited communication with physicians and others).

However, Hutchinson (1990) warns that responsible subversion may have negative as well as positive consequences. Nurses who bend the rules may experience sanctions if they are "caught," and rules may become more rigid once this happens. Moreover, if rules are not applied consistently, patients and families may become concerned about inconsistent (and possibly unjust) treatment. Further, in response to Hutchinson's study, Munhall (1990) raised a number of serious ethical questions about responsible subversion. These include questions about the rightness or wrongness of nurses practising according to their own rules, about the ethical principles that underlie nurses' actions when they bend or break rules, about what would happen if everybody broke rules, about whether rule breaking is the only course of action available to the nurse, and so on. Thus, although responsible subversion often helped nurses to mediate the constraints inherent in the social structure of their work, it also had the potential to jeopardize their role and their care of patients and families. Further, in the authors' studies it was observed that rule bending became entrenched so that practice problems were hidden and remained unexamined. Paradoxically, then, responsible subversion has the potential to jeopardize the nurses' enactment of their moral agency. In a sense, responsible subversion may be a "guerrilla tactic" that has the potential to misfire.

CONCLUSION

Beyond Guerrilla Tactics

At the same time as health care workers participate in corporatism, they engage in tactics that mitigate these dominant influences. However, most of these tactics are at the level of the individual and are not necessarily based on a critical awareness of dominance of corporate ideologies and practices. Thus, efforts to preserve quality in the health care system must become increasingly conscious, deliberate, and organized. In particular, nurses' work must be restructured to align with goals of health and the common good and in defiance of corporatism as the driving force in health care. Warnings about the danger to health and health care posed by corporatism must be heeded (e.g. Gibb, 1998; Hiraki, 1998; Mohr & Mahon, 1996; Mohr, 1997; Reinhardt, 1997). Ideologies must be exposed and challenged, "efficiency" re-envisioned, and space for the intellectual, emotional, and body work of nursing must be carved out of the wasteland that corporatism has created in health care. Nurses must take active roles individually and collectively both in countering the erosion of health care and nursing practice and in formulating policy. Collective action will require proactive work through professional nursing associations and unions (Canadian Nurses Association, 1998; Health Canada Office of Nursing Policy, 2000; Walters, 1994).

Unmasking Ideology

This chapter has attempted to make visible some of the ways in which corporate ideologies are enacted within health care, within nursing practice, and by nurses themselves. It is hoped that this will be revealing for nurses and that they will be able to operate with a greater critical awareness of the ways in which ideologies are used to structure their work and of the ways in which they participate in undermining their own values. With this awareness, nurses might challenge the often taken for granted idea that "there is no more money," and recognize such ideas as tricks to hide the fact that money is simply being spent elsewhere (sometimes on expensive systems to keep track of their labour). Nurses might then refuse the corporate rhetoric (Hiraki, 1998) and challenge corporate ideologies. They might also then decide that accepting such ideas and sanctioning one another to work in compliance with corporatism is unacceptable, that it is neither in their interests nor in those of their patients. Collective refusal to comply with corporatism would necessarily put patient needs and health outcomes ahead of corporate imperatives, would foreground alternate ideologies (perhaps ideologies of health, social justice, and the common good), and would require rethinking "efficiency."

Of course, individual nurses cannot do this work alone. There must be sufficient critical awareness of the issues and operating ideologies to make resistance the norm rather than simply the maverick behaviour of an individual. Shifting away from an environment of sanction and compliance would require and contribute to the creation of environments where relationships and trust flourish. Collective action within units, and in collaboration with existing groups such as professional organizations and unions, is necessary to move beyond guerrilla tactics to a full-scale assault on corporatism.

Reimagining "Efficiencies"

This chapter has challenged the strategies currently employed in the name of cost efficiency. The form of efficiency that must be sought is one that takes into account effectiveness, impact on patient well-being, and long-term as well as short-term gains. Providing care that is at once efficient and effective would require that effectiveness be valued and understood (that is, that the goals of care be known), that strategies toward effective care not be thwarted by short-term "efficiencies," and that both be measured. Valuing effectiveness is predicated on an awareness of the dominance and impact of the current preoccupation with "cost constraint." Setting goals of care that aim for effectiveness and health outcomes requires valuing both, and it requires research evidence regarding the relationship between care and health outcomes as well as the political will to implement care that has already been shown to be effective in terms of outcomes.

Health outcomes must be understood as more than individual responses to specific therapies and must be seen as including outcomes for groups and populations (Mitchell, 1993). Outcomes must be thought of beyond what can be achieved and measured within units (such as length of stay), organizations (such as bed numbers), and regions (numbers of staff). As was illustrated above, such measures are often used counterproductively. The authors agree with Armstrong and Armstrong (1996), who note that "effectiveness and efficiency cannot be measured primarily in terms of money spent and people processed" (p. 9). This suggests that measurement in health care must become much more complex, taking into account broader variables such as well-being, relief of suffering, and so on.

In terms of nursing work, the importance of attention to the emotional needs of patients has been illustrated in a variety of contexts (see, for example, Beeber & Charlie, 1998; Smith, 1993; Hodnett & Osborn, 1989; Langer et al., 1998; Thorne, 1993; Yates, 1995). If nurses are to be more effective, as well as efficient, they must value effectiveness in terms of nonphysical care and have adequate control over their work to implement the care that will achieve meaningful health outcomes. Valuing effectiveness is again predicated on critical awareness of the dangers of an emphasis on efficiency regardless of effectiveness, and efficiency that overlooks difficult-to-quantify determinants of health such as social support, emotional support, and psychological well-being. Implementing effective nursing care requires, first, research that links care with broad health outcomes, and second, sufficient nursing control over practice to implement what has been shown to be effective (Nortvedt, in press).

Creating Space for Intellectual and Emotional Work

Promoting the intellectual labour of nursing within the described context is challenging. As has been argued above, nurses do not have time to think, let alone do health promotion, "innovate," lobby for changes in "rules" that are detrimental to care, introduce new or evidence-based practice, or evaluate care in terms of outcomes. And yet, these are the very strategies that are needed to develop a truly more efficient *and effective* health care system. There is beginning a recognition at bureaucratic levels that the bottom has been reached in terms of the cuts that can be made in staffing. However, the damage will not be undone simply by reinstating numbers of positions. In words attributed to Albert Einstein, "The problems we have created cannot be solved at the level of thinking that created them."

Years of "reform" have eroded the culture of health care to one based predominantly on corporate values. Within this culture, the emphasis on efficiency has eroded the foundation for professional nursing practice. In addition to "righting" staffing to levels that can sustain safe care, space needs to be created for nurses to provide the emotional labour that patients require during illness and death experiences. Space needs to be created for nurses to provide reasoned care, based on evidence and research. Such space needs to be created for nurses who provide direct care, rather than allocating the thinking space only to those who practise in roles removed from direct care. This cannot be achieved simply by allocating reasonable staffing levels, but must also be supported by the continued development of clinical advanced nursing practice roles such as clinical nurse specialists, clinical practice leaders, clinical resource nurses, and clinical nurse researchers — roles that can contribute to and support direct care. Intellectual and emotional work must also be supported by greater attention being given, by researchers and educators who are not in direct care, to linking practice, especially body work and emotional and intellectual labour, to health and outcomes. Realistically capturing the indeterminate work of nursing, and supplementing the data captured by current technologies, will require voices from nursing to be heard in policy development from the unit to organizational to social levels.

This chapter was titled "**constrained agency**" to draw attention to the ideological and **structural constraints** to agency within nursing. However, nurses are never without agency. Whether it is an individual nurse offering an alternative to corporate images (perhaps we could see mentally ill patients as casualties of deinstitutionalization rather than as "repeaters" or "users"), or a group lobbying for change or participating in public policy formulation, the structure of nurses' work can be shaped by nurses to the extent that they are willing to take action. Questioning that which has been taken for granted is the first step.

ACKNOWLEDGEMENTS

The research contributing to this paper was supported by a National Health Research and Development Program fellowship (Varcoe) and research grant (Rodney), and by a research grant from the Canadian Nurses Foundation (Varcoe). The authors gratefully acknowledge all the research participants, as well as Dr. Joan Anderson from the University of British Columbia School of Nursing for her guidance. We would also like to acknowledge Dr. Ann Hoffmeyer from Flinders University (Australia) and Dr. Michael Yeo from the Canadian Medical Association for their insightful critical review.

STUDY QUESTIONS

1. What are the relationships between the disvaluing of women and women's work in general and the disvaluing of the emotional labour of nursing?

2. What examples of responsible subversion have you observed? What were the consequences?

3. List the rhetoric currently in vogue in health care. What ideas, images, and assumptions underlie this language?

4. Imagine some situations in which you and the people you work with could constructively challenge the corporate ideology. Provide some examples of how you would achieve this.

GLOSSARY

capping Cost containment measures such as setting a predetermined level or number of activities to be performed within a specific program during a specified time frame; for example, a number of particular organ transplants or surgeries over a 1-year period.

common good The well-being of aggregates (communities and society), not just individuals; some notion of the well-being of communities and society, if arrived at through participatory democratic processes, can provide a moral horizon for work in ethics and public policy.

constrained agency Ideological and structural constraints to agency within nursing such that nurses are unable to act upon their professional responsibilities and accountability.

corporate ideology The taken for granted beliefs, attitudes, and assumptions that bring a business model to health care.

culture The processes that happen between people as individuals and as groups within organizations and society, and that confer meaning and significance; the health care system has its own culture(s).

downsizing Cost containment measures such as bed closures, staff layoffs, and reductions in the length of hospital stay.

emotional labour The effort involved in dealing with other people's feelings and emotions and, in the case of nursing, dealing with the fears and worries of ill patients and their families and promoting the emotional well-being of patients.

globalization The economic, social, and political transformation of the world, such that capital flows around the world to serve the interests of an economically dominant elite.

ideology A set of beliefs, attitudes, and assumptions about the world that justify or explain "what is." Ideologies are not in and of themselves good or bad; when unexamined, however, they can lead to unanticipated consequences.

ideology of scarcity A perception about the state of the economy, fiscal realities, the availability of funds, and budgetary deficits, such that current levels of care are no longer affordable; a view popularized by the media, corporate elite, management elite, and others.

moral distress A situation that occurs when nurses (or other moral agents) are unable to translate their moral choices into moral action because of constraints in the organizational context; the aftermath can include anger, frustration, guilt, and powerlessness.

structural constraints Administrative policies, procedures, and practices, such as allotted labour time and performance evaluation, that set the parameters within which labour is performed.

RECOMMENDED READINGS

Annas, G.J. (1995). Reframing the debate on health care reform by replacing our metaphors. *New England Journal of Medicine, 332*(11), 744–747. An insightful overview of the military and market metaphors that have dominated health care reform in the United States. Although written for a U.S. context, the arguments apply to a significant extent in Canada.

Armstrong, P., & Armstrong, H. (1996). *Wasting away: The undermining of Canadian health care.* Toronto: Oxford University Press. A comprehensive and critical analysis of changes to the Canadian health care system. Uses political economic analysis to examine the impact of health care reform on direct care providers.

Hiraki, A. (1998). Corporate language and nursing practice. *Nursing Outlook, 46*, 115–119. A stinging critique of the misapplication of business rhetoric to health care management.

Mohr, W.K. (1997). Outcomes of corporate greed. *Image: Journal of Nursing Scholarship, 29*(10), 39–45. A study of nurses practising in the United States during major changes to psychiatric care delivery; an ominous warning about the potential impact of for-profit health care.

Mohr, W.K., & Mahon, M.M. (1996). Dirty hands: The underside of marketplace health care. *Advances in Nursing Science, 19*(1), 28–37. A disturbing account of the impact of the marketplace on the quality of care.

Saul, J.R. (1995). *The unconscious civilization.* Concord, ON: Anansi Press. Presents the argument that Canadians operate on myth rather than memory; as a result, sweeping new policy changes are brought in without attention being paid to their political, economic, and social origins and context.

REFERENCES

Aiken, L.H., Clarke, S.P., & Sloane, D.M. (2000). Hospital restructuring: Does it adversely affect care and outcomes? *Journal of Nursing Administration, 30*(10), 457–465.

Anderson, J.M. (2000). Writing in subjugated knowledges: Towards a transformative agenda in nursing research and practice. *Nursing Inquiry, 7*, 145.

Anderson, J.M., Blue, C., & Lau, A. (1991). Women's perspectives on chronic illness: Ethnicity, ideology and restructuring of life. *Social Science and Medicine, 33*(2), 101–113.

Anderson, J.M., Dyck, I., & Lynam, J. (1997). Health care professionals and women speaking: Constraints in everyday life and the management of chronic illness. *Health, 1*(1), 57–80.

Anderson, J., & Reimer-Kirkham, S. (1998). Constructing nation: The gendering and racializing of the Canadian health care system. In V. Strong-Boag, S. Grace, A. Eisenberg, & J. Anderson (Eds.), *Painting the maple: Essays on race, gender, and the construction of Canada* (pp. 242–261). Vancouver: UBC Press.

Annas, G.J. (1995). Reframing the debate on health care reform by replacing our metaphors. *New England Journal of Medicine, 332*(11), 744–747.

Armstrong, P., & Armstrong, H. (1996). *Wasting away: The undermining of Canadian health care.* Toronto: Oxford University Press.

Attridge, C., & Callahan, M. (1987). *Women in women's work: An exploratory study of nurses' perspective of quality work environments* (research report). Victoria, BC: University of Victoria, Faculty of Human and Social Development.

Barry-Walker, J. (2000). The impact of systems redesign on staff, patient, and financial outcomes. *Journal of Nursing Administration, 30*(2), 77–89.

Beeber, L.S., & Charlie, M.L. (1998). Depressive symptom reversal for women in a primary care setting: A pilot study. *Archives of Psychiatric Nursing, 12*, 247–254.

Bendix, R. (1993). Ideology. In W. Outhwaite & T. Bottomore (Eds.), *The Blackwell dictionary of twentieth-century social thought* (pp. 272–273). Oxford: Blackwell.

Benner, P.A., Tanner, C.A., & Chesla, C.A. (with contributions by Dreyfus, H.L., Dreyfus, S.E., & Rubin, J.) (1996). *Expertise in nursing practice: Caring, clinical judgment, and ethics.* New York: Springer.

Blue, A.W., Keyserlingk, E.W., Rodney, P., & Starzomski, R. (1999). A critical view of North American health policy. In H. Coward & P. Ratanakul (Eds.), *A cross-cultural dialogue on health care ethics* (pp. 215–225). Waterloo: Wilfrid Laurier University Press.

Bolaria, B.S. (1994). Income inequality, poverty, food banks, and health. In B.S. Bolaria & H.D. Dickinson (Eds.), *Health, illness, and health care in Canada* (2nd ed., pp. 245–254). Toronto: Harcourt Brace.

Brown, M.C. (1996). Changes in Alberta's medicare financing arrangements: Features and problems. In M. Stingl & D. Wilson (Eds.), *Efficiency vs. equality: Health reform in Canada* (pp. 137–151). Halifax: Fernwood.

Burgess, M. (1996). Health care reform: Whitewashing a conflict between health promotion and treating illness? In M. Stingl & D. Wilson (Eds.), *Efficiency vs. equality: Health reform in Canada* (pp. 153–162). Halifax: Fernwood.

Campbell, M.L. (1987). Productivity in Canadian nursing: Administering cuts. In D. Coburn, C. D'Arcy, G.M. Torrance, & P. New (Eds.), *Health and Canadian society: Sociological perspectives* (2nd ed., pp. 463–475). Toronto: Fitzhenry & Whiteside.

Campbell, M. (1994). The structure of stress in nurses' work. In B.S. Bolaria & H.D. Dickinson (Eds.). *Health, illness, and health care in Canada* (pp. 592–608). Toronto: Harcourt Brace.

Canadian Nurses' Association. (1998). *The quiet crisis in health care.* Paper submitted to the House of Commons Standing Committee on Finance and the Minister of Finance. Ottawa: Author.

Carniol, B. (1995). *Case critical: Challenging social services in Canada* (3rd ed.). Toronto: Between the Lines.

Cassidy, B., Lord, R., & Mandell, N. (1995). Silenced and forgotten women: Race, poverty, and disability. In N. Mandell (Ed.), *Feminist issues: Race, class, and sexuality* (pp. 32–66). Scarborough, ON: Prentice-Hall.

Collins, P.H. (1986). Learning from the outsider within: The social significance of black feminist thought. *Social Problems, 33*(6), 14–32.

Collins, P.H. (1989). The social construction of black feminist thought. *Signs: Journal of Women in Culture and Society, 14*, 745–773.

Collins, P.H. (1993). Toward a new vision: Race, class, and gender as categories of analysis and connection. *Race, sex & class, 1*(1), 25–45.

Corley, M.C., & Mauksch, H.O. (1988). Registered nurses, gender, and commitment. In A. Statham, E.M. Miller, & H.O. Mauksch (Eds.), *The worth of women's work: A qualitative synthesis* (pp. 135–149). Albany: State University of New York Press.

Coward, H., & Ratanakul, P. (Eds.). (1999). *A cross cultural dialogue on health care ethics.* Waterloo, ON: Wilfrid Laurier University Press.

Curran, C.R., & Miller, N. (1990). The impact of corporate culture on nurse retention. *Nursing Clinics of North America, 25*(3), 537–549.

Dant, T. (1991). *Knowledge, ideology and discourse: A sociological perspective.* London: Routledge.

Dick, J., & Bruce, S. (1994). Cost containment: Doing more with less. In J.M. Hibberd & M.E. Kyle (Eds.), *Nursing management in Canada* (pp. 91–107). Toronto: W.B. Saunders.

Dickinson, H.D. (1994). Mental health policy in Canada: What's the problem? In B.S. Bolaria & H.D. Dickinson (Eds.), *Health, illness, and health care in Canada* (2nd ed., pp. 466–481). Toronto: Harcourt Brace.

Doyal, L. (1994). Waged work and well being. In S. Wilkinson & C. Kitsinger, *Women and health: Feminist perspectives* (pp. 65–84). London: Taylor & Francis.

Duncan, S.M. (1992). Ethical challenge in community health nursing. *Journal of Advanced Nursing, 17*, 1035–1041.

Erlen, J.A., & Frost, B. (1991). Nurses' perceptions of powerlessness in influencing ethical decisions. *Western Journal of Nursing Research, 13*, 397–407.

Ferguson-Paré, M. (1997). *Leadership that supports autonomous professional practice of registered nurses.* Unpublished doctoral dissertation, The Fielding Institute.

Foucault, M. (1978). *The history of sexuality: An introduction.* (R. Hurley, Trans.). New York: Random House. (Original work published 1976).

Foucault, M. (1980). *Power/knowledge: Selected interviews and other writings (1972–1977).* C. Gordon, (Ed.). New York: Random House.

Freeman, T., & O'Brien-Pallas, L.L. (1998). Factors influencing job satisfaction on specialty nursing units. *Canadian Journal of Nursing Administration, 11*(3), 25–51.

Fuller, C. (1998). *Caring for profit: How corporations are taking over Canada's health care system.* Vancouver: New Star Books.

Geertz, C. (1973). *The interpretation of cultures.* New York: Basic Books.

Gibb, H. (1998). Reform in public health: Where does it take nursing? *Nursing Inquiry, 5*, 258–267.

Growe, S.J. (1991). *Who cares? The crisis in Canadian nursing.* Toronto: McClelland & Stewart.

Health Canada Office of Nursing Policy. (2000). *Health Canada Office of Nursing Policy: Strategic Priorities 2000–2001.* Ottawa: Author.

Hiraki, A. (1998). Corporate language and nursing practice. *Nursing Outlook, 46*, 115–119.

Hodnett, E., & Osborn, R.W. (1989). Effects of continuous intrapartum professionals support on childbirth outcomes. *Research in Nursing and Health, 12*(5), 289–297.

Hutchinson, S.A. (1990). Responsible subversion: A study of rule-bending among nurses. *Scholarly Inquiry for Nursing Practice, 4*(1), 3–17.

Jameton, A. (1984). *Nursing practice: The ethical issues.* Englewood Cliffs, NJ: Prentice-Hall.

Jennings, B., Callahan, D., & Wolf, S.M. (1987). The professions: Public interest and common good. *Hastings Center Report, 17*(1), 3–10.

Keddy, B., Gregor, F., Foster, S., & Denney, D. (1999). Theorizing about nurses' work lives: The personal and professional aftermath of living with healthcare 'reform.' *Nursing Inquiry, 6*, 58–64.

Ketefian, S., & Ormond, I. (1988). *Moral reasoning and ethical practice in nursing: An integrative review.* New York: National League for Nursing.

Kramer, M. (1974). *Reality shock: Why nurses leave nursing.* St. Louis: C.V. Mosby.

Langer, A., Campero, L., Garcia, C., & Reynoso, S. (1998). Effects of psychosocial support during labour and childbirth on breastfeeding, medical interventions, and mothers' wellbeing in a Mexican public hospital: A randomised clinical trial. *British Journal of Obstetrics and Gynaecology, 105*, 1056–1063.

Laschinger, H.K., Finegan, J., Shamian, J., & Casier, S. (2000). Organizational trust and empowerment in restructured healthcare settings: Effects on staff nurse commitment. *Journal of Nursing Administration, 30*(9), 413–425.

Lawler, J. (1993). *Behind the screens: Nursing, somology, and the problem of the body.* Redwood City, CA: Benjamin/Cummings.

Laxer, J. (1996). *In search of a new left: Canadian politics after the neoconservative assault.* Toronto: Viking.

Laxer, J. (1998). *The undeclared war: Class conflict in the age of cyber capitalism.* Toronto: Penguin Books.

Liaschenko, J. (1993a). *Faithful to the good: Morality and philosophy in nursing practice.* Unpublished doctoral dissertation, University of California, San Francisco.

Liaschenko, J. (1993b). Feminist ethics and cultural ethos: Revisiting a nursing debate. *Advances in Nursing Science, 15*(4), 71–81.

Long, B.C., & Kahn, S.E. (Eds.). (1993). *Women, work, and coping: A multidisciplinary approach to workplace stress.* Montreal & Kingston, Canada: McGill–Queen's University Press.

Lynn, M., & Todoroff, M. (1995). Women's work and family lives. In N. Mandell (Ed.), *Feminist issues: Race, class, and sexuality* (pp. 244–271). Scarborough, ON: Prentice-Hall.

MacPhail, S.A. (1996). *Ethical issues in community nursing.* Unpublished master's thesis, University of Alberta, Edmonton.

McClure, M.L., Poulin, M.A., Sovie, M.D., & Wandelt, M.A. (1983). *Magnet hospitals: Attraction and retention of professional nurses.* Kansas City, MO: American Academy of Nursing.

McGowan, J. (1998). *Hannah Arendt: An introduction.* Minneapolis: University of Minnesota Press.

McQuaig, L. (1993). *The wealthy banker's wife: The assault on equality in Canada.* Toronto: Penguin books.

McQuaig, L. (1998). *The cult of impotence: Selling the myth of powerlessness in the global economy.* Toronto: Penguin Books.

Millette, B.E. (1994). Using Gilligan's framework to analyze nurses' stories of moral choices. *Western Journal of Nursing Research, 16*(6), 660–674.

Mitchell, P. (1993). Perspectives on outcome-oriented care systems. *Nursing Administration Quarterly, 17*(3), 1–7.

Mohr, W.K. (1997). Outcomes of corporate greed. *Image: Journal of Nursing Scholarship, 29*(10), 39–45.

Mohr, W.K., & Mahon, M.M. (1996). Dirty hands: The underside of marketplace health care. *Advances in Nursing Science, 19*(1), 28–37.

Mouffe, C. (1993). *The return of the political.* London: Verso.

Munhall, P.L. (1990). Response to "Responsible subversion: A study of rule-bending among nurses." *Scholarly Inquiry for Nursing Practice, 4*(1), 19–22.

Nagle, L.M. (1999). A matter of extinction or distinction. *Western Journal of Nursing Research, 21*(1), 71–82.

Noblit, G.W., & Hare, R.D. (1988). *Meta-ethnography: Synthesizing qualitative studies.* Newbury Park, CA: Sage.

Northcott, H.C. (1994). The politics of austerity and threats to Medicare. In B.S. Bolaria & R. Bolaria, *Women, medicine and health* (pp. 7–24). Saskatoon: University of Saskatchewan.

Nortvedt, P. (in press). The clinician's gaze: The contribution of ethical sensitivity to clinical knowledge. *Scholarly Inquiry for Nursing Practice* (in press).

Oberle, K., & Grant, N. (1994). *Results of the AARN initiative regarding the impact of health care cuts* (unpublished research report). Edmonton: Alberta Association of Registered Nurses.

Oberle, K., & Tenove, S. (2000). Ethical issues in public health nursing. *Nursing Ethics, 7*(5), 425–438.

O'Brien-Pallas, L.L., Baumann, A.O., & Villeneuve, M.J. (1994). The quality of nursing work life. In J.M. Hibberd & M.E. Kyle (Eds.), *Nursing management in Canada* (pp. 391–409). Toronto: W.B. Saunders.

O'Neil, J.D. (1987). Health care in a central Canadian arctic community: Continuities and change. In D. Coburn, C. D'Arcy, G.M. Torrance, & P. New (Eds.), *Health and Canadian society: Sociological perspectives* (2nd ed., pp. 141–158). Toronto: Fitzhenry & Whiteside.

Phillips, S.S., & Benner, P. (1994). Preface. In S.S. Phillips & P. Benner (Eds.), *The crisis of care: Affirming and restoring caring practices in the helping professions* (pp. vii–xi). Washington, DC: Georgetown University Press.

Picard, A. (2000). *Critical care: Canadian nurses speak for change.* Toronto: HarperCollins.

Rachlis, M., & Kushner, C. (1989). *Second opinion: What's wrong with Canada's health care system and how to fix it.* Toronto: Harper & Collins.

Rachlis, M., & Kushner, C. (1994). *Strong medicine: How to save Canada's health care system.* Toronto: HarperCollins.

Reinhardt, U.E. (1997). Spending more through "cost control": Our obsessive quest to gut the hospital. *Nursing Outlook, 45,* 156–160.

Rodney, P.A. (1997). *Towards connectedness and trust: Nurses' enactment of their moral agency within an organizational context.* Unpublished doctoral dissertation, University of British Columbia, Vancouver.

Rodney, P., & Starzomski, R. (1993). Constraints on the moral agency of nurses. *Canadian Nurse, 89*(9), 23–26.

Saul, J.R. (1995). *The unconscious civilization.* Concord, ON: Anansi Press.

Saul, J.R. (1997). *Reflections of a Siamese twin: Canada at the end of the twentieth century.* Toronto: Penguin Books.

Scanlon, C. (1996–1997). Impact of cost containment on patient welfare concerns nurses. *American Nurses Association Center for Ethics and Human Rights Communique, 5*(2), 1–4.

Sherwin, S. (1992). *No longer patient: Feminist ethics & health care.* Philadelphia: Temple University Press.

Sherwin, S. (1998). A relational approach to autonomy in health care. In S. Sherwin et al. (Eds.), *The politics of women's health* (pp. 19–47). Philadelphia: Temple University Press.

Shindul-Rothschild, J., Berry, D., & Long-Middleton, E. (1996). Where have all the nurses gone? Final results of our patient care survey. *American Journal of Nursing, 96*(11), 25–39.

Sibbald, B. (1997). Delegating away patient safety. *Canadian Nurse, 93*(2), 22–26.

Smith, C.E. (1993). Quality of life in long-term total parenteral nutrition: Patients and their family caregivers. *Journal of Parenteral and Enteral Nutrition, 17,* 501–506.

Smith, D.E. (1987). *The everyday world as problematic: A feminist sociology.* Toronto: University of Toronto Press.

Smith, D.E. (1990). *Conceptual practices of power: A feminist sociology of knowledge.* London: Routledge.

Smith, D.E. (1992). Sociology from women's experience: A reaffirmation. *Sociological Theory 10*(1), 88–98.

Smith, D.M. (2000). *Moral geographies: Ethics in a world of difference.* Edinburgh: Edinburgh University Press.

Starzomski, R., & Rodney, P. (1997). Nursing inquiry for the common good. In S.E. Thorne & V.E. Hayes (Eds.), *Nursing praxis: Knowledge and action* (pp. 219–236). Thousand Oaks, CA: Sage.

Stelling, J. (1994a). Nursing metaphors: Reflections on the meaning of time. In B.S. Bolaria & R. Bolaria, *Women, medicine and health* (pp. 205–217). Saskatoon: University of Saskatchewan.

Stelling, J. (1994b). Staff nurses' perceptions of nursing: Issues in a woman's occupation. In B.S. Bolaria & H.D. Dickinson (Eds.), *Health, illness, and health care in Canada* (2nd ed., pp. 609–626). Toronto: Harcourt Brace.

Stephenson, P. (1999). Expanding notions of culture for cross-cultural ethics in health and medicine. In H. Coward & P. Ratanakul (Eds.), *A cross-cultural dialogue on health care ethics.* Waterloo, ON: Wilfrid Laurier University Press.

Storch, J.L. (1992). Ethical issues. In A.J. Baumgart & J. Larsen (Eds.), *Canadian nursing faces the future* (2nd ed., pp. 259–270). St. Louis, MO: Mosby Year Book.

Storch, J.L. (1996). Foundational values in Canadian health care. In M. Stingl & D. Wilson (Eds.), *Efficiency vs. equality: Health reform in Canada* (pp. 21–26). Halifax: Fernwood.

Storch, J.L., & Meilicke, C.A. (1994). Political, social, and economic forces shaping the health care system. In J.M. Hibberd & M.E. Kyle (Eds.), *Nursing management in Canada* (pp. 19–36). Toronto: W.B. Saunders.

Swanson-Kauffman, K.M. (Ed.). (1987). *Women's work, families, and health: The balancing act.* New York: Hemisphere.

Taylor, C. (with Gutmann, A., Rockefeller, S.C., Walzer, M., & Wolf, S.) (1992). *Multiculturalism and "The politics of recognition."* Princeton, NJ: Princeton University Press.

Taylor, C. (1995). *Philosophical arguments.* Cambridge, MA: Harvard University Press.

Thomas, J. (1993). *Doing critical ethnography.* Newbury Park, CA: Sage.

Thorne, S. (1993). *Negotiating health care: The social context of chronic illness.* Newbury Park, CA: Sage.

Varcoe, C. (1997). *Untying our hands: The social context of nursing in relation to violence against women.* Unpublished doctoral dissertation. Vancouver: University of British Columbia.

Varcoe, C. (2001). Abuse obscured: An ethnographic account of emergency unit nursing practice in relation to violence against women. *Canadian Journal of Nursing Research, 32*(4).

Walters, V. (1994). The social construction of risk in nursing: Nurses' responses to hazards in their work. In B.S. Bolaria & H.D. Dickinson (Eds.), *Health, illness, and health care in Canada* (2nd ed., pp. 627–643). Toronto: Harcourt Brace.

Watson, S.D. (1994). Minority access and health reform: A civil right to health care. *Journal of Law, Medicine & Ethics, 22*, 127–137.

Wilkinson, J.M. (1985). *Moral distress in nursing practice: Experience and effect.* Unpublished master's thesis, University of Missouri, Kansas City.

Wilkinson, J.M. (1989). Moral distress: A labor and delivery nurse's experience. *Journal of Obstetric, Gynecologic and Neonatal Nursing, 18*(6), 513–519.

Wolf, S.M. (1994). Health care reform and the future of physician ethics. *Hastings Center Report, 24*(2), 28–41.

Woodward, C., Shannon, H., Cunningham, C., McIntosh, J., Lendrum, B., Rosenbloom, D., & Brown, J. (1998). *Re-engineering in a large teaching hospital: A longitudinal study.* Working paper, Centre for Health Economic Policy Analysis, Ontario.

Yates, B.C. (1995). The relationship among social support and short- and long-term recovery outcomes in men with coronary artery disease. *Research in Nursing and Health, 18*, 193–203.

Yarling, R.R., & McElmurry, B.J. (1986). The moral foundation of nursing. *Advances in Nursing Science, 8*(2), 63–73.

Yeo, M., & Ford, A. (1996). Integrity. In M. Yeo & A. Moorhouse (Eds.), *Concepts and cases in nursing ethics* (2nd ed., pp. 267–306). Peterborough, ON: Broadview Press.

Yyelland, B. (1994). Structural constraints, emotional labour and nursing work. In B.S. Bolaria & R. Bolaria, *Women, medicine and health* (pp. 231–240). Saskatoon: University of Saskatchewan.

NOTES

1. *Ideology* can be defined as "a shared set of fundamental beliefs, attitudes, and assumptions about the world that justify 'what is'" (Thomas, 1993, p. 8). Ideologies are usually taken for granted because they provide the conceptual basis for our theory and our

research (Thomas, p. 8). Ideologies are not in and of themselves good or bad (Bendix, 1993; Dant, 1991; Thomas, 1993). However, making ideologies explicit can further critical inquiry in nursing and other disciplines (Hiraki, 1998; Rodney, 1997).

By *corporate* ideology, we mean the beliefs, attitudes, and assumptions that bring a business model to health care. A corporate ideology takes direction from the operation of the marketplace and management and organizational theories (Hiraki, 1998, p. 117). As a consequence, health policy and health care delivery are "based upon economic and political values rather than values reflecting the broader social responsibilities of individuals in community" (Storch, 1996, p. 25).

2. Moral distress occurs when nurses (or other moral agents) are unable to translate their moral choices into moral action because of constraints in the organizational context. The aftermath can include anger, frustration, guilt, and powerlessness (Jameton, 1984; Rodney & Starzomski, 1993; Wilkinson, 1989).

3. *Culture* is more than race or ethnicity. It includes the processes that happen between people as individuals and as groups within organizations and society, and that confer meaning and significance (Geertz, 1973; Rodney, 1997; Stephenson, 1999). Those of us in health care tend to see culture as residing in patients/clients and families. We need to understand that the health care system that we operate in has its own culture(s) (Coward & Ratanakul, 1999).

4. The global economy is part of *globalization*. Globalization "refers to the transformation—economic, social, and political — that has been underway since the 1970s.... It refers not simply to the ways the world has been changing, but also to the ways the economically dominant want the world to change to serve their interests" (Laxer, 1996, pp. 21–22). The negative consequences of globalization include national and international insecurity caused by cuts to labour forces and social programs (Laxer, 1998; McQuaig, 1998; Smith, 2000). However, the consequences of globalization are not all necessarily negative. Cuts to labour forces and social programs do not have to be inevitable (McQuaig, 1998), and globalization can further international human rights initiatives (Smith, 2000).

   For the purposes of this chapter, it can be understood that globalization has led to the dominance of a corporate ideology in health care. And a corporate ideology has had a profound — and often negative — impact on the culture of health care delivery.

5. The *common good* may be understood in terms of the well-being of aggregates (communities and society), not just individuals (Jennings, Callahan, & Wolf, 1987; Rodney & Starzomski, 1993). It should be noted that it is not unproblematic to try to define *the* common good. There is a danger that an autocratic (even totalitarian) process may be used to define it (Mouffe, 1993; Taylor, 1992). Nonetheless, some notion of the well-being of communities and society, if arrived at through participatory democratic processes, can provide a moral horizon for work in ethics and public policy (McGowan, 1998; Mouffe, 1993; Taylor, 1992).

6. This was the perception of many of the nurses in our two studies. Whether physicians and/or managers *actually* embraced a corporate ideology is an empirical question for other research. Indeed, nurses themselves often (unwittingly) embraced a corporate ideology by not questioning it.

7. Such indeterminate work is also unaccounted for when performed by nurses in managerial, educational, and advanced practice roles. And it is unaccounted for when it is performed by physicians, pastoral care workers, physiotherapists, social workers, and other members of the health care team.

8. The term "efficient" is placed in quotes to draw attention to the fact that the type of efficiency being referred to is only "efficient" in the sense of dealing with more patients in less time, and not in the sense of overall efficiency connected with health outcomes or immediate or long-term benefits for patients.

9. We are intentionally using mixed corporate and military metaphors here. Western biomedicine has been dominated by these two metaphors, which reflect "the quest for control that seems to define both modern medicine and modern politics" (Annas, 1995, p. 747). It is our contention that the quest for control is problematic for nurses, patients, families, and communities.

10. Yyelland (1994) distinguishes nurses' emotional labour from their technical labour. We are using the term "emotional labour" as one of many aspects of nurses' work, one that is concerned with promoting the emotional well-being of patients and harmony among patients and health care professionals.

11. In British Columbia during 1998 and 1999, physicians were publicizing their "donations" of time by counting the number of days by which they claim to be subsidizing the health care system. While physicians can thus claim to be donating, for example, 52 days of unpaid work to the system, similar donations of nursing time are uncounted and unremarked.

12. Overlooking the well-being of patients, families, and communities is not the intention of a corporate focus on "outcomes." However, the authors' research and a growing number of other studies (e.g., Aiken, Clarke, & Sloane, 2000; Mohr, 1997) warn that it is the result.

13. Traditional perspectives on moral agency reflect a notion of individuals engaging in self-determining or self-expressive choice (Sherwin, 1992; Taylor, 1992). In addition to this traditional view, there are perspectives that see moral agency as enacted through relationships in particular contexts (Rodney, 1997; Sherwin, 1992, 1998; Taylor, 1992).

14. As Benner, Tanner, & Chesla (1996) claim, "even in clinical situations, where the ends are not in question, there is an underlying moral dimension: the fundamental disposition of the nurse toward what is good and right and action toward what the nurse recognizes or believes to be the best good in a particular situation" (p. 6).

PART 3

Inequality and Health Care

It has long been known that social and economic inequality is related to health status and the utilization of health care services. Not until the elucidation of the health field concept in the 1974 Lalonde Report, however, did health care service planners begin to look seriously at the implications of this relationship for health care policy and service delivery. The health field concept entails the rather simple notion that health status is determined by a number of interacting factors: human biology and genetics, lifestyle choices and behaviours, the nature of the social and physical environments, and the nature and organization of the health care system.

Initially, policymakers focused on altering lifestyle choices and behaviours as the most promising means to achieve health. Thus considerable efforts have gone into stop-smoking campaigns, reducing impaired driving, improving diets, and increasing exercise, among other things. More recently, attention has focused on the effects of social and economic inequality on health status. The policy consequences of this shift of focus have resulted in more attention being paid to how structural inequalities based on income, education, age, gender, and race can be reduced to improve overall population health status. This is a radical departure from the near-exclusive focus on the health care system that dominated policymaking and public debate for the past several decades.

Despite strong evidence that economic inequalities result in reduced life chances and decreased health status, the poverty in Canadian society has increased over the past 25 years. For many people, poverty is a temporary condition. Some, including single-parent families, people of Aboriginal ancestry, members of visible minorities, and those with low levels of educational attainment, however, are at high risk for long-term poverty.

Bolaria draws our attention to the relationship between poverty, health status, and life opportunities and the use of food banks in Chapter 7. He points out that since the first food bank opened in Edmonton in 1981, the number of food banks across the country has increased steadily. Bolaria also points out that increased poverty and the growth of the food bank system indicate a public policy failure. Changes in welfare and tax policies are among the causes of growing poverty in Canada. Giving food to the poor is a valiant but desperate attempt to deal with the symptoms of a very serious problem. In the long run, this approach is doomed to failure. Bolaria clearly highlights this problem and throws down the gauntlet to health policymakers.

Social inequality and poverty are directly linked to lower health status. This is true regardless of the chosen indicators of health status: life expectancy at birth, infant mortality, psychomotor and growth retardation, or emotional disturbances. For the Aboriginal population of Canada, the negative health consequences of social inequality and poverty are amplified. In Chapter 8, Frideres paints a grim picture of the life chances and health status of Canada's Aboriginal population. He attributes the plight of the Aboriginal peoples to several factors, including colonial and racist policies that contributed to the destruction of indigenous cultures and communities and their replacement with Western culture and institutions, including Western medicine, which emphasizes the individual causes and cures of illness. Failure to address the issues of low health status and life chances at the social policy level perpetuates the causes of the problem.

7

Income Inequality, Poverty, Food Banks, and Health

B. SINGH BOLARIA University of Saskatchewan

INTRODUCTION

Poverty, malnutrition, hunger, and disease have come to be identified with underdeveloped Third World countries. While the significance and concentration of these problems in the Third World cannot be overstated, neither have the advanced capitalist countries eliminated economic inequalities and poverty. The inequalities of wealth and income produce differential **life chances** — chances for material and social rewards. Poverty translates into dependency on food banks, malnutrition and hunger, ill health, short life expectancy, and homelessness, to mention only a few of its effects (Bolaria & Wotherspoon, 2000).

Canada is a highly stratified society, which has widespread disparities in wealth, income, power, and prestige. These inequalities have important implications for people's lives. This chapter explores the linkages between income inequality, poverty, and life chances, with particular emphasis on food banks and health.

INCOME INEQUALITY AND POVERTY

Income inequality is an important dimension of social stratification. An examination of income distribution data reveals wide income disparities among Canadians. These data also show that there has been very little change in the share of income held by Canadians in different income categories over time (National Council of Welfare, 1988, 1989, 1990a, 1997). For instance, families in the lowest quintile had only 6.1 percent of the total income in 1951 and 6.3 percent in 1986. The corresponding figures for the highest quintile were 41.1 percent and 39.4 percent — more than six times the lowest quintile's share. The figures for unattached individuals reveal that in 1986 the lowest quintile had 5.3 percent of the total income. In contrast, the highest quintile had 44.7 percent of the total income — more than eight times the bottom group's share. The income distribution for unattached individuals was even more skewed in 1951 (National Council of Welfare, 1988). Income inequalities persist in Canada.

A significant number of Canadians live in poverty. The most common measure used to establish the poverty line is the low-income cut-offs used by Statistics Canada. These cut-offs are set at levels where, on average, 56.2 percent of income is spent on the necessities of life — food, clothing, and shelter (National Council of Welfare, 1997). There is no single cut-off line for all of Canada, because living costs vary by family size and place of residence. It should also be noted that "poverty lines only establish the upper limit of the low income population. Most poor Canadians live on incomes that are hundreds and more often thousands of dollars under the poverty line" (National Council of Welfare, 1989, p. 5).

Poverty figures have fluctuated with the economic conditions in this country. Although poverty declined in the 1970s, it increased substantially during the first half of the 1980s as a result of the 1981–82 recession (National Council of Welfare, 1988). Despite some movement, by the late 1980s the poverty rates had not returned to pre-recession levels.

Table 1 shows national trends in poverty from 1980 to 1998. In 1980, the number of people living in poverty was a little over 3.6 million and the poverty rate was just over 15 percent. Both the number of people who lived in poverty and the poverty rate fluctuated throughout the 1980s. These figures rose throughout 1982–84, declined in 1985–89, and rose again in the 1990s. Since 1989, poverty rates have increased amid high unemployment rates, cutbacks in social assistance, and economic restructuring leading to downsizing and wage reductions. During the years 1995–97, poverty rates exceeded 17 percent: five million Canadians lived in poverty. In 1998, there was a slight decrease in the poverty rate to 16.4 percent, the lowest rate since 1992.

TABLE 7.1 *Poverty Trends, All Persons, 1980–1998*

Year	No. of Persons Living in Poverty	Poverty Rate (percent)
1980	3 624 000	15.3
1981	3 643 000	15.3
1982	3 951 000	16.4
1983	4 406 000	18.2
1984	4 397 000	18.1
1985	4 170 000	17.0
1986	3 976 000	16.0
1987	3 912 000	15.6
1988	3 744 000	14.8
1989	3 487 000	13.6
1990	3 821 000	14.6
1991	4 227 000	16.0
1992	4 320 000	16.1
1993	4 775 000	17.4
1994	4 795 000	16.6
1995	5 070 000	17.4
1996	5 190 000	17.6
1997	5 300 000	17.8
1998	4 910 000	16.4

Source: National Council of Welfare (1999, Table 2, p. 10). Reproduced with the permission of the Minister of Public Works and Government Services Canada, 2000.

As Table 2 shows, child poverty figures followed the same general pattern as statistics for the general population. Child poverty increased in the early part of the 1980s, declined during the next few years, and rose again in the 1990s. The stated commitment by the federal and provincial governments to eradicate child poverty has not been realized, and poverty rates for children have exceeded 20 percent in some years. Nearly one and a half million, or more than one in five, children are poor.

Certain groups face a high risk of poverty. These include families headed by women, unattached or elderly women, unemployed, those with irregular participation in the labour force, and persons with low educational levels (National Council of Welfare, 1997). Women overall face a much higher risk of poverty than men, a phenomenon that has come to be known as the "**feminization of poverty**" (National Council of Welfare, 1990a).

Because the vast majority of Canadians earn their income from wage employment, labour market characteristics that determine which jobs are well paid are particularly important in any discussion of poverty. For instance, those in managerial and professional occupations and their families are unlikely to live in poverty, compared with those in the service industries. Occupations with an above-average risk of poverty include farming, fishing, forestry, sales, clerical, and services (National Council of Welfare, 1997).

Clearly, wide income disparities and poverty persist in Canada. Income inequality and poverty have an important influence on the lives of individuals. Max Weber saw class as closely linked to people's life chances; that is, their chance to acquire material

TABLE 7.2 *Poverty Trends, Children Under 18, 1980–1998*

Year	No. of Children under 18 Living in Poverty	Poverty Rate (percent)
1980	984 000	14.9
1981	998 000	15.2
1982	1 155 000	17.8
1983	1 221 000	19.0
1984	1 253 000	19.6
1985	1 165 000	18.3
1986	1 086 000	17.0
1987	1 057 000	16.6
1988	987 000	15.4
1989	934 000	14.5
1990	1 105 000	16.9
1991	1 210 000	18.3
1992	1 218 000	18.2
1993	1 415 000	20.8
1994	1 334 000	19.1
1995	1 441 000	20.5
1996	1 481 000	20.9
1997	1 439 000	20.3
1998	1 327 000	18.8

Source: National Council of Welfare (1999, Table 3, p. 11). Reproduced with the permission of the Minister of Public Works and Government Services Canada, 2000.

goods and other amenities (Gerth & Mills, 1958). Economic and social inequalities produce inequality of opportunities and life chances, which are reflected in such measures
as education, living standards, housing, health, and consumption patterns.

Most relevant to the discussion in this chapter is the link between income inequalities and consumption patterns. Chossudovsky points to

> the dual and divided structure of social consumption and of consumer goods markets
> between necessary subsistence goods on the one hand and luxury and semi-luxury goods
> consumed by the privileged upper-income groups on the other hand.... This duality in the
> structure of social consumption, while more pronounced in peripheral social formulations,
> is also present in the advanced capitalist countries. (1983, p. 76)

In addition to the differences in the goods they consume, persons with different
income levels devote a different percentage of their money income to necessary subsistence goods. Families and unattached individuals in the lowest quintile spend 57.5 percent of their income on the necessities of life. The corresponding figure for the second
lowest quintile is 45.6 percent. Family units in the highest quintile spend 33 percent of
their income on the necessities of life (National Council of Welfare, 1989, p. 13).

Chossudovsky notes that "food is by far the most important component of necessary consumption." Adequate production and supply of food in themselves do not
assure adequate levels of food consumption and nutrition. Consumption levels are
influenced by the social distribution of food to different groups in the population
(Chossudovsky, 1983), which itself is a function of income distribution.

Since the early 1980s, it has become increasingly evident that a large number of
Canadians depend on **food banks**. The very existence of food banks indicates that
hunger and poverty have become permanent features of Canadian society.

FOOD BANKS

Since the first food bank opened in Edmonton in 1981, food banks and similar organizations have been established in many towns and cities across Canada (Canadian
Association of Food Banks, 1989; Riches, 1986; Oderkirk, 1992; Webber, 1992). As Table
3 indicates, by 1984 there were 75 food banks in Canada, mostly in the western
provinces. The number of food banks continued to increase through the 1980s. By 1991,
there were 292 food banks in various parts of Canada; by 1997, 508 communities had
one or more food banks. This growth continues as the economy further experiences the
effects of economic recession, restructuring, and unemployment.

It is estimated that two million Canadians used food banks in 1991. By 1997, in one
month alone (March of that year) 669 877 Canadians received emergency food assistance
(Canadian Association of Food Banks, 1997, p. 1). Children account for a large number
of food bank users. While 25 percent of the Canadian population was under age 18, over
40 percent of the food bank beneficiaries in 1997 were in that age group (Canadian
Association of Food Banks, 1997, p. 1). For over two thirds (68 percent) of the food bank
users, welfare was the primary source of income (Oderkirk, 1992). It is evident that many
Canadians depend on food banks and other charitable meal operations for their daily
food (Riches, 1986, p. 13). The very existence of food banks and their proliferation indicate

TABLE 7.3 *Food Banks in Canada, 1981–1997 (Selected Years)[1]*

	1981	1984	1988	1989	1990	1991	1997
Newfoundland	0	0	1	1	1	17	30
Prince Edward Island	0	0	2	2	2	3	3
Nova Scotia	0	2	8	14	14	27	33
New Brunswick	0	2	27	34	35	40	48
Quebec	0	2	5	5	5	11	446
Ontario	0	4	19	33	35	88	174
Manitoba	0	1	1	3	3	4	13
Saskatchewan	0	5	5	5	8	11	21
Alberta	1	12	16	26	24	40	63
British Columbia	0	47	42	36	34	51	71
Canada	1	75	126	159	161	292	905[2]

1. Estimates from 1988 to 1991 from the Canadian Association of Food Banks do not include Salvation Army Family Services Divisions food banks. Growth during this period can be attributed to the creation of new food banks and to the registration of existing food banks with the association.
2. Includes 1 in Yukon and 2 in the Northwest Territories. The actual number of food banks is much higher because some food banks collect food on behalf of, and distribute food to, a number of smaller agencies or affiliates in a given area.

Source: Oderkirk (1992); Canadian Association of Food Banks (1997[2], 1992); Riches (1986).

the extent to which hunger and poverty have become regular features of advanced societies. The growing demand for their services has forced food banks to expand beyond their own distribution centres in order to distribute food through programs and centres such as community kitchens, women's shelters, and AIDS service organizations that feed specific client groups (Greater Vancouver Food Bank Society, 1998, pp. 1, 3).

POVERTY, FOOD BANKS, AND HEALTH

Social medicine is primarily concerned with the social, economic, and environmental conditions in society that produce illness and mortality. Epidemiological data clearly demonstrate the differential health status of the population by socioeconomic status. The health gap between the rich and the poor continues to exist in Canada, where the principle of universality was a major impetus to the introduction of medical care in the sixties (National Council of Welfare, 1990b; Grant, 1988). Upper-income Canadians live longer, healthier, and more disability-free lives on average than poor Canadians. This gap in health status is primarily due to the "debilitating conditions of life that poverty forces upon people" (National Council of Welfare, 1990b, p. 6). Social and material conditions of existence such as poor housing, poor nutrition, poor neighbourhoods, and poor environment all contribute to high mortality in the low income population. High mortality levels in poor neighbourhoods are well documented (Thomson, 1990; National Council of Welfare, 1990b). Evidence indicates that the poorer the area, the shorter the life expectancy of both men and women. Data also show that children of parents in the poorest neighbourhoods have twice the infant mortality rates of children in the richest neighbourhoods. High mortality, high disability, and low health status of Aboriginal people are associated with environmental, economic, social, and living conditions of the population

(Borsellino, 1990; Mao et al., 1992). Other studies lend support to the general conclusion that low income people not only have high mortality and morbidity, but low utilization of health services (Driver, 1991; Shah et al., 1987; Grant, 1988).

A number of studies show the relationship between low incomes and inadequate diets (Nutrition Canada, 1975; Myres & Kroetsch, 1978; Reid & Miles, 1977). Poverty, nutrition, and hunger are also closely linked to health status (Epp, 1986; Wilkins & Adams, 1983; Wigle & Mao, 1980). A report published by the Minister of Health revealed that "men in the upper income groups can expect 14 more disability-free years than men with a low income; in the case of women, the difference is eight years" (Epp, 1986, p. 398). Other evidence associates poverty with malnutrition, psychomotor and growth retardation, emotional disturbances, and visual difficulties. These problems are even more acute among Aboriginal people (Shah & Farkas, 1985).

The adverse health affects of poverty for children start during pregnancy; they have significant impact on complications during pregnancy, low birth weight of children, handicaps, poor growth, and intellectual and emotional disorders (National Council of Welfare, 1975; Brown, 1989). Child mortality rates are higher for poor children than their wealthy peers (Fine, 1989). Hess (1989, p. 5) outlines how children in poverty face both direct and indirect risks to their physical and mental well-being due to greater likelihood of "substandard housing, overcrowding, exposure to toxic substances, high traffic density, neighborhood crime and insufficient recreational facilities," among other things. In poor neighbourhoods, the infant death rate is nearly double the rate in rich neighbourhoods, and poor children are more likely to suffer from chronic health problems and more likely to die from injuries than non-poor children (Canadian Institute of Child Health, 1994, p. 128).

The cumulative effect of poverty, malnutrition, hunger, and ill health is the extensive reproduction of poverty. All of these things influence poor children's learning ability and performance in school (Chu, 1989; National Council of Welfare, 1975), which subsequently affects job prospects, employment patterns, and earnings. As a report by the National Council of Welfare (1975, p. 1) states: "To be born poor in Canada does not make it a certainty that you will live poor and die poor — but it makes it very likely."

Low income and poverty force upon people many debilitating conditions which produce poor health, shorter lives, high infant mortality, and other physical and mental health problems for the disadvantaged. Dependency on food banks furthers these disadvantages. In this context, one of the questions most frequently raised is whether the food banks meet the diet and nutritional needs of their clients. While Canadian studies that provide systemic evidence on this subject are lacking, the evidence from elsewhere suggests that the provision of food assistance in itself cannot be equated with nutritional and dietary adequacy (Rauschenbach et al., 1990; Emmons, 1987; Laven & Brown, 1985; Carrillo et al., 1990; Reuler, 1989; Wood & Valdez, 1991). Poverty and homelessness are also likely to increase as "disadvantages" accumulate for individuals and groups, and with differential social status and power relations and differential medical and nutritional needs of the individuals. For instance, even in the food bank population, women and children are likely to be at a higher risk than men. Factors that need to be considered here include women's reproductive health (Martin, 1989; Pollock, 1988), nutritional health needs during pregnancy, and children's nutritional needs.

The effects of malnutrition and vitamin deficiencies have begun to appear in some cases. Mo Ali, physician and hematologist, points out in this regard:

> We're seeing more patients who suffer from blood diseases by lack of vitamins. One of the vitamins is folic acid, and that's present in fresh vegetables and fresh fruit. People who are living on canned food from food banks are the people we are starting to see in age groups I have not seen before, people in their 20s and 30s. They become anemic. They become weak and tired. They have to walk and line up for food, jobs, clothing, shelter. It is really sad what is happening (*The Globe and Mail*, December 22, 1992, p. A4).

Folic acid, for instance, also prevents neural tube defects (Laxdal, Habbick, & Bolaria, 1993).

Researchers have also ignored the "hidden injuries" of food bank dependency and their association with health status. The negative social attributes, such as **social stigma** and shame, which are usually associated with poverty, are likely to be exacerbated by dependency on food banks (Eales, 1989; Sennett & Cobb, 1973; Matza, 1966; Coleman & Cressey, 1984; Tarasuk & MacLean, 1990). Shame, degradation, stigma, disrepute, sense of failure, loss of self-respect, self-blame, and powerlessness are likely to be disruptive of social relationships, both in and out of the family, with negative consequences such as social isolation and unhealthy social environment within the household.

Whereas previous research addressed the general issue of socioeconomic status and health (for a review of these studies, see Hay, 1994), a number of recent studies in Canada and elsewhere have focused on the specific topic of food insecurity, hunger, and health-related consequences and outcomes (Tarasuk & Davis, 1996; Kendall, Olson, & Frongillo, 1996; Tarasuk & Beaton, 1999; McIntyre, Travers, & Dayle, 1999; James et al., 1997; Johnson, 1994; Hamelin, Habicht, & Beaudry, 1999; Rose, 1999; Olson, 1999; Roberts et al., 1999; Davis & Tarasuk, 1994; Tarasuk, 1994; Jacobs, Kuhnlein, & Gray-Donald, 1998). These studies, with varying degrees of focus, highlight the importance of **food insecurity** and health and nutrition outcomes, as well as the social implications of food insecurity in the household. For instance, worsening food insecurity was associated with decreased consumption of nutritional food and fruit and vegetables, an overall reduction in food intake, and an increase in disordered eating patterns (Kendall, Olson, & Frongillo, 1996; Olson, 1999; Rose, 1999). The human development and social implications of food insecurity include physical impairment, loss of productivity for adult members, learning difficulties in school, feelings of powerlessness, stigmatization, shame, and decreased social participation (Hamelin, Habicht, & Beaudry, 1999; McIntyre, Connor, & Warren, 2000; Tarasuk & Beaton, 1999). While children's feeding programs may meet food needs, McIntyre, Connor, & Warren (2000) argue that these programs stigmatize the families, increase institutional control, continue dependency, and reproduce inequalities. These charitable programs also have a limited capacity to address problems of food insecurity and hunger that arise in the context of persistent inequality and poverty (Tarasuk & Beaton, 1999). A critical assessment of these programs is required in the broader context of economic restructuring, high levels of unemployment and poverty, and reduced social spending (Tarasuk & Davis, 1996).

CONCLUSION

Data presented in this chapter indicate that wide income disparities and poverty persist in Canada. Economic and social imbalances produce inequalities of opportunities, differential life chances, and different social consumption patterns. A duality of social consumption patterns is linked to income levels — while upper-income and rich Canadians have disposable income for luxury goods, at the other extreme, low-income and poor Canadians are often unable to buy even necessary subsistence goods, including food. Since the early 1980s, it has become increasingly evident that a large number of Canadians depend upon food banks. The continuous existence of food banks indicates that poverty, malnutrition, and hunger have become permanent features of Canadian society.

Low income and poverty forces upon people many debilitating conditions that produce poor health, shorter lives, high infant mortality, and other physical and mental health problems for the disadvantaged. Dependency on food banks only exacerbates these conditions and further increases the health risks for the dependent populations.

STUDY QUESTIONS

1. *Discuss the statement that the material conditions of existence and debilitating conditions of life that poverty forces upon people produce poor health and shorter lives for the disadvantaged.*
2. *Discuss the physical and psychological health consequences of dependency on food banks.*
3. *Canada is one of the richest countries in the world and certainly produces abundant food. How, then, can we explain hunger and malnutrition in this country?*
4. *Discuss the relationships among inequality, poverty, hunger, and health.*
5. *Negative social attributes such as social stigma, disrepute, and shame, which are usually associated with poverty, are likely to be exacerbated by dependency on food banks. Discuss the linkages between negative social attributes and social, psychological, and physical wellness.*

GLOSSARY

feminization of poverty Conditions in which women face a higher risk of poverty than men and comprise a growing population of the poor.

food banks Voluntary agencies established to distribute food to the hungry; sustained by public and private sector donations of time, food, and money.

food insecurity The inability to acquire nutritionally adequate and safe foods in socially acceptable ways.

income inequality A pattern of income distribution in which relatively stable disparities exist in the relative share of income received by different segments of the population.

life chances Opportunities to acquire material goods, necessary services, and desirable living conditions.

social stigma Negative social and personal characteristics that are often attributed to individuals as a result of their dependency on public and private agencies and programs.

RECOMMENDED READINGS

Bolaria, B.S., & Wotherspoon, T. (2000). Income inequality, poverty and hunger. In B.S. Bolaria (Ed.), *Social issues and contradictions in Canadian society* (pp. 73–90). Toronto: Harcourt Brace. An analysis of poverty in relation to structures of income inequality and unequal life chances; examines the consequences of poverty for differences in consumption patterns, lifestyles, health, and well-being.

Hay, D.I. (1994). Social status and health: Does money buy health? In B.S. Bolaria & R. Bolaria (Eds.), *Racial minorities, medicine and health* (pp. 9–51). Halifax and Saskatoon: Fernwood Publishing and Social Research Unit. A critical examination of an extensive body of studies from Canada and other countries on the relationship between social inequality and health status.

Robert, S.A., & House, J.S. (2000). Socioeconomic inequalities in health: An enduring sociological problem. In C.E. Bird, P. Conrad, & A.M. Fremont (Eds.), *Handbook of medical sociology* (pp. 79–97). Upper Saddle River, NJ: Prentice-Hall. An examination of the contributions of sociological perspectives and approaches to the understanding and alleviation of socioeconomic inequalities in health in more developed countries and on indicators of physical rather than mental health.

Tarasuk, V. (1994). Poverty, homelessness and health. In B.S. Bolaria & R. Bolaria (Eds.), *Racial minorities, medicine and health* (pp. 53–66). Halifax and Saskatoon: Fernwood Publishing and Social Research Unit. Focuses on the link between poverty, homelessness, and health, examines critical health issues confronting a group of homeless adults, and explores possible directions for responses.

Williams, D.R. (2000). Race, SES and health: The added effects of racism and discrimination. In P. Brown (Ed.), *Perspectives in medical sociology* (3rd ed., pp. 21–39). Prospect Heights, IL: Waveland Press. An overview of the ways in which socioeconomic status (SES) and race combine to affect health status. By drawing upon data from the United States, patterns of racial differences in health and the role that SES plays in accounting for these disparities are examined.

Warnock, J.W. (1987). *The politics of hunger: The global food system*. Toronto: Methuen. An excellent book on the issues of hunger, food production, agriculture and economic development, the distribution of food, and ecology, discussed in historical and contemporary contexts.

Zong, L., & Li, P.S. (1994). Different cultures or unequal life chances: A comparative analysis of race and health. In B.S. Bolaria & R. Bolaria (Eds.), *Racial minorities, medicine and health* (pp. 113–123). Halifax and Saskatoon: Fernwood Publishing and Social Research Unit. Based upon health data from 118 countries, this reading examines the effects of material conditions, racial composition, and lifestyles on health status and health outcomes.

REFERENCES

Bolaria, B.S., & Wotherspoon, T. (2000). Income inequality, poverty and hunger. In B.S. Bolaria (Ed.), *Social issues and contradictions in Canadian society* (pp. 73–90). Toronto: Harcourt.

Borsellino, M. (1990, March). Poor health care, housing blamed for Natives' high disability rate. *Medical Post, 27*, 20.

Bradley, C.F., Ross, S.E., & Warnyea, J.M. (1978, November). *Parent's choice. A comprehensive perinatal programme.* Vancouver Perinatal Health Project.

Brown, J.L. (1989). When violence has a benevolent face: The paradox of hunger in the world's wealthiest democracy. *International Journal of Health Services, 19*(2), 257–277.

Canadian Association of Food Banks. (1989). *Canadian hunger count, 1989. Summary.* Toronto: Author.

Canadian Association of Food Banks. (1997). *Hunger count 1997: A report on emergency food assistance in Canada.* Toronto: Canadian Association of Food Banks.

Canadian Institute of Child Health. (1994). *The health of Canada's children: A CICH profile* (2nd ed.). Ottawa: Author.

Carrillo, T., Gilbride, A., & Chan, M.M. (1990). Soup kitchen meals: An observation and nutrient analysis. *Journal of the American Diet Association, 90*, 989–991.

Chossudovsky, M. (1983). Underdevelopment and the political economy of malnutrition and ill health. *International Journal of Health-Services, 13*(1), 69–87.

Chu, C. (1989). Malnutrition affects learning ability of the poor. In *Star Phoenix*, November 7, p. C4.

Coleman, J., & Cressey, D. (1984). *Social Problems* (2nd ed.). New York: Harper & Row.

Davis, B., & Tarasuk, V. (1994). Hunger in Canada. *Agriculture and Human Values, 11*, 50–57.

Driver, D. (1991, September 17). Poverty linked to higher risks of poor health, death. *The Medical Post, 81.*

Eales, M.J. (1989). Shame among unemployed men. *Social Science and Medicine, 28*(8), 783–789.

Emmons, L. (1987). Relationship of participation in food assistance programs to the nutritional quality of diets. *American Journal of Public Health, 77*, 856–858.

Epp, J. (1986). Achieving health for all: A Framework for health promotion. *Canadian Journal of Public Health, 77*(6), 393–424.

Fine, S. (1989, July 25). Poor children more likely to die than wealthy peers, study finds. *The Globe and Mail*, p. A5.

Gerth, H.H., & Wright Mills, C. (Eds.). (1958). *From Max Weber: Essays in sociology.* New York: Oxford University Press.

Grant, K.R. (1988). The inverse care law in Canada: Differential access under universal free health insurance. In B.S. Bolaria & H.D. Dickinson (Eds.), *Sociology of health care in Canada* (pp. 118–134). Toronto: Harcourt Brace Jovanovich.

Grant, K.R. (1993). Health and health care. In P.S. Li & B.S. Bolaria (Eds.), *Contemporary sociology* (pp. 394–409). Toronto: Copp Clark Pitman.

Greater Vancouver Food Bank Society. (1989). Food bank information kit. Vancouver: Greater Vancouver Food Bank Society.

Greater Vancouver Food Bank Society. (1998). *Food Bank News, 2*(2) (Winter–Spring).

Hamelin, A.M., Habicht, J.P., & Beaudry, M. (1999). Food insecurity: Consequences for the household and broader social implications. *Journal of Nutrition, 129*, 5175–5205.

Hay, D.I. (1994). Social status and health status: Does money buy health? In B.S. Bolaria & R. Bolaria (Eds.), *Racial minorities, medicine and health* (pp. 9–51). Halifax: Fernwood.

Hess, M. (1989). *Children, schools and poverty*. Ottawa: Canadian Teachers' Federation.

Jacobs, S., Kuhnlein, H., & Gray Donald, K. (1998). Food bank users: Sociodemographic and nutritional characteristics." *Canadian Medical Association Journal, 159*(9), 1143–1149.

James, W.P.T., Nelson, M., Ralph, A., & Leather, S. (1997). The contribution of nutrition to inequalities in health. *British Medical Journal, 314*, 1545–1549.

Johnson, S.R. (1994). How nutrition affects food and agricultural policy. *Journal of Nutrition, 124*, 1871S–1877S.

Kendall, A., Olson, C.M., & Frongillo, E.A. (1996). Relationship of hunger and food insecurity to food availability and consumption. *Journal of the American Dietetic Association, 96*, 1019–1024.

Laven, G.T., & Brown, K.C. (1985). Nutritional status of men attending a soup kitchen: A pilot study. *American Journal of Public Health, 75*, 875–878.

Laxdal, O.E., Habbick, B., & Bolaria, R. (1993). Folic acid prevents neural tube defects. *Saskatchewan Medical Journal, 4*(1), 11–14.

Mao, Y., Moloughney, B., Semenciw, R.M., & Morrison, H. (1992). Indian reserves and registered Indian mortality in Canada. *Canadian Journal of Public Health, 83*, 350–353.

Martin, S.L. (1989). *Women's reproductive health*. Canadian Advisory Council on the Status of Women.

Matza, D. (1966). The disreputable poor. In R. Bendix & S.M. Lipset (Eds.), *Class, status and power*. New York: Free Press.

McIntyre, L., Connor, S.K., & Warren, J. (2000). Child hunger in Canada: Results of the 1994 national longitudinal survey of children and youth. *Canadian Medical Association Journal, 163*(8), 961–965.

McIntyre, L., Travers, K., & Dayle, J.B. (1999). Children's feeding programs in Atlantic Canada: Reducing or reproducing inequities? *Canadian Journal of Public Health, 90*, 196–200.

Myres, A.W., & Kroetsch, D. (1978). The influence of family income on food consumption patterns and nutrition intake in Canada. *Canadian Journal of Public Health, 69*(3), 208–221.

National Council of Welfare. (1975). *Poor kids*. Ottawa: Ministry of Supply and Services.

National Council of Welfare. (1987). *Welfare: The tangled safety net*. Ottawa: Ministry of Supply and Services.

National Council of Welfare. (1988). *Poverty profile 1988*. Ottawa: Ministry of Supply and Services.

National Council of Welfare. (1989). *Poverty lines*. Ottawa: Ministry of Supply and Services.

National Council of Welfare. (1990a, Summer). *Women and poverty revisited*. Ottawa: Supply and Services Canada.

National Council of Welfare. (1990b, Autumn). *Health, health care, and medicare*. Ottawa: Supply and Services Canada.

National Council of Welfare. (1997, Autumn). *Poverty profile 1995*. Ottawa: Supply and Services Canada.

National Council of Welfare. (1999). *Poverty profile 1997*. Ottawa: Minister of Public Works and Government Services.

Nutrition Canada. (1975). *Survey report on Indians and Eskimos*. Ottawa: Information Canada.

Oderkirk, J. (1992, Spring). Food banks. *Canadian Social Trends, 24*(6), 6–14 (cat. no. 11-008).

Olson, C.M. (1999). Nutrition and health outcomes associated with food insecurity and hunger. *Journal of Nutrition, 129*, 5215–5245.

Olson, K.W. (1992). *Food security in Edmonton — Organizing for action.* Edmonton: Edmonton Food Policy Council.

Perkins, S. (1974). *Malnutrition and mental development.* International Union of Child Welfare Conference.

Pollock, S. (1988). Feminism and reproduction. In B.S. Bolaria & H.D. Dickinson, *Sociology of health care in Canada* (pp. 167–182). Toronto: Harcourt Brace Jovanovich.

Rauschenbach, B.S., Frongillo, E.A., Thompson, F.E., Anderson, E.Y.J., & Spicer, D. (1990). Dependency on soup kitchens in urban areas of New York state. *American Journal of Public Health, 80*(1), 57–60.

Reid, D.L., & Miles, J.E. (1977). Food habits and nutrition intakes of noninstitutionalized senior citizens. *Canadian Journal of Public Health, 68*(2), 154–158.

Reuler, J.B. (1989). Health care for homeless in a national health program. *American Journal of Public Health, 79*(8), 1003–1035.

Riches, G. (1986). *Food banks and the welfare crisis.* Ottawa: Canadian Council on Social Development.

Roberts, R., Golding, J., Towell, T., & Weinreb, I. (1999). The effects of economic circumstances on British students' mental and physical health. *Journal of American College of Health, 48*, 103–109.

Rose, D. (1999). Economic determinants and dietary consequences of food insecurity in the United States. *Journal of Nutrition, 129*, 5175–5205.

Ross, S.E., & Rutter, A.C. (1978). *Healthiest babies possible: An outreach program.* Vancouver: Vancouver Perinatal Health Project.

Sennett, R., & Cobb, J. (1973). *The hidden injuries of class.* New York: Vintage Books.

Shah, C.P., & Farkas, C.S. (1985). The health of Indians in Canadian cities: A challenge to the health-care system. *Canadian Medical Association Journal, 133*, 859–863.

Shah, C.P., Kahan, M., & Krauser, J. (1987, September 15). The health of children of low income families. *Canadian Medical Association Journal, 137*, 485–490.

Tarasuk, V. (1994). Poverty, homelessness and health. In B.S. Bolaria & R. Bolaria (Eds.), *Racial minorities, medicine and health* (pp. 53–65). Halifax: Fernwood.

Tarasuk, V.S., & Beaton, G.H. (1999). Household food insecurity and hunger among families using food banks. *Canadian Journal of Public Health, 90*, 109–113.

Tarasuk, V., & Davis, B. (1996). Response to food insecurity in the changing Canadian welfare state. *Journal of Nutrition Education, 28*, 71–75.

Tarasuk, V.S., & MacLean, H. (1990, July–August). The institutionalization of food banks in Canada: A public health concern. *Canadian Journal of Public Health, 81*, 331–332.

Thomson, M. (1990, August). Association between mortality and poverty. *B.C. Medical Journal, 32*, 8.

Thomson, M., & Philion, J. (1991, May–June). Children's respiratory hospitalization and air pollution. *Canadian Journal of Public Health, 82*.

Vernon, P.E. (1979). *Intelligence: Heredity and Environment.* San Francisco: W.H. Freeman.

Webber, M. (1992). *Food for thought.* Toronto: Coach House Press.

Wiecha, J.L., Dwyer, J.T., & Dunn-Strhecker, M. (1991, July–August). Nutrition and health services needs among the homeless. *Public Health Reports, 106*(4), 364–374.

Wigle, D.T., & Mao, Y. (1980). *Mortality by income level in urban Canada*. Ottawa: Health and Welfare Canada.

Wilkins, R., & Adams, O. (1983). *Healthfulness of life*. Montreal: Institute on Public Policy.

Wilson, B., & Steinman, C. (2000). *Hunger count 2000: A surplus of hunger*. Toronto: Canadian Association of Food Banks.

Winkleby, M.A. (1990). Comparison of risk factors for ill health in a sample of homeless and nonhomeless poor. *Public Health Reports, 105*(4), 404–409.

Wood, D., & Valdez, B. (1991). Barriers to medical care for homeless families compared with housed poor families. *American Journal of Diseases in Children, 145*, 1109–1115.

8

Overcoming Hurdles:
Health Care and Aboriginal People

JIM S. FRIDERES   University of Calgary

INTRODUCTION

Since the arrival of Europeans in North America, there has been inextricable pressure on the Aboriginal way of life. Beginning with a more benign impact on the way of life of the **Aboriginal people**, the Canadian state inexorably began to assimilate them. This chapter will show how, over time, colonialism penetrated Aboriginal institutional orders, specifically their traditional health care system and health practices.

Canadians have, for many years, chosen to employ behaviour embedded in the principle of Jeremy Bentham's Panopticon — a building designed so that guards could watch prisoners but prisoners were unable to see the guards (Foucault, 1977). The principle of such a building was that prisoners would know they were being watched and thus would always be on their best behaviour. In the end, they would internalize their "model" behaviour and strive to act and think as society dictated. The Panopticon model underlies Canada's assumptions and conceptualization of its relationship to Aboriginal people — unidirectional and hierarchical. It is the belief that coercive control directed toward Aboriginal peoples would eventually result in their losing their Aboriginal characteristics and assimilating into Canadian society.

This intrusion and impact was exacerbated by Europeans' belief that sickness is generated and located totally within an individual's body. The locus of cause tends to be focused on the individual. Thus, Canadians tend to view health care and health risks in terms of the individual, rather than in the context of society or of the actions taken by vested interest groups such as the Canadian Medical Association or multinational corporations (Bush et al., 1996). As Bolaria (1979) points out, this individual-centred conceptualization has led to a curative orientation, in which technical medical solutions are offered to solve the individual's problems, and the social, economic, and political causes of ill health are ignored. He goes on to point out that this position obscures the extent to which health and illness depend on socially determined ways of life.

SOCIAL PROFILE OF ABORIGINAL PEOPLE

More than three quarters of a million people are identified as being at least partially of Aboriginal origin. Table 1 identifies various categories of Aboriginal people and their distribution in Canada. There are many dimensions in which Aboriginal people differ from other Canadians. For example, Aboriginal children live in a very different family structure: fewer than half (43 percent) of Aboriginal families include married couples, compared with nearly three quarters of the general Canadian population. One fourth of Aboriginal families are common-law couples (compared with only 10 percent of the general Canadian population), and one third of the Aboriginal families are "lone parent" families, while 16 percent of other Canadian families are of this type. Nearly half of the Aboriginal population lives in rural areas (compared with less than 20 percent of the general Canadian population). Aboriginal people have, on average, more children than do non-Aboriginals (3.4 compared to 1.9), and they show a high dependency ratio (the number of people who are either too young or too old to work relative to the number of people of working age — usually defined as ages 15–65). The Aboriginal population is considered very young: nearly 40 percent of Aboriginal people (compared with 22 percent of non-Aboriginal) are under 15 years of age, and only 3 percent are over 65 (compared with 9 percent of non-Aboriginal).

The information in Table 2 reveals the extent of urbanization of Aboriginal people for selected urban centres. Overall, nearly half the Aboriginal population reside (permanently or temporarily) in large urban centres. When the numbers are compared with earlier data, it is clear that there has been a substantial urbanization of Aboriginal people, not unlike the case for the general Canadian population. This change in residence has significant social and cultural implications for the older generation as well as for the generation now growing up. Although some Aboriginal institutions exist in urban areas, such as the Plains Indian Cultural Survival School in Alberta, most Aboriginal youth attend provincially funded primary or secondary schools and participate in institutions that are part of the dominant society.

Table 3 identifies some important sociodemographic attributes of Aboriginal people that further distinguish them from the general Canadian population: low educational attainments, low income, and low involvement in the labour force, all which reflect a quality of life that is considerably less than that of the average Canadian. For example, more than half the dwellings on **reserves** require minor or major renovations or replacement.

Figure 1 reveals the annual expenditures of the Department of Indian Affairs and Northern Development for Aboriginal people. It shows that nearly $1 billion is spent on direct health care for Aboriginal people; this cost has continued to rise in the past decade.

In summary, the statistics show that Aboriginal people have a low participation rate in the labour force, low educational attainments, low job status, and low incomes. They are further restricted by geographic concentration in rural and isolated geographic areas. Aboriginal people are, for the most part, concentrated at the bottom of the class hierarchy of Canadian society. This position is primarily a result of government policies that created and maintained a relationship of perpetual dependency (Dunning, 1959; Carstens, 1971). Paine (1977) referred to this relationship as "welfare colonialism," and

TABLE 8.1 *Total Canadian Aboriginal Population by Aboriginal Group, 1996*

| | Total Population | | Aboriginal Population | | | | |
	Total[1]	Percentage Aboriginal	North American Indian[2,3]	Métis[2]	Inuit[2]	Percentage Living Off Reserve
Canada	28 528 125	2.82	554 290	210 190	41 080	53
Newfoundland	547 160	0.2	5 430	4 685	4 265	70
Prince Edward Island	132 855	0.1	825	120	15	68
Nova Scotia	899 970	0.1	11 340	860	210	27
New Brunswick	729 630	0.2	9 180	975	120	29
Quebec	7 045 080	2.1	47 600	16 075	8 300	36
Ontario	10 642 790	1.3	118 830	22 790	1 300	65
Manitoba	1 100 295	11.7	82 990	46 195	360	42
Saskatchewan	976 615	11.4	75 205	36 535	190	50
Alberta	2 669 195	4.6	72 645	50 745	795	57
British Columbia	3 689 755	3.8	113 315	26 750	815	56
Yukon	30 655	20.2	5 530	565	110	93
Northwest Territories	64 120	61.9	11 400	3 895	24 600	98

1. Total North American Indian, Métis, and Inuit populations do not equal the total Aboriginal population because 6415 persons reported identifying with more than one group.
2. Single and multiple responses have been combined.
3. Counts for North American Indian may be affected by the incomplete enumeration of 77 Indian reserves and settlements in the 1996 Census, depending on the geographic area under study.

Source: Statistics Canada, *1996 Census*, Nation Tables, p. 4.

TABLE 8.2 *Aboriginal Identity Population in Selected Census Metropolitan Areas[1]*

	Total Population	Total Aboriginal Population	Aboriginal Population as Percentage of Total Population
Toronto	4 232 905	16 100	0.4
Winnipeg	660 055	45 750	6.9
Regina	191 480	13 605	7.1
Saskatoon	216 445	16 160	7.5
Calgary[2]	815 985	15 200	1.9
Edmonton	854 230	32 825	3.8
Vancouver[2]	1 813 935	31 140	1.7
Ottawa-Hull	1 000 935	11 605	1.2

1. People who reported identifying with at least one Aboriginal group: North American Indian, Métis, or Inuit.
2. These CMAs contain, within their boundaries, Indian reserves that were incompletely enumerated during the 1996 Census. Consequently, their counts of North American Indians are affected by this incomplete enumeration.

Source: Statistics Canada, *1996 Census*, Nation Tables, p. 13.

TABLE 8.3 *Aboriginal Income Recipients, Average Total Income and Number of Earners, Average Earnings, by Age Groups and Level of Schooling, Canada, 1995*

Age Groups and Highest Level of Schooling	Population 15 Years and Over	Income Recipients		Earners	
		Percent	Average 1995 Income ($)	Percentage of Earners	Average 1995 Earnings ($)
Total: Age groups/ Highest level of schooling	518 590	91	15 699	57	17 382
15–24 years	143 795	77	6 930	49	6 984
25–34 years	135 905	96	16 270	66	17 024
35–44 years	107 705	96	20 941	70	22 385
45–54 years	65 260	94	21 385	66	24 861
55–64 years	37 615	95	16 261	43	21 598
65 years and over	28 310	99	14 897	11	15 596
Less than secondary school graduation	277 765	86	11 897	43	13 499
Less than university degree	223 505	96	18 628	73	18 913
University degree	17 325	99	31 896	86	31 690

Note: 20 percent sample data.

Source: Statistics Canada, *1996 Census*, Nation Tables, p. 16.

FIGURE 8.1

Federal Expenditures on Programs Directed to Aboriginal Peoples, 1995–1996 ($ million)

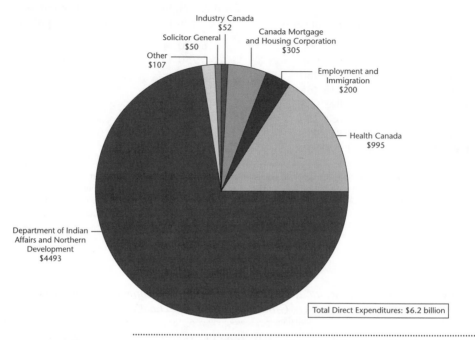

Source: Compiled using information from Canada (1997).

it was described as "coercive tutelage" by Dyck (1997). Tanner (1983) points out that the colonial structure emerged over an extended period and in different forms, first with the French, then the British, and more recently with a rapidly expanding industrial state. Nevertheless, under the Panopticon principles, the central goal of the federal government in dealing with Aboriginal people has always been to maintain close control over them in almost all aspects of their lives.

TRADITIONAL ABORIGINAL HEALTH CARE

For many Aboriginal people in the past, the traditional understanding of illness was embedded in the system of religious beliefs. Illness was the result of some kind of action taken by an individual, such as the breaking of taboos and allowing an evil spirit to influence the behaviour of another person. Aboriginal people traditionally identified three kinds of illness: visible injuries that were a result of physical causes, such as bone fractures and lacerations; diseases caused by some invisible external event, confirmed indirectly by the behaviour of the sick person (e.g., smallpox, influenza, or cancer); and a residual category, which included mental illness.

Traditional health care, as practised by Aboriginal societies, was not only a way of dealing with private troubles and uncertainties, but also an integral part of social relationships and cultural patterns of belief. It involved both a practitioner and a patient, and the actions taken by the medical practitioner reinforced the existing social order (Assembly of First Nations, 1994; Lajeunesse, 1993). Aboriginal people used their traditional health care system as a form of social control. Like other systems, it aimed at producing a healthy person who could work and produce goods for domestic consumption and enhance the viability of the community.

At the outset of his or her curative regimen, the traditional Aboriginal health care practitioner generally applied routine medicines and practised the rituals associated with them. The assumption was that there was some metaphysical basis for the illness and that the rituals and medicines would have a curative power. Many medicines were developed to treat a variety of illnesses. If the illness did not pass, more powerful shamanistic methods — prayers and chants — would be employed (Sealy & McDonald, no date). Because Aboriginal people viewed illness as a result of some foreign object or spirit having entered the space surrounding an individual, the task of the medicine man or woman, or **shaman**, was to remove the foreign object or spirit.

Aboriginal healing circles and the medicine wheel reflect the world and the events taking place as a circle — a view different from the Euro-Canadian view of order, which is hierarchical and one-directional. In the Aboriginal circle perspective, the community is interconnected, consisting of the land, the people, and the nonphysical world. A central value of Aboriginal culture is to live life to its fullest, not only for oneself but for one's family. In short, a balance between all aspects of the physical and spiritual world is necessary if healing is to take place.

Throughout the nineteenth and well into the twentieth centuries, traditional Aboriginal health care activities were increasingly discouraged and discontinued as various government agencies declared them inappropriate or, sometimes, illegal. In the period after World War II, Aboriginal people were still living in isolated rural communities with local subsistence economies, reliant on hunting, fishing, and trapping, which were supplemented by seasonal labour in the dominant technological society. During this time, the federal Indian Affairs department was the sole provider of educational and medical activities on the reserves. The major problem confronting Aboriginal people was the precipitous intrusion of white society into their way of life; high rates of neurosis and alcoholism resulted as they attempted to deal with the rapid changes imposed upon them. Eyer and Sterling (1977) point out that the economic and cultural forces imposed on Aboriginal people by the government and its agencies created a great deal of stress by disrupting communal ties and by trying to mould Aboriginal people into competitive, striving individuals.

HEALTH CARE POLICY: WHO IS RESPONSIBLE?

Government involvement in health care for many non-Aboriginal Canadians is a relatively recent phenomenon, even though the federal government has been involved in "providing" health care for Aboriginal people since the eighteenth century. However, as Meilicke and Storch (1980) point out, prior to Confederation there was some government involvement in health care issues. The government's position was that the health and social needs of Canadians were family concerns and were to be dealt with by families and voluntary or religious organizations. Heagerty (1934) points out that there are few references to any measures being taken by the provincial or federal governments to prevent the spread of smallpox, typhus, and other diseases that frequently decimated the Aboriginal population. Only when various epidemics threatened the local non-Aboriginal population did provinces and/or cities become involved in health care (Hasting & Mosley, 1964).

Discussions between **First Nations** (another name that status **Indians** use to identify themselves) and the federal government over health care issues begin with a belief by the federal government that, with certain exceptions, it does not have any legal or **fiduciary obligations**. First Nations disagree and claim the right to special treatment. Disputes between First Nations and the federal government over health issues revolve around three components: the definitions of health; the difference in the way health policy is implemented for Aboriginal people; and the funding of First Nations health services, including the statutory, constitutional, and fiduciary obligations of the federal government regarding the provision of health services to Aboriginal people (Speck, 1989).

The most recent policy — the transfer policy — reflects an agreement between the two levels of government to disagree on the issue of obligations. Nevertheless the federal government has accepted some responsibility with regard to Aboriginal health. Under Health and Welfare Canada, a current budget of approximately $900 million is to be spent on six major health programs: community health services, environmental health and surveillance, noninsured health benefits, national Aboriginal alcohol and drug abuse, hospital services, and management services. Although there is no direct federal government legislation for the provision of these services, custom and historical commitment provide the basis and rationale for covering their cost. There are some exceptions, such as the references to the provision of a "Medicine chest" in Treaty 6. In this **treaty**, the Cree of Alberta were able to force the government to add a provision that would ensure that their medical needs would be the responsibility of the crown.

Until 1945, the Department of Indian Affairs was the sole provider of medical health care services to Aboriginals on reserves. In that year, these services were transferred to the Department of Health and Welfare, where they have remained. In 1962, Indian Health Services (a division of Health and Welfare) was merged with six other federal health programs to form the Medical Services Branch. In 1964, **treaty Indians** were defined as insured persons under provincial medicare. The contemporary phase of health care issues emerges from the 1969 "White Paper" policy that suggested the elimination of distinct, separate services for Aboriginals and that they receive health care services from provincial governments (Weaver, 1981). Although this policy was officially withdrawn, the government has, on occasion, tried to covertly implement some of the recommendations. Nevertheless, by 1970, the present structure of Indian Health Services was in place.

In 1980, Justice Thomas Berger was commissioned by the federal government to study and make recommendations as to how the federal government and First Nations could consult with each other on health issues in a meaningful manner. As Young (1984) points out, Berger recommended intensive, regular consultations that would lead to greater Aboriginal involvement in the design, management, and control of health care services in their communities. By 1981, a proposal to transfer responsibility for health care services to Aboriginal communities was approved. In 1982, Indian health services standards were developed and introduced as a way of measuring the extent to which Aboriginal health needs were being met.

In 1986, Health and Welfare (Medical Services Branch) announced a new policy initiative: Indian Health Transfer Policy. This new policy was to facilitate a developmental approach to health care and services to Aboriginal communities and was centred on the concept of self-determination. It was hoped that it would lead to First Nations autonomy and community control of health care services (Speck, 1989). The Transfer Policy in health care is a continuation of the "devolution policy" developed by Indian and Northern Affairs Canada a decade earlier, in that it proposes that a larger share of the responsibility now allocated to the federal government be taken on by First Nations.

There is considerable tension between the two parties with regard to this transfer. Speck (1989) points out that First Nations are denied self-determination, which in turn denies them the opportunity to create conditions whereby Aboriginal health could be improved. For example, she notes that the federal government continues to administer health services as an isolated "thing" that is separate from the political, social, and economic dimensions of life — a fact that Aboriginal people and others have consistently identified as one of the major problems in Aboriginal health care.

Today, in all but three of the provinces, insurance premiums are paid for everyone by provincial governments, who take payments from tax revenue. A variety of arrangements exist in these provinces for payment of premiums by registered Aboriginal people, ranging from bulk payments to general means tests. As Speck (1989) points out, the specific features that differentiate Aboriginal from non-Aboriginal health services are the payment of medical and hospital insurance premiums by the federal government for three provinces, the provision of public health services by the federal government rather than the provincial government, and the federal funding of additional noninsured services for Aboriginal people (p. 193). Nonetheless, full medical services are provided to Aboriginal people, although the actual practice varies from one province to another, depending upon the standards set by each.

PROGRAMS AND THE PROVISION OF MEDICAL SERVICES

The federal government has assumed jurisdiction over the health of Aboriginal people throughout Canada. Although the *Indian Act* says little about specifics (see section 73[1]) and its main focus is on preventing the spread of infectious diseases, there remains strong financial commitment to Aboriginal health care through a variety of programs (Woodward, 1989). The first major program operated by Health and Welfare Canada focuses on communicable disease control, health education, mental health, nursing, and the provision of medical advice and assistance. The estimated annual cost of this program is about $300 million.

The second program is the noninsured health benefits program, which has an annual expenditure of over $500 million. Through this program, Aboriginal people are provided general health care by having access to provincial medicare systems and supplemental programs. It also covers the provincial health insurance premium and user fees. In addition, the program includes the transportation of patients, dental services, and other medical appliances and services. This program was established to achieve equity, that is, to ensure that all Aboriginals will be treated alike in all provinces. Prior to 1978, Health and Welfare provided these benefits on the basis of need. New guidelines drawn up by cabinet in 1979 were met with stiff opposition, and one year later they were withdrawn. They were replaced with a new health policy one year later that allowed doctors and dentists to determine whether or not a person needed health services, as well as what those services would be.

The third major program is the community health activities, in which funding is provided to train and employ local health care workers. For example, in 1982, the National Aboriginal Alcohol and Drug Abuse Program was put in place. This experimental program expanded its role over time and deals with treatment, rehabilitation, and education at an annual cost of over $50 million.

Health involves more than hospital care and medicine. If areas of social assistance and welfare services are considered part of the health services afforded to Aboriginal people, the costs of these services increase by $650 million and $250 million respectively. These programs differ from previous ones in that most funds directed toward social assistance are directly administered by the bands themselves.

The provision of services for Aboriginal people is carried out through all three levels of government. Services provided by provincial and municipal agencies are generally fully reimbursed by the federal government. At the federal level, the Medical Services Branch has over 200 doctors (less than 1 percent are Aboriginal) and over 1000 nurses (about 10 percent are Aboriginal). More than 500 community health workers are also contracted by Medical Services to provide health care for Aboriginal people. Nearly all the community health workers are Aboriginals. On a per capita basis, the Medical Services Branch spends about the same per year for each Aboriginal person as is spent on each non-Aboriginal person (Grescoe, 1981). Health services are also provided through contributions and contract arrangements with Aboriginal organizations, bands, and post-secondary educational institutions. They carry out this program under four main activities: health care and treatment services, public health services, involvement of Aboriginals in the health care system, and the provision of physical facilities (DIAND, 1984).

In summary, the overall structure for providing medical and health services to Aboriginal people is complex. At the national level, several government agencies interact to set policies, determine programs, and establish funding levels. They include the deputy minister of health and welfare, director general: policy and evaluation, the treasury board, and the directors of Indian/**Inuit** policy, planning and evaluation. At the provincial level, the regional director oversees the implementation of the programs for each health zone, which involves doctors, nurses, and environmental health officers. In addition, provincial authorities provide health services for which Aboriginal people may be recipients. At the local level, for those bands involved in health care delivery, band councils make decisions regarding training programs and determining who will be admitted to various health programs (Frideres & Gadacz, 2001).

DOMINANT CULTURE VIEWS ON ABORIGINAL HEALTH AND ILLNESS

Over the years, traditional Aboriginal health care practices have been ridiculed by the practitioners of modern Western medicine. Non-Aboriginal people, unfamiliar with the substances and methods used in Aboriginal medicine, saw its practices as primitive, irrational, and ignorant. From their ethnocentric and racist perspective, the use of shamans was evidence of paganism and heathenism; they persistently argued that shamans were evil and that Christian prayers were more efficacious in curing illness (Sealy & McDonald, no date). These moral entrepreneurs, who carried out their destruction of Aboriginal health care practices with relentless zeal, were aided by the government's willingness to accept the medical profession's definition of what was appropriate and acceptable in health care methods. To secure the primacy of this definition, laws were introduced that would ensure that traditional Aboriginal ways would be phased out and new ways legitimized. As a result, the Western medical model became the dominant model and many traditional medicinal practices and products were forced underground.

To combat the plethora of social problems facing Aboriginal communities, some have taken up traditional healing activities or combined Aboriginal perspectives with more modern medicinal practices. Others have used traditional methods to deal with increasing levels of alcohol and substance abuse (Jefferson, 1994). Their long-term effectiveness is unknown; moreover, their inability to obtain long-term funding places the programs on shaky ground. However, like more modern programs, unless the social and economic environment is changed, these programs have little chance of success. The influence of structural processes is too powerful for most individuals to resist. In certain communities, much of this traditional knowledge has disappeared completely.

Although the dominant society's medical system may be utilized by Aboriginal people, their traditional health care provides them with a sense of security not obtainable through modern practices. Thus, they tend to retain and utilize some of the traditional approaches, under specific conditions, along with more modern health care practices. On many of the reserves, traditional health care remains viable, if not universally used. To the extent that Aboriginal people are isolated and **institutionally complete** on the reserve, the use of such traditional techniques is reinforced (Sivell-Ferri, 1997).

MODERN MEDICINE: UNDERLYING ASSUMPTIONS

For modern medicine to be effective, a number of assumptions must be made. For example, if an individual is ill, the assumption is that treatment will be sought as soon as the symptoms appear. Moreover, it is assumed that if medicines are prescribed, the individual will purchase them, carry out the medicinal regime, and stop behaviours that counter the prescribed medicine. While this model may be a workable one for middle-class families, it is not always successful for those who are poor or have different cultural values. The resurgence of tuberculosis and the high rate of diabetes in Aboriginal communities are perhaps the best modern examples of how modern medical assumptions are not always workable. To provide an individual with a prescription and a set of instructions as to how to use the medicine does not necessarily mean that the individual is able to purchase the medicine, take the dosage in the manner instructed, nor change his or her lifestyle (e.g., eat regular meals, eat meals that reflect proper nutritional standards, or have funds to purchase the proper housing). On many reserves, fewer than 50 percent of the population have easy access to an automobile, and this has major implications for health care and provision.

The basic assumptions upon which Canadian medical thinking, and hence the health care system, rest are the acceptance of germ theory and the ability of people to diagnose and take steps to cure an illness. Both assumptions presuppose that health is the concern of the individual. Most members of the population accept the first condition with little reservation; the second also does not seem to be problematic for many people. However, certain sectors of the population, for example, some Aboriginal people, do not accept the first assumption and find the second difficult to implement. Obviously, those who reject or are unable to accept or implement both these assumptions are at a distinct disadvantage in maintaining good health and consequently in maintaining quality of life. The most serious consequence is a **mortality rate** considerably greater than that among those people who accept germ theory and practise preventive medicine, and who are, in any case, already in a position of low risk with regard to life-threatening illnesses.

INFLUENCES ON HEALTH STATUS

The health of an individual is influenced by four factors: lifestyle, environment, the organizational structures of health care, and biological (genetic) makeup (LaFramboise, 1980). Lifestyle consists of decisions made by an individual that have an impact on overall health, for example, his or her use of alcohol and tobacco, occupation, and physical fitness. There is a tendency to define this component only in terms of "voluntary" decisions. However, many of these seemingly voluntary decisions are actually involuntary or at least severely circumscribed. For example, smoking is a means to reduce hunger pangs, unskilled labourers are forced to take jobs with a high risk of accidents, and the nutritional value of one's diet may be determined by one's financial resources.

The environmental element is the individual's physical and social environment, which includes factors such as air quality, potable water, place of residence, and housing. Health care organization refers to the quality, arrangement, nature, and relationships of people and resources within society to its health care services. This component, usually referred to as the "health care delivery system," includes such elements as medical practices, hospitals and extended care facilities, and the use of antibiotics and other drugs. The final component — biological makeup — refers to the individual's physical and genetic makeup. There is a tendency to view this component as a constant and to consider all people as biologically the same, although there are some known biological predispositions for specific human groups (e.g., sickle-cell anemia among Black people of West African descent).

Health problems experienced by the individual are, theoretically, the result of a "crack" in any one of the above four components. However, each of these components can contribute differentially to illness among different groups of people. As noted, there is a tendency to assume that all Canadians have access to the same health care system and have the same biological makeup, so that these two components are constant. To a certain extent, environment is also viewed as a constant. Thus, there is a tendency for researchers to focus on the individual's lifestyle as determining the quality of health, since it is considered the only variable in the formula (Wirick, 1966).

In other words, politicians, health care practitioners, and the employment system view the Canadian population as homogeneous, or soon to become so. There is a continued insistence that one health care model (the individual technical curative model) is correct and that no others should be recognized. Policy decisions and programs established by the government reflect this fundamental bias. However, it is clear that many social classes and cultural groups outside the mainstream have fundamental problems in adapting to the health care model propounded by the medical profession. Aboriginal people are in double jeopardy: they tend to be shunted into a lower social class, and they are culturally separate from the dominant society. The chapter will now examine how socioeconomic and cultural factors influence Aboriginal people's access to health care services and affect their health.

ABORIGINAL PEOPLE: A HEALTH STATUS REPORT

Many of the statistics about disease and illness among Aboriginal people have been published and are well known (see Bobet, 1990). Diseases of poverty, overcrowding, and poor housing have led to chronic and acute respiratory diseases that take a heavy toll among Aboriginal people. The standardized death rate for the Aboriginal population is more than double that of the general Canadian population — 15.9, compared with 6.6 deaths per 1000 population — and follows a trend that has existed for well over half a century (Nuttal, 1982; Brady, 1983; Canada, 1997), with an average age of death more than 20 years earlier than that of the average non-Aboriginal Canadian.

Nevertheless, the overall trend in Aboriginal mortality shows that it has improved substantially over the past decade. However, there is still a considerable gap between Aboriginals and the general Canadian population. Although the overall death rate among Aboriginal people has decreased by nearly one third since 1978, it is still about 1.5 times the national rate. The gap between Aboriginal people and the general Canadian population is particularly wide for ages 15–44. Aboriginal people in this age group are more than three times as likely to die as non-Aboriginal people (Berger, 1991).

Life expectancy at birth for Aboriginal people continues to improve each year, yet the gap between Aboriginal people and the general Canadian population is still more than 6 years. One of the major factors contributing to the increase in the life expectancy of Aboriginal people is the declining infant mortality rate. Over the past two decades, the rate has decreased by more than 50 percent, from a high of 24 per 1000 in 1980 to less than 12 per 1000 in 1997.

Figure 2 reveals the overall mortality rates in Canada for both Status Indians and the general Canadian population. (The term "Status Indians" describes Aboriginal people who are registered with the federal government as Indians according to the terms of the *Indian Act*.) It shows that in the 1960s, the Status Indian mortality rate was nearly three times that of the general population. Over time there has been a general, slow decline in the Canadian population mortality rate. However, the Status Indian population experienced a sharp drop from 1960 to 1965 and a further significant drop between 1965 and 1990. Since 1980, the decrease has been gradual but consistent and converging with the general Canadian mortality rate. Nevertheless, in relative terms, the Status Indian rate is twice the general Canadian rate.

Mortality Rates by Cause

What are the specific causes of death among Aboriginal people? For the past decade, over one third of all Aboriginal deaths (compared to 8 percent in the general population) are due to accidents and violence. For all age groups up to 63, Aboriginal people are four times as likely as non-Aboriginals to die from these causes. The most common causes are motor vehicles, drowning, and fire. Although these rates are extremely high, they have been reduced by over 40 percent since 1980.

FIGURE 8.2

Mortality Rates per 1000 for Status Indian and Canadian Population, 1960–1998

....

*Estimated

....

Source: Bobet (1990, p. 14). Copyright © Minister of Public Works and Government Services Canada, 2001.

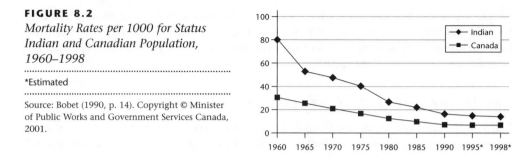

Figure 3 reveals the leading causes of death for Aboriginal people. While the two major causes (injury and poisoning and the circulatory system) have shown dramatic decreases over the past two decades, the data also show that the third leading cause, neoplasm (cancers) is on the increase. Another health problem facing Aboriginal people is the resurgence of tuberculosis. From a high of 84 cases per 100 000 population in 1980, the incidence steadily decreased into the 1990s. By 1994, the incidence of tuberculosis was at an all-time low at 46 cases per 100 000 population for Aboriginal people. However, in recent times, the rate has dramatically increased, and today the rate stands at 81.3 cases per 100 000 population, a rate similar to that evidenced nearly two decades earlier. To fully appreciate this level, consider that today, Africa has a rate of 80.0; alternatively, the rate for all of Canada is 7.4 per 100 000 population. Nevertheless, the data in Figure 3 reveal the stability of these health issues for Aboriginal people. As such, it is clear that government efforts to deal with these issues have not been successful.

Other health issues facing Aboriginal people include diseases previously unknown to them. For example, prior to 1950, diabetes was practically unknown in the Aboriginal

FIGURE 8.3

Aboriginal Mortality Rates by Selected Causes, 1984–1996

....

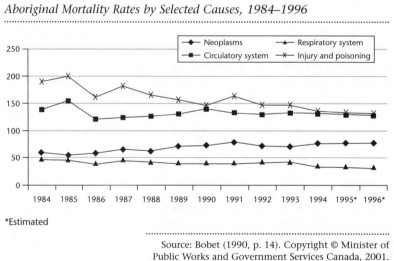

*Estimated

....

Source: Bobet (1990, p. 14). Copyright © Minister of Public Works and Government Services Canada, 2001.

population; today, its incidence is two to five times higher than for the non-Aboriginal population. Health officials in British Columbia report increases of 50–100% between 1992 and 1999. AIDS also has become a major health issue for Aboriginal people, and its incidence is reported to be five times the national level.

Infant mortality has tremendous impact on the population of all societies, since infants (if they live) contribute to the growth of the population when they reach child-bearing age. Over the years there has been a substantial decrease in Aboriginal infant mortality rates. The data show that the infant mortality rate for non-Aboriginals is 6.7 per 1000 while the rate for Aboriginal people is 14.3 per 1000. A closer look at the infant mortality rate shows that Aboriginal perinatal deaths (stillbirths and deaths before one week) are twice as high as they are in the general population. On the other hand, neonatal death (occurring from birth to one month) rates for the two groups are very similar. Postneonatal (one month to one year) death rates are more than three times higher for Aboriginal people. These rates reflect poor housing and other adverse environmental conditions that Aboriginal children are born into.

The effectiveness of the Aboriginal health care system is related as much to the environmental conditions in which Aboriginals live as to the treatment and facilities provided. When health care is provided, it is sometimes countered by social and economic problems, such as overcrowding, poor nutrition, chronic unemployment, and community and family violence. Thus, an Aboriginal person, after receiving effective medical treatment, finds himself or herself returning to the social and economic conditions that created the problem in the first place. In short, the causes of poor mental and physical health are not dealt with.

In present-day Aboriginal communities, compared with the rest of the Canadian population, suicide and self-inflicted injuries are three times higher (six times higher for the 15–24 age group), homicide rates are twice as high, congenital anomalies are 1.5 times higher, and pneumonia is over three times higher. Aboriginal people have five times the rate of child welfare, four times the death rate, three times the violent death, juvenile delinquency, and suicide rates, and twice the rate of hospital admissions of Canada's non-Aboriginal population. Aboriginal people are also exposed to severe environmental hazards: industrial and resource development have polluted water and disrupted fish and game stock for many reserve communities, seriously affecting their quality of life. For example, residents of the White Dog and Grassy Narrows reserves in Ontario were found to have 40 to 150 times more mercury in their blood than does the average Canadian (Bolaria, 1979). Various environmental disturbances have upset other Aboriginal communities, for example, Cluff Lake (uranium pollution), Serpent River (acid discharge), and St. Regis (fluoride pollution).

Considerable effort and funds have been allocated to deal with Aboriginal medical services. However, the social environmental issues that are linked to health have not been attended to. For example, when mercury contaminates a river or lake that Aboriginal people use as a daily food source, community members who eat the fish will become ill and suffer the consequences, both in the short and the long term. On the other hand, if they do not eat the fish, they must look for an alternative source of food. Either course of action will cause health, social, and economic disruption in the community, which in turn has indirect impacts upon the community and its residents.

In summary, the quality of life experienced by Aboriginal people is far inferior to that of non-Aboriginals. How has this come about? These conditions have resulted from the cultural imperialism of the Canadian government and the racist philosophy that promoted the dominant society's insistence on the inferiority of Aboriginal people.

ETIOLOGY IN SOCIETY

Definitions of disease and illness or health have a social as well as pathological component. The physical condition of an individual must be defined as one of illness before the individual can perceive that she or he is ill (Berliner, 1977). If the group, neighbourhood, or community defines the condition as an illness, then certain steps are necessary to correct the condition. On the other hand, if the condition is not so defined by the individual's reference group, it would be inappropriate for the individual to assume a sick role and so the individual would not seek treatment (Kane, Kasteler, & Gray, 1976). Thus the definition of illness in a community will determine the norm of health, or state of health considered normal for its members. An Aboriginal individual living in an Aboriginal community thus interprets his or her own health status as do others in the community. What constitutes illness or sickness will be determined by the definition of the group and the group's reaction to people who exhibit certain symptoms or behaviour. As Kane, Kasteler, and Gray (1976) argue, the Aboriginal definition of reality means living with other Aboriginal people who share the same perspective, values, and beliefs, which are passed from one generation to the next.

Some of the tensions and conflicts experienced by Aboriginal people are inner-directed (e.g., mental illness), whereas others are outer-directed (e.g., accidents, alcohol and drug abuse, domestic violence). For instance, because only a few of the residents of Aboriginal communities are able to participate in the wage economy as productive workers, those with the relevant skills must choose between remaining on the reserve, where job opportunities are few, or leaving the community and entering the larger postindustrial economy. Those able to successfully compete in the larger economy are generally successful, although they are faced again with a choice of maintaining reserve contacts or assimilating into the larger society. To choose the first generally results in the development of "marginal man" and ultimately a return to the reserve. To choose the second means that individuals lose their Aboriginal culture. The process is similar to that faced by immigrants, although immigrants rarely have the option of returning home (Frideres, 1998).

There is also the issue of the middle-class mentality prevalent among professional health care practitioners. Any patient not sharing their values is at a distinct disadvantage. First, the practitioners do not understand the attitudes and lifestyles of lower-class patients. Health care professionals, socialized in a middle-class milieu with the modern medical ethic, are ill-prepared to deal with patients whose behaviour does not conform to middle-class values. They assume that Aboriginal patients share their perspective on illness and health care and that they have the same resources (or access to the same resources) as the middle-class patient or the medical professional. In reality, however, Aboriginal people generally are poor and can manage only the barest of material necessities: heat, food, and clothing. Thus their desires are for material improvements — health is not a high priority, nor is it considered in a specific sense. The day-to-day experience of medical practitioners clearly reinforces the notion that Aboriginal patients do not follow their orders and heal themselves. As a result, Aboriginal people are stereotyped as irresponsible, dirty, and incapable of carrying out orders or taking responsibility for themselves. Negative attitudes are expressed more or less openly, making encounters with health care providers unpleasant for Aboriginal people. Every time they return to the health care facility, they must undergo this experience. The alternative, and common, Aboriginal strategy is to avoid the unpleasant situation by not returning to the practitioner or facility.

Culture creates rules of behaviour for its members, dictating what is expected, encouraged, or allowed. Various subcultures may have different rules. The extent to which a group is institutionally complete, or isolated from other cultural influences, will determine both the extent to which its norms differ from those of the dominant society and the extent to which they are enforced. Cross-cultural influences or memberships will reduce the influence and redefine the situation. Aboriginal people, since they often reside in rural areas, remain an isolated group with a high frequency of contact within the group. All of this has created tight social networks that reinforce their collective definition of reality. Thus, Aboriginal people's attitude and behaviour toward illness and their strategy for dealing with it are a response to how their culture (and the community) defines it and to the types of social support or pressure they receive (Knowlton, 1971).

Because of their poverty and cultural ethos, Aboriginal people have a very tolerant attitude toward what middle-class culture defines as illness. However, when it becomes clear that there is little they can do to prevent an illness or to heal it, they learn to define certain conditions as not illness and thus not worthy of health care services. In other words, poor people learn to live with certain "illnesses" as long as they are not totally physically incapacitated. Since all people in the community take this perspective and share these attitudes, all members of the community learn to view certain debilitating physical conditions as normal.

Aboriginal people, with both lower-class status and a culture different from that of the dominant society, do not respond well to professional health care workers. They prefer to deal with others from a more holistic perspective — taking note of all the aspects of the person with whom they are interacting. In the health care system of the dominant society, there is an elaborate division of labour: nurses are interested only in one aspect of the patient, the X-ray technician in another, the orthopedic surgeon in still another. Aboriginal people find this a foreign experience, both confusing and frustrating (Suchman, 1963). They also perceive the rational, objective, and unemotional manner of health care professionals, inculcated in medical school, as the mark not of a good professional but rather of a cold, heartless person, unsympathetic to the patient (Knowlton, 1971).

In addition, Aboriginal patients tend to resent and resist professional health care workers' extraction of private and personal information from them that usually seems irrelevant. They do not want health care workers to have access to private information without any reciprocity and without being able to control how this information is used — both in the present and in the future (Baca, 1969). Aboriginal women also find that they prefer to deal with women physicians rather than men, so that, unless they are experiencing an acute illness, they tend not to visit male doctors. One other factor that affects the overall health of Aboriginal people is their perception of health care facilities. Because a pattern of health service provided to them has been well established over the years, Aboriginal people have learned to gauge their state of health very differently from non-Aboriginals.

Until recently, medical services were provided to Aboriginal people by the federal govern-ment on a 9-to-5, five-days-a-week basis. There were no home visits and no referrals, nor were any preventative services carried out. If an Aboriginal person became sick at night or on a weekend, she or he would have to define the illness as not serious and wait until morning or, in the case of a weekend, Monday. However, if the illness were in fact life-threatening, she or he would be forced to seek attention from medical personnel at the nearest hospital. For this reason, hospitals, not day clinics or doctors' offices, have become regarded as the most appropriate place to seek health care (Ross, 1992).

Aboriginal people do not utilize health care services in part because of their percep-tion of "health" and "illness." Thus, many do not believe in immunization, because they view the injection of a foreign substance into the body as harmful or potentially harmful. The major utilization of health care services by Aboriginal people generally occurs when a person experiences acute pain or a life-threatening situation. A sick role is adopted under different conditions from those of middle-class, non-Aboriginal peo-ple. This is particularly true when the sick role is regarded as a manifestation of weak-ness, or when it means that an individual would have to be removed from the community and isolated in health care facilities far from friends and kin (Dutton, 1986).

CONCLUSION

The successful adaptation of Aboriginal people to the dominant society requires the denial, or at least the repression, of traditional models of health care in favour of those of the dominant society. In this process, there is a fundamental inequity and dehuman-ization (Weidman, 1980). The dominant group has taken the position that its patterns of behaviour and institutions are not only the best, but morally superior. Behaviours that do not match the dominant group norms are viewed as undesirable. As a result, while Aboriginal people publicly utilize the dominant society's medical service, it is not uncommon for individuals to seek help simultaneously from the traditional health care system. Although Aboriginal people use the dominant health care systems, they continue to regard their own understanding of the natural world as antecedent and superior knowledge (Press, 1978). Unfortunately, modern orthodox practitioners ignore the exis-tence of a traditional health care culture in Aboriginal communities. They are not trained to be aware of it, nor do they have any ability to evaluate it; they deny its existence, or if they acknowledge it, discount its significance to the medical world or to those people using it (Lam, 1980).

Because middle-class white Canadians have accepted germ theory as a legitimate causal explanation for illness, the Canadian lifestyle is organized in such a way as to min-imize the adverse impact of germs by, for example, emphasizing sanitation and refriger-ation. However, those who do not accept this perspective, or who are unable to implement the preventative strategies based on such assumptions, cannot avoid certain diseases or illnesses. Aboriginal people, because of cultural differences and poverty, find themselves unable to implement the preventative strategies.

The dominant society, particularly its health care practitioners, dismiss medicine men or women and shamanism among Aboriginal people as meaningless, even though many prescribed modern medicines are pharmacologically inert (Sealy & McDonald, no date). Despite this, the dominant medical profession still relies upon these medicines and — perhaps more startling — the patients using them get well. This suggests that medicine is not just a function of its pharmacological ingredients, but also of suggestion and social support.

Although health services tend to be concentrated in urban areas, most Aboriginal people live in rural areas. When health professionals enter the rural areas, the "drop-in" mentality resulting from occasional visits is seldom conducive to delivery of adequate service. Medical specialists have little understanding of Aboriginal culture, and language also poses a barrier to communication. When Aboriginal people must travel to distant urban centres to obtain health services, disruptions are even more acute.

Most service and delivery systems are centralized and insensitive to input from local communities, operating on the assumption that Aboriginal patients are passive recipients who should have little or no say in what services are offered, by whom, or where. The bureaucracy of the Medical Services Branch shows that policies emanate from Ottawa and are then implemented by regional administrators and on-site health care workers. There are few ways in which the bureaucracy can be responsive to local concerns or medical issues. In addition, professional autonomy in medical issues at the local level inhibits the involvement of Aboriginal clients. Those services that are offered undermine Aboriginal culture by explicitly or implicitly providing incentives for Aboriginal people to abandon their heritage and be assimilated into the larger, non-Aboriginal society. The dominant society perpetuates this situation despite the obvious fact that one of the most effective ways of improving a people's health lies in individual maintenance. This is more important than having more doctors per capita or improving environmental conditions. An individual's quality of life is highest when she or he functions at a high level, is free from morbidity or impairment, and when his or her vitality and emotional health are high (Lerner, 1973). Rather than denigrating traditional medicine, the dominant society should spend more time learning about Aboriginal health care and how to utilize and integrate it with modern health care practices.

Intergovernmental and interdepartmental divisions of responsibility generate debate and delay when dealing with issues that are health-related but not traditionally defined as such, for example, mercury pollution, where the Department of Indian Affairs and Northern Development (DIAND) and Health and Welfare are jointly responsible (Castellano, 1982). The effectiveness of the entire health care system is related as much to the environmental conditions of Aboriginal communities as to the treatment and facilities provided. Too often, the need for care is engendered by problems associated with overcrowded living conditions leading to contagion and infection, by generally poor nutrition associated with chronic unemployment, by family and community violence, and by the re-emergence of medical problems after effective treatment, when the patient returns to the conditions from which the problems arose. Nevertheless, the Medical Services Branch treats the symptoms, and little is done to address the basic causes of poor health conditions in areas of housing, economic development, employment opportunities, and sanitation — all of which lie within the mandate of DIAND (Canada, 1985).

Until recently there have been few jobs available in Aboriginal communities. Because of low educational achievements, few residents were able to take advantage of even these opportunities. The government has provided social welfare and assistance to the residents; this form of "compensation" takes the place of a wage economy but allows Aboriginals the opportunity to participate, albeit marginally, in the modern industrial economy — as consumers, not producers. Today, with rising educational achievements, more Aboriginal residents are competing for these few jobs. This has resulted in a second layer of frustration and resentment. The first layer is directed toward government and business, which Aboriginal people feel have exploited their communities. The second layer focuses on competing Aboriginal factions who vie for jobs and power. As individuals and families compete for the favour of the reserve power elite, the development of factions has led to considerable tension and conflict in communities. As a result, considerable tension and conflict are endemic in Aboriginal communities.

As the larger society moves into the twenty-first century, it is increasingly directing its attention to preventative health care activities. For example, stop-smoking programs are based on the belief that preventing tobacco use will result in a better quality of life, and advocates of physical exercise promote exercise for the same reasons. Thus, governments are investing in "health promotion" activities that are based on the belief that not only will the health of individuals be better in later life but that this will, in turn, be economically beneficial to society. Unfortunately, this conceptualization is not being applied to Aboriginal communities. Although the federal government spends more than $10 billion annually to deal with the "Indian" problem, little has been done to promote the health of Aboriginals. Almost all programs are reactive and attempt to solve a health or health-related problem.

Over the past quarter century, Aboriginal people have experienced a more positive quality of life, particularly in the area of health. However, in comparison with the general Canadian population, they do not exhibit the same profile. A major gap persists that reflects the poverty in which most Aboriginal people live. Until a more integrated approach is taken to dealing with the problems faced by Aboriginal people, there is no reason to anticipate a great change in their quality of life.

STUDY QUESTIONS

1. *How have historical actions precipitated today's crisis in Aboriginal health care?*
2. *What are the health conditions of Aboriginal people compared with those of non-Aboriginals?*
3. *What are some of the reasons for Aboriginal people not using modern health practices?*
4. *Why has the current health care system failed Aboriginal people?*
5. *How is modern health care similar to the traditional health care practices of Aboriginal people?*
6. *Why should Canadian health care professionals have an understanding of traditional Aboriginal approaches to health care?*

GLOSSARY

Aboriginal government An arrangement in which Aboriginal peoples govern their territories and in which they have jurisdiction and authority over activities occurring there.

Aboriginal people The descendants of the original inhabitants of North America. The Canadian constitution recognizes three groups of Aboriginal peoples: Indians, Métis, Inuit.

fiduciary obligations Obligations based on a relationship between Aboriginal people and the government of Canada that involves a trust or trusteeship.

First Nation A term that came into common usage in the 1970s to replace the term "Indian band"; there is no legal definition of this term.

Indian An Aboriginal person who is not Inuit or Métis; a legal term embedded in the *Constitution Act, 1982.*

Inuit An Aboriginal people of northern Canada.

institutionally complete Of an ethnic community, controlling a variety of institutions, such as religion, education, and commerce, that influence the society in which it operates.

life expectancy On average, the number of years an individual may expect to live at birth.

Métis People of mixed First Nations and European ancestry who identify themselves as Métis; a legal term in Alberta and British Columbia.

mortality rate The number of deaths per year in a cohort of people.

reserve A piece of land set aside by the federal government for use and occupancy by status Indians.

shaman Individuals in the Aboriginal community who are called upon to diagnose a health-related problem or to restore balance on behalf of a community.

treaty A negotiated agreement regarding land and governance between the federal government and a group of Indians. Hundreds of treaties have been signed over the past 200 years.

treaty Indian A status Indian who belongs to a band that signed a treaty with the government of Canada.

RECOMMENDED READINGS

Asch, M. (Ed). (1997). *Aboriginal and treaty rights in Canada: Essays on law, equality and respect for differences*. Vancouver: UBC Press. Intended to provide an interpretive frame of reference for the judiciary and politicians, these essays address the steps Canadian law can take in developing a new relationship with Aboriginal people.

Driben, P. (1985). *We are Métis*. New York: AMS Press. An historical account of the emergence of an ethnic group in Canadian society; identifies current issues facing Métis as well as the organizations they have established to help them achieve their goals.

Frideres, J., & Gadacz, R. (2001). *Aboriginal people in Canada*. Scarborough: Prentice-Hall. A comprehensive overview of Aboriginal people in Canada and an extensive presentation of facts and figures regarding the socioeconomic profile of Aboriginal peoples; presents a historical background of Indian–white relations, discussion of treaties, and information on contemporary issues such as land claims, self-government, and gender issues in Aboriginal communities.

Henderson, S., Benson, M., & Findlay, I. (2000). *Aboriginal tenure in the constitution of Canada*, Scarborough: Carswell. A cross-cultural analysis of Aboriginal and treaty rights and an Aboriginal perspective with regard to constitutional order in Canada.

Li, P., & Bolaria, B.S. (Eds.). (1983). *Racial minorities in multicultural Canada*. Toronto: Garamond Press. Theoretical perspectives on intergroup relations, comparative so that Aboriginal–white relations can be seen as part of the larger Canadian social landscape; provides a sociological perspective and identifies state policies as applied to ethnic groups in Canada; a good understanding of the essential elements of ethnic relations in Canada is presented.

Morse, B. (Ed.). (1985). *Aboriginal people and the law.* Ottawa: Carleton University Press. A discussion of several aspects of Canadian law as it relates to Aboriginal people; presents legal cases over the past century and analyzes court rulings.

REFERENCES

Abella, R. (1984, October). *Report of the commission on equality in employment.* Ottawa: Government of Canada.

Assembly of First Nations. (1994). *Breaking the silence.* Ottawa: Assembly of First Nations Health Commission.

Baca, J. (1969). Some health beliefs of the Spanish-speaking. *American Journal of Nursing, 69,* 2172–2176.

Berger, T. (1991). *A long and terrible shadow.* Vancouver: Douglas & McIntyre.

Berliner, H. (1977). Emerging ideologies in medicine. *Review of Radical Political Economics, 9*(1), 189–218.

Bobet, E. (1990). *The inequalities in health: A comparison of Indian and Canadian mortality trends.* Ottawa: Health and Welfare Canada.

Bolaria, B.S. (1979). Self-care and lifestyles: ideological and policy implications. In J.A. Fry (Ed.), *Economy, class and social reality* (pp. 350–363). Toronto: Butterworths.

Brady, P. (1983). The underdevelopment of the health status of treaty Indians. In P. Li & B.S. Bolaria (Eds.), *Racial minorities* (pp. 39–55). Toronto: Garamond Press.

Bush, P., et al. (1996). *Children, medicines, and culture.* New York: Pharmaceutical Products Press.

Canada. (1985). *Indians and Aboriginal programs: A study team report to the task force on program review.* Ottawa: Supply and Services.

Canada. (1997). *Basic departmental data 1996.* Ottawa: Departmental Statistics Section, Public Works and Government Services Canada.

Carstens, P. (1971). Coercion and change. In R. Ossenberg (Ed.), *Canadian society, pluralism, change and conflict* (pp. 126–148). Scarborough: Prentice-Hall.

Castellano, M. (1982). Indian participation in health policy development: Implications for adult education. *Canadian Journal of Aboriginal Studies, 2*(1), 113–128.

Department of Indian Affairs and Northern Development (DIAND). (1984). *Annual report 1983–84.* Ottawa: Ministry of Supply and Services.

Dunning, R. (1959). Ethnic relations and the marginal man in Canada. *Human Organization, 18*(3), 117–122.

Dutton, P. (1986). Financial, organizational and professional factors affecting health care utilization. *Social Science and Medicine, 23*(7), 721–735.

Dyck, N. (1997). Tutelage, resistance and co-optation in Canadian Indian administration. *Canadian Review of Sociology and Anthropology, 34*(3), 333–348.

Eyer, J., & Sterling, P. (1977). Stress-related mortality and social organization. *Review of Radical Political Economics, 9*(1), 1–44.

Foucault, M. (1977) *"Panopticonism" in discipline and punishment: The birth of prison.* New York: Pantheon.

Frideres, J. (1998). Indigenous peoples of Canada and the United States of America: Entering the 21st century. In L. d'Haenens (Ed.), *Images of Canadianness* (pp. 167–196). Ottawa: University of Ottawa Press.

Frideres, J., & Gadacz, R. (2001). *Aboriginal people in Canada.* Scarborough: Prentice-Hall.

Graham-Cumming, G. (1966). *The influence of Canadian Indians on Canadian vital statistics.* Ottawa: Medical Services Department of National Health and Welfare.

Grescoe, P. (1981). A nation's disgrace. In D. Coburn, C. D'Arcy, P. New, & G. Torrance (Eds.), *Health and Canadian society* (pp. 127–140). Markham, ON: Fitzhenry & Whiteside.

Hasting, J., & Mosley, W. (1964). *Introduction: The evolution of organized community health service in Canada.* Royal Commission on Health Services. Ottawa: Supply and Services.

Heagerty, J. (1934). The development of public health in Canada. *Canadian Journal of Public Health, 25,* 53–59.

Indian and Northern Affairs Canada. (1988). *Basic departmental data.* Ottawa: Minister of Supply and Services.

Jefferson, C. (1994). *Conquest by law.* Ministry of the Solicitor General. Ottawa: Minister of Supply and Services.

Kane, R., Kasteler, J., & Gray, R. (1976). *The health gap: Medical services and the poor.* New York: Springer.

Knowlton, C. (1971). Cultural factors in the non-delivery of medical services to southwestern Mexican Americans. In M. Riedesel (Ed.), *Health-related problems in arid lands* (pp. 118–131). Tempe: Arizona State University Press.

LaFramboise, H. (1980). Health policy: breaking the problem down into more manageable segments. In C. Meilicke & J. Starch, *Perspectives on Canadian health and social services policy: History and emerging trends.* Ann Arbor, MI: Health Administration Press.

Lajeunesse, T. (1993). *Community holistic circle healing.* Ottawa: Ministry of the Solicitor General.

Lam, A. (1980). Traditional Chinese medicine and western medical practice: Personal observations. In M. Staum & D. Larsen (Eds.), *Doctors, patients and society* (pp. 147–151). Waterloo: Wilfrid Laurier University Press.

Lerner, M. (1973). Conceptualization of health and social well-being. In R.L. Berg (Ed.), *Health status indexes* (pp. 1–72). Chicago: Hospital Research and Educational Trust.

Meilicke, C., & Storch, J. (1980). *Perspectives on Canadian health and social services policy: History and emerging trends.* Ann Arbor, MI: Health Administration Press.

Nuttall, R. (1982). The development of Indian boards of health in Alberta. *Canadian Journal of Public Health, 73,* 300–303.

Paine, R. (Ed). (1977). *The white arctic: Anthropological essays on tutelage and ethnicity.* St. John's: Memorial University of Newfoundland, Institute of Social and Economic Research.

Ponting, J.R., & Gibbins, R. (1980). *Out of irrelevance: A socio-political introduction to Indian affairs.* Toronto: Butterworths.

Press, I. (1978). Urban folk medicine: A functional overview. *American Anthropologist, 80,* 71–84.

Ross, R. (1992). *Dancing with a ghost: Exploring Indian reality.* Markham, ON: Octopus Publishing.

Sealy, B., & MacDonald, N. (no date). *The health care professional in an Aboriginal community.* Ottawa: Department of National Health and Welfare.

Sivell-Ferri, C. (1997). *The Ojibwa circle: Tradition and change.* Ottawa: Ministry of Solicitor General, Supply and Services Canada.

Speck, D.C. (1989). The Indian health transfer policy: A step in the right direction, a revenge of the hidden policy? *Aboriginal Studies Review, 5*(1), 187–214.

Suchman, E. (1963). *Social patterns of health and medical care.* New York: New York City Department of Health.

Tanner, A. (Ed.). (1983). *The politics of Indianness.* St. John's: Memorial University of Newfoundland, Institute of Social and Economic Research.

Turshen, M. (1977). The political ecology of disease. *Review of Radical Political Economies, 10*(1), 250–267.

Weaver, S. (1981). *Making Canadian Indian policy. The hidden agenda 1968–1970*. Toronto: University of Toronto Press.

Weidman, H. (1980). Dominance and domination in health care: A transcultural perspective. In M. Staum & D. Larsen (Eds.), *Doctors, patients, and society* (pp. 133–145). Waterloo, ON: Wilfrid Laurier University Press.

Wirick, G. (1966, Winter). A multiple equation model of demand for health care. *Health Services Research*, 301–346.

Woodward, J. (1989). *Aboriginal law*. Toronto: Carswell.

Young, K. (1984). Indian health services in Canada: A sociohistorical perspective. *Social Science and Medicine, 18*(3), 257–264.

PART 4
Women, Family, and Health

Women are health care givers and receivers. In both roles, women's experiences are profoundly influenced by the gendered inequality pervasive in Canadian society.

Bolaria and Bolaria begin this section with a chapter that links women's health status and health care needs to the structured social and economic inequality of their lived experiences. Chapter 9 presents a brief review of gender differences in health and illness patterns and discusses "artefact," genetic, and social–structural explanations of these differences in morbidity and mortality. Differential exposure theory and differential vulnerability theory are discussed to explain general differences in psychological health. Bolaria and Bolaria conclude by addressing various forms of violence against women living in low-income countries and the consequences for women's health and morbidity and mortality.

In Chapter 10, Findlay and Miller focus on the medicalization of women's bodies. Medicalization is the process whereby certain processes and phenomena come to be understood as properly belonging in the domain of medical knowledge and professional control. Two core aspects of women's existence historically have been medicalized: pregnancy, childbearing, and child rearing; and physical appearance, especially as it relates to body weight. Findlay and Miller outline the reasons for, and the means by which, the medicalization of pregnancy, childbearing, and child rearing occurred. They also examine the way in which a concern for women's health, rooted in their role as bearers of future generations, was manifested as a concern with diet, exercise, and weight. In particular, fat was seen as a major health problem that also was symptomatic of an underlying failure of will and self-control. It is in this context that the authors link women's eating disorders, such as anorexia and bulimia, to women's subordinate social status, socialization, and the struggle for autonomy and control. Findlay and Miller argue that although the medicalization of women's bodies is indicative of their general social subordination, women also have an interest in at least some aspects of the medicalization of their bodies and have learned how to use it to their advantage. They conclude that the relationship between women and the medical profession will continue as an ongoing negotiation for control over the definition of health problems and the best means to deal with them.

Varcoe picks up the theme of women's social subordination and links it to their experiences of violence and health in Chapter 11. In this regard she makes three points. First, she argues that various dimensions of inequality compound the impact of violence on women's health. Second, the various dimensions of inequality experienced by women sustain violence by creating barriers to securing adequate means for dealing with it. Finally, she argues that those same dynamics sustain privilege and distance from the problem for some, so they tend not to fully understand the problem or the social foundation of its cause.

Hartrick, in Chapter 12, focuses on women's reproductive work, that is, the biological bearing of children and the day-to-day activities required to sustain the emotional and physical well-being of women's significant others and society in general. She argues that the time, energy, and sacrifice associated with looking after the needs of others may well have negative effects for women's health. Contemporary health reforms, particularly notions of health promotion and the shift in the locus of treatment from hospital to community and home, exacerbate these negative health effects. Hartrick then goes on to consider the social arrangements that perpetuate and sustain women's responsibility for, and obligation to perform, reproductive work.

9

Women's Lives, Women's Health

B. SINGH BOLARIA University of Saskatchewan

ROSEMARY BOLARIA Saskatchewan Institute on Prevention of Handicaps

INTRODUCTION

Socially structured gender inequalities have important consequences for women's lives and their life chances. Women's positions and experiences in society are shaped by their social roles, conventions, economic opportunities, and access to resources. Social and economic inequalities in turn produce variations in health and illness patterns between men and women. Women, however, are not a homogeneous group. The life experiences of some groups of women differ markedly from those of other women and the female population as a whole. For instance, race, ethnic, and class position intersect with gender to produce variations in gender inequality and social variability in health status among women. Racial minority women are doubly disadvantaged because they may encounter inequality due to their race or colour in addition to sex discrimination. Social and economic differentiation and heterogeneity among women produce subgroup differences in health effects and health outcomes. The first part of this chapter presents a brief review of gender differences in health and illness patterns and the sociological explanations often advanced to account for these differences. The last section of the chapter addresses the health consequences of life experienced by women in different social, cultural, and economic contexts and variations in the health consequences of different life experiences.

GENDER, HEALTH, AND ILLNESS

"Women get sicker, but men die quicker" sums up the morbidity and mortality patterns of men and women in developed countries (Lorber, 2000). Improved living conditions, better public health and sanitation, better nutrition, and improved medical care and services have benefited both men and women. Mortality rates have fallen and life expectancy has consistently increased for both men and women (Federal, Provincial and Territorial Advisory Committee on Population Health, 1999a, pp. 323–324; Miles, 1991; Lorber, 2000; Trypuc, 1994). However, health gains have been greater for women.

Current lower mortality for women is a relatively recent occurrence, and the present patterns of longer life expectancy for women emerged at the end of the nineteenth century and only in developed industrialized countries (Miles, 1991; Lorber, 2000). Before the mid-nineteenth century, women suffered from excess mortality, attributable to a comparatively harsher life for women and factors such as frequent pregnancies and poor maternal care (Shorter, 1984; Trypuc, 1994). Social and health advantages have not accrued to all women because women are not a homogeneous group. Social diversity and social stratification among women produce different life chances and variations in health status across individuals and subgroups (Rieker & Bird, 2000; MacIntyre, Hunt, & Sweeting, 1996; Muszynski, 1994).

The health of Canadians in regard to one of the basic indicators of population health has been consistently improving over the years. In 1996, the total (male and female) life expectancy at birth reached new heights, 78.6 years, as a result of the decline in mortality rates. As Table 1 indicates, a female born in 1996 could expect to live to the age of 81.4 and a male to the age of 75.7, a difference of 5.7 years. The life expectancy at birth continues to narrow slowly between sexes. For example, the difference was 7.5 years in 1978 and 5.9 years in 1995 (Federal, Provincial and Territorial Advisory Committee, 1999a, p. 324). As data in Table 1 also show, of the twelve selected OECD countries, Canada ranked third for both male and female life expectancy, behind Japan and Switzerland.

It is also evident that in all OECD countries, females enjoy a decided advantage over males in life expectancy. Women living in poor, less industrialized countries, however, do not fare as well as men in those countries and women in industrialized countries (United Nations Population Fund [UNFPA], 2000; Miles, 1991; United Nations [UN], 1995; Lorber, 2000). Men live longer than women in some countries of Asia and Africa (Miles, 1991). The lives of women in these countries continue to be harsher, due to factors such as feudal cultural practices, excessive violence, lack of control by women over

TABLE 9.1 *Life Expectancy at Birth, Selected OECD Countries, 1996*

Country	Males	Females
Denmark	72.8	78.0
United States	72.7	79.4
Germany	73.6	79.9
United Kingdom	74.4	79.3
New Zealand	74.3	79.8
Netherlands	74.7	80.4
Spain	74.4	81.6
France	74.1	82.0
Australia	75.2	81.1
Canada	75.7	81.4
Switzerland	75.7	81.9
Japan	77.0	83.6

Sources: Organisation for Economic Co-operation and Development (1998). Statistics Canada (1998). Compiled from Federal, Provincial and Territorial Advisory Committee on Population Health (1999, Figure 84b, p. 324).

their bodies and reproduction, frequent pregnancies, poor nutrition, and poor obstetric care (UN, 1995; UNFPA, 2000). Women in poor countries also have shorter lives than do their sisters in the advanced countries. The differences in women's life expectancies between the rich and poor countries in some cases is 20 years or more (UN, 1995). Racial, ethnic, and class differences among women in advanced countries produce sub-group variations in life expectancy. For example, the estimated life expectancy for a registered Indian woman born in 1991 is considerably shorter than that of other Canadian females born that year — 74 and 81 years, respectively (Statistics Canada, 1995, p. 149). Data from the United States indicate that longevity rates vary considerably by race and income (Rieker & Bird, 2000; Syme & Yen, 2000).

It is evident from the above discussion that gender differences in life expectancy are closely linked to a nation's level of economic development. The higher the level of development, the longer the overall life expectancy of the population, the greater the increase in women's longevity, and the wider the differences between men and women (Miles, 1991; UN, 1995). Subgroup differences by race and income levels continue to persist in advanced countries.

While women on average live longer than men, they also report more illness than men, and there is some variation in mortality and causes of death. The data on Canadian standardized death rates by cause and sex are reported in Table 2. In 1996, the male mortality rate (per 100 000 population) was 836, compared with 517 for women. Overall, the mortality rate in 1996 was 653, which is among the lowest rates in industrialized countries. The major causes of deaths for both men and women were **cardiovascular diseases** and cancers: 226 and 185 per 100 000, respectively. Among the specific causes of deaths, coronary heart disease (CHD) was the most important: 133 per

TABLE 9.2 *Age-Standardized Deaths by Cause and Sex, Canada, 1996*

Cause	Deaths per 100 000 Population		
	Male	Female	Both Sexes
Cancer (all)	231	153	185
Lung cancer	72	33	49
Breast cancer	0	29	—
Cardiovascular diseases*	288	179	226
Coronary heart disease (CHD)	184	95	133
Stroke	51	43	47
Respiratory (all)	82	4	58
Pneumonia/Influenza	29	18	22
Accidents (all)	63	25	43
Suicide (all)	21	6	13
Total	836	517	653

*Cardiovascular disease: All heart disease plus stroke and atherosclerosis.

Source: Statistics Canada (1999). Compiled from Federal, Provincial and Territorial Advisory Committee on Population Health (1999, Table 82, p. 318).

100 000. The male mortality rates are significantly higher than female rates for general and specific causes such as cardiovascular diseases, cancers, CHD, and respiratory illnesses. As Table 2 shows, the death rates for cardiovascular diseases were 288 for males and 179 for females, and corresponding death rates for cancers were 231 and 153, respectively. It should also be noted that since 1970 the death rates for most of the primary causes have declined. This decline is particularly significant in the case of heart disease in general and coronary heart disease in particular (Federal, Provincial and Territorial Advisory Committee on Population Health, 1999a, p. 317).

The data on **hospital separations** by diagnostic group and sex are reported in Table 3. These data are important because they provide information on morbidity and health problems requiring hospitalization. The overall rate of separations was 9837 per 100 000 in 1998–99 in Canada. The highest rate of separations was for pregnancy (1379 per 100 000 population, or 2731 per 100 000 females). This is followed by circulatory diseases, digestive diseases, and respiratory diseases.

Women were more likely (11 277 per 100 000) than men (8368 per 100 000) to be hospitalized in 1998–99. While pregnancy accounts for much of this difference, women were also more likely to have been hospitalized for cancer, mental disorders, digestive diseases, genitourinary diseases, and musculoskeletal diseases. Men, on the other hand, were more likely to have been hospitalized for circulatory and respiratory diseases and for injuries and poisoning.

The data on mental disorders treated in psychiatric and acute-care hospitals are reported in Table 4. For 1997–98, the total separation rate was 1451 per 100 000. Overall female rates (1507 per 100 000) are markedly higher than male rates (1394 per 100 000). For particular causes, female rates are higher than male rates for affective psychoses, neurotic disorders, adjustment reaction, depressive reaction disorder, and senile and

TABLE 9.3 *Hospital Separations by Diagnostic Group and Sex, Canada, 1998–1999*

Diagnostic Group	Rate per 100 000 Population		
	Male	Female	Both Sexes
Neoplasms	643	794	719
Mental disorders	494	573	534
Circulatory diseases	1 706	1 277	1 489
Respiratory diseases	1 017	901	958
Digestive diseases	1 077	1 123	1 100
Genitourinary diseases	423	785	606
Pregnancy	—	2 731	1 379
Musculoskeletal diseases	399	457	428
Injury and poisoning	867	767	816
Total all diagnostic groups	8 368	11 277	9 837

Source: Canadian Institute for Health Information (2001a, Tabular Reports, Table 1, pp. 1–8). Compiled from Federal, Provincial and Territorial Advisory Committee on Population Health (1999, Table 77, p. 301).

TABLE 9.4 *Separations from Psychiatric Hospitals and Acute-Care Hospitals, by Diagnosis and Sex, Canada, 1997–1998*

	Rate per 100 000 Population		
Diagnosis	Male	Female	Both Sexes
Senile and presenile organic psychotic conditions	87	126	107
Schizophrenic psychoses	145	108	127
Affective psychoses	151	253	202
Neurotic disorders	96	184	140
Alcohol dependence	223	71	146
Drug dependence	51	44	47
Adjustment reaction	64	89	77
Depressive reaction disorder	84	156	120
Other	305	344	324
Total all diagnoses	1 394	1 507	1 451

Note: Comorbid diagnoses of psychiatric and addiction conditions have been included in addition to those found in the main diagnosis. This has resulted in higher rates than in previous releases.

Source: Canadian Institute for Health Information (2001b). Compiled from Federal, Provincial and Territorial Advisory Committee on Population Health (1999, Table 76, p. 298).

presenile organic psychotic conditions. On the other hand, male rates are higher than female rates for schizophrenic psychoses and alcohol and drug dependency.

The data reported above indicate that women are more likely than men to be hospitalized for physical illness and mental disorders. The causes of hospitalization are also different for male and female populations.

Differences in morbidity and mortality patterns between men and women are evident in other areas (Federal, Provincial and Territorial Advisory Committee on Population Health, 1999a; Statistics Canada, 1995; Trypuc, 1994). For instance, while men are more likely than women to commit suicides, women are twice as likely as men to be depressed and their depression lasts longer. Women are also more likely than men to report conditions such as allergies, migraine headaches, and arthritis and rheumatism. These conditions impair women's functional health and cause activity limitations. While conditions such as arthritis as a cause of activity limitation are reported more frequently by women, men report conditions such as heart, back, and limb problems as causing activity limitation.

Women are also more likely than men to visit health professionals, visit a general practitioner, make more frequent visits to doctors, and use emergency health services. Women are also more likely than men to have had a recent eye examination and physical examination. Women also use more antidepressant drugs than men, which is consistent with higher levels of depression experienced by women.

Similar patterns of morbidity and mortality in male and female populations exist in other advanced countries (see, for example, Miles, 1991; Lorber, 2000; Rieker & Bird, 2000). How can these differences and contradictions in morbidity and mortality be explained? The following section discusses the explanations most often advanced.

EXPLANATIONS OF GENDER DIFFERENCES
IN MORBIDITY AND MORTALITY

The subject of male and female differences in morbidity and mortality patterns has received considerable attention. While acknowledging that these explanations are not mutually exclusive, Miles (1991, pp. 10–12) lists three possible ways to account for these differences: "artefact," genetic causation, and social causation. Some researchers argue that these differences are an "artefact," rather than real. Their main argument is that while women's health status is not any worse than men's, women are more likely to take notice of their symptoms, are inclined to see a physician and seek treatment, and are more willing to respond to health surveys (see Miles, 1991, pp. 10–12).

Biological and genetic differences (sex chromosomes and hormones) have also been used to explain morbidity and mortality differences between men and women. Statistics that are often used to show female "superiority" refer to differences in male and female conception, fetal mortality, stillbirths, and infant mortality rates (for review, see Trypuc, 1994; Miles, 1991). It is also argued that females, due to their biological and genetic constitution, reproductive anatomy, and physiology, may be endowed with resistance to certain diseases.

The third general explanation focuses on the social–structural context of women's and men's lives. Social and economic inequalities and socially constructed gender roles have important consequences for men's and women's lives and produce variations in health and illness patterns. Social and economic inequalities produce differential opportunities and life chances; social roles and related activities expose men and women to different health risks (Muszynski, 1994; Trypuc, 1994; Rieker & Bird, 2000; Miles, 1991; Lorber, 2000). The focus here is on the social production of health and illness. Social and economic inequality produce negative health outcomes and poor health status for women. Also, it is argued that male socialization and lifestyles expose men to riskier, aggressive, and dangerous behaviour. For instance, men have higher mortality due to motor vehicle accidents. Men are also more likely to indulge in excessive smoking, drinking, and substance abuse, with negative health consequences (Federal, Provincial and Territorial Advisory Committee on Population Health, 1999a, 1999b; Trypuc, 1994). On the other hand, it is pointed out that the often demanding and contradictory social roles of women produce negative health outcomes. For instance, domestic work responsibility and a caring role in the family, combined with the increasing participation of women in the paid work force, may contribute to elevated stress levels among women.

Two theoretical perspectives are advanced to explain gender differences in psychological health: differential exposure theory and differential vulnerability theory. Rieker & Bird (2000, p. 102) state: "Both theories attribute gender differences in psychological well-being to the social organization of men's and women's lives. The former emphasizes the extent to which men and women are exposed to particular stressors, whereas the latter focuses on men's and women's responses to those stressors." According to the differential exposure theory, women experience hardships and stressors to a greater extent than do men because of their disadvantaged position relative to men in the work force and the inequitable division of work in the household. Married women in particular experience work overload due to paid work outside the home as well as a majority of the household work; this overload may produce higher levels of psychological distress. Women "caught" in these circumstances may also perceive a lack of control over their lives, which in turn can increase psychological distress and depression.

According to the differential vulnerability theory, the effects of particular stressors differ for men and women for a variety of reasons. For instance, men and women may attach different meanings and significance to paid work and family roles because of different normative expectations about work and family responsibilities (Simon, 1995). Sociocultural beliefs and normative expectations may affect men's and women's self-evaluations as parents and spouses. Women are more likely than men to experience role conflict and to see their work and family roles as competing rather than integral, and thus they experience more guilt and stress than men (Simon, 1995). That the consequences of housework and employment differ for men and women and produce different health outcomes is supported by other research evidence (for review, see Miles, 1991; Rieker & Bird, 2000; Trypuc, 1994; Lorber, 2000; Muszynski, 1994). Normative sociocultural expectations and society's treatment of women affect their mental health. As Paltiel (1987, p. 234) states: "Every woman's mental health is affected by the way her society regards and treats unmarried or married women, childless women, mothers, poor women, assaulted women, divorced women, minority women, disabled women, widows, aged women, or women with aspirations."

Patterns of health and illness have everything to do with women's lives, work, employment opportunities, life experience, and social and economic circumstances. However, it should be noted that social, economic, and other disadvantages do not accrue to all women equally (MacIntyre, Hunt, & Sweeting, 1996). Women are not a homogeneous group, but, rather, are diversified and stratified by class, race, and ethnicity. The social patterning of health and disease are also differentially experienced by various subgroups (Walters, Lenton, & McKeary, 1995). For instance, women with low income and low education levels report poorer health, and "unhealthy" lifestyles are also associated with lower income and lower education (Walters, Lenton, & McKeary, 1995). Racial minority women often experience ill health because of unhealthy work environments and harsher working conditions in areas such as farm labour, textiles and sewing, and domestic work (for review, see Bolaria & Bolaria, 1994a, 1994b, 1994c). Aboriginal women in Canada have shorter life expectancies than the overall female population (Statistics Canada, 1995). Health status inequalities and the social patterning of disease between diverse groups of women are supported by research findings from other countries (see Walters, Lenton, & McKeary, 1995; Rieker & Bird, 2000).

In summary, sociological research on gender and health has focused on how socially structured gender inequalities and socially constructed gender roles contribute to differences in women's and men's physical and mental health. Social patterning of health and disease are also differentially experienced by various subgroups of women, according to their social class, race, and ethnicity. Race, class, and gender are important determinants of life experiences and contribute to differences in physical and mental health.

WOMEN, VIOLENCE, AND HEALTH

Violence against women, its consequences for women's health, and its impact on morbidity and mortality are being increasingly recognized. In 1990, dealing with violence and rape involving women aged 15–44 accounted for an estimated 5 percent of the global health budget (World Bank, 1993). Violence and abuse are associated with numerous health and social problems, including depression, child abuse, suicide, and substance abuse. Battered women face higher risk of miscarriage and low birth weight babies (World Bank, 1993). Violence is also associated with psychiatric morbidity. For example, research from the United States reveals that **battered women** are four to five times more likely to require psychiatric treatment and five times more likely to commit suicide (Stark & Flitcraft, 1991).

Given the importance of violence against women and its health consequences, it is important to discuss the extent of violence and the link between specific forms of violence and their health impact. As Figure 1 indicates, violence against women is widespread and cuts across social, economic, and national boundaries. Selected data in Figure 1 indicate that the percentages of adult women reporting physical assault by a male partner range from a low of 16 percent to a high of 67 percent. The data also show physical assault to be much more common in some lower-income countries. Women face the risk of violence throughout their lives, from infancy to old age, and even before birth (prenatal) in the form of sex-selective abortions.

Table 5 summarizes the type of violence women may face during their life-course. Some forms of violence are more prevalent in some countries than in others, and the extent and risk of violence is mediated by the economic and legal position and rights of women. In early life, the risks girls face include genital mutilation, incest, infanticide, and child prostitution. During adolescence, girls and women face the risk of date and courtship violence, coercive sex and rape, workplace sexual abuse, and forced prostitution. During their reproductive phase, the types of violence women face include **dowry deaths**, partner homicide, and rape. Women are also at a high risk of abuse and violence in old age.

FIGURE 9.1

Percentage of Adult Women Reporting Physical Assault by a Male Partner (in any intimate relationship; selected studies)

....

Source: Heise, Ellsberg, & Gottemoeller. (1999). In United Nations Population Fund (2000, p. 26).

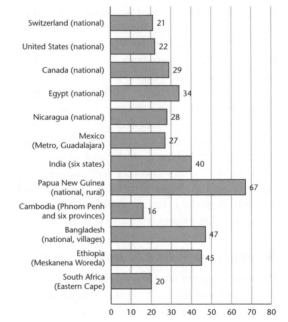

TABLE 9.5 *Gender Violence at Various Stages in a Woman's Life*

Phase	Type of Violence
Prenatal	Sex-selective abortions, battering during pregnancy, coerced pregnancy (rape during war)
Infancy	Female infanticide, emotional and physical abuse, differential access to food and medical care
Childhood	Genital mutilation, incest and sexual abuse, child prostitution, differential access to food, medical care, and education
Adolescence	Dating and courtship violence, economically coerced sex, sexual abuse in the workplace, rape, sexual harassment, forced prostitution
Reproductive	Abuse of women by intimate partners, marital rape, dowry abuse and murders, partner homicide, psychological abuse, sexual abuse in the workplace, sexual harassment, rape, abuse of women with disabilities
Old Age	Abuse of widows, elder abuse (which mostly affects women)

Source: United Nations Population Fund (2000, p. 28).

The universality of this phenomenon threatens women's lives, health, and well-being everywhere, but more so in some low-income countries. In addition to experiencing greater economic disparities, men and women in these countries face social and cultural customs and practices that legitimize subordination, sexual abuse, and violence. In some instances, women even face death if they violate or are suspected of violating certain customs and cultural practices (UNFPA, 2000; UN, 1995; Fischbach & Donnelly, 1996).

The following section discusses certain forms of violence and their associated health and other consequences for women. These forms of violence are prevalent only in certain low-income countries.

Female Genital Mutilation

Female genital mutilation (FGM), often referred to as female circumcision, is practised in many countries, mostly in Africa and western Asian regions. Recent estimates indicate that at least 130 million women have been forced to undergo female genital mutilation or cutting; another two million are at risk each year from this degrading and dangerous practice (UNFPA, 2000, p. 26). The **social surgery** may range from incision and clitorectomy to the most serious form of circumcision, called infibulation (Fischbach & Donnelly, 1996; UNFPA, 2000). The procedure may be performed on infants, females a few years old, or adolescent girls, and is often performed without anesthesia and in unsanitary conditions, and rarely with proper surgical instruments (UNFPA, 1999, 2000; Fischbach & Donnelly, 1996). The practice is intended to preserve the virginity of young girls and the control of female sexuality until marriage. If not circumcised, women may be viewed as sexually permissive. There are many health risks associated with female circumcision, including hemorrhage, infections due to crude and unsanitary instruments, pelvic infections, **chronic conditions** such as urinary tract infections, and, in some cases, infertility. This procedure may also increase the risk of neonatal deaths and stillbirths (UNFPA, 2000; Fischbach & Donnelly, 1996).

Sex-Selective Abortions and Infanticide

Another form of violence against women and girls involves sex-selective abortions and infanticide. UNFPA (2000, p. 25) states that "at least 60 million girls who would otherwise be expected to be alive are 'missing' from various populations, mostly in Asia, as a result of sex-selective abortions, infanticide or neglect." Prenatal gender tests are used to abort female babies in many Asian countries. In countries where these tests are banned, illegal tests are readily available. This practice is most common in countries where male children are preferred and females are considered a liability to the family because of various social customs and cultural practices. One of these costly customs, discussed below, is the institution of dowry, practised in many Asian countries. Female infanticide also takes many girls' lives. The result is that in some Asian countries, there are 105 men for every 100 women (UNFPA, 2000). Neglect, inadequate nutrition, and poor health services also take their toll on girls.

For women these practices pose considerable health risks, including unsafe abortions, frequent and unwanted pregnancies in pursuit of a male child, lack of emergency obstetric care, and infections and hemorrhaging due to complications associated with abortions. Life-saving emergency care is unavailable to women in many of the low-income countries, particularly in rural areas. Unsafe abortions account for a significant number of maternal deaths (World Health Organization [WHO], 1997). It is estimated that about twenty million unsafe abortions are performed each year, causing injuries, suffering, and illnesses to millions of women, and 78 000 deaths (WHO, 1997).

Trafficking, Violence, and Health

Millions of young girls and women are victims of international sex trafficking and forced prostitution (UN, 1995; UNFPA, 2000). It is estimated that about four million girls and women are bought and sold worldwide for prostitution, slavery, or forced marriage (cited in UNFPA, 2000, p. 29). The greatest problem with trafficking is occurring in Asia. According to UNICEF, an estimated 10 000 girls and women enter Thailand from other poor countries for sex work. Some 5000 to 7000 young girls from Nepal end up in brothels in India each year (UNFPA, 2000, p. 29). In India alone, about two million women are said to be in prostitution, and about 400 000 of them are under age 18 (UN, 1995).

Victims of sex trafficking face considerable physical, psychological, and sexual abuse. They are usually isolated, and if they attempt to leave they are faced with physical violence. They are forced to comply with the sexual demands of their clients. Forced and unprotected sex and frequent intercourse with multiple partners put women at risk of sexually transmitted diseases, including HIV and AIDS. Frequent sex and sexual abuse also increase their risk of gynecological problems, including adhesions, infections, chronic pelvic pain, and vaginal bleeding. Sexual abuse and violence and isolation also have negative psychological consequences for these girls and women. These victims of trafficking have almost no access to health care, and their health problems go untreated, which often leads to early deaths (UNFPA, 2000).

Dowry Deaths and Honour Killings

Women and girls are also victims of "dowry deaths," "accidental kitchen deaths," and "bride burning" in many low-income countries. **Honour killings** are often linked to the family's demands for chastity and virginity, a woman's refusal to marry the person chosen by the family, a woman's refusal to stay in an abusive relationship, pregnancy outside of marriage, and even the "dishonour" of having been a victim of rape (World Bank, 1993; UNFPA, 2000; UN, 1995). Rape in some societies is considered as a crime against the woman's family and family honour rather than a violation of women (Heise, 1993). The perpetrators of these killings, who are often members of the victims' own families, often go unpunished by courts because the defence of family honour under these circumstances is often approved and sanctioned by the community and is treated by the courts as a mitigating circumstance (UN, 2000; UNFPA, 2000). These misconceived notions of "family honour" have cost thousands of women their lives; as many as 5000 girls and women are murdered every year for "dishonouring" their families (UNFPA, 2000).

While the true mortality figures related to dowry disputes and unmet dowry demands by the husband and his family remain unknown, these deaths have been reported with increasing frequency on the Indian subcontinent (Jilani, 1992; Heise, 1993; Kelkar, 1991). For instance, 5157 deaths were registered as dowry-related in 1991 (Kelkar, 1991). Typically, the husband and his family make ongoing demands for additional dowry from the bride and her family, which they may not be able to meet. This often leads to an increasing frequency of domestic abuse culminating in the bride's "accidental death," often claimed by the husband to be the result of a "kitchen fire" caused by overheated cooking oil or the bursting of a stove. These deaths are rarely investigated and sometimes may be treated as suicides. With the wife's death, the husband and his family then are free to pursue another, more lucrative, marriage.

Such is the plight of women in societies where they are considered expendable (Jilani, 1992). If they survive sex-selective abortion, infanticide, "honour killings," and "accidental kitchen deaths," many women face social subordination, exploitation, physical and sexual abuse, and violence during their life course. Domestic violence is also linked to various forms of mental disorder, including depression, **post-traumatic stress disorder** (PTSD), phobia, substance use and abuse, and suicide (Fischbach & Donnelly, 1996).

CONCLUSION

The overarching theme of this chapter is that health and illness cannot be understood with reference only to biological phenomena and medical knowledge. Human experiences of health and illness are embedded in economic, social, and cultural contexts, and these factors play an important role in the social distribution of health and illness. Gender is an important part of life; women's and men's different life experiences are shaped by socially structured gender inequality and socially constructed gender roles. Different life circumstances and experiences in turn produce variations in health and illness patterns between men and women. Women, however, are not a homogeneous group. Race and class intersect with gender to produce subgroup differences in health and illness patterns. Women living in poor countries do not fare well relative to women in rich industrialized countries.

In developed industrialized countries, women live longer than men but also experience more illnesses. Women are also more likely than men to be hospitalized for physical illness and mental disorders. The causes of hospitalization are also different for male and female populations. Men are more likely to have been hospitalized for circulatory and respiratory diseases, injuries, and poisoning. In addition to being hospitalized for pregnancy, women are also more likely to have been hospitalized for cancer and digestive, genitourinary, and musculoskeletal diseases. Men are more likely than women to have been hospitalized for schizophrenic psychoses and alcohol and drug dependency. Female rates are higher in areas such as neurotic disorders, affective psychoses, and depressive reaction disorder.

Women are also more likely than men to report conditions such as migraine headaches and allergies, which also impair women's functional health and cause activity limitations. Men, on the other hand, report conditions such as heart and back problems causing activity limitations. Women also visit health professionals more often than men do.

To account for differences in morbidity and mortality, three possible explanations are discussed: "artefact," genetic causation, and social causation, with particular emphasis on the social–structural context of men's and women's lives. Differential exposure theory and differential vulnerability theory are discussed to explain general differences in psychological health. Sociological explanations focus on how socially structured inequality and gender roles contribute to differences in men's and women's physical and mental health. Social and economic subgroup differences among women produce subgroup differences in health status.

The last section of the chapter addressed various forms of violence against women in low-income countries. It examines violence involving female genital mutilation, dowry deaths and honour killings, trafficking in girls and women, sex-selective abortions, female infanticide, and their health consequences for women, and the impact of various forms of violence on morbidity and mortality patterns.

STUDY QUESTIONS

1. *Why do sex differences in mortality and morbidity continue to exist? Give evidence to support the argument that women's health care will not improve until women's position in society improves.*
2. *Discuss the statement that the differential treatment that women receive both as providers and consumers of health care is a manifestation of the patriarchal culture of and gender inequality in the larger society.*
3. *Discuss the extent of violence against women and the relationship between health and various forms of violence.*
4. *Discuss the differential exposure theory and differential vulnerability theory to explain gender differences in psychological well-being.*
5. *Discuss how socioeconomic position, race, and other dimensions of social status interact with gender to produce variations in gender inequality and its health consequences.*
6. *Discuss how socially constructed gender roles and differential opportunities shape men's and women's lives and in turn affect their health.*

GLOSSARY

battered women Women subjected to repeated attacks or multiple blows by a partner.

cardiovascular diseases All diseases of the circulatory system, including ischemic heart disease and stroke.

chronic conditions Conditions having a duration of at least 6 months.

dowry deaths Deaths related to unmet demands of wealth from a bride's family by a husband's family. The most common form of dowry deaths is "kitchen accidents," in which a woman is "accidentally" burned to death by overheated oil or the bursting of a cooking stove.

honour killings The killing of rape victims, women suspected of adultery, women who refuse to marry the person chosen by their families, or women who refuse to stay in an abusive marriage.

hospital separations Patients who are discharged from or die in hospitals.

post-traumatic stress disorder (PTSD) A complex set of symptoms in the aftermath of a psychologically traumatic event and experience; characteristic symptoms include depression, trouble in concentrating, sleep disturbance, and memory impairment.

social surgery Female circumcision, the cultural practice of surgically altering female genitalia, including genital mutilation (circumcision and infibulation).

violence An act involving force or coercion, with the intention of causing physical, psychological, and emotional harm.

RECOMMENDED READINGS

Bolaria, B.S., & Bolaria, R. (Eds.). (1994). *Women, medicine and health*. Halifax and Saskatoon: Fernwood Publishing and Social Research Unit. A collection of articles on a common theme: gendered inequalities have consequences for women as providers and consumers of health care. The wide range of topics includes nursing and gendered division of labour, the medicalization of women's bodies and problems, and social health concerns for women.

Bolaria, B.S., & Bolaria, R. (Eds.). (1994). *Racial minorities, medicine and health*. Halifax and Saskatoon: Fernwood Publishing and Social Research Unit. A collection of articles on women's health issues, particularly those concerning racial minority women and the health consequences of intersection of race, gender, and class.

Federal, Provincial and Territorial Advisory Committee on Population Health. (1999). *Statistical report on the health of Canadians*. Ottawa: Minister of Public Works and Government Services. A collection of a wide range of health status data on gender differences in morbidity and mortality, including causes of deaths, life expectancy, lifestyles, violence, hospitalization, and reproductive health issues.

Fee, E., & Krieger, N. (Eds.). (1994). *Women's health, politics and power: Essays on sex/gender, medicine and public health*. Amityville, NY: Baywood. A collection of essays addressing a broad array of women's health issues from a variety of critical perspectives. Issues covered include women in the health sector, workplace health issues, women's reproductive health, women, and AIDS. The concluding section addresses issues of gender, social policy, and women's lives.

Miles, A. (1991). *Women's health and medicine*. Milton Keynes, PA: Open University Press. This volume focuses on the gender differences in patterns of morbidity and mortality and other topics such as women in medicine and medical control of women.

Subedi, J., & Gallagher, E.B. (Eds.). (1996). *Society, health and disease: Transcultural perspectives*. Upper Saddle River, NJ: Prentice-Hall. A collection of essays focusing on the relationship between health, disease, and different social and cultural settings and on the special health concerns and needs of people in developing countries. Sections on AIDS and domestic violence against women specifically address women's health concerns.

United Nations Population Fund. (2000). *The state of the world population 2000: Lives together, worlds apart: Men and women in a time of change.* New York: UNFPA. A discussion of a wide range of topics pertaining to political, economic, and women's health concerns, including violence and health (trafficking, honour killings), reproductive health, safe motherhood, abortion, female genital mutilation, and sexually transmitted diseases.

REFERENCES

Bolaria, B.S., & Bolaria, R. (Eds.). (1994a). *Racial minorities, medicine and health.* Halifax and Saskatoon: Fernwood Publishing and Social Research Unit.

Bolaria, B.S., & Bolaria, R. (Eds.). (1994b). *Women, medicine and health.* Halifax and Saskatoon: Fernwood Publishing and Social Research Unit.

Bolaria, B.S., & Bolaria, R. (1994c). Immigrant status and health status: Women and racial minority immigrant workers. In B.S. Bolaria & R. Bolaria (Eds.), *Racial minorities, medicine and health* (pp. 149–168). Halifax and Saskatoon: Fernwood Publishing and Social Research Unit.

Canadian Institute for Health Information. (2001a). *Hospital morbidity database, 1995–1996.* Compiled from Federal, Provincial and Territorial Advisory Committee on Population Health (1999). *Statistical report on the health of Canadians.* Ottawa: Minister of Public Works and Government Services.

Canadian Institute for Health Information. (2001b). *Mental health database, 1995–1996.* Compiled from Federal, Provincial and Territorial Advisory Committee on Population Health (1999). *Statistical report on the health of Canadians.* Ottawa: Minister of Public Works and Government Services.

Counts, D.A. (1990a). Domestic violence in Oceania: Introduction. *Pacific Studies, 13*(3), 1–5.

Counts, D. (1990b). Beaten wife, suicidal women: Domestic violence in Kalai, West New Britain. *Pacific Studies, 13*(3), 151–169.

Davis, K. (1995). *Reshaping the female body: The dilemma of cosmetic surgery.* New York: Routledge.

Delahanty, J. (1999). *From social movements to social clauses: Grading strategies for improving conditions for women garment workers.* Ottawa: North-South Institute.

Dixon-Mueller, R. (1994). Abortion policy and women's health in developing countries. In E. Fee & N. Krieger (Eds.), *Women's health, politics and power: Essays on sex/gender, medicine, and public health* (pp. 191–210). Amityville, NY: Baywood.

Doyal, L. (1995). *What makes women sick: Gender and the political economy of health.* London: Macmillan.

Federal, Provincial and Territorial Advisory Committee on Population Health. (1999a). *Statistical report on the health of Canadians.* Ottawa: Minister of Public Works and Government Services.

Federal, Provincial and Territorial Advisory Committee on Population Health. (1999b). *Toward a healthy future: Second report on the health of Canadians.* Ottawa: Minister of Public Works and Government Services.

Fee, E., & Krieger, N. (Eds.). (1994). *Women's health, politics and power: Essays on sex/gender, medicine and public health.* Amityville, NY: Baywood.

Findlay, D.A., & Miller, L.J. (1994). Medical power and women's bodies. In B.S. Bolaria & R. Bolaria (Eds.), *Women, medicine and health* (pp. 115–139). Halifax and Saskatoon: Fernwood Publishing and Social Research Unit.

Fischbach, R.L., & Donnelly, E. (1996). Domestic violence against women: A contemporary issue in international health. In J. Subedi & E.B. Gallagher (Eds.), *Society, health, and disease: Transcultural perspectives* (pp. 316–345). Upper Saddle River, NJ: Prentice-Hall.

Hale, A. (1996). The deregulated global economy: Women workers and strategies of resistance. *Gender and Development, 4*(3), 8–15.

Heise, L. (1993). Violence against women: The missing agenda. In M. Koblinske, J. Timyan, & J. Gay (Eds.), *The health of women: A global perspective* (pp. 171–195). Boulder, CO: Western Press.

Heise, L. (1994). *Violence against women: The hidden health burden*. Washington, DC: World Bank.

Heise, L., Ellsberg, M., & Gottemoeller, M. (1999). Ending violence against women population reports, Series L, No. 11. Baltimore: Johns Hopkins School of Public Health, Public Information Program. In United Nations Population Fund (2000). The State of World Population. New York: Author.

Hubbard, R. (1990). *The politics of women's biology*. New Brunswick, NJ: Rutgers University Press.

Jilani, H. (1992). Whose laws? Human rights and violence against women in Pakistan. In M. Schuler (Ed.), *Freedom from violence: Women's strategies from around the world* (pp. 63–74). Washington, DC: OEF International.

Kelkar, G. (1991). Stopping the violence against women: Issues and perspectives from India. In M. Schuler (Ed.), *Freedom from violence: Women's strategies from around the world* (pp. 75–99). Washington, DC: OEF International.

Lorber, J. (1997). *Gender and the social construction of illness*. Thousand Oaks, CA: Sage.

Lorber, J. (2000). Women get sicker but men die quicker: Gender and health. In P. Brown (Ed.), *Perspectives in medical sociology* (3rd ed., pp. 40–70). Prospect Heights, IL: Waveland Press.

MacIntyre, S., Hunt, K., & Sweeting, H. (1996). Gender differences in health: Are things really as simple as they seem? *Social Science and Medicine, 42*, 617–624.

McLeod, K., & Baris, E. (2000). Globalization and international trade in the twenty-first century: Opportunities for and threats to the health sector in the south. *International Journal of Health Services, 30*(1), 187–210.

Messing, K. (1991). *Occupational safety and health concerns of Canadian women*. Ottawa: Minister of Supply and Services Canada.

Miles, A. (1991). *Women's health and medicine*. Milton Keynes, PA: Open University Press.

Muszynski, A. (1994). Gender inequality and life chances: Women's lives and health. In B.S. Bolaria & R. Bolaria (Eds.), *Women, medicine and health* (pp. 57–72). Halifax and Saskatoon: Fernwood Publishing and Social Research Unit.

Organisation for Economic Co-operation and Development (OECD). (1998). *OECD health data 98*. Paris: Author.

Paltiel, F.L. (1987). Women and mental health: A post-Nairobi perspective. *World Health Statistics Quarterly, 40*, 233–266.

Rieker, P.P., & Bird, C.E. (2000). Sociological explanations of gender differences in mental and physical health. In C.E. Bird, P. Conrad, & A.M. Fremont (Eds.), *Handbook of medical sociology* (5th ed., pp. 98–113). Upper Saddle River, NJ: Prentice-Hall.

Santow, G. (1995). Social roles and physical health: The case of female disadvantage in poor countries. *Social Science and Medicine, 40*, 147–161.

Shorter, E. (1984). *A history of women's bodies*. Harmondsworth: Penguin.

Simon, R.W. (1995). Gender, multiple roles, role meaning, and mental health. *Journal of Health and Social Behavior, 36*(2), 182–194.

Stark, E., & Flitcraft, A. (1991). Spouse abuse. In M. Rosenberg & M. Fenley (Eds.), *Violence in America: A public health approach* (pp. 123–157). New York: Oxford University Press.

Statistics Canada. (1995). *Women in Canada: A statistical report* (3rd ed.). Ottawa: Minister of Industry.

Statistics Canada. (1998). Deaths 1996. *The Daily*, April 16. Ottawa (cat. no. 11-001-XIE).

Statistics Canada, Health Statistics Division. (1999). *Health Indicators, 1999.* Ottawa (cat. no. 82-221-XCB).

Subedi, J., & Gallagher, E.B. (Eds.). (1996). *Society, health and disease: Transcultural perspectives.* Upper Saddle River, NJ: Prentice-Hall.

Sundari, T.K. (1994). The untold story: How the health care systems in developing countries contribute to maternal mortality. In E. Fee & N. Krieger (Eds.), *Women's health, politics and power: Essays on sex/gender, medicine, and public health* (pp. 173–190). Amityville, NY: Baywood.

Syme, S.L., & Yen, I.H. (2000). Social epidemiology and medical sociology: Different approaches to the same problem. In C.E. Bird, P. Conrad, & A.M. Fremont (Eds.), *Handbook of medical sociology* (pp. 365–376). Saddle River, NJ: Prentice-Hall.

Theobald, S. (1996). Employment and environmental hazard: Women workers and strategies of resistance in northern Thailand. *Gender and Development, 4*(3), 16–21.

Trypuc, J.M. (1994). Gender based mortality and morbidity patterns and health risks. In B.S. Bolaria & R. Bolaria (Eds.), *Women, medicine and health* (pp. 73–88). Halifax and Saskatoon: Fernwood Publishing and Social Research Unit.

United Nations (UN). (1995). *The world's women: 1995 trends and statistics.* New York: UN.

United Nations (UN). (2000). *Civil and political rights, including questions of disappearances and summary executions: Report of the special rapporteur, Asma Janhangir.* New York: UN Commission on Human Rights.

United Nations Children's Fund (UNICEF). (2000, January 20). UNICEF: Child sex trafficking must end. Press Release. New York: UNICEF.

United Nations Population Fund (UNFPA). (1999). *Violence against girls and women: A public health priority.* New York: UNFPA.

United Nations Population Fund (UNFPA). (2000). *The state of world population: Lives together, worlds apart, men and women in a time of change.* New York: UNFPA.

Walters, V., Lenton, R., & McKeary, M. (1995). *Women's health in the context of women's lives.* Ottawa: Minister of Supply and Services.

World Bank. (1993). *World development report 1993: Investing in health* (Report No. 11778). Washington, DC: World Bank.

World Health Organization (WHO). (1994). *Ninth general programme of work, 1996–2001.* Geneva: WHO.

World Health Organization (WHO). (1997). *Abortion: A tabulation of available data on the frequency and mortality of unsafe abortion* (3rd ed.). Geneva: WHO.

Yanz, L., Jeffcott, B., Ladd, D., & Atlui, J. (1999). *Policy options to improve standards for women garment workers in Canada and internationally.* Ottawa: Status of Women Canada.

Zimmerman, S. (2000). The medical management of femininity: Women's experiences with silicone breast implants. In P. Brown (Ed.), *Perspectives in medical sociology* (3rd ed., pp. 256–281). Prospect Heights, IL: Waveland Press.

10

Through Medical Eyes:
The Medicalization of Women's
Bodies and Women's Lives

DEBORAH A. FINDLAY Dalhousie University

LESLIE J. MILLER University of Calgary

INTRODUCTION

It has been said that the influence of professional medicine has transformed the body from "an arena of sacred forces to the mundane reality of diet, cosmetics, exercise, and preventative medicine" (Turner, 1984, p. 216). The writer's point is that the human body, once the concern of the priest, is now the business of the doctor. This chapter examines the **medicalization** of women's bodies and women's lives. It begins by considering the historical emergence of modern medical knowledge as a powerful and prestigious perspective on the world and goes on to ask why it is that women's lives, in particular, have become favoured territory for medical intervention. The second part of the chapter looks at two central facets of women's lives — motherhood and child rearing, and bodily appearance — in order to assess the outcome when these activities and conditions are defined as medical problems. In the final section we ask what women stand to gain, as well as lose, when they and others come to see their lives through medical eyes.

THE RISE OF MEDICAL DISCOURSE AND
THE PROFESSIONALIZATION OF MEDICINE

"Medicalization" refers to the process whereby an activity or a condition becomes defined by society at large as an illness (either physical or psychological) and is thereby moved into the sphere of control of the medical profession (Zola, 1972, 1975). Habitual gambling, for example, has been regarded by a minority as a sin and by most people as a leisure pursuit — perhaps wasteful, but a pastime nevertheless. Lately, however, gambling has been described as a psychological illness — "compulsive gambling." It is in the process of being medicalized. The consequences of this shift in **discourse** (i.e., in the way of thinking and talking) about gambling are considerable: for doctors and counsellors, who now have in gamblers a new market for their services or "treatment"; perhaps for casinos, which may find themselves subject to new regulations, insofar as they are deemed to contribute to the "disease"; and, not least, for gamblers themselves, who are no longer treated as sinners or wastrels but as patients, with claims to our sympathy and to our medical insurance plans as well (Conrad & Schneider, 1980).

The concern in this chapter is the medicalization of women's bodies and lives. The modern view is to see the body through medical eyes (as a site of health and sickness); thus, it is hard to grasp that the traditional way of seeing and knowing the body was a religious one. The traditional world view regarded the body as the outward aspect of the soul, and on it appeared the marks of the unending struggle between Good and Evil. Thus, a whole range of problems now taken for granted as medical issues — bodily deformities (e.g., missing limbs, birthmarks), infertility, contagious diseases like the plague, and madness — were customarily regarded as signs of God's displeasure. Similarly, many of the things people did on and with their bodies (e.g., "mortification of the flesh") were done to obtain God's favour; and people dieted (fasted) not for the health of their bodies but for the health of their souls. As Durkheim pointed out, these conditions (and the social reactions they provoked) were visible to all and thus stood as stark reminders of the moral order to which all members of the community were bound (Durkheim, 1964).

Reminders of the religious discourse are still around today — in the Bible, for example, where the mention of health refers to the spirit rather than the body ("There is no health in us"), and in conflicts that sometimes occur between the state and certain religious minorities, who resist the imposition of medical procedures (e.g., blood transfusions) on the grounds that God owns the body and controls what befalls it — not the doctor, not the "ungodly" powers of the state.[1] Despite these lingering remnants of an older world view, the secular discourse of modern medicine has emerged, at least in the West, as the dominant way of thinking and speaking about the body.

HEALING BECOMES "MEN'S WORK"

As medicine began to emerge as a profession in its own right, the lives of ordinary women were of little concern to doctors and other powerful groups, a situation that reflected women's inferior status. For centuries their health needs and the major social events in their lives (notably pregnancy and childbirth) had been left to other women in the community. But as the modern state emerged and began to take a proprietary interest in the health and well-being of its citizens, women, as the creators of those citizens, were gradually encompassed within the sphere of state and medical observation and control. At this point, events like childbirth came to be defined as medical events (Rothman, 1989, p. 77).

But instead of working to improve the skills and training of traditional female healers and midwives, the young, overwhelmingly male medical profession moved to usurp their role in the management of women's health. After a long struggle — and despite the fact that midwives regularly achieved lower maternal mortality rates than physicians (Rothman, 1989, p. 78) — doctors succeeded in discrediting women's traditional expertise (as "ignorance," "superstition," and "incompetence") and, by the early twentieth century, in driving them from the field. The result of this successful poaching operation is that male doctors became society's accepted experts on the subject of women; male doctors came to *define* what counted as health and illness (Lorber, 2000). Twentieth-century science went on to take the male body as the norm for research on women (Tavris, 1992), with the immediate result that many of women's basic functions were seen as "problems" and became subject to medical intervention. Recent analyses show how apparently neutral, objective descriptions of processes such as fertilization were grounded in striking gender stereotypes (Martin, 1991) and generally displayed unintended biases on the part of scientists.

It is this history that forms the backdrop for one feminist criticism of modern mainstream medicine: women's well-being, once the responsibility of other women, has been taken over by a powerful male profession whose androcentric biases were not necessarily apparent. This has not, however, occurred without women's compliance. Sometimes this compliance arose out of women's own choices, such as a preference for the safety and pain relief of medically supervised hospital births over home births. Unwittingly, however, some middle-class women have accepted medical versions of female reproductive processes and thus complied with the medicalization of women's lives (Martin, 1987).

The great prestige that doctors currently enjoy is a relatively recent phenomenon. Until the mid-nineteenth century, surgeons occupied the same low rung on the ladder as barbers — the low status of both owing to the undesirable association with blood. What accounted then, for the rapid rise in power and prestige of the medical perspective? The dominance of medical discourse is related to the *professionalization* of medical practice. Professionalization occurs when an occupational group attains a monopoly over a certain area of expertise. First, the emerging profession must lay claim to the area and establish a legitimate right to treat the group in question. Second, the profession must be able to create a clientele — a market for its services (Turner, 1987, p. 140). This was especially important in the nineteenth century, as physicians turned their attention from major infectious diseases to pregnancy, childbirth, and child care, and began to medicalize these new areas. Third, the profession must maintain its power, in this case by keeping the status of, income, and demand for doctors high. The modern professional association accomplishes this by controlling training and the number of recruits to the profession, by regulating its own practices and standards, and by securing a legal monopoly over delivery of its services, so that licensed doctors are the only legitimate practitioners of medicine and competition is reduced to a minimum (Torrance, 1987, p. 15; Freidson, 1970).

Finally, the power of the medical profession was aided by medicine's crucially important alliance with science. It is interesting to note that before the twentieth century, doctors were not uniformly in favour of a close relation between "the healing arts" and science, but as the nineteenth century drew to a close, they recognized science as the wave of the future, and "there was no longer any doubt that the scientific subjects and the laboratory belonged in the medical curriculum" (Ludmerer, 1985, pp. 102–104). Doctors followed this through by affiliating themselves with "progressive" institutions of learning and technological expertise (universities and research facilities) (Ludmerer, 1985, pp. 107, 231). By defining itself as a scientific endeavour, then, medicine could claim privileged access to the truth about conditions and problems and argue that its approach alone was technical, objective, and bias-free. In short, medicine was able to share the prestige that contemporary society accorded to fields that presented themselves as rational, scientific enterprises.

Many factors, then, contributed to the dominance of the medical perspective, and some scholars argue persuasively that social and political factors rather than strictly medical achievements (e.g., the ability to "conquer" disease) led to that prominence

(Fisher, 1988, p. 134; Rothman, 1989). Whatever the case, the medical profession continues to struggle today to maintain its dominant position by warding off competitors (e.g., naturopaths, nurses, midwives, paramedics) and by expanding its services into ever-new markets — most recently, the "beauty business" (Wolf, 1991; Fisher, 1988, p. 141). Once again, women's bodies offer a lucrative new territory for profit-making.

Feminists have argued that the fact that women's "problems" are more frequently medicalized than others' amounts to a real reduction in women's control over their own lives. Such a loss has important practical implications. The medical profession may discover a problem with women's bodies when women themselves feel that none exists, thus needlessly enmeshing them in the medical system. Or it may perceive interactional or structural problems as medical ones, prescribing pills and surgery when social and political change is called for (as when menopause, for example, is extracted from the larger issue of women's aging and seen as the narrowly medical problem of hormonal changes rather than the political and social issue of the status loss experienced by postreproductive women (Lorber, 2000, p. 82). In short, the issue of who gets to define women's needs and problems is an important aspect of power, for that group also gets to determine the solutions.

The following sections provide some concrete examples of how women's lives have been medicalized and of how that development has influenced women's own understanding of these phenomena. First, mothering, child rearing, and childbirth are examined; then the creation of a medical discourse on appearance, diet, and the fitness of women's bodies is discussed.

THE MEDICALIZATION OF MOTHERING, CHILD REARING, AND CHILDBIRTH

Child Rearing and the "Medical Deprivation" Thesis

For many decades, doctors have been regarded as the authority on the correct or ideal way to raise children. Medical advice on child rearing has gained ascendance as a scientific and technical approach, and because it is viewed as both objective and modern, the voice of the doctor on family matters is generally accepted by mothers and in "society" at large.

Because medical advice recommends some practices and family arrangements over others, it has functioned as a means of **social control** over women and their families, albeit in a benevolent form. The roots of this influence lie in the diligent efforts of early medical men, as well as the clergy, to shape the family form and mothering style that gradually emerged among the new bourgeoisie in the eighteenth and nineteenth centuries in Western Europe (Aries, 1962; Davidoff & Hall, 1987; Shorter, 1977). This image of family life (sometimes termed "domestic" or "companionate") is the one most people today still regard as "normal" (despite the fact that fewer and fewer families resemble it): the patriarchal, heterosexual married pair linked through bonds of sentiment to each other and to their natural offspring.

At the heart of this ideal is the notion that the home is the woman's "natural" sphere (as the workplace is the man's), and it followed from this strictly gendered division of social life that mothering and domestic life would be every woman's full-time occupation. This view represented a departure from that of previous eras, in which mothers had invested considerably less time in their children and child care was only one role among many for wives in the premodern world (Shorter, 1977; Hareven, 1989, pp. 44–45). To promote the new ideal of full-time motherhood, doctors actively worked to elevate nurturing to the level of women's "sacred calling," and to promote the middle-class hearthside as the only fit setting for proper child rearing. As this ideal took hold, the involvement of mothers in economic activities, whether around the household or outside it, became increasingly *stigmatized*, and for the first time women's work was described as a threat to the well-being of their children. Efforts to upgrade the status of the full-time mother have occurred in this century too, primarily through the "domestic science" movement, which portrayed homemaking as a scientifically based, efficient "profession" — the wife's worthy (though always unpaid) counterpart to her husband's paid work in the labour force (Hareven, 1989, p. 45). This conception of woman's family work was institutionalized in the educational system in "Home Ec," studied by generations of schoolgirls (Gaffield, 1990, p. 37).

Blaming the Employed Mother

At the same time, women were told by the medical profession that full-time mothering, and nothing less, was the only way to rear a normal, healthy child. The larger context for this doctrine was the mental hygiene movement of the early twentieth century, whose proponents held that "the scientific promotion of well-being in childhood could prevent adult dysfunctions" (Richardson, 1989, p. 2). As the main child rearers, women were the prime target of the mental hygienists and their programs: it was women who were to have their child-care skills and roles scrutinized by psychiatric and other mental health experts concerned with childhood socialization. Thus health professionals acquired the power to set the standards of good mothering and child mental health for society at large and mothers in particular.

It was against this background that the "working mother" would come to be seen as the cause of the medical problem of "maternal deprivation." Deprivation theorists claimed that children needed their mothers on a full-time basis in order to form the emotional attachments believed to be essential for the development of positive mental health. Mother–child attachment was considered necessary to prevent juvenile delinquency, psychiatric disorders, mental "subnormality," and "acute distress and affectionless psychopathy" in the child (Miller, 1991, p. 70; Rutter, 1981, p. 15). Bowlby's work on maternal deprivation, in particular, has been interpreted as stipulating that mothers be with their children at all times and thus not be employed in the labour force. Riley (1983, p. 100) has pointed out how the concept of "continuous mothering" was interpreted narrowly to mean 24-hour-a-day care by mother alone, in a manner that precluded any absence from the home. By the 1950s, the medical view on child rearing had become entrenched as common sense, in the attitude that "we all know that children need their mothers at all moments" (Riley, 1983, p. 100).

How was the medical perspective on correct child rearing enforced? Occasionally health professionals physically removed "at risk" children from parents who were deemed unfit, as in the now notorious case of the Dionne "quints" of Callander, Ontario.[2] More often, however, the medical perspective was enforced indirectly, that is, through persuasion rather than coercion. This kind of social control works through medical depictions of the "horrors" (including homosexuality, criminality, and madness) predicted to result in children of mothers who failed to heed the medical experts. In effect, doctors used the threat of illness to produce conformity in the same way that village priests had used the threat of hellfire.

It is easy to paint the medical profession as victimizing generations of helpless mothers who struggled vainly to resist their views, but the reality is not so simple. Modern-minded women in the nineteenth century were themselves persuaded that science (and especially medical science) was the key to a better future, and many eagerly seized upon these new concepts and attempted to put them into practice in their own homes. They promoted these ideas, as well, in the homes of others, especially among families of the "ignorant" or "depraved" classes. In Britain, France, and elsewhere, respectable ladies of the middle and upper classes felt it their duty to carry the doctor's message about healthy child rearing into the "slums" (and in North America, into immigrant communities): soap and water, better diet, regular bedtimes, and school attendance (Donzelot, 1979; Lewis, 1986; Ehrenreich & English, 1979; Valverde, 1991).

Such efforts at family reform along the lines set out in medical doctrine created real conflicts for working-class women, for the advice promoted a middle-class standard of living and a style of mothering that many could not hope to attain. These poor mothers (and often their children) had to work. Historical evidence shows that they continued to do so, but under an increasing barrage of medical criticism.

The negative consequences of the maternal deprivation thesis are not restricted to women of an earlier era. Many women today must face the charge of "bad mothering" the concept carries with it, and must resolve conflicts between economic pressure to be in the labour force and social, including medical, admonitions against doing so (Gaskell, 1988). Sociological studies regularly fail to find support for the maternal deprivation thesis as it pertains to mothers who work outside the home (Etaugh, 1974; Kamerman & Hayes, 1982). Nevertheless, the view that the employed mother will rear the bad, or mad, child retains the secure status of received wisdom. Even *The Globe and Mail* reported the results of its own 1991 poll under the headline: "Working Parents Spark Concern: Canadians worry the well-being of the nation's children is being sacrificed" (November 5, 1991, p. A4).

Thus the medical legacy of Bowlby's deprivation thesis continues to influence government policy on matters such as daycare funding and educational curriculum. And it continues to colour women's own views on their proper role in the family and on their careers (see Brannen & Wilson, 1987). It is safe to conclude that the medical discourse on "correct" mothering still produces confusion and ambivalence in women who choose to work for pay, and guilt in those who must.

Childbirth and the Prenatal Period

The medicalization of mothering has not been restricted to the child-rearing period, however; the processes of pregnancy, labour, and childbirth have gradually come to be controlled and reconstructed as medical issues or problems. More recently, this control has even been extended to the *potentially* pregnant woman — and hence all women of childbearing years fall into the realm of medical scrutiny (Balsamo, 1999).

The history of the medicalization of childbirth is one of a gradual takeover of the responsibilities of female midwives by largely male obstetricians. This shift was also a struggle between a more holistic view of childbirth as a "natural" process and the obstetrician's reliance on a scientific model, in which childbirth was treated as a potentially pathological condition (Leavitt, 1986, p. 208; Ehrenreich & English, 1979, pp. 111, 140).[3] Doctors were trained to intervene in the process and at first were called in to assist midwives only when there were complications. Obstetricians had exclusive access to some of the tools of the trade, such as forceps, which could help in cases of difficult birth. But obstetricians in the eighteenth century had relatively low status and power (Lewis, 1986). To a fair degree, they were controlled by the aristocratic women whom they served and hence had little of the professional autonomy needed to impose their own definitions of how childbirth should be conducted (Lewis, 1986, pp. 3–4). For working-class women, the birthing process was still female-dominated and they were assisted by midwives who themselves were often working-class immigrants to North America. Although the prestige of science was on the rise in this era, many obstetricians were at first ambivalent about adopting "scientific" medicine. Only when it was socially accepted (particularly by the nineteenth century) and hence, advantageous to the developing professional status of medicine, was scientific medicine fully adopted (Leavitt, 1986, p. 208; Morantz-Sanchez, 1985, p. 241).

Women's own demands also played a part in the medicalization of childbirth. Considering the historically high risk of infant and maternal mortality in childbirth (in early twentieth-century Britain, childbirth was the third highest cause of death among women aged 15–45), it is not surprising that women demanded an approach that they saw — though not always correctly — as providing greater safety. Moreover, obstetricians were able to provide women with pharmaceutical means of pain relief, such as the early twentieth-century "twilight sleep," which combined scopolamine and morphine, and many women demanded these medications during labour (Sandelowski, 1984, p. 6). Although initiated by women themselves, these developments inevitably took the management of labour out of their hands. Moreover, the safe administration of anesthesia meant that childbirth was moved into the hospital under medical control. Thus women chose safety and pain relief, but at the same time relinquished control over a process that had been formerly "theirs" (Sandelowski, 1984, pp. 17–20; Leavitt, 1986, pp. 134, 140).

The extent to which women themselves have accepted this new medical definition and discourse on childbirth is debated. We have suggested that women's own views of childbirth have been influenced by medical approaches (Currer & Stacey, 1986, p. 97). Yet research by Graham and Oakley indicates that women think less in terms of medicalized childbirth as a pathological condition, and more in terms of it as a natural process (Currer & Stacey, 1986, p. 97; Walters, 1994).[4] They outline two quite different perspectives — the medical and the maternal — which arise out of the two frames of reference.[5] These frames emerge from the different social positions of doctors and patients as these two groups interact (Graham & Oakley, 1986, pp. 114–115). Women tend to draw on their own bodily experiences and their lives as a whole in their contextualization of the processes of pregnancy and childbirth, while for obstetricians the processes are physiological ones, embedded in medical knowledge (Graham & Oakley, 1986, pp. 100–101). Moreover, age, race, and social class appear to influence the degree to which women are prepared to adopt a medicalized view of childbirth.[6] The medical perspective certainly carries greater formal authority.

MAKING PREGNANCY A "MEDICAL PROBLEM"

The medicalization process has increasingly been extended to the period prior to childbirth — pregnancy and the prenatal period — as well. Oakley (1986, p. 135) describes this process as part of the development of preventative medicine generally. Medicine was also allied with the state in developing prenatal (antenatal) care as a way of controlling the health and fertility rates of the population (Oakley, 1986, p. 34). From the 1950s on, after maternal mortality had been substantially reduced, obstetric attention became more focused on the fetus; this meant that women became "obstetric patients" in need of monitoring during the prenatal period (Balsamo, 1999; Oakley, 1986, pp. 213, 252). Just as the professional focus on mothers' child-rearing practices involved a concern with producing healthy adults and "perfecting" society, prenatal care expressed a social concern for the fetus in its role as a future family member and citizen of a nation (Oakley, 1986, p. 252). Moreover, a new patient was being created, in the form of the developing embryo or fetus (Balsamo, 1999).

The development of ultrasound technology has been a key tool for obstetricians to be able to observe the fetus; technical knowledge was essential to the profession's claim to expertise (Oakley, 1986, pp. 182–183). Subsequent NRTs (new reproductive technologies), such as in vitro fertilization, have justified further intervention and involvement in the pregnant woman's body. Here too obstetricians could argue that their knowledge was superior to the traditional knowledge of midwives. Prior to the development of technical intervention into the environment of the fetus, obstetricians (like midwives and women themselves) had to depend for a diagnosis of pregnancy upon "subjective" or "folk" signs of fetal activity, such as "quickening" (Oakley, 1986, p. 182). "Quickening" belonged to a repertoire of traditional (feminine) tools and expertise, which was rapidly discredited by professional medicine as myth and superstition.

But prenatal care also meant the entrenchment of "the definition of all pregnancies as potentially pathological" and this gave medicine and the state "an unprecedented degree of license over the bodies and approved life-styles of women" (Oakley, 1986, p. 2). For example, we now witness a revival of the 1950s' discourse on the need for mother–infant **bonding** during and immediately following childbirth. The medical and psychological rhetoric around bonding comes out of the concern to prevent the physical and psychological neglect of the child; but by making "bonding" an essential part of childbirth, the health profession also sends powerful messages about the "right way" women are to give birth (as naturally and drug-free as possible) and relate to the baby (e.g., breastfeeding is promoted and even glorified; see Wall, 2000). Oakley hypothesized that this type of control over mothers' behaviour has been extended into the prenatal period. She showed that some doctors believe ultrasound is useful for having the mother see her fetus, so that a "bond" will be created and she will become a "good" mother. In this way prenatal bonding is added "to the repertoire of reproductive activities named and controlled by obstetricians" (Oakley, 1986, p. 185). Here we see how psychological rhetoric unites with technology to further medicalize women's bodies.

A more recent development is the emergence of the public health discourse of fetal rights. This discourse pits the interests of the mother against the fetus and has led to the widely publicized prosecution of mothers (often young, Black or Aboriginal, single, and poor) who are addicted to drugs or alcohol. The recent visibility of problems such as FAS (fetal alcohol syndrome) has brought increased demands for the surveillance and control of these already disenfranchised women, whose maternal "excesses" are seen to endanger their victimized fetuses (Balsamo, 1999).

The question then arises whether women tend to resist or buy into medical discourse on prenatal care. Rarely have women's attitudes to such prenatal techniques as ultrasound fetal monitoring been assessed, and the extent of maternal satisfaction with the experience of prenatal care can be considered questionable (Oakley, 1986, pp. 183, 184). One study indicated that when pregnant women receive more detailed feedback regarding the test results from the person providing the prenatal care, they feel more positive about the care (Oakley, 1986, pp. 184–185). Another indicated that working-class mothers in particular felt their need for information was not satisfied (Oakley, 1986, p. 245). So it seems that while women may believe that prenatal visits are necessary to ensure their own health and that of their babies, they may be less than pleased with the whole experience. But the appeal and influence of the medical perspective is pervasive, and many concepts have been popularized and taken over by mothers as their own. "Bonding," for example, is accepted by many mothers as a truism, and (like the recent emphasis on breastfeeding) has been taken up by the alternative health movement as well. It is ironic that this movement, which claims to offer a more "natural" (i.e., demedicalized) childbirth experience, should include "better parent–child bonding" as one of its features, a concept with clear origins in the professional medical lexicon.

In sum, while obstetric and prenatal care is often desired by mothers and can certainly provide advantages for them and their children, it is constructed and delivered in a profoundly class- and gender-divided culture. Moreover, women (pregnant and nonpregnant alike) buy that care at the cost of reduced control over their own lives. In 1986, Oakley noted:

> In these circumstances the wombs of women — whether already pregnant or not — are containers to be captured by the ideologies and practices of those who, to put it most simply, do not believe that women are able to take care of themselves. (p. 292)

By 1999, Balsamo would observe that women were increasingly seen as being unable to take care of their fetuses as well. The new discourse of fetal rights made the control of women's bodies and lives a matter that was not only medically justified, but morally necessary.

THE MEDICALIZATION OF WOMEN'S APPEARANCE

This section considers how the physical appearance and shape of women's bodies have come under medical control. This development has been part of a broader sociohistorical trend toward social control of all bodies, and this trend is discussed first. Then the discussion turns to some of the forms that this control takes for women in particular, and the part that the medical perspective plays in that outcome. Throughout, it is important to keep in mind the question of how women themselves perceive and deal with this medicalization process.

There is a long and interesting history of ideas about the meaning of physical appearance, the beauty of human bodies, and the face. Specifically, appearance has been and still is an important influence in the development of a "self" and our assessment of the selves of others. Synnott (1989, p. 611) states that a "beauty mystique," in which beauty and goodness are equated, originated with the Greeks and Romans: body and soul were taken to mirror each other. The notion that beauty is the reflection of inner goodness still prevails. It can be heard in the advice of beauty experts, for example, who tell us that "beauty comes from within," and in the results of many studies that show that people attribute crimes more readily to "ugly" suspects than to "handsome" ones. Synnott (1989, p. 632) suggests that the causal order may be gradually reversing, however, so that physical beauty is increasingly treated as the first, essential step toward internal, psychological beauty. (See also Chapter 14 of this book regarding the pathology of body image.)

Still, strong traces of past attitudes to the body persist, especially, as we shall see, in the eating disorders experienced by women. Historically, the need to develop a self, particularly a purified and spiritual self, has been achieved through religious asceticism — the denial of bodily needs (Bordo, 1990, p. 83). But in earlier eras, fasting and other denials of the flesh were practised by elite social groups, mainly aristocrats and priests. Bordo and others note that although treatises on diet can be found in the fifteenth and sixteenth centuries in Western Europe, they were always part of a religious discourse about renunciation and the control of "animal passions" and "appetites" (Bordo, 1990, p. 83; Turner, 1984, pp. 165–170).

Policing the Body

The early modern era brought an important change in this pattern: for the first time, an interest was taken in the ordinary individual, who until then had been an undifferentiated part of a faceless "horde" or "rabble." Foucault argues persuasively that the source of this new interest was the modern state, which began, with emerging professional groups as its instruments, to observe and document the lives and bodies of the masses in the interest of producing useful and productive citizens (Foucault, 1979; Donzelot, 1979). The most important of these professional groups was the medical doctors, and we have noted how an emerging and powerful alliance between general practitioners and mothers allowed the state an important point of entry into, and control over, the private sphere of the family, especially the bodily habits of its members, including the mother herself (Donzelot, 1979; Turner, 1984). An emphasis on useful and productive bodies, the raw material for the creation of a productive labour force, was added by the seventeenth-century Cartesian model of the body as a machine (Bordo, 1990, p. 86).

The mechanical image contributed to the development of the medical rationalization and classification of the body, including diet regimens, in which input and output could be mathematically calculated and managed (Turner, 1982, pp. 258–259). In contrast to the earlier religious treatises on diet, nineteenth- and twentieth-century medical writings regarded a dietary regime as a condition of efficient labour, and hence they were intended for the working class (Turner, 1984, p. 170).

FAT BECOMES UNHEALTHY

One important mark of the modern, secular discourse on diet is its relentless focus on body weight. As the modern "scientific" approach to diet and food intake slowly diffused down the social ladder, a large stomach — the old symbol of wealth — faded into history. In the early twentieth century, the modern concept of the calorie allowed the quantification of nutrition based on an economist's notion of physiological equilibrium (as energy flow in and out of the body). Following the emergence of calorie-counting, insurance companies and the medical profession constructed an association of overweight or "obesity" with death, an association based on studies of men but automatically applied to women as well (Schwartz, 1986, pp. 154–156). These and later developments (the linking of fat to heart disease and the classification of bodies into types, like "mesomorph") united to focus on overweight as the major threat to the worker's productivity under capitalism; as a result, the medical profession, backed by the state and business interests, began to recommend a lifelong vigilance over body weight in the form of dieting and exercise (Schwartz, 1986, pp. 189, 223). This approach to diet, while still heavy with moral overtones, was a far cry from earlier religious conceptions. In the transition to modernity, concludes Turner, "The vocabulary of passions, desires and humours was replaced by the discourse of calories and proteins" (1984, p. 170).

Doctors' Group Taking Aim in Fight against Fat

A new group launched Monday by doctors wants obesity treated and funded as a disease as part of a united front against fat.

Doctors can't bill the provinces for treating obesity on a regular basis because it's not considered an illness, Dr. David Lau, president of Obesity Canada, told a news conference.

But the World Health Organization says a global epidemic of obesity is behind a range of illnesses, said Lau, a University of Ottawa professor and endocrinologist....

About half of Canadians are overweight, including one-third who are obese, and that puts them at increased risk of diabetes, heart disease, high blood pressure and other common health woes.... "You're dealing with a complex disease that has a whole bunch of consequences, and there are a lot of costs involved," said Lau....

But while ample girths are driving up health care costs, the issue of how much weight is too much has become a heavy topic.

Lau recognizes the mixed messages. While one Australian company is raking in proceeds for an anti-cellulite pill now sold in Canada, eating disorders especially among teen girls and the lobby for fat acceptance have never been more high-profile.

Lau said that's one reason Obesity Canada is focusing on feeling good, and not looking good.

"We're concerned about the health risk of obesity, and not the body image."

As Obesity Canada becomes a "credible source of information" and does more research on weight problems, it may ask the provinces to work weight counselling and treatment into fee schedules because doctors are the "gatekeepers of health," said Lau....

Source: Marlene Habib, *The Mail-Star*, Halifax, Tuesday, April 13, 1999, pp. A1–A2. Reprinted with permission of The Halifax Herald Limited.

In general, the monitoring of health and body weight, which originated "outside" the individual in the state and the medical profession, has been largely taken over by those individuals themselves, bearing out arguments for a shift in the form of social regulation from **policing** by others to self-policing in modern Western society (Foucault, 1979; Elias, 1978). However, there are important gender and class exceptions to this rule. First, men have traditionally been less inclined to "police" or monitor their own bodily appearance and state of health than have women. This difference is rooted in a broad cultural tendency to value men for their economic resources rather than their appearance,[7] and in a cultural script that makes women the custodians of health care for the whole family, not just themselves (Charles & Kerr, 1988, pp. 82–83, 237; Trypuc, 1994, pp. 268, 270–271). Second, the working class is less likely to self-police body weight and health than is the middle class. Pressure on the working class to do so is largely exerted externally by the state, the medical profession, and the middle class (Edgely & Brissett, 1990).

Critics of the contemporary obsession with fitness argue that the middle class equates health (or at least a fit appearance) with success and worldly achievement and is in favour, moreover, of regulating those in the society who will not conform to the middle-class standard (Edgely & Brissett, 1990). Early in the 1990s, for example, the Alberta government considered a proposal allowing doctors to give patients an "annual report card [covering] ... health indicators like blood pressure, weight, smoking and cholesterol levels." Stating that "businesses have been doing this for years" in Japan and Europe, the president of the Alberta Medical Association noted with approval that bosses say to their employees: "We notice you are 40 pounds overweight and smoking two packs of cigarettes. We would like that changed and we'll give you so many months to do that. And we'll check you out again" (Doctors give top marks, *Calgary Herald*, December 6, 1991, p. B1).

It is interesting to note that the cultural fear of fat is now directed to children as well as adults and has led to the control of women's bodies out of medical concern for the fat of the fetus (Schwartz, 1986, p. 269). The idea that too many fat cells in fetal life and childhood will lead to adult obesity has led doctors and mothers to restrict the weight gain that occurs in pregnancy (Schwartz, 1986, pp. 296–297). To that end, it became necessary to monitor pregnant women's bodies more closely through prenatal care. Here again, the degree to which women have taken up or resisted this medical discourse is unclear. However, faced with the prospect of having fitness and body weight monitored and graded from the womb to the workplace, and perhaps into old age, one begins to grasp the far-reaching authority society has granted to the medical profession.

Is Beauty Healthy?

If the medical profession is concerned with regulating the bodies of all citizens, why does this chapter focus especially on women? It touched on one reason earlier: women, especially mothers, are assigned cultural responsibility for the health and appearance of other family members, as part of the larger feminine role. Therefore, as a group, women become the crucial bridge between the medical profession and the rest of the family. It is frequently mothers who first take up medical discourse as their own, and who watch over and regulate the bodily practices of their husbands and children, from their personal hygiene to their calorie intake (Donzelot, 1979; Frykman & Lofgren, 1987; Miller 1987).

Women not only monitor the bodily practices of others, they monitor their own, and with a vengeance. This is the second reason for the focus on women. Western society teaches women to attach extraordinary significance to appearance, and while concern is a desirable thing, the obsession with appearance, especially in the form of predominantly female disorders like **anorexia nervosa**, is nothing short of disastrous. Certain sociocultural forces invite an excessive concern for "feminine beauty," and medical rhetoric itself acts to exacerbate the already powerful cultural demands on women to overemphasize their bodily appearance.

Although all members of society must evince some concern for the "presentation of self," the concern for bodily appearance has a special place in the lives of women. The norm that charges women with maintaining the "respectable" appearance of the home and its members — their clothing, bodies, hygiene, and demeanor — emerged in the late eighteenth century. It is embedded in the larger Western conception of femininity and was strongly tied to the ideal of bourgeois respectability (for a summary of this argument, see Miller & Penz, 1991, pp. 150–152; Davidoff & Hall, 1987, chap. 8). The hegemonic success of this norm today is reflected in the central place it occupies in the socialization of girls, who learn at a young age that their willingness to control their bodies — to stand up straight, to look neat and tidy — is the key to achieving a social identity (Haug et al., 1987).

The legacy of these kinds of messages is twofold: 1. the way women manage their appearance is invested, by themselves and by others, with greater social significance than in the case of men; and 2. women tend to respond to social demands with **bodywork** throughout their lives (Miller & Penz, 1991, p. 151). This means, for example, that the slim, "well-groomed" woman will be deemed to be socially competent, while women who "let themselves go," especially to fat, are seen as socially irresponsible — even as a threat to the social order. Moreover, the link between social responsibility and body regulation that has been described here is reaffirmed and enforced medically; that is, the medical perspective tends to identify women who fail to "keep up appearances" as suffering from health (psychological) problems. The equation of appearance ("beauty") with health is becoming widespread, according to Wolf (1991, p. 227), and the hugely lucrative fitness industry (for example) positions itself in a way that deliberately blurs the line between health and beauty. Moreover, the concern for health is made still more fashionable through its association with the liberation of women from the chains of domesticity (Spitzack, 1990). Thus beauty, health, and liberation are combined in contemporary society into a powerful package promoting the thin, controlled body, and this package has considerable appeal for women. As Wolf (1991, p. 27) remarks, "medical discourse tells women that beauty and bodywork is the prescription for health, and who can argue with health?"

The connection between health and cultural standards of beauty is by no means a natural one. Feminine ideals of beauty in other eras and societies have demanded distinctly unhealthy practices, ranging from tight corseting and genital mutilation to suntanning (Wilson, Garvin, & McMullan, 1999). In this connection, cosmetic surgery is today one of the medical profession's most lucrative specialties, and doctors are involved in the active marketing of such questionable procedures as liposuction and breast augmentation, the latter even to girls as young as 14 years of age. Thus, while the medical profession sometimes presents itself as the moral guardian of our health and well-being, at other times it looks more like the amoral technician who will help women (and men) in the search for the designer body, wherever it leads.

The air of legitimacy that the medical rhetoric of health lends to contemporary beauty ideals has other undesirable results as well. These include the expectation that women will divert their life energies into beauty work (Wolf, 1991, pp. 14, 16), and the idea that it is the public duty of all good citizens, especially women, to monitor the "health achievements" of others (Edgley & Brissett, 1990, p. 259). Again, it is the prestigious medical rhetoric of health that puts these activities on the moral high ground and stigmatizes those who do not comply with the labels of "deviant" or "sick." Observers of contemporary life have remarked that medicine has replaced the church as society's moral arbiter: disease is the contemporary sin, and health the new religious salvation.

In presenting these arguments, it is not suggested that women should never take care of their bodies or appearance. Rather, the issue is one of "lack of choice" in women's lives (Wolf, 1991, p. 272). Women experience intense social pressure to conform to ideal body images. As de Swaan (1990, p. 1) comments, "Whatever becomes a possibility for many turns into a necessity for everyone."[8] When the thin-body ideal is so prevalent and is considered the epitome of health, it makes it difficult to choose not to struggle to attain that ideal. This predicament leads women to a permanent state of health surveillance and continuous confessions of bodily flaws and "sins" (Spitzack, 1990, p. 3), followed by corrective attempts to "normalize" the body through diets, exercise, surgery, and so on (Spitzack, 1990, pp. 4, 9). This whole process reveals women's deep insecurity regarding their bodies, an insecurity presented by medicine as normal and right (MacNevin, 1992, pp. 26–27).

From the medical perspective, women's "problems" — their fat, their insecurity, and their "lack of will" — lie in women themselves, but feminist scholars disagree. Many women's groups attempt to persuade women that "the problem" is not in their bodies but in the cultural forces that create the demand to be thin. Such forces include the patriarchal image of feminine beauty as passive and vulnerable, or sexualized and available, a prestigious medical discourse that always presents itself as acting in the woman's best interests, and a business community that profits from the search for slimness or "fitness" through the sale of diet aids, workout videos, and exercise classes and fashions. Women's groups argue that the woman's body is the site but not the source of her problems, and they attempt to support women who would challenge cultural demands for the one "right" body. But the escape from the narrow repressive body ideal has proved to be no easy matter. Too often, these efforts are played out on the body in a distorted form: in anorexia, for example, or in yet more bodywork (e.g., body building and "working out").

THE MEDICALIZATION OF WOMEN'S DISORDERS: ANOREXIA NERVOSA AS A "DISEASE"

Although there is some indication that men are under increasing pressure to be fit and thin, disorders like anorexia in recent years, and "hysteria" and agoraphobia in the nineteenth century, are overwhelmingly disorders of women. Next to their gendered character, their most notable feature is their historical dimension; leaving aside "holy anorexia," a form of religious self-starvation encountered in the Middle Ages, they all belong to the last half of the nineteenth century or to the twentieth and twenty-first — they are disorders of the modern age.

This fact, among others, has suggested to feminist scholars that they are responses to historically specific conditions that put greater pressure on women than on men. The earliest clinical records of anorexia in its modern sense seem to be from the 1860s (Turner, 1987, p. 106; 1984, p. 183). The traditional psychoanalytic interpretation of the roots of anorexia is that it represents rejection of femininity, for the woman's body becomes more boy-like and her menstrual periods eventually cease (Boskind-Lodahl, 1976, pp. 343–345). More recently, it has been suggested that anorexia, like agoraphobia and hysteria, is linked with women's position in a society that creates contradictory expectations (Turner, 1987, p. 106; Orbach, 1979, p. 167). One of those contradictions entails the expectation that women will be feminine and domestic at home while aggressively pursuing middle-class achievement in the public sphere (Turner, 1984, p. 196). It is very difficult for a young woman to satisfy demands to be demure and passive at home, but competitive and assertive in the workplace. Here again, these theories suggest that middle-class women, in particular, may be pressed by their parents to be "feminine" achievers — that is, dependent and independent at the same time (Turner, 1987, p. 107; Chernin, 1985).

According to other researchers, a second contradiction can be found in the ethos of consumer capitalism, which sends mixed messages to women with regard to body management. These writers hold that late capitalism, in particular, sets up a contradiction around gratification: on the one hand, our "producer-selves" are expected to control our appetites and desires, while our "consumer-selves" are encouraged to indulge them (Turner, 1984; Bordo, 1990, p. 96). This tension is obvious when advertisements for tempting foods are followed by articles on instant diets (Bordo, 1990, p. 97). It is evident, too, in the pressure women experience to desire and consume beauty products in order to achieve "the natural look"; such campaigns simultaneously advocate consumption and denial. Bordo (1990, p. 97) contends that social contradictions of this sort are dealt with partly by the institutional schism between our rigid daytime lives, when we are in control and "in order," and our evenings and weekends, which are organized around the release of bodily desire through indulgence (in makeup, clothing, food, liquor, and leisure toys). The compartmentalization of the consumer and producer parts of our selves, she says, leads some women to favour one side or the other — in anorexia, or obesity, or bulimia, the latter replaying the excesses of both indulgence and denial in its binges and purges. But none of these attempts to deal with the tensions are socially acceptable, as Bordo (1990, pp. 97, 99) points out: women who are anorexic may be admired at first, but eventually hide their skeletal bodies from public view, while the obese are rejected as disgusting and are especially scorned for fat stomachs, "the symbol of consumption."

In addition to identifying the various contradictions and tensions placed upon modern women, most of these analyses share the view that anorexia represents the adolescent girl's effort to take control over her life in the face of these contradictory demands. The question they often fail to address, however, is this: why do girls respond to these dilemmas in the language of the *body*? Why are power and control sought there, rather than in the workplace, say, or in politics, or in personal relationships? How is it that the same young women who demand control over their bodies also made *The Rules* (and its sequel) a 1990s best-seller?

Bodywork: Cultural Implications for Girls and Women

For an answer, it is useful to return to an earlier point about the special importance attached to women's appearance in contemporary culture. The message of girls' earliest socialization is that bodywork will be the key to full social membership. This means that girls learn to see bodywork as the appropriate way to achieve their goals in the world, and they carry this lesson with them throughout their lives. Women bodybuilders, for example, state that they expect their workouts to lead to improvements in many other aspects of their lives, from public speaking to making love (Miller & Penz, 1991; Spitzack, 1990), and never see it as odd that one should be expected to guarantee the other. Men do not voice the same expectations (*Calgary Herald,* November 17, 1991, p. B8).

It is no surprise then that women's dilemmas, as well as their aspirations, are worked out in the mother tongue of appearance. With respect to the anorexic girl, control over body weight, of which she so often speaks, appears to her as control over her life. In short, for girls, bodywork is the normal way to relate to the world. The body is their workplace. From this perspective, the anorexic girl is not a "deviant" who has violated the appearance norms of her society; she is, rather, its star pupil. These women share with other nonanorexic women the cultural conviction that the body is the proper forum for their views; in addition, they share the specific body ideal (thinness) with "normal" women of all social classes (Boskind-Lodahl, 1976, pp. 345–346; Orbach, 1979, p. 167; Szekely, 1988, p. 18).

It is these kinds of cultural *continuities* that the medical approach to anorexia conceals. Medical discourse is premised on the gulf between "normal" nonanorexic and "abnormal" anorexic women; by classifying them as healthy or sick, it places the two groups on opposite sides of the fence and eclipses all that they share. Moreover, the medical perspective again seeks the causes of anorexia in individual biographies, an interpretation that fails to recognize the role that "normal" gender socialization and "normal" structural impasses play in that "disease." Accordingly, medical treatment of anorexia focuses on the individual and her family, pointing to the girl's abnormal rejection of femininity rather than to the larger social–structural dilemmas women experience in capitalist and patriarchal societies. Here, the medical explanation, as in all of the phenomena we have discussed, leaves these larger factors untouched.

CONCLUSION

This final section weighs the consequences of medicalization on women's lives. First, it reviews the main negative effects, then it considers whether there are positive outcomes as well. Finally, it asks whether recent "woman-centred" health movements are able to provide significant alternatives to mainstream professional medicine.

The Pros and Cons of Medicalization

Perhaps the most important negative result of the medical perspective on women's lives is its tendency to individualize and depoliticize their problems. In all of the examples discussed, women's problems are blamed on themselves (that is, they are viewed as personal, psychological matters), and this diagnosis leads to an avoidance of essential social and institutional remedies. The medical model tells women, "The problem is with *you*, so *you* must do the changing." The authors of this chapter find this approach misguided: it treats the female, but leaves dominant patriarchal conceptions of femininity untouched.

The second negative result of medicalization concerns the manner in which the medical rhetoric of illness is deployed to produce conformity to social norms of family. The idea that sickness will befall women who deviate from their "natural" — that is, social — gender roles runs through the history of Western thought. One of the earliest examples occurs in Platonic writings from the fifth century B.C. According to Plato, and to Hippocrates, the famous Greek physician of the same era, women's failure to bear children, and thus to fulfill their "natural function," would cause the uterus to rebel and to attack the rest of the body. Plato wrote:

> [T]he animal [the uterus] within them is desirous of procreating children, and when remaining unfruitful long beyond its proper time, gets discontented and angry, and wandering in every direction through the body, closes up the passages of the breath, and, by obstructing respiration, drives them to extremity, causing all varieties of disease. (cited in Greenglass, 1982, p. 209)

With the benefit of hindsight, it is easy to dismiss such notions as merely bizarre; but singular efforts to produce social conformity by invoking the medical rhetoric of disease have persisted into our own time. In the nineteenth century, medical opinion held that women who had "too much" schooling would suffer an array of ailments, from depression to an atrophied uterus; thus, "no reading" was often the medical prescription for restoring them to health (Greenglass, 1982, p. 211). The previous section outlined how the maternal deprivation thesis of Bowlby and others in the 1950s was used to pressure women to conform to the ideal of full-time child rearing, and how contemporary medical thinking pushes women to accept a punishingly narrow body ideal. The point of these examples is not to ridicule the medical knowledge of the past but to show how medical discourse has been, and continues to be, deployed in ways that limit women's options — in behaviour, in appearance, and in relationships (Fausto-Sterling, 1986; Lorber, 2000).

But while the negative effects of medicalization on women's lives are considerable, it would be a mistake to portray women as the inevitable victims of medical discourse. The medical rhetoric of health and illness originated with the medical profession, but it is not wholly "owned" by doctors, and this means that it is available to be used by other groups, including women, to achieve their own ends. Women have discovered, for example, that the visibility of formerly "invisible" problems like woman abuse, or premenstrual syndrome, is increased substantially once they are labelled as "medical problems." As such, these conditions are more likely to draw public attention and sympathy, to attract research funding, and to appear on the political agenda. Women at the beginning of the twentieth century used the findings of medical science and the rhetoric of health to regulate the sexual activity of their husbands, for example, and in general, to acquire a greater say in marital relations (Morantz, 1984). Thus, even if women's groups are wary of the medical view and its implications, they have also recognized that certain advantages may flow from adopting it as a strategy. In these instances, women, like other relatively low power groups in society, see that if they cannot change the system that favours the medical perspective, they can at least borrow its discourse and reap some of its benefits for themselves.

Second, women may welcome a medical approach to some issues just because it releases them from stigma and moral responsibility for "the problem"; you cannot be blamed (at least not explicitly) for a "disease" you did not choose to get. The stigma of alcoholism is reduced when it is medicalized as a chemical disorder, for example, and obesity is more acceptable when it is no longer called "the sin of gluttony" but rather a "glandular disorder" or a psychological problem called "compulsive eating." As noted in

---

Is It in Men's Interests to Have Their Lives Increasingly Medicalized?

Manopause Legitimate Health Concern — MDs

Condition not phase, says poll.
The telltale symptoms can include suddenly growing a ponytail, acquiring a shiny new sports car or picking up a much younger woman.

Middle-aged men have gone through phases involving one or all of the above for years, but physicians are now acknowledging the trend as a legitimate medical condition.

In a recent Angus Reid survey, 78 percent of family physicians polled said they believe men experience something similar to menopause as they age. And 71 percent of doctors polled agreed that andropause, or manopause as some would call it, can affect a man's quality of life something like the way menopause affects a woman's....

The president of the Canadian Andropause Society said there should be no question about the validity of the condition.

"We know that andropause is real and that it can be a serious health concern for men," said Dr. Roland Tremblay, a professor of medicine at Laval University in Quebec City.

Andropause describes the gradual decline in men of the hormone testosterone, which usually happens between the ages of 40 and 55. Men going through that process might also find themselves increasingly irritable and suffering a loss of energy, agility, decreased sex drive, anxiety, weight gain and sleep disturbances....

"The good news is that it is also diagnosable and easily treatable," Dr. Tremblay said. That usually means testosterone replacement therapy.

But a urology professor at Dalhousie medical school said testosterone replacement therapy can be dangerous for older men because it causes prostate cancer.

"I'm more or less opposed to it," said Dr. Harmurari Tewari, who is not convinced that andropause exists. "Of course you get old and your body starts to give way," he said. "But nobody has proven there is any male menopause."

He suspects the major push behind recognizing the condition is from the pharmaceutical companies that manufacture hormone replacements....

And the sports cars and younger women?

"That's not a medical condition," he said. "That's everybody who's a normal person who has that. Everybody has to prove to themselves that, 'Hey, I'm 50, but I can still go. I can have a younger woman and keep her happy.' Some people are built like that...."

Source: Jeffrey Simpson, *The Mail-Star*, Halifax, Tuesday, April 20, 1999, pp. A1–A2. Reprinted with permission of The Halifax Herald Limited.

the first section of this chapter, the consequences of such discursive shifts are quite concrete: instead of shunning the guilty parties, or locking them up, we extend them our sympathy and send them for treatment. Furthermore, medicalization not only lightens the burden of stigma, it also transfers the responsibility for the treatment of the problem from the sufferer to the doctor: the behaviour is now the doctor's problem (Conrad & Schneider, 1980, p. 248). The relief and security such a transfer provides may serve a real therapeutic purpose.

Alternatives to the Medical Model: A Realistic Assessment

What alternatives are there to the powerful medical model? As noted above, women can sometimes turn medical rhetoric to their own advantage. They have also resisted medicalization in a more radical fashion by trying to change mainstream medical practices or by sidestepping them altogether. For example, they have tried to escape the control of the medical profession by supporting midwifery and natural-childbirth movements, by challenging the power hierarchies within doctor–patient relationships, and by forming self-help groups that emphasize self-help care (Fox, 1990, p. 410). In addition, strong advocacy has emerged for patients' "right to know" and to decide on matters of their own health. These developments all represent a move toward "client control" (de Swaan, 1990, p. 71; Fox, 1990, p. 410).

But, while these movements are sometimes touted as a **demedicalization** of women's lives, they do not represent a wholesale rejection of modern medicine, partly because of the respect accorded to doctors both by society at large and by women themselves (Fox, 1990, p. 412). Despite the new interest that science is showing in alternative or traditional medicine, most people can scarcely imagine, nor would they choose, a world without modern medical expertise. Even the midwife's opposition to the doctor is mainly occupational; her training and information is largely drawn from the same body of knowledge, and the gulf between her perspective and that of the traditional midwife in a peasant society is immense. To some degree, those in the industrialized "first world" are all held hostage to modern medicine. In part, this is the case because medical discourse often involves the assumption that everyone agrees with it as "obviously the best," and this limits their ability to conceive of alternative frameworks and new definitions of problems (Gusfield, 1989, p. 436).

It is far more likely, then, that women will achieve not a demedicalization of their bodies, but a greater voice in the ways they are treated by the medical profession — in short, informed choice and a greater degree of power. Clients could gain greater influence over the conditions under which medical expertise is applied; for example, women could determine where they give birth, how and when anesthesia is administered, and when an obstetrician or general practitioner is to be in attendance (de Swaan, 1990, p. 71). Moreover, there are signs that mainstream medicine is permeable to a range of consumer demands, notably alternative and traditional techniques and philosophies (e.g., acupuncture), and will be broadened by these inclusions. We have seen, for example, how the midwifery and natural-childbirth movements have had some of their procedures brought into the hospital setting. These developments include "birthing rooms," "rooming-in" of the newborn with the mother, prenatal Lamaze classes, and preparation for pain control in natural childbirth. Certainly, many of the early concerns of the natural childbirth movement have been taken up by mainstream medicine because they serve other medical aims (such as the lowering of maternal and fetal mortality rates), and it can be argued therefore that mainstream medicine has merely co-opted the concerns of these earlier, antiprofessional movements. But on the other hand, it is clear that these developments also address mothers' concerns and demands, albeit primarily those of middle-class mothers.

What is occurring, then, is not a demedicalization but an ongoing negotiation between two power groups, a two-way relationship in which the underdogs (women and other clients of the medical profession) are gaining increased leverage and muscle. It would appear, however, that these gains must be constantly defended, for with each new development (the new reproductive technologies, for example), the medical profession seems to be ready to disempower women anew.

We conclude that women are not the passive victims of medical institutions. They have been controlled by mainstream professional medicine, but they have also influenced it on occasion (Findlay, 1990). Like other groups, they have turned the profession's prestigious rhetoric to their own advantage. In the end, the encounter between women and the medical profession is much like women's encounter with other institutions of social control — neither victory nor defeat, but an ongoing struggle.

ACKNOWLEDGEMENT

The authors thank Carol Berenson, M.A., for her research assistance with the revised version of this chapter.

STUDY QUESTIONS

1. *Recently we have read of two new "diseases": SAD (seasonal affective disorder) and micromastia (small breasts). Discuss the consequences for women and for doctors when these conditions are medicalized.*

2. *How can women's food consumption practices, including anorexia and obesity, be interpreted as rational from women's own standpoint, rather than as "disorders" or "diseases"? Consider this issue in light of the sociocultural context in which women live and eat.*

3. *Do natural-childbirth movements depart from the medicalized approach to pregnant and labouring women that Oakley says views women as "containers of fetuses"? Which aspects of natural childbirth might actually perpetuate that view of women? Consider, for example, what natural childbirth advocates assume to be "natural" for women.*

4. *Consider the current popularity of "working out" and fitness classes (e.g., Tae-Bo). What messages are conveyed to women and girls — in the media but also in the youth subculture — about the relationships between health and beauty? How are women and girls persuaded to participate in these "goods" and practices?*

5. *Compare traditional or folk wisdom on pregnancy, childbirth, and child rearing (e.g., "spare the rod and spoil the child") with modern medical and psychological opinion on the same topics. Using your experience, assess the degree to which one form of knowledge has replaced the other. In any given situation, which form appears to carry more authority? Why?*

GLOSSARY

anorexia nervosa   A behaviour in which individuals, most often young women, severely restrict their food intake. Anorexia results in damaged health or even death.

bodywork   All effort expended in the maintenance or improvement of physical appearance and health; shopping for cosmetics and clothing, dyeing one's hair, exercising, and dieting fall into this category.

bonding   The formation of a strong emotional tie between a mother and her infant; presumed to be beneficial and necessary to the child.

demedicalization   The removal of a condition or activity from the category of disease, at which point the medical profession no longer has the sole responsibility for defining and treating that condition.

discourse   The broad linguistic frameworks within which people perceive, think, and speak about the world, and also the ordinary language-in-use.

medicalization   The process that defines a condition or activity as a disease or an illness; treatment of the condition is then considered the responsibility of the medical profession.

policing   The process by which powerful social groups, such as physicians, control others through scrutiny and documentation (rather than force), in order to bring them into line with dominant or "normal" social standards of acceptability. While the term is borrowed from the legal sphere, it is used by sociologists to refer to forms of social and moral rather than legal constraint.

social control   The result of formal and informal rules or pressures being imposed on individuals or groups to influence their activities and behaviours. Teasing is an example of informal social control.

RECOMMENDED READINGS

Bordo, S. (1993). *Unbearable weight: Feminism, western culture and the body.* An examination of the female body as a socially contested political issue in postmodern culture; focuses on discourses and conceptions of women's bodies, and relates theory to eating disorders, the reproduction of femininity, and motherhood.

Davis, K. (1995). *Reshaping the Female Body: The dilemma of cosmetic surgery.* An exploration of the needs and motives of women who pursue cosmetic surgery; offers a feminist critique of the complex issues involved in medical and surgical intervention into women's bodies, as well as women's own, active role in the decision to reshape their appearance through surgery.

Lorber, J. (2000). *Gender and the social construction of illness.* A useful text in the *Gender Lens* series that explores the interaction between gender as a social institution on the one hand and Western medicine as a social institution on the other. Lorber brings a feminist awareness of power and politics to illnesses that have been considered to be physical, including PMS and AIDS, and concludes with a chapter on feminist health care.

Martin, E. (1987). *The woman in the body: A cultural analysis of reproduction.* Boston: Beacon Press. An analysis of medical discourse on women's reproductive processes, focusing on menstruation, birthing, and menopause; also contrasts the scientific medical approach with the alternative metaphors created by different social classes of women themselves.

Wolf, N. (1991). *The beauty myth.* Toronto: Vintage Books. An argument that a new form of social control is pressuring women to focus on bodily appearance as their chief area of social achievement; demonstrates the beauty myth's influence through discussion of several issues, including anorexia and cosmetic surgery.

REFERENCES

Aries, P. (1962). *Centuries of childhood: A social history of family life.* New York: Vintage Books.

Balsamo, A. (1999). Public pregnancies and cultural narratives of surveillance. In A.E. Clark & V.L. Olesen (Eds.), *Revisioning women, health and healing: Feminist, cultural and techno-science perspectives* (pp. 231–253). New York: Routledge.

Berton, P. (1977). *The Dionne years.* Toronto: McClelland & Stewart.

Bordo, S.R. (1989). The body and reproduction of femininity: A feminist appropriation of Foucault. In A.M. Jagger & S.R. Bordo (Eds.), *Gender/body/knowledge* (pp. 13–33). New Brunswick, NJ: Rutgers University Press.

Bordo, S.R. (1990). Reading the slender body. In M. Jacobus, E. Fox Keller, & S. Shuttleworth (Eds.), *Body politics: Women and the discourses of science* (pp. 83–112). New York: Routledge.

Bordo, S.R. (1993). *Unbearable weight: Feminism, western culture and the body.* Berkeley: University of California Press.

Boskind-Lodahl, M. (1976, Winter). Cinderella's stepsisters: A feminist perspective on anorexia nervosa and bulimia. *SIGNS, 2*(2), 342–356.

Brannen, J., & Wilson, G. (Eds.). (1987). *Give and take in families. Studies in resource distribution.* London: Allen & Unwin.

Brown, C. (1993). The continuum: Anorexia, bulimia, and weight preoccupation. In C. Brown & K. Jasper (Eds.), *Consuming passions: Feminist approaches to weight preoccupation and eating disorders* (pp. 53–68). Toronto: Second Story Press.

Buchanan, K.S. (1993). Creating beauty in blackness. In C. Brown & K. Jasper (Eds.), *Consuming passions: Feminist approaches to weight preoccupation and eating disorders* (pp. 36–52). Toronto: Second Story Press.

Charles, N., & Kerr, M. (1988). *Women, food and families.* Manchester & New York: Manchester University Press.

Chernin, K. (1985). *The hungry self: Women, eating and identity.* New York: Harper & Row.

Conrad, P., & Schneider, J.W. (1980). *Deviance and medicalization: From badness to sickness.* St. Louis: C.V. Mosby.

Currer, C., & Stacey, M. (Eds.). (1986). *Concepts of health, illness and disease: A comparative perspective.* Leamington Spa: Berg.

Davidoff, L., & Hall, C. (1987). *Family fortunes: Men and women of the English middle class, 1780–1850.* London: Hutchinson.

de Swaan, A. (1990). *The management of normality: Critical essays in health and welfare.* London & New York: Routledge.

Doctors give top marks to patient report cards. (1991, December 6). *Calgary Herald,* p. B1.

Doctor's group taking aim in fight against fat. (1999, April 13). *Halifax Mail-Star,* pp. A1–A2.

Donzelot, J. (1979). *The policing of families.* New York: Pantheon Books.

Durkheim, E. (1964 [1933]). *The division of labour in society.* New York: Free Press.

Edgley, C., & Brissett, D. (1990). Health Nazis and the cult of the perfect body: Some polemical observations. *Symbolic Interaction, 13*(2), 257–279.

Ehrenreich, B., & English, D. (1979). *For her own good: 150 years of the experts' advice to women.* Garden City: Anchor Books.

Elias, N. (1978 [1939]). *The history of manners.* New York: Urizen Books.

Etaugh, C. (1974). The effects of maternal employment on children: A review of the research. *Merrill-Palmer Quarterly, 20*, 71–98.

Fast tracks. (1991, November 17). *Calgary Herald*, p. B8.

Fausto-Sterling, A. (1986). Hormonal hurricanes: Menstruation, menopause, and female behavior. In L. Richardson & V. Taylor (Eds.), *Feminist frontiers III* (pp. 329–430). New York: McGraw-Hill.

Findlay, D.A. (1990). *Women and medical knowledge in the 1950s: A study of the process of social construction.* Ph.D. Dissertation, McMaster University, Hamilton.

Fisher, S. (1988). *In the patients' best interest: Women and the politics of medical decisions.* New Brunswick, NJ: Rutgers University Press.

Foucault, M. (1979). *Discipline and punish: The birth of the prison.* New York: Vintage.

Fox, R.C. (1990). The medicalization and demedicalization of American society. In P. Conrad & R. Kern (Eds.), The *sociology of health and illness: Critical perspectives* (3rd ed., pp. 390–394). New York: St. Martin's Press.

Freidson, E. (1970). *Professional dominance: The social structure of medical care.* New York: Aldine.

Frykman, J., & Lofgren, 0. (1987). *Culture builders: A historical anthropology of middle-class life.* New Brunswick, NJ: Rutgers University Press.

Gaffield, C. (1990). The social and economic origins of contemporary families. In M. Baker (Ed.), *Families: Changing trends in Canada* (2nd ed.). Toronto: McGraw-Hill Ryerson.

Gaskell, J. (1988). The reproduction of family life: Perspectives of male and female adolescents. In A. Tigar McLaren (Ed.), *Gender and society* (pp. 146–168). Toronto: Copp Clark Pittman.

Graham, H., & Oakley, A. (1986). Competing ideologies of reproduction: Medical and maternal perspectives on pregnancy. In C. Currer & M. Stacey (Eds.), *Concepts of health, illness and disease: A comparative perspective* (pp. 97–116). Leamington Spa: Berg.

Greenglass, E.R. (1982). *A world of difference: Gender roles in perspective.* Toronto: John Wiley & Sons.

Gusfield, J.R. (1989, December). Constructing the ownership of social problems: Fun and profit in the welfare state. *Social Problems, 36*(5), 431–441.

Hareven, T.K. (1989). American families in transition: Historical perspectives on change. In A.S. Skolnick & J.H. Skolnick (Eds.), *Family in transition* (6th ed., pp. 39–57). Glenview, IL: Scott, Foresman.

Haug, F., et al. (Eds.). (1987). *Female sexualization.* London: Verso.

In search of the perfect man. (2001, March 17). *Calgary Herald*, p. OS1.

Kamerman, S., & Hayes, C.D. (Eds.). (1982). *Families that work: Children in a changing world.* Washington, DC: National Academy Press.

Leavitt, J.W. (1986). *Brought to bed: Childbearing in America, 1750–1950.* New York: Oxford University Press.

Lewis, J. (1986). The working class wife and mother and state intervention, 1870–1918. In J. Lewis (Ed.), *Labour and love: Women's experience of home and family, 1850–1940* (pp. 99–120). London: Basil Blackwell.

Lorber, J. (2000). *Gender and the social construction of illness.* Walnut Creek, CA: AltaMira Press.

Ludmerer, K.M. (1985). *Learning to heal: The development of American medical education.* New York: Basic Books.

MacNevin, A.L. (1992). *Step 'n pump: A social inquiry into aerobically exercised femininity.* M.A. Thesis, Dalhousie University, Halifax.

Manopause legitimate health concern — MDs. (1999, April 20). *Halifax Mail-Star*, pp. A1–A2.

Martin, E. (1987). *The woman in the body. A cultural analysis of reproduction.* Boston: Beacon Press.

Martin, E. (1991). The egg and the sperm: How science has constructed a romance based on stereotypical male-female roles. *Signs: A journal of women in culture and society, 16*(3), 485–499.

Miller, L. (1987, Winter). Uneasy alliance: Women as agents of social control. *Canadian Journal of Sociology, 12*(4), 345–361.

Miller, L. (1991). Family problems and problem families. In B.S. Bolaria (Ed.), *Social issues and contradictions in Canadian society* (pp. 57–85). Toronto: Harcourt Brace Jovanovich.

Miller, L., & Penz, 0. (1991, August). Talking bodies: Female body builders colonize a male preserve. *Quest, 43*(2), 148–163.

Morantz, R.M. (1984). The perils of feminist history. In J.W. Leavitt (Ed.), *Women and health in America* (pp. 239–245). Oxford: Oxford University Press.

Morantz-Sanchez, R.M. (1985). *Sympathy with science: Women physicians in American medicine.* Oxford: Oxford University Press.

Morse, J., Young, D.E., & Swartz, L. (1991). Cree healing practices and western health care: A comparative analysis. *Social Science Medicine, 32*(12), 1361–1366.

Oakley, A. (1986). *The captured womb: A history of the medical care of pregnant women.* Oxford: Basil Blackwell.

O'Neil, J., & Kaufert, A. (1990). The politics of obstetric care: The Inuit experience. In W.P. Handwerker (Ed.), *Births and power: Social change and the politics of reproduction* (pp. 53–68). Boulder, CO: Westview Press.

Orbach, S. (1979). *Fat is a feminist issue.* New York: Berkley Books.

Richardson, T.R. (1989). *The century of the child: The mental hygiene movement and social policy in the United States and Canada.* Albany: State University of New York Press.

Riley, D. (1983). *War in the nursery: Theories of the child and mother.* London: Virago.

Rothman, B.K. (1989). Women, health and medicine. In J. Freeman (Ed.), *Women: A feminist perspective* (pp. 77–86). Mountainview: Mayfield.

Rutter, M. (1981). *Maternal deprivation reassessed.* Harmondsworth: Penguin.

Sandelowski, M. (1984). *Pain, pleasure, and American childbirth: From the twilight sleep to the Read method, 1914–1960.* Westport: Greenwood Press.

Schur, E.M. (1984). *Labelling women deviant: Gender, stigma, and social control.* Philadelphia: Temple University Press.

Schwartz, H. (1986). *Never satisfied. A cultural history of diets, fantasies and fat.* New York: Anchor Books.

Shorter, E. (1977). *The making of the modern family.* New York: Basic Books.

Spitzack, C. (1990). *Confessing excess: Women and the politics of body reduction.* Albany: State University of New York Press.

Strong-Boag, V. (1982). Intruders in the nursery: Childcare professionals reshape the years one to five, 1920–40. In J. Parr (Ed.), *Childhood and family in Canadian history* (pp. 160–178). Toronto: McClelland & Stewart.

Synnott, A. (1989). Truth and goodness, mirrors and masks — Part I: A sociology of beauty and the face. *British Journal of Sociology, 40*(4), 607–636.

Szekely, E. (1988). *Never too thin.* Toronto: Women's Press.

Tavris, C. (1992). *The mismeasure of woman.* New York: Simon & Schuster.

Torrance, G.M. (1987). Socio-historical overview. In D. Coburn, C. D'Arcy, G.M. Torrance, & P. New (Eds.), *Health and Canadian society* (2nd ed.). Markham, ON: Fitzhenry & Whiteside.

Trypuc, J.M. (1994). Women's health. In B.S. Bolaria & H.D. Dickinson (Eds.), *Health, illness, and health care in Canada* (2nd ed., pp. 260–275). Toronto: Harcourt Brace.

Turner, B.S. (1982, June). The government of the body: Medical regimens and the rationalization of diet. *British Journal of Sociology, 33*(2), 254–269.

Turner, B.S. (1984). *The body and society.* Oxford: Basil Blackwell.

Turner, B.S. (1987). *Medical power and social knowledge.* London: Sage.

Valverde, M. (1991). *The age of light, soap and water: Moral reform in English Canada, 1885–1925.* Toronto: McClelland & Stewart.

Walker, G.A. (1990). *Family violence and the women's movement: The conceptual politics of struggle.* Toronto: University of Toronto Press.

Wall, G. (2000). Moral constructions of motherhood in breastfeeding discourses. Paper presented at the Annual Meeting of the Canadian Sociology and Anthropology Association, Edmonton, Alberta.

Walters, V. (1994). Women's perceptions regarding health and illness. In B.S. Bolaria and H.D. Dickinson (Eds.), *Health, illness, and health care in Canada* (2nd ed., pp. 307–325). Toronto: Harcourt Brace.

Wertz, R.W., & Wertz, D.C. (1977). *Lying-in: A history of childbirth in America.* New York: Free Press.

Wilson, K., Garvin, T., & McMullan, C. (1999). The bronzed aesthetic: The social construction of women's tanning. In M. Denton, J. Hadjukowski-Ahmed, M. O'Connor, & I. Zeytinoglu (Eds.), *Women's voices in health promotion* (pp. 204–216). Toronto: Canadian Scholars' Press.

Wolf, N. (1991). *The beauty myth.* Toronto: Vintage Books.

Working parents spark concern: Canadians worry the well-being of the nation's children is being sacrificed. (1991, November 5). *The Globe and Mail,* p. A4.

Zola, I.K. (1972). Medicine as an institution of social control. *Sociological Review, 20,* 487–504.

Zola, I.K. (1975). In the name of health and illness: On some sociological consequences of medical influence. *Social Science and Medicine, 9,* 83–87.

NOTES

1. The recent debates around the cancer treatment of young Tyler Dueck in Saskatchewan remind us that there still exist powerful traditional alternatives to the secular discourse of modern medicine, and more generally, that discourses exert strong moral and emotional holds over us.

2. Shortly after their birth in the 1930s, the Dionne quintuplets were taken from their poor, French-speaking parents to be scientifically reared by physicians and psychiatrists in a morally and physically "hygienic" laboratory environment (the birth of quintuplets being an exceedingly rare event in an era before fertility drugs). In 1998, the three remaining Dionne "quints" successfully sued the government of Ontario for the emotional and financial exploitation they endured as children.

3. O'Neil and Kaufert describe a similar (but more recent) process in the Canadian North and argue that the rapid medicalization of childbirth in Inuit communities has also functioned as a form of cultural colonization. Their article discusses obstetric policy as "one aspect of the penetration of southern institutions and controls into the lives of people living in the Canadian North" (1990, p. 416).

4. See Walters (1994) for a more general discussion of the limits of medicalization and the resilience of lay perspectives on health issues. Walters concludes that "women borrow from medicine as appropriate, transform and integrate this information with their own

understandings" (p. 312). She argues that women's own perceptions are too rarely examined, and that when they are, they reveal that they have not been medicalized to the degree that critics suppose.

5. Morse, Young, and Swartz (1991) make a parallel argument that contrasts healing practices among the Cree (holistic, caring, and integrated) with Western health care (individualistic, cure-based, grounded in a mind–body split). They suggest that the medical problem of "noncompliance" with Western medical regimes of treatment be seen rather as the clash of two worldviews.

6. Martin (1987, pp. 139–155) argues that there are more issues for a Black working-class woman to contend with than for a white, middle-class woman, and that the former is more likely to encounter medical mismanagement and inadequate information from professionals on matters related to childbirth. On this basis, Martin suggests that Black women are less likely to adopt the medical perspective as their own.

7. Men's increasing interest in their appearance is now widely covered in the popular press. A recent article in the *Calgary Herald* entitled "In Search of the Perfect Man" states that Canadian men spent $16 million on hair-colouring products in 2000, and that 11 per-cent of all cosmetic surgery (mainly liposuction) is performed on men (a figure based on combined American and Canadian statistics) (*Calgary Herald*, March 17, 2001, p. OS1). It is notable that these procedures, however, still tend to be framed within the stereo-typical gendered cultural discourses: men who undergo cosmetic surgery typically say that they are doing it "to give themselves a competitive edge in the workplace," while women claim that they are doing it "for themselves."

8. Buchanan (1993) discusses the impact of dominant norms of beauty (slim, blonde, straight hair) on Black women.

11

Inequality, Violence, and Women's Health

COLLEEN VARCOE   University of Victoria

INTRODUCTION

Although violence is understood to be gendered and women are understood to be by far the majority of victims of violence — violence also interacts with other intersecting forms of inequality. Inequalities along the lines of class, age, ability, sexual orientation, and racialization compound and are compounded by the effects of violence on women's health. Thus, violence against women must be understood in the context of these other forms of violence.

The purpose of this chapter is to explore the ways in which certain pervasive forms of inequality (particularly gender, **racialization**, and poverty) interact with violence to affect women's health. This chapter will draw on literature as well as the author's research to explicate the links between violence, various forms of inequality, and women's health in Canada. In doing so, this chapter is intended to contribute to the developing understanding of violence against women that goes beyond a gender analysis and to contribute to the promotion of strategies to counter violence that are rooted in an understanding of women's diversity. In particular, it draws attention to the ways in which people in positions of professional privilege and power can reproduce and reinforce, or resist and oppose, the dynamics of inequality and violence.

This chapter will draw on three studies the author has conducted in partnership with others. An ethnographic study conducted over two years in two hospital emergency units and their communities examined health care practice in relation to violence against women (Varcoe, 1997, 2001). A second study of women's experiences of formal support services in relation to abuse explored how those experiences were shaped both by professionals and by the women themselves. Finally, an action research study with women who have been battered by partners is in progress (Varcoe, Jaffer, & Irwin, 2000). This study aims to improve the ways in which services in the health care, legal, and social welfare systems respond to violence against women.

EVOLVING UNDERSTANDINGS OF VIOLENCE

Violence against women has been recognized as a significant social problem only since the late 1960s and early 1970s. The three intervening decades have seen efforts, primarily by women themselves, to have the scope of the problem *believed* by the public. There is now wide acceptance that violence against women is a global problem of epidemic proportions. Further, the gendered nature of violence has been increasingly understood. Violence is largely a women's problem, both because women are most often on the receiving end of abuse and because they have taken most of the responsibility for decreasing and dealing with violence. Violence in the home (often referred to by the somewhat diminishing and gender-neutral term "domestic violence"), sexual assault and **sexual harassment**, by known and unknown assailants, and **corporate violence** are deeply gendered.

The Scope and Gendered Nature of Violence

In Canada the enormity of the problem of violence and its gendered nature have been clearly established. In 1993, Statistics Canada conducted a national population survey, the Violence Against Women Survey (VAWS). In this survey, researchers interviewed a randomly selected national sample of 12 300 women by telephone. The data from this study have been analyzed by various researchers, including Rodgers (1994), Ratner (1995), Johnson (1996), and Kerr and McLean (1996), providing the most comprehensive picture of the problem in Canada to date.

The VAWS estimated that one in every two women in Canada over the age of 18 had experienced at least one incident of sexual or physical assault, and that 10 percent were the victims of assault in the year preceding the survey (Johnson, 1996; Rodgers, 1994). In congruence with global statistics on wife abuse (Heise, Pitanguy, & Germain, 1994) and numerous U.S. studies (see Barnett, 2000; Koss, 1990; Tjaden & Thoennes, 1998), 29 percent of women in Canada who had ever been married or lived in a common-law relationship reported being physically or sexually assaulted by a marital partner at least once during the relationship (Johnson, 1996; Rodgers, 1994). Johnson extrapolated these figures to the population, estimating that over 2.6 million Canadian women have experienced physical or sexual assault, and that of the 6.69 million women currently in a marital relationship, 1.02 million (15 percent) have been assaulted.

Corporate violence, which encompasses hazardous working conditions and environments, including sexual harassment, has been less well studied but is also deeply gendered (Hinch & DeKeseredy, 1994). Although no national studies have been conducted to estimate the full extent of violence in the workplace, the scope and gendered nature of the problem can be appreciated from the many small-scale studies, especially those conducted in occupations where women predominate. For example, Poster (1996) found that 75 percent of 999 psychiatric nursing staff in Canada, the United States, the United Kingdom, and South Africa reported being assaulted at least once during their careers. Coombes (1998) reported a survey that indicated that one of every two nurses was at risk of physical assault, and Carroll and Morin (1998) reported that one third of nurses working in general areas were affected by workplace violence. Arnetz, Arnetz, and Soderman (1998) found that the incidence of violence toward practical nurses was 31 incidents per 100 person years.

While sexual harassment is usually discussed in relation to employment contexts and in the context of power relations, such as between teachers and students or between doctors and patients, this narrow definition is problematic (Kelly & Radford, 1998). Kelly and Radford explain that women in positions of authority are harassed (e.g., female teachers by male students), many women's places of employment are also their homes (e.g., "domestic" workers), and many women are harassed outside of employment contexts. The VAWS illustrates this clearly as it found that 23 percent of Canadian women had been assaulted by a nonspousal known man and 23 percent by a stranger, with sexual violence (including unwanted sexual touching and violent sexual assault) being much more common than physical assault outside of spousal relationships (Johnson, 1998).

Evolving Theoretical Perspectives

In addition to the scope and gendered nature of violence being delineated, during the past three decades the ways violence is understood have also evolved. Theorists from across disciplines have attempted to understand violence by focusing attention on and seeking causal explanations for violence in three spheres: individuals, couples or dyads, and society (Bograd, 1988; Gelles, 1993). Stark and Flitcraft (1991) label these three perspectives the interpersonal model, the family violence model, and the gender-politics model.

INTERPERSONAL MODELS

Initial attempts to make sense of violence against women tried to explain violence by focusing on individual and interpersonal relationships. These views emphasized the psychology of the victim and perpetrator and their interrelationships. The initial focus on the characteristics of victims led to victim-blaming theories of violence, such as the theory of learned helplessness, which diverted attention from the situation to the victim and labelled women's reasonable responses to unreasonable situations as odd (Wardell, Gillespie, & Leffler, 1983). More recent attention to the psychology of the perpetrator shifted the locus of causes of violence to the psychopathology of the perpetrator but continue to leave power, gender relations, and other forms of oppression unexamined. Dobash and Dobash (1992) argue that the focus on the individual has been popularized by the media in ways that perpetuate common understandings of violence as strictly a problem of abnormal individuals who need psychiatric help. This focus on the psychology of individuals suggests that violence is an aberrance of a few husbands rather than a predominant pattern of behaviour, excuses men, implicates women, and concludes that the differences between abused and nonabused women are the causes rather than the consequences of abuse (Bograd, 1988). Causal explanations of violence related to the psychology of the individual leave power and gender relations unexamined and consider violence in isolation from the social and historical contexts in which it occurs.

FAMILY VIOLENCE MODELS

The second set of perspectives on violence focuses on dyads or families, and seeks explanations of the causes of violence in social relations within couples and families. These perspectives, predominant in most research on violence (Silva, 1994), tend to be gender-neutral, treat power inequities as only one factor among many, and explain violence as resulting from external stresses and breakdown of the family, rather than as a part of most normally functioning families (Bograd, 1988; Stanko, 1988). As with the focus on individuals, a focus on dyads or families limits an analysis of the influence of the social context. These approaches leave the role of women in society and families out of analyses of violence.

GENDER-POLITICAL MODELS

The third set of perspectives, variously labelled "feminist" or gender-political, tend to explain violence as arising from the social context and contribute an analysis of the influence of gender and power relations to theorizing violence (Yllö, 1993). Feminist perspectives take into account the gendered nature of violence. However, feminist perspectives have been criticized as inadequate for understanding violence from at least two positions.

Some authors (e.g., Dutton, 1994; Gelles, 1993; Letellier, 1994) argue that **feminism** is insufficient because it is limited to using a single variable (**patriarchy**) to explain the existence of wife abuse, and use evidence of men who are not violent and violence in same-sex relationships to contend that patriarchal ideology does not account for male violence. These authors tend to reject feminism in favour of continued support for the interpersonal or family violence model or in favour of an integration of the various perspectives (e.g., Dutton, 1994; Miller, 1994; Tolman & Bennett, 1990; Renzetti, 1994).

Other authors such as Crenshaw (1994), Mahoney (1994), Mosher (1998), and Phillips (1998) critique the limitations of a feminist perspective from a different vantage point. They argue that while violence is deeply gendered, other forms of oppression are equally important in understanding violence against women. These authors argue that although gender analysis is important, gender can be seen as "overly determinate" in understanding violence. "While gender is a significant factor, other kinds of oppression, such as that based on race and class, are seen to be equally important" (Mosher, 1998, p. 140). Mosher categorizes the various perspectives somewhat differently than earlier authors do, combining individual and family-oriented approaches under what she terms the "therapeutic" perspectives, and distinguishing feminist perspectives, which foreground gender, from the "intersecting oppression perspective," which considers how other forms of oppression are magnified by each other and magnify the violence in women's lives. From this perspective, the experience of violence is seen as being influenced profoundly by the intersections of multiple social locations of privilege and oppression.

Dobash and Dobash (1992) claim that "by the late 1980s, public accounts had chipped away at persistent images of the violence as a problem confined to the working class, ethnic groups or the poor" (p. 5). Yet such images persist today, informing individual and state responses to violence against women. At every stage of this author's research on violence, she was referred repeatedly by members of the public and service providers to places associated with poor and racialized people.

Acceptance is growing that violence is an enormous social problem that is deeply gendered. However, understandings of violence against women have been largely viewed in abstraction from women's lives, and the interpersonal–therapeutic models continue to dominate common understandings of violence. Thus, attention to violence has largely focused on individuals and on discrete acts of violence rather than on the social context within which violence occurs. Such understandings lead to interventions that deal with individuals and their specific acts rather than with the patterns from which those acts arise. When attention is turned to the sociopolitical context of violence, feminist analyses tend to focus on gender oppression, and the influences of other intersecting forms of oppression are rarely taken into account. Although feminist perspectives have increased public awareness of the gendered nature of violence, violence and its impact on women's lives must be understood within the context of a culture of violence that encompasses the violence of racism, poverty, heterosexism, and other forms of inequity. It is thus from this perspective that the remainder of this chapter will proceed.

VIOLENCE AT THE INTERSECTIONS

The limitations of a gender-only analysis of violence against women have been force-fully articulated and attention has been turned toward the importance of other forms of oppression by authors such as hooks (1984), Richie and Kanuha (1993), Walker (1995), and Agnew (1998). Moving beyond a gender analysis of violence, recent theorists use the concept of **intersectionality** to understand violence (Crenshaw, 1994; Mahoney, 1994; Mosher, 1998; Phillips, 1998). "Intersectionality" refers to the interaction between forms of oppression (e.g., racism, classism, sexism) in ways that magnify one another (Brewer, 1993; Collins, 1993). For example, the experience of being poor (or racialized, or disabled, or aged) is not simply an "added" form of oppression for a woman; rather, being poor magnifies the oppression inherent in being a woman. Similarly, being racialized amplifies poverty, as does disability, and so on. Intersectionality addresses the ways in which various forms of oppression reinforce each other and interact. Thus, for example, a First Nations woman who finds it difficult to find employment because of racism is kept poor, and so on.

The central purpose of this chapter is to illustrate that violence, like any other woman's health issue, must be understood from the vantage point of intersectionality, because intersecting forms of inequality interact with violence to affect women's health. There are three major points to this argument. The first is that inequities compound the impact of violence. The second is that the dynamics of inequity and violence create barriers to obtaining meaningful support in dealing with violence, and thus sustain violence in the lives of more oppressed women. The third point is that these dynamics also sustain privilege and notions of superiority, and thus they distance persons of privilege from violence.

INEQUITIES COMPOUND THE IMPACT OF VIOLENCE

Intersecting inequities magnify the experience of violence in women's lives in at least three ways. First, less privileged women are exposed to more forms of violence, and thus to more violence. Second, the less privileged a woman, the greater are the costs of disclosure of intimate violence. Third, the more forms of oppression a woman experiences, the more constrained are her "choices."

Less Privilege Means More Violence

Less privileged women are exposed to more violence. This is not to say that violence is more common among less privileged people, but rather that less privilege renders people more vulnerable. For example, women with disabilities are made vulnerable to violence by their disabilities and by the fact that they often must rely on others to provide many forms of support, and they are thus vulnerable to a large range of people. Approximately 15 percent of women in Canada have disabilities (Health Canada, 1993), and up to half of these women have experienced violence (DisAbled Women's Network, 1989). To take another example, women who are racialized are exposed to the violence of racism as a matter of course. Thus, for racialized women, violence in intimate relationships occurs within a context of daily exposure to racism. Finally, national surveys in the United States have repeatedly illustrated that poverty constitutes a significant risk factor for abuse by male partners (Browne & Bassuk, 1997).

Less Privilege Means More Costly Disclosure

Disclosure of abuse incurs costs for all women. For most women, including nonracialized people, disclosure of abuse is constrained by cultural norms, religious beliefs, and family pressures.[1] According to the women interviewed by the author, the disclosure of intimate violence means at least embarrassment and shame. As Koss notes: "When people acknowledge their status as victims, inevitably some degree of devaluation is incurred" (1990, p. 374). In addition, decision making is often taken out of women's hands following a disclosure of intimate violence. Therefore disclosure often has personal, social, and economic costs that extend beyond the initial act of disclosure. For example, one woman described the costs of disclosure (which she saw as ruining her son's chances for a scholarship and university, and potentially causing her to lose her home) after her husband had beat her particularly badly:

> If I go to the cops tonight (and I knew damn well if I made a complaint it was out of my hands) — what I really wanted to do was get this documented, okay? I knew if I went there it was out of my control so I had to sit back and "What am I going to do?"

There are costs associated with disclosure for the woman, her family, and her community regardless of her level of privilege. In the author's various studies, many women spoke of those constraints in terms of the loss of privilege.

> [My husband] was earning somewhere around two hundred to three hundred thousand a year, he covered the mortgage but it was very difficult, I mean I didn't have enough money to buy myself a pair of jeans, it was awful, very, very difficult.... I didn't realize the legal system, once he moved out, how awful it was for women, I didn't realize the cost of child care, I didn't realize the difficulty of getting care for my kids if I was working nights or evenings...all of that was not known to me, and the year that I was separated, that all became known to me.... I had so little support from anyone...because of him being a [professional], it really felt that people were really biased against me...even in my family you know, they didn't really understand that I should be leaving a marriage.

For most women, disclosure and the subsequent pressure to leave abusive partners means a drastically reduced income. Although many people feel that more privileged women have "more to lose," disclosure is in fact most costly for women who experience more inequities, because they have fewer options and resources.

Inequities mean that women have fewer resources and fewer choices about how much violence they have to endure. Women who must rely on others for various forms of support and care (such as women who are disabled or frail, and elderly women) often must choose between enduring the abuse or losing the care. This may mean not only the loss of a home and income but also the irreplaceable loss of direct care. Women who have fewer employment opportunities (due to age, racism, and so on) must tolerate more sexual harassment, not only because they need their jobs, but also because they have less power to expose the harassment. Given the invisibility of lesbian battering (Bernhard, 2000; Ristock, 1991; Turrell, 2000), lesbians are unlikely to find meaningful social support among formal services, and disclosure is likely to incur homophobic and heterosexist responses. Lesbians may fear such responses, fear disbelief, and fear the impact of disclosure on the lesbian community — fears that may be exploited by abusive partners. For example, in a recent study (Varcoe, Jaffer, & Irwin, 2000), a lesbian who had been battered by her partner did not call the police when beaten because her partner threatened to tell the police that the woman who had been beaten had "started it" and because she thought "of course the cops would believe her or treat us both like freaks."

The costs of disclosure are particularly evident in the especially toxic consequences for racialized women. Dobash and Dobash (1992) note that for racialized women to seek assistance in dealing with intimate violence is considered unacceptable both by racialized communities and by the women themselves because responses (such as arrest) are seen as "further act(s) of racial oppression against men of colour"(p. 52). Women from racialized communities must choose between exposing their communities to further racism (itself a form of violence) or tolerating violence. In her study of resources for Canadian women from Asia, Africa, and the Caribbean, Agnew (1998) illustrates how seeking help risks "the loss of sympathy and support from their families and other members of the ethnic or racial community" (p. 8). Dobash and Dobash note that racialized women "are in fact being expected to bear the brunt of gender violence within a racial or ethnic group in order that the group itself or its violent members not be exposed to further racial oppression" (p. 53). Despite the documentation of these problems, the impact on women's use of the formal systems is unknown. In the United States, studies such as the National Violence Against Women Survey (Tjaden & Thoennes, 1998) and others (see Barnett, 2000) indicate that African American women are more likely to seek help than Anglo-American women, suggesting that women from racialized communities are to some extent paying the costs of disclosure. Similar studies have not been carried out in Canada.

Less Privilege Means Fewer Choices

The more forms of oppression a woman experiences, such as poverty, racialization, and disability, the more constrained are her "choices." Poverty is particularly constraining. Women's vulnerability to violence is increased by economic and social disparities between men and women. Gurr, Mailloux, and Kinnon (1996) point out that financial and psychological independence are key factors that deter women from entering or staying in abusive relationships. Women's lack of economic independence often limits their ability to leave abusive situations, and poverty limits access to services in multiple ways.

Levinson's (1989) comparative study of 90 small-scale and peasant societies indicated that the strongest predictor of wife abuse was sexual economic inequality. Wife abuse occurred more frequently in societies in which husbands controlled family wealth and thus had more economic and decision making power. In Canada, the VAWS indicated that the 1-year incidence of wife assault was twice as high for women who were unemployed or earned less than $15 000 per year than for all other socioeconomic groups. Lambert and Firestone (2000) note that "women who are able to at least equalize their occupational prestige with their partner suffer fewer types of abuse than women whose prestige is lower than their partner's and women from lower socioeconomic households" (p. 50). These economic barriers to living violence-free are magnified by the effects of racism, cultural norms, language, disabilities, and age (see Gurr, Mailloux, & Kinnon, 1996).

Thus in Canadian society, where men tend to have more economic and decision making power, wife abuse occurs at disgraceful rates, and the same inequities that foster abuse also limit women's options for entering or leaving abusive relationships. Inequities compound one another, and inequities compound violence by increasing women's vulnerability to abuse, thus increasing the costs of disclosure and limiting options for dealing with abuse.

INEQUITIES CREATE BARRIERS TO SUPPORT

Intersecting forms of oppression limit women's possibilities of obtaining meaningful support in several interacting ways. First, inequities limit access to support. Second, because services have become professionalized and are now largely provided by "mainstream" well-educated members of the dominant culture, services tend to be designed with similar women in mind. Thus, services are fewer and less appropriate for women who are further from the dominant culture. Third, women who are more disadvantaged or marginalized have less power in relation to those providing service.

Inequities Mean Less Access

Access to support is limited both directly and indirectly by inequities. Poverty, which is of course compounded by racism, disability, age, and so on, is particularly limiting. At the most concrete level, the costs of services (such as legal fees and counselling), of transportation to services in both urban and rural settings, and of child care during support can directly limit access. The understanding of complex legal and social welfare systems may be limited by education and literacy levels. Further, women's paid and unpaid work may leave little time to sort through these complex systems. A woman who has casual, part-time, minimum-wage employment will not have the luxury of paid time off to attend services such as support groups or counselling, or to consult lawyers, police, and so on. Language barriers will further compound all of the access issues (Agnew, 1998).

Geography is a source of inequity of particular importance to Canadian women. Women in rural and isolated communities have considerably less access than urban women to all forms of social support. In the VAWS, the number of rural women who contacted or stayed in a transition house or shelter, got their own place, or stayed in a hotel was too small to report, compared with 15 percent of urban women who did so

(Levett & Johnson, 1997). Although they were somewhat more isolated from family, friends, and neighbours, rural women relied on family and friends to the same extent as did urban women, but were somewhat more likely than urban women to return home (79 percent compared with 67 percent). However, rural women were slightly more likely to contact a social service agency, and, despite being geographically more distant from medical services, rural women who were injured were as likely as urban women to receive medical attention for their injuries (Levett & Johnson, 1997). This suggests that rural women often do the added work to overcome the additional barriers to access.

Inequities Mean Less Appropriate Support

Even when women can access services, those services are often inappropriate or inadequate, reflecting and further magnifying existing inequities based on age, language, disability, sexual orientation, and racialization. For example, services for older women are often lacking. In a recent study of services offered by transition houses in British Columbia, Hightower et al. (1999) found that only 1–2 percent of the women served were over 60 years of age, although women over 60 years of age comprise 22 percent of the adult female population. Some of the reasons suggested for this discrepancy included a lack of staff training and awareness of the dynamics of abuse of older persons, lack of facilities for those with disabilities, and challenges in providing assistance with medications and physical care to those who require such care. The services were thought to be particularly inadequate for older women with disabilities or language barriers, and older women living in poverty. Overall, Hightower et al. and others (e.g., Vinton, 1997) conclude that service has been oriented to the needs of younger women with children. Services for older abused women are often guided by a medical model that views all older adults as vulnerable and dependent, creating services that are more in line with a child abuse model.

The appropriateness and accessibility of services for women who are racialized, women who speak little English, and lesbians has also been questioned. Racism pervades human-service provision in Canada (Henry et al., 2000). With particular regard to services for women who have experienced abuse, Agnew (1998) conducted an extensive study of services in Canada (primarily Eastern Canada). She described widespread racism in mainstream social and legal services for women who had experienced abuse. She also described institutionalized racism, such as employment practices that lead to service providers who are not representative of the diversity of the communities they serve, and inadequate funding for community-based services. In Canada and other Western countries, women seeking assistance in relation to abuse within health care services commonly encounter racism and classism (Campbell et al., 1994; Dobash & Dobash, 1992; Hampton & Newberger, 1988; Varcoe, 1997), factors that likely deter access and disclosure and certainly diminish the benefit of service.

Women who speak limited English (this includes some immigrant women, francophone women in English-dominated regions, and women who speak Aboriginal languages) find services less accessible and appropriate in most areas. For example, a survey of resources in Greater Vancouver illustrated that services for francophone women experiencing abuse are difficult to find and may not be affordable (e.g., psychologists), thus limiting French-speaking women's support for dealing with abusive partners (Dubois,

Dussault, & Lévesque, 1994). For women who are immigrants, citizenship issues and unfamiliarity with institutional systems further compound the problems of access throughout the legal, health care, and social welfare systems (Varcoe, Jaffer, & Irwin, 2000). For many immigrant women language, isolation, and economic fears are also barriers to support.

With the well-placed emphasis on men as batterers, violence in lesbian relationships has only recently been acknowledged (Hamberger, 1994). Lesbians commonly encounter barriers to health care (Stevens & Hall, 1988; Davis, 2000), and evidence exists that in other systems, responses by service providers in relation to violence may be particularly compromised for lesbian women (e.g., Agnew, 1998; Wise & Bowman, 1997).

Inequities Mean Less Power

When service is obtained, women of less privilege have less power in relation to those providing service. With less power in relation to service providers, women are more at the mercy of service providers and thus even less likely to find those services useful. Women with less power are more readily scrutinized, have less power to resist the contingencies that professionals place on the provision of service, and may be viewed as less deserving of service.

Poverty, racialization, and other forms of inequity make individuals more open to the health care provider's scrutiny. In this author's study of emergency units (Varcoe, 1997, 2001), she observed and was told by health care providers that they were less likely to ask questions about abuse of wealthy, nonracialized people. One nurse working in a setting that served a large First Nations reserve as well as a wealthy population said:

> I'll just say "Maybe this could be," rather than really "Look let's deal with this, I think there is some violence here," which I would do with the [Native] Indian women, which I probably wouldn't do with the [wealthier] ladies.

Health care providers commonly associated and anticipated violence with poor and racialized people, despite the fact that they were aware that violence crosses all socio-economic levels and cultures. Paradoxically, although they were likely to assume abuse as an issue among poor and racialized women, they also tended to view poor and racialized women as less deserving of care and support. In a disturbing example, nurses reported that a physician refused to call the sexual assault team to examine a First Nations woman who had been drinking, calling her "a societal derelict." Such judgements were not based directly on class and race alone, but rather on a complex of judgements in which individual women were seen as deserving to different extents. Women who were seen as undeserving of support in relation to violence included women who abused alcohol and drugs and women who had been offered help before and "refused" help, or returned frequently — behaviours that were seen as individual choices rather than as reflecting larger social issues. For example, a social worker told of supporting a particular woman:

> She had been in a transition house, left the house to go and try to reconnect with this partner, been badly beaten again and was now in Emerg awaiting some repair surgery...her situation was quite appalling to some of the nurses, [and my role was] also dealing with the judgment that she was the undeserving patient because of the drug addiction.

Health care providers also made support contingent on women accepting profes-sional definitions of the problem and solutions. "Definitional contingency," which Lempert (1997) described as enacted by friends and family members of women who experience violence, was extended by health care providers. Support was often not offered or was withdrawn from women who were perceived as not making decisions that health care providers thought best. Because women with less privilege have less power in relation to service providers, these dynamics are more likely to play out along the lines of existing inequities.

Intersecting inequities mean that certain women have less service and support for dealing with violence. The more inequity a woman experiences, the less likely she is to find appropriate, meaningful support in dealing with violence in her life. And, the more inequity she experiences, the less power she has in relation to those providing support.

THE DYNAMICS OF INEQUITY AND VIOLENCE SUSTAIN PRIVILEGE

The dynamics between violence and inequity are self-perpetuating, sustained positions of privilege and notions of superiority, and distance persons of privilege from violence. This maintenance of the status quo of inequity and violence is actualized primarily through stereotyping. These stereotypes include associating violence with people of less privilege (particularly poor and racialized people) and associating certain characteristics such as passivity and acceptance of abuse with those same people (Agnew, 1998).

Inequity fosters violence, which in turn fosters inequity. The greater the inequities a given woman experiences, the more forms of violence she is exposed to and the less likely she is to receive meaningful support. The more violence she must endure, the more inequity is entrenched. So, for example, a woman who is poor and unable to afford independent housing, legal fees, and other services that might help decrease the violence in her life, is kept in violence and kept poor.

These dynamics also sustain positions of privilege and notions of superiority. When women who are marginalized in some way are recognized as abused, rather than others associating violence with vulnerability and visibility, such women may be judged as being more "prone" to being battered. In a study of emergency units and their commu-nities (Varcoe, 1997, 2001), health care providers commonly associated violence with the racialized groups in their community but attributed the association to race, rather than to the vulnerabilities associated with racism or to the visibility occasioned by appearance. When asked about their experiences in dealing with violence against women, health care providers tended to recall only racialized women. They more easily recalled women they identified by race, tended to anticipate and observe violence among racialized women, and thus more often recognized abuse among racialized women, reinforcing their ideas about among which people and communities violence occurred.

When increased scrutiny of racialized and poor women identifies violence, the iden-tification of violence is interpreted as further evidence that the particular group is *more violent* rather than *more visible* to those in positions of power. Rather than the dispro-portionate barriers to disclosure being seen and being attributed to inequities, women are seen as not wanting help. When women do not use or access services, this is not seen as reflecting inadequate service but rather, in a victim-blaming manoeuvre, is again often explained as not wanting help. Limited choices are not seen for what they are, but rather are considered choices women make (see also Mahoney, 1994; Mosher, 1998). Thus, if a woman must choose between poverty and abuse, she is blamed either for tolerating abuse or for being poor. If a woman must choose between abuse and exposing her community to racial stereotypes about violence, either the stereotypes are reinforced or she is blamed for tolerating abuse (and other racial stereotypes about women in certain groups — such as passivity and tolerance for violence — are reinforced).

The dynamics of inequality and violence are often dismissed by using the concept of culture. In Canadian society, "culture" is often conflated with "race" and used to explain all sorts of social problems and behaviours. In respect to violence, such ideas can be used to dismiss abuse as a "cultural problem" among certain people. Thus culture is a concept often used to mask the dynamics between inequity and violence. For example, in an ethnographic study (Varcoe, 1997), referring to racialized groups, both racialized and non-racialized people told the author that it was "against their culture" to disclose abuse.

The dynamics of inequality and violence reinforce stereotypes that associate violence with the less privileged. Women who are seen to endure violence (despite the fact that they may be doing so partially in resistance to other forms of oppression) may be judged as being accepting of violence. Increased exposure to violence may be seen as a failing on the part of the woman. Similarly, if less service decreases the effectiveness of women's attempts to limit the violence they endure, then that ineffectiveness may be attributed to the woman. Finally, given the greater scrutiny of less privileged women by powerful service providers, less privileged groups may be perceived as being more violent.

These stereotypes in turn serve to maintain the superiority of more privileged people (particularly racial and class superiority) and to distance those more privileged from violence. The logic here is that violence is a problem of the "other" and thus is not a problem of those with more privilege; it is a problem of "those people" and by contrast, is *not* a problem of "my" people. Thus a person of privilege is superior because of membership in a seemingly less violent group, and violence is a problem that is at a distance from those persons and groups. Ideas about violence work to maintain notions of racial superiority among those with white-skin privilege, and ideas about race and class work to keep violence at a distance from those with privilege. Furthermore, these demeaning stereotypes particularly put racialized women in the position of protecting their communities by enduring individual violence.

The dynamics of inequality and violence "work" for people in privileged positions. And professional service providers are at the interface between the worlds of privilege and women who require service. The increased visibility of marginalized people and increased scrutiny by professionals are fuelled by stereotypical thinking and biased expectations, all of which magnify the appearance of an increased incidence of violence among poor and racialized people, an appearance that in turn fosters demeaning stereotypes.

IMPLICATIONS

Attempts to address inequities and violence in relation to women's health generally focus on the accessibility and appropriateness of services rather than on the correction of fundamental inequities within our society. Improvements to service provision generally take the form of providing services for particular marginalized groups and of promoting "cultural sensitivity" in mainstream services. These strategies are inadequate and must be replaced with strategies that address fundamental social inequities and strategies to provide services that are based on critical awareness of inequity and actively seek to redress those inequities.

Address Fundamental Social Inequities

Anti-violence work must be accompanied by active strategies to address social inequities. Lack of economic resources seriously compromises women's ability to change their circumstances and live in safety (Browne & Bassuk, 2000). Since economic independence is the greatest determinant of women entering and leaving abusive relationships (Gurr, Mailloux, & Kinnon, 1996), strategies that increase the financial and psychological independence of women, particularly women who are marginalized by other inequities such as racialization, disability, and age, are far more likely to have an impact on reducing violence against women than any violence-specific programs. Social policies that promote equity in hiring practices and wages; social housing; subsidized child care; legal aid, divorce, and child-support laws that foster equity; and so on should be supported by all who wish to reduce violence against women.

Base Services on a Critical Awareness of Inequities

Anti-violence services need to be based on a critical understanding of all forms of inequity and integrated with services that attempt to address such inequities. The intersecting impacts of disability, mental illness, poverty, racism, ageism, and heterosexism must be considered in the planning, improvement, and delivery of services. Individual women's experiences of violence must be understood within the context of their lives and the inequities they experience, and support must be provided based on that understanding. This means that support must be woman-centred and promote economic independence. Mills (1996) argues that rather than insisting that a woman leave her partner, a woman-centred approach to economic independence is required to explore all the woman's options and recognize "that her uncertainty and emotional and cultural loyalties demand a safe and non-judgemental space in which to explore these issues" (p. 266).

Mills (1996) has argued for replacing the criminal model of response with an integrated social response in the form of "domestic violence commissions" that would place control in the hands of women themselves and address economic independence as well as the violence the woman has experienced. Wuest and Merritt-Gray (1999) concur and argue that helpers must go beyond simply facilitating access to resources. Rather, they argue, women need more than just access to financial aid; they need to know how to create long-term financial security. Women need more than police protection; they need the judicial system to support their economic independence through the division of assets, child support, and the maintenance of their personal boundaries.

Addressing the inequities that women face that are based on gender and are magnified by all other forms of inequity must begin with dealing with economic issues. Simultaneously, active strategies to address particular forms of oppression are essential to interrupt the dynamics of inequality and violence. Considering anti-racist strategies may provide ideas for approaches that are also consciously anti-heterosexist, anti-ageist, anti-ableist, and so on.

Replace "Multiculturalism" with Anti-Racism

The improvement of mainstream anti-violence services must move beyond the ideology of **multiculturalism**, which pervades Canadian society (Henry et al., 2000; Ng, 1993a, 1993b), and beyond the passive notion of "cultural sensitivity." Multiculturalism is inadequate to the goal of eradicating racism because its focus is on improving the behaviour of "**prejudiced** individuals," which overlooks the ways in which racism is deeply embedded in language, structures, and institutions. In a multicultural analysis of service, the problem is defined as mismatches between "minority" and dominant cultures, which overlooks political and economic forces and makes the "different" culture the problem. The focus in improving services from a multiculturalism perspective is on bringing "culture" into care, which often confuses culture with "ethnicity," and perpetuates the use of racial categories. Multiculturalism assumes a "level playing field" between individuals, which overlooks the historical impact of colonization, immigration, and racism. The related notion of cultural sensitivity is similarly insufficient. Such an idea relies on the passive "sensitivity" of members of dominant groups to the "difference" of "others" and leaves inequity unexamined.

Actively anti-racist approaches would include changing language, structures, and institutions. Racism is manifest in structures and service delivery through lack of access to appropriate programs and services for racialized women, inadequate funding for ethnoracial community-based agencies, lack of minority representation in social agencies, ethnocentric values and counselling services, and monocultural or ad hoc "multicultural" models of service delivery. Meaningful change would thus include improved funding for community-based agencies (without further entrenching racial stereotypes), hiring practices that ensure that the diversity in any given community is reflected in the social locations of those providing service, and the development of anti-racist models of service delivery that take into account the inequities that women experience and the impact of those inequities on women's lives and communities.

Mosher (1998) asks if it would not be preferable to discern what would make it possible for a woman "to take care of her race, her community, her husband [or partner] and herself without having to choose among them" (p. 148). To move toward that preferable option, those who are in positions of professional privilege must examine their stance in relation to inequities and violence. People in such positions have the option of using their privilege in ways that oppose the dynamics of inequality and violence toward improving women's health rather than maintaining the status quo.

ACKNOWLEDGEMENTS

This research was supported by a National Health Research and Development Program fellowship, by a research grant from the Canadian Nurses Foundation, and by two grants from the British Columbia Health Research Foundation. The author gratefully acknowledges all the research participants, the members of "Women in Action," and Dr. Joan Anderson for her guidance.

STUDY QUESTIONS

1. What privileges do you personally experience? How do these privileges shape your assumptions, values, and beliefs? What sensitivities and "blind spots" do your privileges create?

2. What are your beliefs about the demographics of violence against women?

3. What do you believe is the extent of violence within the community with which you identify? What influences the ideas you hold?

4. In what ways has the ideology of multiculturalism influenced your thinking about how human services ought to be provided?

GLOSSARY

classism An assumption of superiority in relation to a group of people of a given rank or status (usually socioeconomic) in the community.

corporate violence Behaviour and actions of persons in authority within the corporation, including acts of omission that endanger the health and safety of employees and other persons.

feminism A point of view that considers women as oppressed and exploited; includes both a commitment to changing the condition of women and the adoption of a critical perspective toward dominant intellectual traditions and methodologies.

gendered Of a given phenomenon, influenced and varied by the gender of the persons involved; for example, work, caregiving, and income are different for men and women and thus are "gendered."

intersectionality The interaction between forms of oppressions (such as racism and sexism) in ways that magnify one another; for example, being racialized is not an "added" form of oppression for a woman; rather it magnifies that oppression (Brewer, 1993; Collins, 1993).

multiculturalism An approach to culture and "difference" in diverse, multiracial, multilingual societies that has arisen from the general social theory of cultural pluralism. Cultural pluralism holds that all cultures are "equal" but different. Multiculturalism emphasizes culture as a determinant of behaviour and "difference" (rather than, for example, structural inequities), and is often associated with cultural relativism, the idea that each culture has its own values and should be judged by its own standards. Multiculturalism is enshrined in Canadian society, in various laws and in commonsense understandings of Canada. In health care, multiculturalism has been increasingly associated with calls for "cultural sensitivity," meaning that health care providers should be "tolerant" of and sensitive to the "differences" of "other" cultures (nondominant groups).

patriarchy The system of male domination over women — the rule of husbands, male bosses, and other men in social, economic, and political institutions.

prejudiced Holding an unreasonable, unjustified bias; having a preconceived opinion that is usually unfavourable.

racialization The process by which people are labelled according to particular physical characteristics or arbitrary ethnic or racial categories, and then dealt with in accordance with beliefs related to those labels (Agnew, 1998). This process is based on the concept of race, "a socially constructed phenomenon based on the erroneous assumption that physical differences such as skin colour, hair colour, and texture, and facial features are related to intellectual, moral or cultural superiority. The concept of race has no basis in biological reality and as such has no meaning independent of its social definitions" (Henry et al., 2000, p. 4).

sexual harassment Conduct that occurs in a gender-stratified context and in a context of differential power relationships and that often involves sexual remarks, sexual touching, demands for sex, sexual impositions, and other unwanted and offensive conduct.

violence An act involving force or coercion and that causes physical, psychological, or emotional harm to others.

RECOMMENDED READINGS

Barnett, O.W. (2000). Why battered women do not leave: Part 1: External inhibiting factors within society. *Trauma, Violence & Abuse, 1*(4), 343–372. A current and extensive analysis of the social context of violence against women and the social barriers to living violence-free.

Bayne-Smith, M. (Ed.). (1996). *Race, gender and health.* Thousand Oaks, CA: Sage. An examination of the health of women of colour in the context of their lives and living conditions. The excellent coverage of these areas brings together the most recent empirical evidence.

Bolaria, B.S., & Bolaria, R. (Eds.). (1994). *Women, medicine and health.* Halifax and Saskatoon: Fernwood Publishing and Social Research Unit. A wide range of essays concerning women's health status and health concerns as they relate to women's socioeconomic status, gendered division of labour, and women's work. One common theme of the essays is that women's subordinate position in the health sector and inequalities in health are manifestations of socially structured gender inequalities.

Fineman, M.A., & Mykitiuk, R. (1994). *The public nature of private violence.* New York: Routledge. A compilation of a variety of excellent critical analyses of racism, conceptualizations of violence against women, sexual assault, and child abuse.

Fischbach, R.L., & Donnelly, E. (1996). Domestic violence against women: A contemporary issue in international health. In J. Subedi & E.B. Gallagher (Eds.), *Society, health and disease: Transcultural perspectives* (pp. 316–345). Upper Saddle River, NJ: Prentice-Hall. A comprehensive analysis of violence against women and its health consequences, with a focus on low-income countries; summarizes a number of studies on violence and health and includes an extensive list of relevant references.

Johnson, H. (1996). *Dangerous domains: Violence against women in Canada.* Toronto: Nelson. A comprehensive analysis of the nature and extent of violence in Canadian families.

Labour Canada. Women's Bureau. (1991). Occupational safety and health concerns of Canadian women: A background paper. Ottawa: Minister of Supply and Services Canada. A discussion of a number of health issues for women, with a focus on women's lives and work patterns and associated health risks and outcomes. Working conditions in traditional female jobs and their effects on women's health and risks associated with jobs commonly held by women are the primary focus.

Smaje, C. (2000). Race, ethnicity and health. In C.E. Bird, P. Conrad, & A.M. Fremont (Eds.), *Handbook of medical sociology* (pp. 114–128). Upper Saddle River, NJ: Prentice-Hall. An overview of the current research and thinking in this domain of medical sociology; the primary focus is on the contemporary situation in the United Kingdom and the United States.

Statistics Canada. (2000). *Women in Canada: A gender-based statistical report.* Cat. no. 89-503-XPE. Ottawa: Statistics Canada. A good resource of empirical data on socioeconomic status and the demographic composition of Canadian women; includes statistics on women's health, education, labour force characteristics, and income and earnings. A major section is devoted to immigrant women, visible minority women, and Aboriginal women.

REFERENCES

Agnew, V. (1998). *In search of a safe place: Abused women and culturally sensitive services.* Toronto: University of Toronto Press.

Allman, K.K.M. (1992). Race, racism, and health: Examining the "natural" facts. In J.L. Thompson, D.G. Allen, & L. Rodrigues-Fisher, *Critique, resistance and action: Working papers in the politics of nursing* (pp. 35–52). New York: NLN.

Arnetz, J.E., Arnetz, B.B., & Soderman, E. (1998). Violence toward health care workers: Prevalence and incidence at a large regional hospital in Sweden. *AAOHN, 46*(3), 107–114.

Barbee, E.L. (1992). Ethnicity and woman abuse in the United States. In C.M. Sampselle (Ed.), *Violence against women: Nursing research, education and practice issues* (pp. 153–166). New York: Hemisphere.

Barnett, O.W. (2000). Why battered women do not leave: Part 1: External inhibiting factors within society. *Trauma, Violence & Abuse, 1*(4), 343–372.

BC Task Force on Family Violence. (1992). *Is anyone listening? Report of the British Columbia Task Force on Family Violence.* Victoria, BC: Ministry of Women's Equality.

Bernhard, L.A. (2000). Physical and sexual violence experienced by lesbian and heterosexual women. *Violence against women, 6*(1), 68–79.

Bograd, M. (1988). Feminist perspectives on wife abuse: An introduction. In K. Yllö & M. Bograd (Eds.), *Feminist perspectives on wife abuse* (pp. 11–26). Newbury Park, CA: Sage.

Brewer, R.M. (1993). Theorizing race, class and gender: The new scholarship of Black feminist intellectuals and Black women's labour. In S.M. James & A.P.A. Busia, *Theorizing black feminisms: The visionary pragmatism for Black women* (pp. 13–30). London: Routledge.

Browne, A., & Bassuk, S.S. (1997). Intimate violence in the lives of homeless and poor housed women: Prevalence and patterns in an ethnically diverse sample. *American Journal of Orthopsychiatry, 67*(2), 261–278.

Campbell, J.C., Pliska, M.J., Taylor, W., & Sheridan, D. (1994). Battered women's experiences in the emergency department. *Journal of Emergency Nursing, 20*(4), 280–288.

Carroll, V., & Morin, K.H. (1998). Workplace violence affects one-third of nurses: Survey of nurses in seven SNA's reveals staff nurses most at risk. *American Nurses, 30*(5), 15.

Collins, P.H. (1993). Toward a new vision: Race, class, and gender as categories of analysis and connection. *Race, Sex & Class, 1*(1), 25–45.

Coombes, R. (1998). Violence: The facts. *Nursing Times, 94*(43), 12–13.

Culley, L. (1996). A critique of multiculturalism in health care: The challenge for nurse education. *Journal of Advanced Nursing, 23*, 564–570.

Crenshaw, K.W. (1994). Mapping the margins: Intersectionality, identity politics, and violence against women of color. In M.A. Fineman & R. Mykitiuk (Eds.), *The public nature of private violence* (pp. 93–118). New York: Routledge.

Davis, V. (2000). Lesbian health guidelines. *Journal of the Society of Obstetricians and Gynaecologists of Canada, 22*, 202–205.

DisAbled Women's Network (DAWN). (1989). *Beating the odds: Violence against women with disabilities.* Position Paper #2. Toronto: DAWN.

Dobash, R.E., & Dobash, R.P. (1988). Research as social action: The struggle for battered women. In K. Yllö & M. Bograd (Eds.), *Feminist perspectives on wife abuse* (pp. 51–74). Newbury Park, CA: Sage.

Dobash, R.E., & Dobash, R. (1992). *Women, violence and social change.* London: Routledge.

Dubois, M.-F., Dussault, M., & Lévesque, M. (1994). *Que ça change!! Rapport du Comité consultatif sur la violence.* Vancouver: Réseau-Femmes Columbie-Britannique.

Dutton, D. (1994). Patriarchy and wife assault: The ecological fallacy. *Violence and Victims, 9*(2), 167–182.

Gelles, R.J. (1993). Introduction. In R.J. Gelles & D.R. Loseke (Eds.), *Current controversies on family violence* (pp. 1–9). Newbury Park, CA: Sage.

Grillo, T., & Wildman, S. (1995a). Obscuring the importance of race: The implications of making comparisons between racism and sexism (or other isms). In R. Delgado, *Critical race theory: The cutting edge* (pp. 564–572). Philadelphia: Temple University Press.

Grillo, T., & Wildman, S. (1995b). Sexism, racism and the analogy problem in feminist thought. In J. Adleman & G.M. Enguídanos, *Racism in the lives of women: Testimony, theory and guides to antiracist practice* (pp. 171–180). New York: Harrington Park Press.

Gurr, J., Mailloux, L., & Kinnon, D. (1996). *Breaking the links between poverty and violence against women*. Ottawa: Health Canada.

Hamberger, L.K. (1994). Domestic partner abuse: Expanding paradigms for understanding and intervention. *Violence and Victims, 9*(2), 91–94.

Hampton, R.L., & Newberger, E.H. (1988). Child abuse incidence and reporting by hospitals: Significance of severity, class and race. In G.T. Hotaling, D. Finkelhor, J.T. Kirkpatrick, & M.A. Straus, *Coping with family violence: Research and policy perspective.* (pp. 212–221). Newbury Park, CA: Sage.

Health Canada. (1993). *Family violence against women with disabilities*. Ottawa: National Clearinghouse on Family Violence.

Heise, L.L. (1994). Gender-based abuse: The global epidemic. In A.J. Dan (Ed.), *Reframing women's health: Multidisciplinary research and practice* (pp. 233–250). Thousand Oaks, CA: Sage.

Heise, L.L., Pitanguy, J., & Germain, A. (1994). *Violence against women: The hidden health burden*. World Bank Discussion Paper #255. Washington, DC: World Bank.

Henry, F., Tator, C., Mattis, W., & Rees, T. (2000). *The colour of democracy: Racism in Canadian society*. Toronto: Harcourt Canada.

Higginbotham, E.B. (1992). African-American women's history and the metalanguage of race. *Signs: Journal of Women in Culture and Society, 17*(21), 251–274.

Hightower, J., Smith, G., Ward-Hall, C., & Hightower, H.C. (1999). *Meeting the needs of abused older women?* A British Columbia and Yukon transition house survey. Unpublished manuscript. BC Institute Against Family Violence, Vancouver.

Hinch, R., & DeKeseredy, W. (1994). Corporate violence and women's health at home and in the workplace. In B.S. Bolaria & H.D. Dickinson (Eds.), *Health, illness, and health care in Canada* (pp. 326–344). Toronto: Harcourt Brace.

hooks, b. (1984). *Feminist theory: From margin to center*. Boston, MA: South End Press.

Johnson, H. (1996). *Dangerous domains: Violence against women in Canada*. Toronto: Nelson.

Johnson, H. (1998). Rethinking survey research on violence against women. In R.E. Dobash & R.P. Dobash (Eds.), *Rethinking violence against women* (pp. 23–51). Thousand Oaks, CA: Sage.

Kelly, L., & Radford, J. (1998). Sexual violence against women and girls. In R.E. Dobash & R.P. Dobash (Eds.), *Rethinking violence against women* (pp. 53–76). Thousand Oaks, CA: Sage.

Kerr, R., & McLean, J. (1996). *Paying for violence: Some of the costs of violence against women in BC*. Victoria, BC: Ministry of Women's Equality.

Koss, M.P. (1990). The women's mental health research agenda: Violence against women. *American Psychologist, 45*(3), 374–380.

Lambert, L.C., & Firestone, J.M. (2000). Economic context and multiple abuse techniques. *Violence Against Women, 6*(1), 49–67.

Lempert, L. (1997). The other side of help: Negative effects in the help-seeking processes of abused women. *Qualitative Sociology, 20*(2), 289–309.

Letellier, P. (1994). Gay and bisexual male domestic violence victimization: Challenges to feminist theory and responses to violence. *Violence and Victims, 9*(2), 95–106.

Levett, A., & Johnson, H. (1997). *A statistical comparison of women's experiences of violence in urban and rural settings*. Ottawa: Canadian Centre for Justice Statistics, Statistics Canada.

Levinson, D. (1989). *Family violence in cross-cultural perspective*. Newbury Park, CA: Sage.

Mahoney, M.R. (1994). Victimization or oppression? Women's lives, violence, and agency. In M.A. Fineman & R. Mykitiuk (Eds.), *The public nature of private violence* (pp. 59–92). New York: Routledge.

Miller, S.L. (1994). Expanding the boundaries: Toward a more inclusive and integrated study of intimate violence. *Violence and Victims, 9*(2), 183–194.

Mills, L. (1996). Empowering battered women transnationally: The case for postmodern interventions. *Social Work, 41*(3), 261–268.

Mosher, J. (1998). Caught in tangled webs of care: Women abused in intimate relationships. In C.T. Baines, P.M. Evans, & S.M. Neysmith, *Women's caring: Feminist perspectives on social welfare* (2nd ed.). Oxford: Oxford University Press.

Ng, R. (1993a). Sexism, racism, Canadian nationalism. In H. Bannerji (Ed.), *Returning the Gaze: Essays on racism, feminism and politics* (pp. 182–196). Toronto: Sister Vision Press.

Ng, R. (1993b). Multiculturalism as ideology: A textual analysis. In M. Campbell & A. Manicom (Eds.), *Knowledge, experience and ruling relations: Studies in the social organization of knowledge* (pp. 35–48). Toronto: University of Toronto Press.

Phillips, D.S.H. (1998). Culture and systems of oppression in abused women's lives. *Journal of Obstetrical and Gynecological Nursing, 27*, 678–683.

Poster, E.C. (1996). A multinational study of psychiatric nursing staffs' beliefs and concerns about work safety and patient assault. *Archives of Psychiatric Nursing, 10*(6), 365–373.

Ratner, P.A. (1993). The incidence of wife abuse and mental health status in abused wives in Edmonton, Alberta. *Canadian Journal of Public Health, 84*(4), 246–249.

Ratner, P. (1995). *Societal responses as moderators of the health consequences of wife abuse*. Unpublished doctoral dissertation. University of Alberta, Edmonton.

Rattansi, A. (1995). Just framing: Ethnicities and racisms in a "postmodern" framework. In L. Nicholson & S. Seidman, *Social postmodernism: Beyond identity politics* (pp. 250–286). Cambridge: Cambridge University Press.

Renzetti, C.M. (1994). On dancing with a bear: Reflections on some of the current debates among domestic violence theorists. *Violence and Victims, 9*(2), 195–200.

Richie, B.E., & Kanuha, V. (1993). Battered women of color in public heath care systems: Racism, sexism and violence. In B. Bair & S.E. Cayleff (Eds.), *Wings of gauze: Women of color and the experience of health and illness*. Detroit: Wayne State University Press.

Ristock, J. (1991). Beyond ideologies: Understanding abuse in lesbian relationships. *Canadian Women's Studies, 12*(1), 74–79.

Rodgers, K. (1994). Wife assault: The findings of a national survey. *Juristat: Service Bulletin, Canadian Center for Justice Statistics, 14*(9), 1–22.

Silva, N. (1994). Towards a feminist methodology in research on battered women. In A.J. Dan (Ed.), *Reframing women's health: Multidisciplinary research and practice* (pp. 290–298). Thousand Oaks, CA: Sage.

Stanko, E.A. (1988). Fear of crime and the myth of the safe home: A feminist critique of criminology. In K. Ylló & M. Bograd (Eds.), *Feminist perspectives on wife abuse* (pp. 75–88). Newbury Park, CA: Sage.

Stark, E., & Flitcraft, A. (1991). Spouse abuse. In M. Rosenburg & M. Fenely (Eds.), *Violence in America: A public health approach* (pp. 123–155). New York: Oxford University Press.

Statistics Canada. (2000). Women in Canada: A gender-based statistical report. Ottawa: Author (cat. no. 89-503-XPE).

Stevens, P.E., & Hall, J.M. (1988). Stigma, health beliefs and experiences with health care in lesbian women. *Image: Journal of Nursing Scholarship, 20*(2), 69–73.

Tjaden, P., & Thoennes, N. (1998). *Prevalence, incidence, and consequences of violence against women: Findings from the national violence against women survey.* Washington, DC: U.S. Department of Justice, National Institute of Justice and Centers for Disease Control and Prevention.

Tolman, R.M., & Bennett, L.W. (1990). A review of quantitative research on men who batter. *Journal of Interpersonal Violence, 5,* 87–118.

Turrell, S.C. (2000). A descriptive analysis of same-sex relationship violence for a diverse sample. *Journal of Family Violence, 15,* 281–293.

Varcoe, C. (1996). Theorizing oppression: Implications for nursing research on violence against women. *Canadian Journal of Nursing Research, 28*(1), 61–78.

Varcoe, C. (1997). *Untying our hands: The social context of nursing in relation to violence against women.* Unpublished doctoral dissertation. University of British Columbia, Vancouver.

Varcoe, C. (2001). Abuse obscured: An ethnographic account of emergency unit nursing practice in relation to violence against women. *Canadian Journal of Nursing Research, 32*(4), 95–115.

Varcoe, C., Jaffer, F., & Irwin, L. (2000). *Project violence-free year one.* Report to the BC Health Research Foundation. Unpublished Manuscript. University of Victoria, Victoria, BC.

Vinton, L. (1997). *Questions and answers about older battered women.* http://www.state.fl.us/doea/Home/Publications/Older_Battered_Women/older_battered_women.html.

Walker, L.E.A. (1995). Racism and violence against women. In J. Adelman & G.M. Enguídanos (Eds.), *Racism in the lives of women: Testimony, theory, and guides to antiracist practice* (pp. 239–249). New York: Harrington Park.

Wardell, L., Gillespie, D.L., & Leffler, A. (1983). Science and violence against wives. In D. Finkelhor, R. Gelles, G. Hotaling, & M. Straus (Eds.), *The dark side of families* (pp. 69–84). Beverly Hills, CA: Sage.

Wildman, S., & Davis, A.D. (1995). Language and silence: Making systems of privilege visible. In R. Delgado, *Critical race theory: The cutting edge* (pp. 573–579). Philadelphia: Temple University Press.

Wise, A.J., & Bowman, S.L. (1997). Comparison of beginning counselors' responses to lesbian vs. heterosexual partner abuse. *Violence and Victims, 12*(2), 127–135.

Wuest, J., & Merritt-Gray, M. (1999). Not going back: Sustaining the separation in the process of leaving abusive relationships. *Violence Against Women, 5*(2), 110–133.

Yassi, A., Tate, R., Cooper, J., Jenkins, J., & Trottier, J. (1998). Causes of staff abuse in health care facilities: Implications for prevention. *American Association of Occupational Health Nursing, 46*(10), 484–491.

Ylló, K. (1993). Through a feminist lens: Gender, power and violence. In R.J. Gelles & D.R. Loseke (Eds.), *Current controversies on family violence* (pp. 47–62). Newbury Park, CA: Sage.

NOTE

1. "Culture" is often thought of only in relation to racialized people, a common feature of Canadian democratic racism (Henry et al., 2000) that is especially problematic in relation to violence.

12

Women's Reproductive Work:
A Precarious Obligation

GWEN HARTRICK   University of Victoria

INTRODUCTION

Reproductive issues are central to women's **health** in most parts of the world (Garcia Moreno, & Claro, 1994). These issues are increasingly located in the broader framework of **reproductive work**, which includes the biological bearing of children as well as the daily activities necessary to sustain the physical and emotional well-being of significant others and of society in general. Women's reproductive work has profound implications for their health and well-being. The sheer volume of women's domestic reproductive labour has major implications for women's health (Doyal, 1995, p.28). In poorer countries, women literally work themselves to death, and in more affluent countries, women's reproductive work is associated with an increased incidence of depression and other illnesses (Doyal, 1995).

The health of women and families has traditionally been considered complementary. Consequently, policymakers and health care practitioners often fail to recognize the time, energy, and material resources that women expend in their daily work of taking care of family health and the impact this has on women's own health (Messias et al., 1997). This chapter examines how the reproductive work necessary for the promotion of family health may well contravene the promotion of women's health. The social arrangements that perpetuate and sustain women's responsibility for, and obligation to, reproductive work are considered in light of the costs of that obligation to women's own well-being.

WOMEN'S HEALTH AND THEIR REPRODUCTIVE WORK

Health is "created and lived by people in the settings of their everyday life, where they learn, work, play, and love" (World Health Organization [WHO], 1986). Therefore, in considering women's health it is important to begin by analyzing the major areas of activity that constitute women's lives. Examining women's lives and areas of activity can illuminate the impact of these activities on their health and well-being. According to Doyal (1995), the cumulative effects of various activities are the major determinants of women's health. Since activities that affect health are not merely a matter of personal choice and are often facilitated and constrained by social and material structures and conditions (Poland, 1992), such an analysis must consider the social and material conditions that direct women's reproductive work (Angus, 1994).

WOMEN'S REPRODUCTIVE WORK

Although biology decrees women's role in procreation, social arrangements mandate their responsibility for the reproductive work of maintaining the health and well-being of society. As a consequence of their biological capacity for reproduction, women in most societies are closely tied to and identified with the domestic world of home, family, and household (Doyal, 1995). Kabeer (1991) asserts that households comprise "the bundle of relationships in a society through which reproductive activities are organized" (p. 10). The daily activities of women are largely concerned with reproduction and the physical subsistence and well-being of others (Smith, 1987). This responsibility is shouldered both biologically and socially.

Biological Reproductive Work

The event of bearing a child is highly significant in every culture throughout the world (Callister, 1995). "Childbirth is a universally celebrated event and an occasion for dancing, fireworks, flowers or gifts" (Royston & Armstrong, 1989, p. 9). The status of "mother" continues to be a central element in the definition of a normal adult female, and in most cultures, women are pressured to prove their femaleness by becoming mothers (Doyal, 1995; Gonzalez, 2000). Both women who do not want children and those who want children but cannot conceive live with the pressure of family, religious, and societal expectations that they bear children. Consequently, procreation has been found to be a central construct in women's identity (Chodorow, 1978; Humphrey, 1977; Mahlstedt, 1985) and self-esteem (Johnson, 1996). Women have reported that when they fail to fulfill this prescribed societal norm of procreation they experience an assault on their personal identity, self-concept, and body image (Gonzalez, 2000).

Doyal (1995) contends that the inherent societal pressure and expectation to procreate impedes the opportunity for women to make real choices about their procreation and ultimately their health. This lack of choice can have penetrating effects on women's health. For example, the pressure to be a mother draws many women into the world of high technology, **gynecology**, and **obstetrics**. Women may turn to technology in the hope of finding a solution to the "problem" of infertility. New technologies such as in vitro fertilization (IVF) or gamete intrafallopian tube transfer (GIFT) are hailed as miracle solutions (Doyal, 1995). Although both members of an infertile couple may find this search for a technological solution difficult, research suggests that women experience the greatest distress and are most anguished by their "failure" to conceive (Greil, Leitko, & Porter, 1988). Given the high cost (e.g., the stress of participating in IVF programs, the invasiveness of the process, the risks associated with the drugs) and the relatively low success rate, the search for a technological solution can have harmful effects on women's well-being and health.

Social Reproductive Work

Care is at the core of women's history and has been the main focus of their activity (Colliere, 1986). In examining the cultural roots of women's caring, Colliere asserts that women's reproductive role made them responsible for every aspect of reproduction, including childbearing and rearing, nurturing and nourishing. According to Colliere, since death is linked with birth, women were also in charge of the sick and elderly. This responsibility continues today.

Most of this **caring labour** is carried out in the home. Although in the Western world there is an **ideology** of separate spheres (Armstrong & Armstrong, 1994; Drover & Kearns, 1993), where home is supposedly "a restful haven from the world of commerce" (Angus, 1994, p.26), for many women home is not a site of leisure. Rather, it is a place where there are no temporal boundaries to the work required of them. In the home, women engage in multiple activities, including housework, child care, the emotional care of others, care of the elderly, and so forth (Armstrong & Armstrong, 1994). All of this work is essentially focused on reproducing and sustaining the health and well-being of family members. Commonly, women juggle the care of children with the care of aging parents and other family members while simultaneously participating in the labour force. For example, over 85 percent of the care given to elderly Canadians is provided by family (Chapell, Strain, & Blandford, 1986). This family caregiving is most often assumed by women, particularly by women in mid-life (Wuest, 1993).

Graham (1983) asserts that in essence this caring work has been the defining characteristic of women's self-identity and their life work. However, viewing caring labour as a natural responsibility of women conceals the constraints, costs, and consequences for women (Baines, Evans, & Neysmith, 1998). The ideology that separates the spheres of employment and home may conceal the long-term costs in poverty and poor health that women incur as they assume the responsibility for family health.

THE GENDER DIVISION OF LABOUR AND THE INVISIBILITY OF WOMEN'S REPRODUCTIVE WORK

In considering the effects that women's reproductive work may ultimately have on their health and well-being, it is essential to consider the broader social arrangements that render reproductive work stressful or fatiguing (Angus, 1994; Wuest, 1993). Angus (1994) contends that the dominant order that divides labour according to **gender** may be one of the major determinants of poor health in women (Angus, 1994). This division of labour, accomplished through the prevailing set of **normative conceptions** and ideologies about what activities are appropriate for men and women, gives women little choice about whether or not to accept reproductive obligations. Existing social arrangements create legal, gendered, and moral expectations that women take up their reproductive work (Opie, 1994).

Although gender divisions of responsibility have evolved and even softened somewhat during the past few decades, the contemporary family continues to be largely constituted by this gender division, which defines certain work as domestic, female, and unpaid, and other work as public, male, and paid (Drover & Kerans, 1993). For example, although women are increasingly entering the public workforce, as evidenced by the large increase in dual earning families (71 percent of couples with children under 19 were dual earners in 1990, compared with 30 percent in 1970), women continue to be responsible for household chores. While more couples are sharing housework, most often women continue to be responsible for the regularly required chores, such as meal preparation and child care (Armstrong & Armstrong, 1994; Devereaux, 1993). In contrast, men participate in more episodic tasks such as home maintenance (Armstrong & Armstrong, 1994; Devereaux, 1993). In general, working mothers have less respite from demands than do their partners, and the time-consuming nature of those demands in the home sphere leaves little time for self-renewal or leisure (Angus, 1994).

Preston (1994) found that the combined effects of gender role and marital status contributed significantly to the variance in women's health. Specifically, of four marital contexts studied (married men and married women and unmarried men and unmarried women), married women were in the poorest health and the most vulnerable to stress. Other research has also shown marriage to be more rewarding for men than for women (Coombs, 1991). Married women have higher rates of mental disorders (Kessler & McRae, 1981); for example, in one study men described dissatisfaction with marriage yet were in good health, while women were more likely to say they were happily married but exhibited much poorer mental health (Bernard, 1972). Gove (1984) contends that gender differences in physical and mental illness can be explained by the demands of the female nurturant role. Similar to Bernard's (1972) description of the housewife syndrome, which consists of nervousness, fainting, insomnia, trembling hands, nightmares, and other anxiety symptoms, Gove (1984) emphasizes the deleterious effects that the unending demands of reproductive work can have on women's health.

Overall, the gendered division of labour sanctifies women's responsibility for the reproductive work of society. These socially structured arrangements foster the expectation that women take up the responsibility for nurturing and sustaining their family and/or significant others. However, the recognition of women's reproductive work and their contributions to societal well-being have been hindered by the artificial splitting of the private and public sphere of work (Angus, 1994). Because this work is done in the home and is therefore "invisible," the consequences of bearing this responsibility and carrying out the work are also invisible (Laurence, 1992). Often, the burnout and stress experienced by women caregivers is viewed as a personal limitation or failure while the effects of women's reproductive work on their health are ignored or overlooked.

REPRODUCTIVE WORK AND THE COST TO WOMEN

Research has documented the high price that women may pay to ensure the people they love are cared for (Neysmith, 1998). Although recent workforce trends indicate that women's responsibilities and workloads have increased, these trends have not been reflected in greater economic security or increased health and social benefits (Messias et al., 1997). The double workplace of home and paid employment makes time a "critical resource for employed women as they seek a position of health for themselves amid the demands of home and career" (Angus, 1994, p. 28). In addition, the increased number of women in the paid workforce has not reversed the invisibility and devaluation of the unpaid work women do or the inequity they experience (Messias et al., 1997).

The unpaid work required of women may lead them to make choices that decrease their opportunity for economic benefit. For example, they may take time out of their career life to raise a family and as a result face career stagnation, lower income, and a smaller pension for later life. Although women are no more likely than men to be absent from work due to illness, in 1991 they lost an average of 17.5 days because of personal responsibilities, compared with 3.9 days lost by men (Phillips & Phillips, 1993).

The Cost of Being in Relation and Caring

The nature of reproductive work — long hours, isolation, and continual demands — may be both stressful and fatiguing. Not only does physical work need to be done, but also the "emotional housework" of managing relationships, ensuring harmony between household members, and promoting the emotional health of others needs to be carried out (Doyal, 1995). Varcoe and Turris (1999) found that some women bear this family responsibility for relationships to the extent that they tolerate violence and severe injury. In studying the experiences of women who have been battered, these researchers found that the women's ideas about themselves as mothers and their commitment to their children profoundly shaped their decisions, particularly the decision to remain in the relationship. "Relationship work is primarily seen as women's work, and such ideas add to pressure for women to enter, maintain, and remain in relationships with partners (Varcoe & Turris, 1999, p.15). The ideology of **familism** and the normative expectation that women selflessly care for their family and maintain caring relationships place their well-being in a precarious situation.

Women as Primary Caregivers During Family Illness

As part of their reproductive work and caring labour, women often assume the responsibility for any family members with illness or a chronic health condition. Thirty-one percent of children live with chronic conditions (Newachuk & Taylor, 1992), and their families are the primary caregivers. In these families, women provide most of the care (Stewart et al., 1994). Mothers who care for children with chronic conditions report physical and psychological strain and are at increased risk of health problems such as depression, anxiety, loneliness, and role strain (Stewart et al., 1994).

A study that looked at mothers' experiences of support while caring for their chronically ill child illustrated the pervasive impact of the child's condition on the mother's health and well-being (Stewart et al., 1994). Many mothers described the time-consuming and unrelenting routines of managing their child's symptoms and condition. Even when children were old enough to assume some of the tasks of care, the burden of responsibility continued for mothers. Of the mothers in the study, 94 percent lacked time to meet their own needs. These women described fatigue, the need for "me" time, and not enough time to maintain their own health. Only 16 percent of mothers received practical support (e.g., direct care for the child) from their husbands.

Health care professionals were often condescending. In particular, mothers felt that health professionals were often critical, emphasizing where the mothers were lacking in their caregiving or knowledge. Neither the mothers nor their partners had considered change in maternal or paternal role expectations beyond the care of the child's illness:

although the fathers may have begun to participate in caring for the child's illness, the division of other household responsibilities was not changed to accommodate the extra work required of the mother. Mothers in the study appeared isolated: the support they received was scattered and inadequate (Stewart et al., 1994).

In a study of the effects of home care on caregivers, Gayno (1990) found that women caregivers had more physical health problems. Younger women who were caregivers found the caregiving to be psychologically burdensome. There was a "cycle of neglect" as the stress of prolonged caregiving wore the women down and their own health began to suffer. Gayno concluded that although caring for a disabled family member may be a family choice, an obligation, or even a normative experience, it may well be detrimental to a woman's emotional and physical health.

Aronson (1991) describes the internal struggle that women experience between self-enhancement and self-sacrifice. This struggle results in feelings that the woman is never doing enough. For example, in examining women's choice to stay home with their children or return to the workforce, women are "damned if they do and damned if they don't when it comes to working inside or outside the home" (Ontario Advisory Council on Women's Issues [OACWI], 1990, p. 16). If women choose to return to work, they risk being viewed as "selfish"; if they choose to stay home, they experienced pressure and criticism about not using their intelligence and strengths. Women who assume the dual roles of home and employment face fatigue from double responsibilities, the stressors of inadequate daycare, disruption of family life, and limited benefits (OACWI, 1990).

Even for women who work full-time in the home, depression appears to be an occupational hazard, especially if they have young children (Doyal, 1995). Ultimately, the emotional and physical labour required in the home, combined with the normative expectations and obligations that are placed on women, may foster a sense of guilt and failure. For some women these feelings result when they are unable to carry out the overwhelming obligations, whereas for others the feelings are sparked when they find the expected reproductive work unrewarding or frustrating (Aronson, 1991; Angus, 1994).

HEALTH PROFESSIONALS: HOW DO THEY PERPETUATE POOR HEALTH IN WOMEN?

Canadian culture is dominated by normative expectations that women find both difficult to meet and difficult to relinquish (Wuest, 1998). Even as women's reproductive work and the consequences of that work become visible through documented research, the acceptance of this caring as a "normal" family responsibility and, thereby, women's responsibility, continues (Baines, Evans, & Neysmith, 1998). Health professionals who have been educated and socialized in this ideology and in behaviours that support and perpetuate it continue to confer the responsibility for caregiving on women (Waitzkin, 1991). Anderson and Elfert (1989) found that health professionals played a major role in preserving women's caregiving roles. Similarly, Wuest's (1993) study of caregivers revealed that health professionals continue to reinforce the normative expectation that women are responsible for family health.

The Dilemma of Family-Centred Care

In investigating women's caring, Wuest (1998) found that the competing and changing demands of caring in the current health and social structures of Eastern Canada were highly problematic for women. Women experienced daily struggles, altered prospects, and ambivalent feelings as a result of the competing demands of caring for themselves, their partners, and family members. The expectations of others as well as the expectations they had internalized had a profound influence on what women judged to be legitimate boundaries of care (Wuest, 1998). For example, within the study, women described instances of caring that were based on obligation and duty as opposed to love or commitment. In those situations, the expectation to care was intensified by social, professional, or familial expectations.

Of particular concern is the rhetoric and move to "family-centred care." This ideology places a huge responsibility on women. Although the intent to recognize the significance of family and family members in the health and healing process is laudable, "family-centred care" often translates into the assumption that women are the responsible, primary caregivers for ill family members. For example, a woman who may not have the capacity to take up the responsibility for her elderly mother (and subsequently refuses to do so) may face judgement and harsh criticism from health professionals who assume that it is only right that a daughter cares for her mother. For example, a nurse who worked in an emergency department regularly heard astonished and disdainful comments bestowed on daughters who refused to take their elderly mothers or mothers-in-law home with them, especially when "there was no other place for her to go."

Similarly, mothers are often required to fit into the normative scripts of "caring mother" (Hartrick, 1997). In a study that explored women's experience of self while actively engaged in motherhood, Hartrick (1997) described how the women were profoundly affected by health practitioners who had expectations about what the women should be doing and experiencing in their mothering role. After receiving help, the women often felt deflated, since the expectations of the health practitioners added to the great expectations they were already struggling to meet as mothers.

Wuest (1998) contends that because health care reforms in Canada are creating an increased societal expectation on women to care, health professionals now more than ever need to recognize the vulnerability of women. The above research findings emphasize the importance of health professionals supporting women from an early age to identify their own health needs in relation to their familial roles and responsibilities.

The Necessity of Limiting Women's Reproductive Work

In addition to conferring the responsibility for reproduction and caring to women, Wuest (1998) emphasizes that health professionals have given little attention to establishing limits on women's caring. As declining health care resources place more and more responsibility for health care on families, little consideration has been given to just how much caring work women have the capacity to do. Although the struggle that women have in balancing caring for self and caring for others has been identified in the women's health literature (Lemkau & Landau, 1986), women live in a society that seems to expect them to have a "natural" desire and ability to provide endless care.

The assumption that women's caring capacity is endless may ultimately conflict with the promotion of family and societal well-being. Whether acknowledged or not, women's capacity for caring is bounded. Although many women attempt to extend those boundaries, at some point they do become overloaded: they no longer can provide the emotional labour required to nurture emotionally healthy children and families. The refusal of the state (and of the people who make up the state) to accept the responsibility for ensuring adequate daycare, wages, and other resources to support women's well-being will ultimately translate into less "reproduction" of family health.

The understanding that health is a socially determined phenomenon requires health professionals to look beyond the level of the individual to the **hegemonic structures** that give rise to normative expectations that are deleterious to women's health. As Wuest (1993) asks, if women are not equal partners in society, how might they suddenly be partners in health care? For health policy to be responsive to women's health needs (and ultimately family and societal needs), it must recognize the complexity of women's lives and the diversity of women's experiences. There must be an understanding of the real experience of women as they go about their daily lives and live in families.

Health professionals have an important responsibility to ensure that women have the opportunity to speak of their experiences and "make claims on their own behalf" (Aronson, 1991, p. 164). Health practitioners must take the responsibility for illuminating their own normative assumptions about women's roles and begin deconstructing the biases and myths perpetuated in the health care system (Messias et al., 1997).

RETHINKING HEALTH POLICY

Societal conceptualizations of women and work affect the formulation of health and social policy and the ways in which these policies affect the lives and health of women (Messias et al., 1997). Often the provision of care "is presented as the *raison d'être* of health and social services" (Baines, Evans, & Neysmith, 1998, p. 7). However, if health is a social phenomenon (WHO, 1986) and if women's health is adversely affected by the social responsibility for reproductive work, it is essential to look at how women might be relieved of this normative expectation. The material and ideological structures that require women to be dutiful and undemanding require not only scrutiny but transformation (Aronson, 1998).

Reitsma-Street and Neysmith (in press) contend that the social rights of Canadian citizens to claim public funding for social and health care are increasingly diminishing. The national child care program has ended, family allowances no longer exist, and entitlement to elder care and safe housing is gone from the public agenda. These authors contend that downsizing and restructuring are made to appear inevitable when other options have not been considered. Moreover, these policies can only serve to perpetuate poor health in women.

Of fundamental concern is that health and social policy will continue to be based on old, stereotypical images and historical ideologies. For example, the Canadian government's priority of deficit reduction has meant that services traditionally provided by the welfare state have been downloaded to family, and thereby women (Baines, Evans, & Neysmith, 1998). The notion of community-based health care that has become a dominant feature of Canadian health care reform merely transfers the economic responsibility to the family (Neysmith, 1998). Since family responsibilities are women's responsibilities, women caregivers bear the brunt of this policy change. As health policy mandates family-based care, the demands on women increase, as does the isolation they experience (Wuest, 1993). It is time to consider the implications for women as the state restructures and retreats from public caring (Baines, Evans, & Neysmith, 1998).

The view that women's work consists of reproduction is reflected in past and current health and social policy (Messias et al., 1997). Policymakers have equated women's health care with promoting women's health during childbearing. However, as Wuest (1993) asserts, understanding women's social reality is essential for the development of responsive health policies that address the health needs of women. Although a broader view of women's health across their lifespan is beginning to be recognized, policymakers and health care providers have not seriously considered the effect of social arrangements on women's health. As Canadian health care policy emphasizes health promotion through self-care, mutual aid, and greater community-based services and there is a move toward increasingly locating health care in the community and "closer to home," the essential social, physical, and economic supports have not been included (Wuest, 1993). In essence, Canada's forward-looking health care reform has been used to justify the reduction of institutionalized services and increasing family responsibility (Laurence, 1992). Guberman (1990) asserts that underlying this move to family involvement is the assumption that there is a woman available who is able, willing, and committed to care.

To effect women's health, the connection must be drawn between women's structural position in society (and in families) and their own health experience. This requires a consideration of how the normative expectations of reproductive work, such as the caring and responsibility for family health, is integrated into women's subjective experiences of their lives, and of how normative expectations influence the obligation and willingness of women to care for children, the elderly, and other family members, at the risk of their own health, financial security, and social status.

Political rhetoric and written policy couched in language that implies the naturalness of families' caring work and obligations fail to acknowledge the interests of women as either providers or receivers of care (Aronson, 1998). Women's health is only a concern insofar as it ensures women are able to carry on caring for family members.

> Thus, we see social programs intended to shore up their efforts...such programs as caregiver support groups and respite care serve to provide minimal short-term relief, but with the intention of sustaining the present division of care rather than changing it or asking whether it is in women's best interests to be, effectively, pressed into caregiving. (Aronson, 1998, p. 118)

CONCLUSION

Historically, women's health care has been synonymous with a narrow concept of reproductive health. However, recently health has been redefined to include health promotion throughout the life span. There is now a recognition that understanding women's health requires an awareness of the context of women's lives (Expert Panel of Women's Health [EPWH], 1997). This recognition "warrants examination of economic, social, political, and environmental circumstances for women." Since the ideology of familism dominates social organization in Western society (Dalley, 1990), and since women are the central mechanism for the maintenance of family well-being, this ideology offers limited opportunities for women.

Although the normative expectation of women's reproductive work currently serves the family as well as society at large, the cost to women is substantial. With the onset of an aging population, these arrangements will eventually be of detriment to society as well. By 2031, Canadians age 65 and older will form 21 percent of the population (Corelli, 1986). Women will comprise the majority of the very old. As Covan (1997) points out, research has shown that "frail old women fare worse than do frail old men" (p. 341). Consequently, the future may be bleak if these existing social and fiscal arrangements continue.

Some advocates of women's health have proposed a shift from viewing women's health as "gynecology" to "GYN-ecology, the fit between a woman and her environment" (EPWH, 1997, p. 7). To move forward in the promotion of women's health and in health policy that will effect positive change, it is essential that the functional aspects of women's reproductive health — the ability to perform multiple roles, adapt to the stresses of daily living, and control their overall well-being — be addressed.

STUDY QUESTIONS

1. *In what ways have you adopted the normative expectations that women are "natural" caregivers? For example, what do you assume a "good mother," a "good daughter," or a "good wife" is, does, and looks like?*
2. *How does an emphasis on family-centred health care have the potential to jeopardize women's health?*
3. *How might health professionals begin to effect the systemic changes required for women's health (and, ultimately, family health) to be promoted?*

GLOSSARY

caring labour   The innumerable daily, routine, preventative, monitoring, promotional, and emotional tasks women perform to maintain and build the health of their families and, by extension, the health of society (Heller, 1986).

familism   A dominant ideology that assumes the nuclear family is the primary structure for the organization of daily life and functions of caring; this ideology includes relationships of domination and subordination and the division of domestic labour according to gender (Wuest, 1993).

gender   Culturally determined cognitions, attitudes, and belief systems about females and males. The concept varies among cultures, changes over time, and differs in terms of who makes the observations and judgements (Worell & Remer, 1992, p. 9).

gynecology   The science of the physiological functions and diseases of women.

health   The extent to which an individual or group is able to realize aspirations and satisfy needs and to change and cope with the environment (World Health Organization [WHO], 1984).

hegemonic structures The organized assemblage of meanings and practices; the central and dominant system of ideas or processes that saturate the consciousness of society, organize the educational, economic, and social world, and are expressed in the values and actions of society (Grundy, 1987).

ideology The dominant ideas of a group or culture (Grundy, 1987).

normative conceptions The taken-for-granted, socially constructed assumptions and beliefs about what is normal and natural, which shape people's expectations of their own and others' actions.

obstetrics A branch of medicine dealing with childbirth and the processes immediately preceding and following it.

reproductive work The biological bearing of children as well as the daily activities necessary to create and sustain the physical and emotional well-being of significant others and of society in general.

RECOMMENDED READINGS

Angus, J. (1994). Women's paid/unpaid work and health: Exploring the social context of everyday life. *Canadian Journal of Nursing Research, 26*(4), 23–42. A review of literature from various disciplines to obtain a description of the working lives of Canadian women. The author contends that normative thought and social ideology may obscure the extent and value of women's contributions.

Baines, C., Evans, P., & Neysmith, S. (1998). *Women's caring: Feminist perspectives on social welfare*. Toronto: Oxford University Press. An examination of the implications of women's caring work, recognizing the significance of class and race in structuring inequities.

Doyal, L. (1995). *What makes women sick: Gender and the political economy of health*. London: Macmillan. A study of two aspects of modern medicine: knowledge generated in the biomedical framework is combined with that from other disciplines to develop a more holistic understanding of women's health and illness, and the impact of medical practices on women's health is critically reviewed and compared with that of other factors influencing their well-being.

Wuest, J. (1993). Institutionalizing women's oppression: The inherent risk in health policy that fosters community participation. *Health Care for Women International, 14*, 407–417. A feminist exploration of the assumptions underlying "partnership health policy" that increasingly requires family involvement in health care and community-based health services. The impact of such policy on women's health is examined, including the responsibilities and societal expectations of women as family caregivers.

Wuest, J. (1998). Setting boundaries: A strategy for precarious ordering of women's caring demands. *Research in Nursing and Health, 21*, 39–49. A report of research findings from a grounded theory study that examined the strategies that women use to manage the dissonance created by caring demands; intended to guide the practice of health professionals working with women caring for themselves and others.

REFERENCES

Anderson, J., & Elfert, H. (1989). Managing chronic illness in the family: Women as caregivers. *Journal of Advanced Nursing, 14*, 735–745.

Angus, J. (1994). Women's paid/unpaid work and health: Exploring the social context of everyday life. *Canadian Journal of Nursing Research, 26*(4), 23–42.

Armstrong, P., & Armstrong, H. (1994). *The double ghetto* (3rd ed.). Toronto: McClelland & Stewart.

Aronson, J. (1991). Dutiful daughters and undemanding mothers: Contrasting images of giving and receiving care in middle and later life. In C. Baines, P. Evans, & S. Neysmith (Eds.), *Women's caring: Feminist perspectives on social welfare* (pp. 272–299). Toronto: McClelland & Stewart.

Aronson, J. (1998). Dutiful daughters and undemanding mothers: Contrasting images of giving and receiving care in middle and later life. In C. Baines, P. Evans, & S. Neysmith (Eds.), *Women's caring: Feminist perspectives on social welfare* (2nd ed., pp. 114–139). Toronto: Oxford University Press.

Baines, C., Evans, P., & Neysmith, S. (1998). Women's caring: Work expanding, state contracting. In C. Baines, P. Evans, & S. Neysmith (Eds.), *Women's caring: Feminist perspectives on social welfare* (2nd ed., pp. 272–299). Toronto: Oxford University Press.

Bernard, J. (1972). *The future of marriage.* New York: World.

Callister, L. (1995). Cultural meanings of childbirth. *Journal of Obstetrics, Gynecology and Neonatal Nursing, 24*(4), 327–331.

Chapell, N., Strain, L., & Blandford, A. (1986). *Aging and health care: A social perspective.* Toronto: Holt, Rinehart & Winston.

Chodorow, N. (1978). *The reproduction of mothering.* Berkeley: University of California Press.

Colliere, M. (1986). Invisible care and invisible women as health care-providers. *International Journal of Nursing Studies, 23*(2), 95–112.

Coombs, R.H. (1991). Marital status and personal well-being: A literature review. *Family Relations, 40*, 97–102.

Corelli, R. (1986, October 6). A matter of care. *Maclean's*, pp. 50–53.

Covan, E. (1997). Cultural priorities and elder care: The impact on women. *Health Care for Women International, 18*, 329–342.

Dalley, G. (1990). *Ideologies of caring: Rethinking community and collectivism.* New York: Macmillan.

Devereaux, M. (1993, Autumn). Time use of Canadians in 1992. *Canadian Social Trends*, 13–16.

Doyal, L. (1995). *What makes women sick. Gender and the political economy of health.* London: Macmillan.

Drover, G., & Kearns, P. (1993). New approaches to welfare theory: Foundations. In G. Drover & P. Kerans (Eds.), *New approaches to welfare theory* (pp. 3–31). Cheltenham, UK: Edward Elgar.

Expert Panel on Women's Health (EPWH). (1997). Women's health and women's health care: Recommendations of the 1996 AAN Expert Panel of Women's Health. *Nursing Outlook, 45*(1), 7–15.

Garcia Moreno, C., & Claro, A. (1994). Challenges from the women's health movement: Women's rights versus population control. In G. Sen, A. Germain, & L. Chen (Eds.), *Population policies reconsidered: Health, empowerment and rights* (pp. 47–63). Cambridge, MA: Harvard University Press.

Gayno, S. (1990). The long haul: The effects of home care on caregivers. *IMAGE: Journal of Nursing Scholarship, 22*(4), 208–212.

Gonzalez, L. (2000). Infertility as a transformational process: A framework for psychotherapeutic support of infertile women. *Issues in Mental Health, 21*, 619–633.

Gove, W.R. (1984). Gender differences in mental and physical illness: The effects of fixed roles and nurturant roles. *Social Science and Medicine, 19*, 77–91.

Graham, H. (1983). Caring: A labour of love. In J. Finch & D. Groves (Eds.), *A labor of love: Women, work, and caring* (pp. 13–30). London: Routledge & Kegan Paul.

Greil, A.L., Leitko, T., & Porter, K. (1988). Infertility: His and hers. *Gender and Society, 2*(2), 172–199.

Grundy, S. (1987). *Curriculum: Product or praxis*. London: Falmer Press.

Guberman, N. (1990). The family, women, and caregiving: Who cares for the caregivers. In V. Dhruvarajan (Ed.), *Women and well-being* (pp. 67–78). Kingston & Montreal: McGill–Queen's University Press.

Hartrick, G.A. (1997). Women who are mothers: The experience of defining self. *Health Care for Women International, 18*(3), 263–278.

Heller, A. (1986). *Health and home: Women as health guardians*. Ottawa: Canadian Advisory Committee on the Status of Women.

Humphrey, M. (1977). Sex differences in attitudes to parenthood. *Human Relations, 30*, 737–749.

Johnson, C. (1996). Regaining self-esteem: Strategies and interventions for the infertile woman. *Journal of Obstetric, Gynecologic and Neonatal Nursing, 25*(4), 291–295.

Kabeer, N. (1991). *Gender, production and work: Rethinking the household economy*. Discussion Paper 288. Brighton, UK: Institute of Developmental Studies, University of Sussex.

Kessler, R.C., & McRae, J.A., Jr. (1981). Trends in the relationships between sex and psychological distress: 1957–1976. *American Sociological Review, 46*, 443–452.

Laurence, M. (1992). Womancare–health care: Power and policy. *Canadian Woman Studies, 12*, 31–34.

Lemkau, J.P., & Landau, C. (1986). The selfless syndrome: Assessment and treatment considerations. *Psychotherapy, 23*, 227–232.

Mahlstedt, P.P. (1985). The psychological components of infertility. *Fertility and Sterility, 43*, 335–346.

Martin, E. (1987). *The woman in the body: A cultural analysis of reproduction*. Milton Keynes: Open University Press.

Messias, D., Regev, H., Im, E., Spiers, J., Van, P., & Meleis, A. (1997). Expanding the visibility of women's work: Policy implications. *Nursing Outlook, 45*, 258–264.

Newachuk, P.W., & Taylor, W.R. (1992). Childhood chronic illness: Prevalence, severity and impact. *American Journal of Public Health, 82*, 364–371.

Neysmith, S. (1991). From community care to a social model of care. In C. Baines, P. Evans, & S. Neysmith (Eds.), *Women's caring: Feminist perspectives on social welfare* (pp. 272–299). Toronto: McClelland & Stewart.

Neysmith, S. (1998). From home care to social care: The value of a vision. In C. Baines, P. Evans, & S. Neysmith (Eds.), *Women's caring: Feminist perspectives on social welfare* (pp. 233–249). Toronto: Oxford University Press.

Ontario Advisory Council on Women's Issues (OACWI). (1990). *Women and mental health: A background paper*. Toronto: Author.

Opie, A. (1994). The instability of the caring body: Gender and caregivers of confused older people. *Qualitative Health Research, 4*(1), 31–50.

Phillips, P., & Phillips, E. (1993). *Women and work: Inequality in the Canadian labour market*. Toronto: James Lorimer.

Poland, B. (1992). Learning to 'walk the talk': The implications of sociological theory for research methodologies in health promotion. *Canadian Journal of Public Health, 83* (Suppl. 1), S31–S46.

Preston, D. (1994). Marital status, gender roles, stress, and health in the elderly. *Health Care for Women International, 16*, 149–165.

Reitsma-Street, M., & Neysmith, S. (in press). Restructuring and community care work: The case of community resource centers for families in poor urban neighbourhoods. In S. Neysmith (Ed.), *Restructuring caring labour: Discourse, state practice and everyday life*. Toronto: Oxford University Press.

Royston, E., & Armstrong, S. (1989). *Preventing maternal deaths*. Geneva: World Health Organization.

Smith, D. (1987). *The everyday world as problematic: A feminist sociology*. Toronto: University of Toronto Press.

Stewart, M., Ritchie, J., McGrath, P., Thompson, D., & Bruce, B. (1994). Mothers of children with chronic conditions: Supportive and stressful interactions with partners and professionals regarding caregiving burdens. *Canadian Journal of Nursing Research, 26*(4), 61–82.

Thomas, V. (1994). Using feminist and social structural analysis to focus on the health of poor women. *Women & Health, 22*(1), 1–15.

Varcoe, C., & Turris, S. (1999). *"Battered women" as agents: Negotiating formal support*. Unpublished manuscript.

Waitzkin, H. (1991). *The politics of medical encounters*. New Haven, CT: Yale University Press.

Worell, J., & Remer, P. (1992). *Feminist perspectives in therapy. An empowerment model for women*. New York: John Wiley & Sons.

World Health Organization (WHO). (1984). *Health promotion: A discussion document on the concept and principles*. Geneva: Author.

World Health Organization (WHO). (1986). Ottawa charter for health promotion. *Canadian Journal of Public Health, 77*, 425–473.

Wuest, J. (1993). Institutionalizing women's oppression: The inherent risk in health policy that fosters community participation. *Health Care for Women International, 14*, 407–417.

Wuest, J. (1998). Setting boundaries: A strategy for precarious ordering of women's caring demands. *Research in Nursing and Health, 21*, 39–49.

PART 5

The Health of Children, Youth, and the Elderly

Current thinking and research is increasingly of the view that the advantages and disadvantages that characterize one phase of life carry over into subsequent stages of life. The implications of this perspective for policymakers are clear; those things that determine the health and well-being of children and youth will continue to determine the health status of adults and the elderly. Although concern about the health and well-being of children and youth is a policy objective in its own right, the prevailing view gains increased policy relevance in the context of an aging society. The three chapters in this section examine the determinants of health for children, youth, and the elderly.

It is widely believed that one's experiences from conception to the age of 6 years are the most important in connecting and sculpting the brain's neurons. Healthy development during this phase of the life cycle improves learning, behaviour, and health into adulthood. Bolaria and Bolaria, in Chapter 13, explore the relationship between inequality (particularly income inequality), poverty, family environment, and child health. Specifically, they look at changing patterns of infant mortality and at a number of key determinants of child health status, including an examination of low birth weight and lifelong morbidity, the nature of family life and health status, and child mental health and the psychosocial environment. The pattern that emerges is very clear: the various dimensions of inequality, particularly income inequality, are directly related to poor child health status.

Schissel, in Chapter 14, picks up the theme of inequality and health status as it relates to adolescents. His main argument is that the health problems of youth are the result of their social, economic, and political marginalization in contemporary Canadian society. To develop this argument, he provides an overview of the physical and emotional jeopardy faced by youth in the contexts of their lived experiences in school, athletics, the labour market, the underworld of crime, and the criminal justice system. An overarching reality for an increasing proportion of youth is poverty, which exposes them to increased health risks.

Penning, in Chapter 15, looks at the social construction of aging and health and its consequences in the Canadian health care context. She argues that the application of biomedical concepts and criteria for understanding the aging process results in the medicalization of aging and the aged — the view that aging is a clinical condition. Because the concerns of the aged and the consequences of aging often are not amenable to effective management in the context of the hospital-based acute health care system, the elderly are often stigmatized as both inappropriate and problematic users of health care services. As a result, they are increasingly channelled into community-based facilities and home care. The paradox is that, unlike medicare, community-based care and home care are not always covered by public health care insurance. Thus, the rise of community-based care corresponds to a trend toward the reprivatization of the Canadian health care system. This reprivatization takes at least two forms: an increase in private, for-profit health care services, and an increased reliance on unpaid, voluntary health care provisions, usually by family members, mainly women. The implications of these processes, both for the nature and organization of the Canadian health care system and for the health status of volunteer care givers in the community, warrant close attention.

13

Inequality, Family, and Child Health

B. SINGH BOLARIA University of Saskatchewan

ROSEMARY BOLARIA Saskatchewan Institute on Prevention of Handicaps

INTRODUCTION

In the past few years, children's lives and well-being have received considerable attention from researchers, health experts, politicians, and policymakers. Much of the study and discussion has focused on the links between inequality and opportunities. Inequalities of wealth and income produce unequal life chances — the opportunities for material and social rewards. Poverty translates into homelessness, ill health, short **life expectancy**, malnutrition, and hunger, to mention only a few of its effects (Bolaria & Wotherspoon, 2000).

Political and social concerns about child poverty led in 1989 to an all-party resolution in the House of Commons to end child poverty by the year 2000. One of the first publications to present a comprehensive picture of the health profile of Canada's children was prepared by the Canadian Institute of Child Health (CICH, 1994). Although public awareness of many of the issues of child health has increased, poverty and its consequences remain prominent in many areas of children's lives. This chapter focuses on the health risks and health outcomes associated with socioeconomic inequalities and the physical and social environments in which children live.

INEQUALITY AND POVERTY

Income inequality is an important dimension of social stratification. An examination of income distribution data reveals wide income disparities among Canadians. The data also show the small change in the share of income held by Canadians in different income categories over time (National Council of Welfare, 1999; Bolaria & Wotherspoon, 2000). Income inequalities persist in Canada. The richest 20 percent of the families in 1996 had 44.8 percent of all income before transfers and taxes, compared with only 2.1 percent for the poorest 20 percent. This situation improves somewhat when income distribution is considered after transfer payments: 40.6 percent of the income goes to the richest 20 percent, and only 6.1 percent to the poorest 20 percent (Statistics Canada, 1998a). More recent figures indicate that while the average family income in Canada is on the rise, the richest fifth of the population gained the most (Little & Stinson, 2000). Income disparities between rich and poor families have increased recently; in 1998, the top 20 percent received $5.40 for every $1.00 that went to the bottom 20 percent. The corresponding figures were $4.80 for every $1.00 in 1994 (Little & Stinson, 2000, p. A1).

A significant number of Canadians live in poverty (National Council of Welfare, 1999). The number of poor people was nearly 5.1 million in 1997 and the poverty rate was 17.2 percent. Poverty figures fluctuate with economic conditions, particularly fluctuations in the labour market. Poverty rates have increased amid high unemployment rates, economic restructuring that has forced job losses and wage cuts, and cutbacks in social spending.

Child poverty figures follow the same general patterns as the statistics for the general population. In 1997, almost 1.4 million children, of slightly more than 7 million children, were poor — a poverty rate of 19.6 percent (National Council of Welfare, 1999). Obviously, children are poor because they live in poor families. Poverty rates vary by family structure. Poverty rates are relatively low for two-parent families and quite high for families with single-parent mothers. Certain groups face a high risk of poverty. These include unemployed persons, people whose participation in the labour force is irregular, those with low educational levels, and those in certain occupations.

Wide income disparities and poverty persist in Canada. They produce an inequality of opportunities and life chances and have negative outcomes for individuals in low-income and poor families. "Poverty of opportunity" and family income levels are factors detrimental to healthy child development and child well-being (Ross & Roberts, 1999).

Most relevant to the discussion in this chapter is the link between income inequality, poverty, family environment, and child health, which is the focus of the following sections. First, the chapter discusses the health status of low-income and poor children in areas such as **infant mortality**, birth weight, injuries, and emotional development. Then it focuses on the health risks and health outcomes associated with specific family environments.

INEQUALITY, POVERTY, AND HEALTH STATUS

Social medicine is primarily concerned with the social, economic, and environmental conditions in society that produce patterns of **morbidity** and mortality. **Epidemiological** data in Canada and elsewhere show a persistent and pervasive association between socioeconomic status and health status (Link & Phelan, 2000; Zong & Li, 1994; Mirowsky, Ross, & Reynolds, 2000; World Health Organization [WHO], 1995; Syme & Yen, 2000; Hay, 1994). Those who are advantaged with respect to socioeconomic status are also advantaged in health status. Those with high incomes, for instance, live longer, healthier, and more disability-free lives on average than those who are poor. Similar patterns of disease, illness, and mortality prevail for children (Reading, 1997; CICH, 1994; Ross & Roberts, 1999; Ross, Scott, & Kelly, 1996; Health Canada, 1999; Saskatchewan Institute on Prevention of Handicaps, 1997). Poor housing, poor nutrition, poor neighbourhoods, and poor environments all contribute to high morbidity and mortality in low-income and poor populations.

Research findings from Canada and other countries on specific dimensions of child health are discussed below. These findings provide persuasive evidence on the association between structural determinants and the variation in health risks and health outcomes for children.

INFANT MORTALITY

Infant mortality is one of the most important indicators of population health of a country. It is "the best available overall indicator of health and development" (WHO, 1995, p. 5). Infant mortality is also strongly associated with adult mortality. If infant mortality is high, adult mortality is also likely to be high (Gray, 1993).

The infant **mortality rate** in Canada has declined steadily. In 1960, the **infant mortality rate** for Canada was slightly over 27. By 1993, it had dropped to 6.3 (Statistics Canada, 1995; Ross, Scott, & Kelly, 1996). In 1996, for the first time, the infant mortality rate dropped below 6 — 5.6 per 1000 live births, and a little more than half these deaths (3.3 per 1000) occurred in the first seven days of life. The **perinatal mortality** rate in 1996 was slightly under 7 (6.7). There has been a substantial decline in these rates since 1974 (Federal, Provincial and Territorial Advisory Committee on Population Health [FPTAC], 1999b, pp. 305–306; Statistics Canada, 1999b; Statistics Canada, Health Statistics Division, 1999).

Although overall infant deaths have declined substantially, class, race, and regional differences persist in child health (FPTAC, 1999a; Ross & Roberts, 1999). The infant mortality in the Aboriginal population is almost twice that of the general population (Frideres, 2000, p. 205; CICH, 1994, p. 141). Children of parents in the poorest neighbourhoods have twice the infant mortality rates of children in the richest neighbourhoods (Ross, Scott, & Kelly, 1996, p. 9; CICH, 1994, p. 141).

Infant mortality rates vary by income groups. Those in the lower-income groups experience above-average infant mortality rates (FPTAC, 1999a, p. 75). The infant mortality rate in 1996 was highest in the Northwest Territories (12.2 per 1000); among the provinces, Saskatchewan ranked highest (8.4) and Quebec lowest (4.6) (FPTAC, 1999b, p. 307, Table 78).

With respect to infant mortality, Canada does not rank very favourably with other advanced countries; its standing has declined in recent years. For instance, in 1990 Canada ranked fifth among the seventeen OECD countries; its ranking dropped to twelfth by 1996 (FPTAC, 1999b, p. 306). As Table 1 shows, in 1996, Japan had the lowest infant mortality rate (3.8) and the United States the highest (7.8). Finland, Sweden, and Norway all had infant mortality rates of 4. Other countries with infant mortality rates above 7 were Greece and New Zealand. It is apparent that the association between socioeconomic status and health status arises very early in life — "the first injustice" (Gortmaker & Wise, 1997) — and "this first injustice is followed by an enduring association between socioeconomic status and the risk of death that persists throughout adult life (Link & Phelan, 2000, p. 34). This association is persistent across time and in many countries. There are various reasons for variations in infant mortality rates, including low birth weights, preventable communicable diseases, malnutrition, household income, and the mother's education (Price, 1994; Kloos, 1994; Singh & Yu, 1995; Reading, 1997).

TABLE 13.1 *Infant Mortality Rates, Selected OECD Countries, 1996*

Country	Infant Mortality Rates (Deaths per 1000 live births)
Japan	3.8
Finland	4.0
Sweden	4.0
Norway	4.0
Switzerland	4.7
France	4.9
Luxembourg	4.9
Germany	5.0
Austria	5.1
Denmark	5.2
Ireland	5.5
Canada	5.6
Australia	5.8
United Kingdom	6.1
Greece	7.3
New Zealand	7.4
United States	7.8

Source: Organisation for Economic Co-operation and Development (1998). Statistics Canada (1999). Compiled from Federal, Provincial and Territorial Advisory Committee on Population Health (1999b, Figure 78C, p. 306).

HEALTH AT BIRTH: BIRTH WEIGHT

Weight at birth is one of the most important measures of overall health and well-being later in life (McCormick, 1985; McCormick et al., 1992; Wilkins, Sherman, & Best, 1991). The standard definition of low birth weight is less than 2500 grams (5.5 pounds) at birth (Statistics Canada, 1999). The average weight at birth of a full-term infant is 3400 grams (7.5 pounds). Low birth weight is the major cause of infant mortality. Children who survive face a high risk of other developmental and health-related problems, such as impaired learning and neurodevelopment and loss of sight and hearing (McCormick, 1985; McCormick et al., 1992). The negative effect of low birth weight extends into adult life and contributes to differences in mortality (Reading, 1997). Several factors are associated with low birth weight, including the mother's age, health, tobacco and alcohol use during pregnancy, and nutrition, as well as premature delivery.

The data on low birth weight are presented in Table 2. Almost 6 percent of all live births in Canada in 1996 resulted in low birth weight (Statistics Canada, 1998b). Low-birth-weight children are likely to be born to very young mothers (10–14 years) and to older mothers (45 and older). For instance, 9.3 percent of the low-birth-weight children were born to mothers 10–14 years of age, and 10 percent to mothers 45 years of age and older (Statistics Canada, 1998b). The risk of low-birth-weight children increases for mothers 40 years of age and older. Mothers younger than 15 years of age and those 45 years of age and older are almost twice as likely to have an underweight newborn infant as is the average Canadian mother. Premature births account for over half of low-birth-weight infants. Teen mothers are more likely to have babies with low birth weight and prematurity (Ng & Wilkins, 1994), and both the teen mother and the unborn child are at risk of poor nutrition and poor health outcomes (Schor, 1995, p. 97).

Maternal health and nutrition during pregnancy are important factors in healthy pregnancy and in the weight and health of the newborn. Income levels are closely linked to consumption patterns (Chossudovsky, 1983). The adequate production and supply of food, in themselves, do not ensure adequate levels of food consumption and nutrition. Consumption levels are influenced by the social distribution of food to different groups in the population, which itself is a function of income distribution (Chossudovsky, 1983). Food availability, food security, food deprivation, and hunger are problems faced by low-income Canadians (Philp, 1998; CICH, 1994; Bolaria & Wotherspoon, 2000); an estimated 7.5 percent of Canadians report food availability as a problem (CICH, 1994, p. 136). The percentages are higher for Aboriginal people (8.3 percent) and for Inuit (12.7 percent) (CICH, 1994, p. 136). The contradictions associated with "hunger in the midst of plenty" are starkly illustrated by the rise of food banks across Canada in the past two decades. About two million Canadians used food banks in 1991; in March 1997 alone, 669 877 Canadians received emergency food assistance. Children account for a large number of food bank users (Canadian Association of Food Banks, 1997, p. 1). There is "serious deterioration in household food security in Canada" in the 1990s (Canadian Association of Food Banks, 1997, p. 6), and the growing demand for their services has forced food banks to expand their distribution services beyond their own centres to various other programs, centres, and service organizations (Greater Vancouver Food Bank Society, 1998, p. 1, 3) (see also Chapter 7 of this book, pp. 134 to 135). The provision of food in itself cannot be equated with nutritional and dietary adequacy (Rauschenbach et al., 1990; Carrillo, Gilbride, & Chan, 1990; Wood & Valdez, 1991). Women and children, in particular, face high health risks and negative health outcomes (CICH, 2000; Wilson & Steinman, 2000; McIntyre, Connor, & Warren, 2000; Tarasuk & Beaton, 1999). Factors that need to be considered here include women's

TABLE 13.2 *Low Birth Weight in Canada, by Mother's Age, 1996*

Age of Mother	Number of Births <2500 g*	Percentage of All Live Births
10–14	21	9.3
15–19	1 516	7.0
20–24	3 934	5.9
25–29	6 107	5.3
30–34	6 195	5.6
35–39	2 730	6.4
40–44	487	8.1
45+	23	10.0
Total	21 025	5.8

*Excludes births in age group where age of mother is unknown.

Source: Statistics Canada (1999b). Compiled from Federal, Provincial and Territorial Advisory Committee on Population Health (1999a, Table 3.3, p. 77).

reproductive health and nutritional health needs during pregnancy, and children's nutritional needs. The effects of malnutrition and vitamin deficiencies have begun to appear in some cases (Bolaria & Wotherspoon, 2000). Adequate diet can prevent certain health risks; vitamins such as folic acid, for instance, prevent neural tube defects (Laxdal, Habbick, & Bolaria, 1993).

Mother's lifestyle and social consumption patterns can also contribute to poor birth outcomes. Evidence indicates that infants of mothers who smoke during pregnancy are more likely to have low birth weight than those of nonsmokers (Single et al., 1995). Infants born to mothers who smoke during pregnancy also have higher rates of respiratory illness and sudden infant death syndrome (Blair et al., 1996; DiFranza & Lew, 1995). Smoking during pregnancy is related to education and income. Mothers with lower education are more likely to smoke during pregnancy; teen mothers are twice as likely to smoke as are mothers age 25 and older (FPTAC, 1999a, p. 77).

Alcohol consumption during pregnancy can be harmful to the unborn, and overindulgence can cause fetal alcohol syndrome (FAS) and fetal alcohol effects (FAE) (for review, see Loney, 1994). FAS is expressed in certain abnormalities such as growth retardation, damage to the nervous system, and facial anomalies in children exposed to high levels of alcohol *in utero* (Loney, 1994). Certain groups appear to have a higher incidence of FAS; these include Black people, Aboriginal people, and children born to mothers with low socioeconomic status.

Low incomes, poverty, dependency on food banks, poor nutrition, and inadequate health care all contribute to low birth weight and high infant mortality. The low-birth-weight rate is significantly higher (1.4 times higher) in poor than in rich neighbourhoods (CICH, 1994, p. 128). Canada ranked in the middle among the industrialized countries in low-birth-weight infants. Table 3 indicates that, in 1995, Canada (5.5 percent) ranked sixth, tied with Switzerland. Finland had the lowest percentage of low-

TABLE 13.3 *Births Less Than 2500 grams, Selected OECD Countries, 1995*

Country	Percentage of All Births in Hospitals
Finland	4.1
Sweden	4.4
Iceland	4.7
Denmark	5.1
Norway	5.3
Switzerland	5.5
Canada	5.5
Austria	5.7
Germany	6.1
New Zealand	6.1
France	6.2
United States	7.3
Japan	7.5

Source: Organisation for Economic Co-operation and Development (1998). Compiled from Federal, Provincial and Territorial Advisory Committee on Population Health (1999b, Figure 64b, p. 256).

birth-weight infants (4.1 percent). Other countries that ranked above Canada were: Sweden (4.4 percent), Iceland (4.7 percent), Denmark (5.1 percent), and Norway (5.3 percent). Japan and the United States had the highest percentage of births below 2500 grams, 7.5 percent and 7.3 percent, respectively.

Social inequality also affects growth and height. Children from poor families are generally shorter than rich children. Failure to achieve height potential is not only an indication of past health impairment but also of the health outlook for the future (see Reading, 1997, p. 463).

The National Longitudinal Survey of Children and Youth found that children born prematurely (before 37 weeks' gestation) were 1.6 times as likely to experience slower motor and social development as were children who were not premature. Low-birth-weight infants were 2.3 times as likely to experience slow development (Statistics Canada, 1996).

INJURIES

Injuries are one of the least-recognized public health problems in Canada today. The costs associated with injuries are enormous, not only in direct dollar costs but also, more importantly, in the loss of life and human potential (Saskatchewan Institute on Prevention of Handicaps, 1996; FPTAC, 1999b, pp. 248–250, 319–322). In 1993, injuries in Canada may have resulted in more than $7 billion in direct health care and compensation costs (Cushman, 1995).

Injuries are the leading cause of death for Canadian children and youth between the ages of 1 and 19. For children over the age of 4, injuries cause more deaths than all other causes of death combined. Saskatchewan children 1 to 4 years of age and youth 15 to 19 years of age have the highest rates of injury deaths for children among all provinces in Canada (CICH, 1994). In addition, nonfatal injuries result in impairment and disabilities for many young people.

Fatalities account for only a small proportion of the health and economic costs of injuries. Recent figures on young people indicate that "for every injury related death, there are 40 hospitalizations and an estimated 670 emergency room visits for treatment of injuries" (Herbert et al., 1999, p. 39). In 1996, 1280 persons under the age of 20 died from injuries — 30.5 percent of all deaths in this age category. Injury mortality rates are also higher for males than for females (Herbert et al., 1999, p. 40).

The recognition of injuries as a leading cause of death in children has resulted in more research and comprehensive information on this subject. The data from hospitals participating in the Canadian Hospitals Injury Reporting and Prevention Program (CHIRPP) is one of the primary sources on types, sites, location, and activity at the time of injury (Health Canada, 1998). Data are reported for children and youth up to age 19. Almost 96 000 injured children were treated in 1997 in the emergency departments of participating hospitals; 57 percent of them were injured while involved in sports or leisure activities. Home and school were the primary locations of injuries: 44 percent at home and 19 percent in schools. Younger children were more frequently injured at home than were adolescents. Adolescents were more likely to be injured while involved in sports or leisure activities. Fractures, open wounds, and superficial injuries were the most common injuries (20 percent for each category) and the most frequent sites of injuries were head or neck (35 percent), arm (34 percent), and leg (20 percent).

Injuries, in addition to causing suffering and death, also are a major financial cost to the society. The economic cost of injuries to Canadians of all ages is in the billions of dollars, and other related costs, such as property damage and insurance claims, add billions to the total cost (Moore, Mao, & Zheng, 1997).

The Saskatchewan Institute on Prevention of Handicaps (1996) reports comprehensive data on child injury, hospitalization, and deaths in Saskatchewan for the period 1989–1994. During this period, nearly 69 percent of all deaths to children and youth aged 1 to 19 years were due to injuries. A large number of injuries result in hospitalization. During this 6-year period, 28 321 hospital admissions of Saskatchewan children and youth under 20 years of age were due to injuries. These hospitalizations represent 102 297 days of stay.

Table 4 shows the leading cause of injury deaths for all Saskatchewan children and youth under 20 years of age was motor vehicle traffic (31 percent), and the leading cause of injury-related hospitalization was falls (25 percent). Among children under 1 year of age, injury was not a major cause of death, accounting for less than 4 percent of all deaths. Drowning or choking (39 percent) were the leading cause of death, and falls (32 percent) were the leading cause of injury-related hospitalizations.

Among children 1 to 4 years of age, the leading injury causes of death were drowning or choking (31 percent) and fire and flame (24 percent). The major causes of injury-related hospitalizations, however, were falls (28 percent) and poisoning (25 percent). For children 5 to 9 years of age, the leading injury cause of death was drowning or choking (23 percent), and the leading cause of injury-related hospitalizations was falls (46 percent).

As children get older, the causes of death and hospitalization change considerably. Among children 10 to 14 years of age, the largest number of injury deaths was caused by motor vehicle traffic injuries (37 percent), and hospitalization for injury was most often caused by falls (27 percent). The major causes of injury deaths and injury-related hospitalizations for youth 15 to 19 years of age were motor vehicle traffic and self-injury. Motor vehicle traffic injuries accounted for 44 percent of injury deaths and 20

TABLE 13.4 *Leading Causes of Injury Deaths and Hospitalizations, by Age Group, for Saskatchewan Children, 1989–1994*

Age Group	Leading Causes of Injury Deaths	Leading Causes of Injury-Related Hospitalization
0–1 year	Drowning and choking: 39%	Falls: 32%
1–4 years	Drowning and choking: 31% Fire and flame: 24%	Falls: 28% Poisoning: 25%
5–9 years	Drowning and choking: 23%	Falls: 46%
10–14 years	Motor vehicle traffic injuries: 37%	Falls: 27%
15–19 years	Motor vehicle traffic injuries: 44% Self-injury: 30%	Motor vehicle traffic injuries: 20% Self-injury: 15%

Source: Based on data compiled by the Saskatchewan Institute on Prevention of Handicaps (1996, pp. viii–ix).

percent of injury-related hospitalizations. Self-injury caused 30 percent of injury deaths and 15 percent of injury-related hospitalizations (Saskatchewan Institute on Prevention of Handicaps, 1996, pp. viii–ix). The Saskatchewan study shows that among children under age 10, the most common cause of injury death was drowning or choking, and in the older age groups, motor vehicle traffic was the leading cause of injury deaths, followed by self-injury. The causes of injury deaths were different from the causes of injury hospitalizations: falls accounted for one quarter of all injury hospitalizations; for children of all ages, the leading cause of injury deaths was motor vehicle traffic.

The Saskatchewan study also found differences among various groups in injury-related hospitalizations and deaths. The highest rates of injury-related hospitalizations occurred among treaty Indian children, followed by northern children in all age groups, except 10–14-year-old males. Rural males 10 to 14 years of age had the second-highest rate of injury-related hospitalization. For ages 5 and older, the lowest injury hospitalization rates occurred among children in urban communities. Under age 5, the lowest rates were found among rural and urban children. There were also variations in injury-related deaths among various groups. For instance, for urban, rural, and northern children and youth under 20 years of age, the leading cause of injury death was motor vehicle traffic. The figures for the rural group were much higher than the urban group — 46 percent and 29 percent, respectively. For treaty Indian children and youth, however, the leading cause of injury death was self-injury, at 22 percent, followed by drowning or choking (16 percent), fire and flame (13 percent), and motor vehicle–pedestrian (11 percent). In Canada, the death rate for Aboriginal children as a result of injuries is much higher than that of the total population of Canadian children: almost four times higher for infants; five times higher for preschoolers; and three times higher for teenagers (MacMillan, Walsh, & Jamieson, 1999).

Differential risk of injury and death is associated with the socioeconomic background of children and the physical and social environments in which children live. Poor children face a high risk of injury, illness, and death because they often live in **substandard housing**, houses with damp walls and ceilings, rotting porches and steps, and crumbling foundations (Ross, Scott, & Kelly, 1996; CICH, 1994). Social variations in accidents, accidental injury, and accident rates are evident from research in other countries (Reading, 1997). Writing on this topic, Reading (1997, p. 464) states: "Because accidents are "place-specific" — that is, they happen in part because of the risks associated with the place they occur — these geographical variations indicate more clearly the links between social disadvantage, environmental risk, and accidental injury."

PSYCHOSOCIAL, MENTAL HEALTH, AND CHILD WELL-BEING

Other dimensions of child development and child health also deserve consideration. For instance, low birth weight, as well as being linked to infant mortality and adult morbidity and mortality, can also result in physical and mental disabilities. Since low birth weight is more prevalent in poor families and poor neighbourhoods, child disabilities are also linked to low-income and poor families. Poor children are also more likely to suffer from psychological and mental health problems (Ross, Scott, & Kelly, 1996; Ross & Roberts, 1999; CICH, 1994). Poor children are more likely than nonpoor children to have chronic health problems, problems at school, and psychiatric problems, and they are less likely to feel good about themselves (CICH, 1994, p. 128). They are also more likely to have vision, hearing, speech, or mobility problems (Ross & Roberts, 1999). Other evidence also indicates poor social and emotional health of children from low-income and poor families in areas such as school performance, emotional disorders, high levels of indirect aggression, hyperactivity, and conduct disorders (CICH, 1994, p. 151; Canada, 1991; Offord, Boyle, & Racine, 1989; Ross & Roberts, 1999; Offord & Lipman, 1996). Marked differences existed among income groups on various measures of emotional and behavioural disorders; poor children were the most disadvantaged in behavioural impairment in social relationships and psychosocial problems (Offord & Lipman, 1996).

Other indicators raise concerns about the well-being of Canadian children and youth: low self-esteem, depression, high life stress levels, substance abuse, smoking, and intentional injuries. The continuing high rate of suicide among youth, particularly in Aboriginal populations, points to young people's distress (FPTAC, 1999a).

Canadian children and youth are, however, doing well in many areas, and there is a continuous decline in morbidity and mortality in this group. For instance, child and youth injury death rates and injury-related hospitalizations have been decreasing during the past two decades. Over the past 20 years, the injury death rate for children in the first year of life has decreased by 80 percent. During the same period, the injury death rate for children 1 to 4 years of age decreased 56 percent. For children 5 to 9 years of age the decrease was 60 percent, and for youth 15 to 19 the decrease was 33 percent (CICH, 1994).

Since 1980, injury hospitalization rates have also declined: 28 percent for infants; 24 percent for children 1 to 4 years of age; 18 percent for boys 5 to 14 years of age; 11 percent for girls 5 to 14 years of age; and 17 percent for youth 15 to 19 years of age (CICH, 1994, p. 273). Similar decreases were reported by Hu and Wesson (1994) for metropolitan Toronto, where hospitalizations due to injuries declined 25 percent for most injury causes since 1986. In Canada, there is also a steady decline in infant mortality rates and increasing life expectancy. While these are positive signs, social variations in health status, opportunities, quality of life, and well-being persist because of socioeconomic disparities.

FAMILY AND CHILD HEALTH

Increasingly, social scientists, policymakers, and social epidemiologists are recognizing the family as an important factor in the health of infants, children, and youth. Social relations and the family environment, as well as forces external to the family, have important effects on child health.

Abuse and violence in families puts mothers and children at greater risk of negative health outcomes. Abuse and violence affect the physical as well as emotional and psychological health and well-being of victims (Saskatchewan Institute on Prevention of Handicaps, 1996, 1997; Modeland, Bolaria, & McKenna, 1995; Schor, 1995; Fischbach & Donnelly, 1996; Ross & Roberts, 1999; Health Canada, 1996; Committee on Wife Assault, 1991). Family violence and sexual and physical assaults against spouses and children are extensive in Canada and in other countries (Fischbach & Donnelly, 1996; Statistics Canada, 1994; Statistics Canada, Canadian Centre for Justice Statistics, 1997; Health Canada, 1996). In 1996, 22 percent of about 23 000 assaults reported to police agencies involved children under 18 years of age. Sexual assaults accounted for nearly one fourth of the total assaults against children (Statistics Canada, Centre for Justice Statistics, 1997). Family members were responsible for one third of sexual assaults and one fourth of physical assaults on children. Girls were the victims in 80 percent of sexual assaults by family members. The federal government reported that, in five study sites (Calgary, Edmonton, Regina, Saskatoon, and Hamilton) between 1988 and 1992, there was an increase in the number of cases of child sexual abuse reported to police. About three quarters of the victims were female, most victims were under age 12, and about one fifth were under age 5. The vast majority (over 94 percent) of accused abusers were male. Most abusers were adults, but approximately one quarter were under age 18 (Vanier Institute of the Family, 1994, p. 134).

Family-related homicides are another source of data on family violence. Most of the victims are killed by a spouse, another family relative, or someone known to the victims (FPTAC, 1999b, p. 55). Children are also victimized when mothers have to escape to shelters or transition homes from abusive homes. A large number of women and children are compelled to use shelters; for example, on May 31, 1995, 2316 women accompanied by 2217 children were in shelters across Canada to escape violence and abusive circumstances (Statistics Canada, Canadian Centre for Justice Statistics, 1998). Other evidence also points to the protection that many children need from abuse and neglect. Between 1987 and 1993, the number of Saskatchewan families receiving child protection services increased from approximately 2600 to 3476. Between 1989 and the end of 1993, the deaths of 30 Saskatchewan children were attributable to abuse and neglect (Saskatchewan Education, Training and Employment, 1994b, p. 59).

Children living in violent situations are abused emotionally as a consequence of witnessing or being subject to the violent behaviour of their fathers or their mothers' partners. This is of particular concern because 39 percent of women in violent marriages report that their children have witnessed the violence against them. In one out of three families in which the mother is assaulted, the children are also directly abused (Saskatchewan Education, Training and Employment, 1994b). Infants born to women who have been abused during pregnancy are at greater risk of negative health outcomes, including preterm birth, low birth weight, and death of the fetus (Modeland, Bolaria, & McKenna, 1995). Children who witness spousal violence are at a higher risk of substance abuse in later life, as well as risking depression and emotional problems (Health Canada, 1996). Other forms of violence that have negative health and development outcomes include neglect, verbal abuse, and maltreatment.

Income is a major factor in the overall well-being of families. Ross and Roberts (1999, p. 5) show that "children in low-income families are twice as likely to be living in poorly functioning families as children in high-income families. The incidence of poor family functioning decreases steadily as family incomes rise from under $20,000 to $50,000." Children in low-income families are also more likely to be living with a parent who often exhibits signs of depression and to grow up with parents who themselves suffered childhood trauma and who are chronically stressed (Ross & Roberts, 1999, pp. 6–8). Children and adolescents in these circumstances are more likely than others to exhibit behavioural and emotional problems.

Exposure to other environmental factors in the household and the consumption patterns of parents and adult family members can have negative health effects on infants. Alcoholism in the family is a problem for about 10 percent of all children under age 18, and being raised in such a family is one of the most stressful conditions for children (Vanier Institute of the Family, 1994, p. 131). Prenatal exposure to alcohol can have negative health consequences for infants, leading to alcohol-related birth defects or fetal alcohol syndrome (FAS) (Habbick et al., 1996).

Many Canadian preschoolers live in environments in which they are exposed to cigarette smoke. According to Canada's health promotion survey, 26 percent of households with preschoolers have at least one smoker living in the house, and 20 percent have two or more smokers (CICH, 1994, p. 50). The survey also found that almost half of poor parents with children under 15 years of age reported that they smoked cigarettes daily. In comparison, about one fifth of parents in the highest income level reported daily cigarette smoking (CICH, 1994, p. 124). Preschool children who are regularly exposed to tobacco smoke have an increased risk of contracting infectious diseases (Reichert, 1995, p. 19), ear infections, asthma, and allergies (DiFranza & Lew, 1995), and are at a greater risk of acute respiratory illnesses, including pneumonia, bronchitis, and impaired lung functioning (Health Canada, 1998).

Maternal smoking is more common among low-income women, youth, poorly educated women, and unmarried women (CICH, 1993, p. 28). Infants born to women who smoke during pregnancy have higher rates of low birth weight, respiratory illness, and sudden infant death syndrome (Blair et al., 1996; DiFranza & Lew, 1995).

Other social environmental factors in the family that are linked to child health and development include family structure (e.g., single- or two-parent family), parenting skills, and an emotionally stable family environment (Beiser et al., 1998; Saskatchewan Institute on Prevention of Handicaps, 1997, 2000; Brink & Zessman, 1997; Schor, 1995; FPTAC, 1999a, pp. 71–93). The physical environment, including adequate housing and safe neighbourhoods, is also linked to child health (Ross, Scott, & Kelly, 1996, p. 14; CICH, 1994, p. 137; Reichert, 1995, p. 17; Ross & Roberts, 1999, pp. 14–16). Low-income families are more likely to live in inadequate and unsafe housing and in problem neighbourhoods.

The socioeconomic status of the family is crucial in the family's ability to cope with the child health issues discussed above. Children in low-income families are less likely to have access to health services, particularly services that are not socially funded, such as dental care and eye care.

CONCLUSION

Child health and well-being have received considerable attention in the past few years. Although there has been a steady improvement in the health status of Canadian children, variations by socioeconomic status persist. Whereas overall infant mortality rates and infant deaths have steadily declined, class, race, and neighbourhood differences persist in child health. Inequality and poverty are linked to high infant mortality, low birth weight, high risk of injury deaths, child disabilities, and poor psychosocial development and mental health. The social and economic health of the family, as well as the social and economic forces external to the family, have important effects on child health.

Improvement in the social and material conditions of existence of children and the elimination of child poverty and child hunger have been in the forefront of public policy debate in Canada and internationally. Although the House of Commons voted unanimously to "seek to achieve the goal of eliminating poverty among Canadian children by the year 2000," Canada ranks near the bottom in the fight against child poverty among the world's richest nations (Philp, 2000). According to the UNICEF report, Sweden led all countries in the fight against poverty, followed closely by other Nordic countries (Norway, Finland, and Denmark), while Canada ranked seventeenth among 23 industrialized countries (Philp, 2000). Food insecurity and hunger remain daily experiences of thousands of children in Canada (Wilson & Steinman, 2000; CICH, 2000; Tarasuk & Beaton, 1999; McIntyre, Connor, & Warren, 2000). Millions of children in poor countries face poverty, exploitation, abuse, hunger, and poor health (UNICEF, 2000). In view of this, a broad strategy is required to address issues of child health: accessibility to and the availability of a wide range of health services, the elimination of child poverty and hunger, and programs and policies to provide safe and secure physical and social environments for healthy child development.

STUDY QUESTIONS

1. *Discuss the relationship between family income and factors critical to the well-being of children.*
2. *Discuss the factors associated with differential infant mortality rates by class and race.*
3. *Discuss the relationship between family's social environment and children's health.*
4. *Discuss the association between infant mortality and adult mortality. Why is infant mortality one of the most important indicators of population health?*
5. *What is meant by poverty of opportunity? How does poverty of opportunity relate to children's health?*
6. *Discuss the relationship between maternal lifestyle, the availability of and accessibility to maternal care, and children's health.*
7. *Discuss the statement that "Infant mortality is the best available overall indicator of health and development status of a country."*

GLOSSARY

epidemiological Relating to epidemiology; the study of factors related to the distribution of disease in a population.

infant mortality The death of a live-born infant in the first year of life.

infant mortality rate The number of deaths in the first year of life per 1000 live births.

life expectancy The length of time a person born in a given year is expected to live.

morbidity The distribution of sickness and disease in a given population.

mortality rate The total number of deaths in a population in a specific time period divided by the total population.

perinatal mortality Combination of stillbirths and deaths within the first 7 days of life.

substandard housing Houses with major problems, such as poor plumbing, poor sanitation, and broken windows.

RECOMMENDED READINGS

Canadian Institute of Child Health (CICH). (2000). *The health of Canada's children: A CICH profile* (3rd ed.). Ottawa: Author. A comprehensive resource profiling child health in Canada, from pregnancy, birth and infancy to childhood and youth. This publication also covers Aboriginal children and youth, the mental health of children and youth, children and youth with disabilities, children's environmental health, and the health outcomes of income inequality.

Federal, Provincial and Territorial Advisory Committee on Population Health. (1999). *Toward a healthy future: Second report on the health of Canadians.* Ottawa: Minister of Public Works and Government Services. Summarizes the most recent information on the health status of Canadians, including self-rated health, psychological well-being, selected conditions and diseases, major causes of death, and life expectancy. Chapter 3 is particularly relevant to the topic of child health.

Health Canada. (1999). *Measuring up: A health surveillance update on Canadian children and youth.* Ottawa: Author. An important health surveillance update on infant health, childhood cancer, vaccine-preventable diseases, respiratory health, child injury, HIV, and sexual health.

Ross, D.P., & Roberts, R. (1999). *Income and child well-being: A new perspective on the poverty debate.* Ottawa: Canadian Council on Social Development. An important contribution to the debate on child poverty and children's development that attempts to define an unacceptable level of inequality among families or determine the level of "poverty of opportunity." The authors examine a number of elements of child development and conclude that family income plays a crucial role in the child development process.

Ross, D.P., Scott, K., & Kelly, M. (1996). *Child poverty: What are the consequences?* Ottawa: Centre for International Statistics, Canadian Council on Social Development. An important contribution to child health literature, bringing together key findings from a variety of sources to illustrate the links between family income and healthy child development.

Saskatchewan Institute on Prevention of Handicaps. (1997). *Critical issues in health for Saskatchewan children from birth to age nine, 1989–1994.* Saskatoon: Author. Data on births, deaths, and hospitalizations for children under 10 years of age; provides information on the health status of infants at birth, deaths of children by cause, hospitalized illness, and congenital and genetic disorders, and an examination of hospitalizations and deaths due to injuries.

Saskatchewan Institute on Prevention of Handicaps. (1998). *Critical issues in health for Saskatchewan youth 10–19 years of age, 1989–1994.* Saskatoon: Author. A wide range of data on Saskatchewan youth for 1989–1994. Critical issues included are preventable events, those that may lead to chronic illness and premature death, and the most common causes of hospitalization.

REFERENCES

Barnhorst, R., & Johnson, L.C. (1991). *The state of the child in Ontario.* Toronto: University of Toronto Press.

Beiser, M.F., Hou, F., & Hyman, I. (1998). New immigrant children: How are they coping? Presented at Investing in Children: A National Research Conference (cited in Statistics Canada, 1999). (Violence Against Women Survey, 1993.)

Blair, P.S., Fleming, P.J., Bensley, D., Smith, I., Bacon, C., Taylor, E., Berry, J., Golding, J., & Tripp, J. (1996). Smoking and the sudden infant death syndrome: Results from 1993–95 case-control study for confidential inquiry into stillbirths and deaths in infancy. *British Medical Journal, 3, 13.*

Bolaria, B.S., & Wotherspoon, T. (2000). Income inequality, poverty, and hunger. In B.S. Bolaria (Ed.), *Social issues and contradictions in Canadian society* (pp. 73–90). Toronto: Harcourt Brace.

Brink, S., & Zessman, A. (1997). *Measuring social well-being: An index for social health in Canada.* Ottawa: Human Resources Development Canada.

Campbell, D.R. (1989). The political epidemiology of infant mortality: A health crisis among Montana Indians. *American Indian Culture and Research Journal, 13*(344), 105–148.

Canada. (1991, January). *Children in poverty: Toward a better future.* Ottawa: Standing Senate Committee on Social Affairs, Science and Technology.

Canadian Association of Food Banks. (1997). *Hunger count 1997: A report on emergency food assistance in Canada.* Toronto: Author.

Canadian Institute of Child Health (CICH). (1993). Prevention of low birth weight in Canada: Literature review and strategies. Prepared for Health Promotion Branch, Ontario Ministry of Health.

Canadian Institute of Child Health (CICH). (1994). *The health of Canada's children: A CICH profile* (2nd ed.). Ottawa: Author.

Canadian Institute of Child Health (CICH). (2000). *The health of Canada's children: A CICH profile* (3rd ed.). Ottawa: Author.

Carillo, T., Gilbride, A., & Chan, M.M. (1990). Soup kitchen meals: An observation and nutrient analysis. *Journal of American Dietetic Association, 90,* 989–991.

Chaudhuri, N. (1998). Child health, poverty and environment. *Canadian Journal of Public Health, 89* (Suppl. 1).

Chossudovsky, M. (1983). Underdevelopment and the political economy of malnutrition and ill health. *International Journal of Health Services, 13*(1), 69–87.

Committee on Wife Assault. (1991). *Report on wife assault.* Toronto: Ontario Medical Association.

Cushman, R. (1995). Injury prevention: The time has come. *Canadian Medical Association Journal, 152,* 21–23.

DiFranza, J.R., & Lew, R.A. (1995). Effects of maternal cigarette smoking on pregnancy complications and sudden infant death syndrome. *Journal of Family Practice, 40,* 385–394.

Federal, Provincial and Territorial Advisory Committee on Population Health (FPTAC). (1999a). *Toward a healthy future: Second report on the health of Canadians.* Ottawa: Minister of Public Works and Government Services.

Federal, Provincial and Territorial Advisory Committee on Population Health (FPTAC). (1999b). *Statistical report on the health of Canadians.* Ottawa: Minister of Public Works and Government Services.

Fischbach, R.L., & Donnelly, E. (1996). Domestic violence against women: A contemporary issue in international health. In J. Subedi & E.B. Gallagher (Eds.), *Society, health and disease* (pp. 316–345). Upper Saddle River, NJ: Prentice-Hall.

Frideres, J.S. (2000). First Nations: Walking the path of social change. In B.S. Bolaria (Ed.), *Social issues and contradictions in Canadian society* (3rd ed., pp. 195–227). Toronto: Harcourt Brace.

Gortmaker, S.L., & Wise, P.H. (1997). The first injustice: Socioeconomic disparities, health services technology, and infant mortality. *Annual Review of Sociology, 23,* 147–170.

Gray, A. 1993. Mortality and morbidity: Causes and determinants. In A. Gray (Ed.), *World health and disease* (pp. 21–37). Buckingham, UK: Open University Press.

Greater Vancouver Food Bank Society. (1998, Winter/Spring). *Food Bank News, 2*(2).

Habbick, B.R., Nanson, J.L., Snyder, R.E., Casey, R.E., & Schulman, A.L. (1996). Foetal alcohol syndrome in Saskatchewan: Unchanged incidence in a 20-year period. *Canadian Journal of Public Health, 87,* 204–207.

Hay, D.I. (1994). Social status and health status: Does money buy health? In B.S. Bolaria & R. Bolaria (Eds.), *Racial minorities, medicine and health* (pp. 9–52). Halifax and Saskatoon: Fernwood Publishing and Social Research Unit.

Health Canada. (1996). *Wife abuse: The impact on children.* Ottawa: National Clearinghouse on Family Violence.

Health Canada. (1998). Laboratory Centre for Disease Control, Canadian Hospitals Injury Reporting and Prevention Program (CHIRPP) Data Base, 1998.

Health Canada. (1999). *Passive smoking: Nowhere to hide.* Ottawa: Author.

Herbert, M., Lipskie, T., MacKenzie, S., & Rusen, I.D. (1999). Child injury. In I.D. Rusen & C. McCourt (Eds.), *Measuring up: A health surveillance update on Canadian children and youth* (pp. 39–48). Ottawa: Minister of Public Works and Government Services.

Hu, X., & Wesson, D.E. (1994). Fatal and non-fatal childhood injuries in Metropolitan Toronto, 1986–1991. *Canadian Journal of Public Health, 85,* 269–273.

Human Resources Development Canada (HRDC) and Statistics Canada. (1996). *Growing up in Canada: National longitudinal survey of children and youth* (cat. no. 89-550-MPE N01).

King, A., Wold, B., Tudor-Smith, C., & Harel, Y. (1997). *The health of youth: A cross-national survey, 1993–1994.* World Health Organization Regional Series: European Series, No. 69.

Kloos, H. (1994). The poorer third world. In D.R. Phillips & Y. Verhasselt (Eds.), *Health and development* (pp. 199–215). London: Routledge.

Laxdal, O.E., Habbick, B., & Bolaria, R. (1993). Folic acid prevents neural tube defects. *Saskatchewan Medical Journal, 4*(1), 11–14.

Link, B.G., & Phelan, J.C. (2000). Evaluating the fundamental cause explanation for social disparities in health. In C.E. Bird, P. Conrad, & A.M. Fremont (Eds.), *Handbook of medical sociology* (5th ed., pp. 33–46). Upper Saddle River, NJ: Prentice-Hall.

Little, B., & Stinson, M. (2000, June 13). Average family enjoying best income in a decade. *The Globe and Mail,* pp. A1, A7.

Loney, E.A. (1994). Fetal alcohol syndrome: Research and prevention issues. In B.S. Bolaria & R. Bolaria (Eds.), *Women, medicine and health* (pp. 341–363). Halifax and Saskatoon: Fernwood Publishing and Social Research Unit.

MacMillan, H., Walsh, C., & Jamieson, E. (1999). Children's health. Ottawa: First Nations and Inuit Regional Health Survey National Steering Committee.

McCormick, M.C. (1985). The contribution of low birth weight to infant mortality and child morbidity. *New England Journal of Medicine, 312,* 82–90.

McCormick, M. et al. (1992). The health and development status of very low birth weight children at school age. *Journal of the American Medical Association, 267,* 2204–2208.

McIntyre, L., Connor, S.K., & Warren, J. (2000). Child hunger in Canada: Results of the 1994 national longitudinal survey of children and youth. *Canadian Medical Association Journal, 163*(8), 961–965.

Mirowsky, J., Ross, C.E., & Reynolds, J. (2000). Links between social status and health status. In C.E. Bird, P. Conrad, & A.M. Fremont (Eds.), *Handbook of medical sociology* (5th ed., pp. 47–67). Upper Saddle River, NJ: Prentice-Hall.

Modeland, A., Bolaria, R., & McKenna, A. (1995). Domestic violence during pregnancy. *Saskatchewan Medical Journal, 6,* 4–9.

Moore, R., Mao, Y., & Zheng, I. (1997). *Economic burden of illness in Canada, 1993.* Ottawa: Health Canada, Laboratory Centre for Disease Control.

National Council of Welfare. (1990). *Health, health care and medicare.* Ottawa: Supply and Services Canada.

National Council of Welfare. (1999). *Poverty profile 1997.* Ottawa: Minister of Public Works and Government Services Canada.

National Council of Welfare. (2000). *Justice and the poor.* Ottawa: Minister of Public Works and Government Services.

Nelson, M.D. (1996). Socioeconomic status and childhood mortality in North Carolina. In P. Brown (Ed.), *Perspectives in medical sociology* (pp. 83–88). Prospect Heights, IL: Waveland Press.

Ng, E., & Wilkins, R. (1994). Maternal demographic characteristics and rates of low birth weight in Canada, 1961 to 1990. *Health Reports, 6,* 241–253.

Offord, D., Boyle, M., & Racine, Y. (1989). *Ontario child health study: Children at risk.* Toronto: Queen's Printer.

Offord, D., Boyle, M.H., Szatmari, P., Rae-Grant, N.I., Links, P.S., Cadman, D.T., Byles, J.A., Crawford, J.W., Blum, H.M., & Byrne, C. (1997). Ontario child health study. *Archives of General Psychiatry, 44,* 832–836.

Offord, D., & Lipman, E. (1996). Emotional and behavioural problems. In *Growing up in Canada: National longitudinal survey of children and youth.* Ottawa: Human Resources Development Canada and Statistics Canada.

Organisation for Economic Co-operation and Development (OECD). (1998). *OECD health data 98: A comparative analysis of 29 countries.* Paris: Author.

Philp, M. (2000, June 13). Canada ranks high in child poverty. *The Globe and Mail,* pp. A1, A8.

Price, P. (1994). Maternal and child health care strategies. In D.R. Phillips & Y. Verhasselt (Eds.), *Health and development* (pp. 135–155). London: Routledge.

Rauschenbach, B.S., Frongillo, E.A., Thompson, F.E., Anderson, E.Y.J., & Spicer, D. (1990). Dependency on soup kitchens in urban areas of New York State. *American Journal of Public Health, 80*(1), 56–60.

Reading, R. (1997). Poverty and health of children and adults. *Archives of Disease in Childhood, 76,* 463–467.

Reichert, P. (1995). Background information for the development of the Aboriginal head start program in Saskatchewan. Regina: Common Knowledge Social Research.

Ross, D.P., & Roberts, P. (1999). *Income and child well-being: A new perspective on the poverty debate.* Ottawa: Canadian Council on Social Development.

Ross, D.P., Scott, K., & Kelly, M. (1996). *Child poverty: What are the consequences?* Ottawa: Centre for International Statistics, Canadian Council on Social Development.

Saskatchewan Education, Training and Employment. (1994a). Saskatchewan children "at risk" demographic risk factors. Regina: Government of Saskatchewan.

Saskatchewan Education, Training and Employment. (1994b). Working together to address barriers to learning; Integrated school-linked services for children and youth at risk. Regina: Government of Saskatchewan.

Saskatchewan Institute on Prevention of Handicaps. (1996). *Child injury in Saskatchewan: Injury hospitalizations and deaths 1989–1994.* Saskatoon: Saskatchewan Institute on Prevention of Handicaps.

Saskatchewan Institute on Prevention of Handicaps. (1997). *Critical issues in health for Saskatchewan from birth to age nine 1989–1994.* Saskatoon: Author.

Saskatchewan Institute on Prevention of Handicaps. (2000, June). Background paper for the development of a national statement on shaken baby syndrome. Unpublished Paper, Saskatchewan Institute on Prevention of Handicaps, Saskatoon.

Schor, E.L. (1995). The influence of families on child health. *Pediatric Clinics of North America, 42,* 89–102.

Singh, G.K., & Yu, S.M. (1995). Infant mortality in the United States: Trends, differentials and projections, 1950 through 2010. *American Journal of Public Health, 85,* 957–964.

Single, E., Robson, L., & Xie, X. (1995). *The costs of substance abuse in Canada.* Ottawa: Canadian Centre on Substance Abuse.

Statistics Canada. (1994). *Violence against women survey 1993*. Ottawa: Author.

Statistics Canada. (1995). *Vital statistics, births and deaths 1993*. Ottawa: Supply and Services.

Statistics Canada. (1996). *Growing up in Canada: National longitudinal survey of children and youth*. Ottawa: Human Resources Canada.

Statistics Canada. (1997). *National population health survey, 1996–1997*. Ottawa.

Statistics Canada. (1998a). *Income after tax, distribution by size in Canada, 1996*. Ottawa: Ministry of Industry.

Statistics Canada. (1998b, July 8). Births 1996. *The Daily*. Ottawa: Statistics Canada (cat. no. 11-001-XIE).

Statistics Canada. (1998c, April 16). Deaths 1996. *The Daily*. Ottawa: Statistics Canada (cat. no. 11-001-XIE).

Statistics Canada. (1999). *Compendium of vital statistics 1996*. Ottawa: Statistics Canada (cat. no. 84-214-XPE).

Statistics Canada, Canadian Centre for Justice Statistics. (1997, November). *Assaults against children and youth in the family 1996*. Ottawa: Statistics Canada (cat. no. 85-002-XPE, vol. 17, no. 11).

Statistics Canada, Canadian Centre for Justice Statistics. (1998, May). *Family violence in Canada: A statistical profile 1998*. Ottawa: Statistics Canada (cat. no. 85-224-XPE).

Statistics Canada, Health Statistics Division. (1999). *Health indicators 1999*. Ottawa: Statistics Canada (cat. no. 82-221-XCB).

Syme, S.L., & Yen, I.H. (2000). Social epidemiology and medical sociology: Different approaches to the same problem. In C.E. Bird, P. Conrad, & A.M. Fremont (Eds.), *Handbook of medical sociology* (5th ed., pp. 365–376). Upper Saddle River, NJ: Prentice-Hall.

Tarasuk, V.S., & Beaton, G.H. (1999). Household food insecurity and hunger among families using food banks. *Canadian Journal of Public Health, 90*, 109–113.

United Nations Children's Fund (UNICEF). (2000). *The state of the world's children 2000*. New York: Author.

Vanier Institute of the Family. (1994). *Profiling Canada's families*. Ottawa: Author.

Wilkins, K. (1995). Causes of death: How the sexes differ. *Health reports, 7*, 32–43.

Wilkins, R. (1995). Mortality by neighborhood income in urban Canada, 1986–1991. Poster presented at the Conference of the Canadian Society for Epidemiology and Biostatistics, St. John's, NF, August 16–19, 1995.

Wilkins, R., Sherman, G.J., & Best, P.A.F. (1991). Birth outcomes and infant mortality by income in urban Canada, 1986. *Health Reports, 3*(1).

Wilkinson, R. (1996). *Unhealthy societies: The afflictions of inequality*. New York: Routledge.

Wilson, B., & Steinman, C. (2000). Hunger count 2000: A surplus of hunger. Ottawa: Canadian Association of Food Banks.

Wood, D., & Valdez, B. (1991). Barriers to medical care for homeless families compared with housed poor families. *American Journal of Diseases in Children, 145*, 1109–1115.

World Health Organization (WHO). (1995). *The world health report: Bridging the gap*. Geneva: WHO.

Zong, L., & Li, P.S. (1994). Different cultures or unequal life chances: A comparative analysis of race and health. In B.S. Bolaria & R. Bolaria (Eds.), *Racial minorities, medicine and health* (pp. 113–123). Halifax and Saskatoon: Fernwood Publishing and Social Research Unit.

14

The Pathology of Powerlessness: Adolescent Health in Canada

BERNARD SCHISSEL University of Saskatchewan

INTRODUCTION

Adolescent health is an important political, economic, and personal issue for several reasons. First, patterns of physical and emotional health in adolescence — including ways of dealing with health problems either preventively or therapeutically — quite often follow individuals throughout their lives. Secondly, the health problems that youth face are often the result of their position as second-class citizens in a world created by and for adults and in a society in which profit is sacrosanct. This second point is important for understanding adolescent health and frames the arguments set out in this chapter. When one strips away the empty rhetoric of children and youth being the nation's most valued and valuable resource, one finds that the problems of adolescent health are largely preventable, are often the result of youth emulating adult behaviour or attempting to live up to the expectations of adults, and are often the result of the stresses and strains of a world in which youth have little political and economic impact on the society they share with adults. This relative powerlessness often places youth in jeopardy, especially youth who live on the margins of the society. The jeopardy of having little political or economic impact, coupled with living in conditions of poverty, often results in adolescents using and abusing drugs and alcohol to kill the pain (Schissel & Fedec, 1999; Webber, 1992). The risk for all youth, especially marginalized youth, occurs in a political–economic context in which the substances that place youth at risk are largely manufactured by legitimate adult-owned corporations (Chisholm, 1996; Diller, 1998). Youth substance abuse will be explored later in this chapter, but for now, suffice it to say that youth, in many respects, are victims of an adult world where a "business as usual" ethic frames the danger that jeopardizes the health of Canadian adolescents.

This chapter, then, explores the physical and emotional jeopardy in which Canadian youth find themselves. It explores the primary contexts in which youth live, including school, athletics, the labour market, the social world, and the "underworld" of crime and youth justice. Essentially, this chapter illustrates that the health of youth is a generic issue that involves education, justice, and social welfare as much as it does medicine. In the end, it illustrates that much of the physical and emotional damage to youth is social and political in origin and that, as a consequence, the public policy reaction to issues of youth health rarely focus on the health of the community in which youth live.

HEALTH AND POVERTY

This first section illustrates the overall levels of health for Canadian adolescents and ties these levels to socioeconomic factors. The underlying argument is that health status for youth depends on their placement in the socioeconomic hierarchy. In short, living on the margins, below the poverty line, on the streets, and in abusive contexts predisposes youth to poor health.

Figures 1 through 5 illustrate how living in poverty is probably the greatest health risk for adolescents with respect to physical illness, mental health, high-risk behaviours, and injury. The data are derived from the National Population Health Survey of Canada (Statistics Canada, 1998). The analysis in the figures is based on the relationship between family income and indicators of health for male and female youth in Canada. Figure 1 is based on a self-report indication of general health. Family income is reported by quintiles, in which the population is divided into five numerically equal categories. All the graphs and figures presented in this chapter are based on findings that are statistically significant (based on two-way analyses of variance and chi-square where appropriate).

The self-assessment of health variable shows quite clearly that youth in the highest income categories have the lowest levels of poor health; this is especially apparent for female youth. In fact, three times as many low-income female youth have poor health (9.5 percent) compared with high-income female youth (3.1 percent). Notably, a greater percentage of females overall reveal poor health than do males, although the poorest youth of both genders are the least healthy.

With regard to adolescent mental health, the estimates in Canada are that between 15 to 20 percent of youth between 10 and 19 years of age have a major mental disorder

FIGURE 14.1

Percentage of Canadian Youth with Poor Health, by Income Level

Source: Based on Statistics Canada (1998).

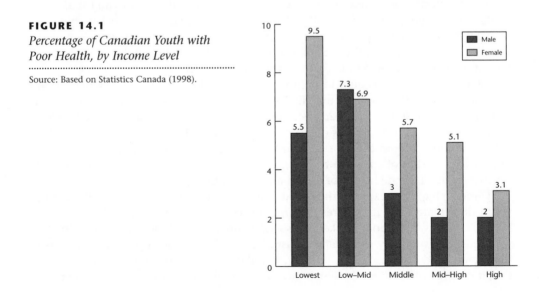

(Kutcher, 1996). Consistent with the argument in this chapter, the conventional work on youth and mental health shows quite clearly that psychological and emotional health problems for children and youth are closely tied to adverse life situations, including living in privation, low educational attainment, poor housing conditions, and family dysfunction associated with living as an underclass (Offord, 1989). Figure 2 is based on a self-report of the number of weeks youth say they are depressed in one year.

Figure 2 shows that, overall, youth experience a significant amount of depression, to the extreme of 15 weeks per year for low-income females and 8.29 weeks per year for high-income males. Furthermore, it is significant that depression is more common among the poorest youth and that the degree of depression decreases as income increases. Males and females experience generally the same amount of depression, although female percentages are slightly higher. This finding is contrary to almost all research on gender and depression, which shows that females of all ages experience more depression than males, at least in clinical contexts (Muszynski, 1994; Trypuc, 1994; Northcott, 1991).

Figure 3 further illustrates the connections between mental health and socioeconomic circumstance by focusing on the levels of stress that Canadian youth experience (based on a series of indicators of stress incorporated in the National Population Health Survey).

Health research is quite clear that stress leads to both physical and emotional health risk and that poverty predisposes youth to stress and ultimately to health risk (Canadian Institute of Child Health, 2000; Baxter, 1993). As with previous indicators of health, stress decreases as income increases, and levels of stress are highest for the lowest-income category for female and male youth. Furthermore, it appears that at all income levels, girls experience higher levels of stress than do boys.

Figures 4 and 5 are intended to complete this introductory section by illustrating two specific physical manifestations of ill health: asthma and arthritis. Asthma serves as a health indicator because it is purported to have both physical–genetic and psychological origins (McCreary Centre Society, 1994). Several things are important about asthma

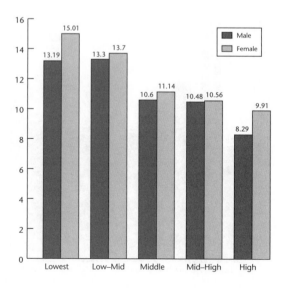

FIGURE 14.2

Number of Weeks of Feeling Depressed for Canadian Youth, by Income Level

Source: Based on Statistics Canada (1998).

FIGURE 14.3

General Chronic Stress Index for
Canadian Youth, by Income Level

Source: Based on Statistics Canada (1998).

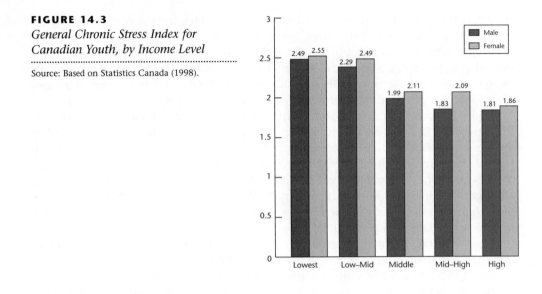

and youth. First, asthma is the most common chronic illness in children and youth. Second, it has been on the rise in the last 20 years in Canada, from 2 percent in 1978 to 12.2 percent in 1997 for children and youth under 20 years of age (Canadian Institute of Child Health, 1998, 2000; Senthilsevan, 1998). Third, American research has indicated that deaths from asthma are four times as prevalent among Black youth as among white youth, indicating a rather marked connection to social class (Morbidity and Mortality Weekly Report, 1996). The overall conclusions in most of the research on asthma and children and youth suggest a strong correlation with environmental conta-

FIGURE 14.4

Percentage of Canadian Youth with
Asthma, by Income Level

Source: Based on Statistics Canada (1998).

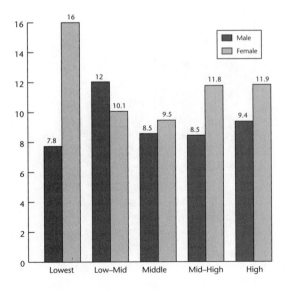

minants and exposure to air-borne and ingested substances that trigger asthmatic reactions (Canadian Institute of Child Health, 1998).

Most noticeable in Figure 4 is the overwhelming impact of poverty on rates of asthma for low-income girls. Interestingly, the same effect is not apparent for boys. Furthermore, for boys, rates of asthma vary little across income categories, except for the low–mid income category, with a relatively high percentage of 12. Lastly, it is significant that girls have higher rates of asthma overall than do boys. This gender difference may be attributable, in part, to higher rates of smoking among girls than among boys. Income differences are somewhat easier to explain given the higher incidences of smoking among lower-income youth and the often-recorded high levels of exposure to environmental contaminants that lower-class people experience relative to their wealthier counterparts.

Arthritis, although it is thought to be less psychosomatically determined in its origins than conditions like asthma, has a probable socioenvironmental antecedent. Adolescent arthritis may originate with impaired nutrition and exposure to environmental threats, resulting in triggering factors such as childhood influenza, rubella, and pneumonia. Research in Manitoba has suggested that these triggering factors and the corresponding incidence of rheumatoid arthritis in adolescents are higher among rural Aboriginal youth, who tend to live in communities marked by relative privation (Oen, Fast, & Postl, 1995). An analysis of levels of arthritis presents a different set of assumptions than those of the study of asthma. First, arthritis is ostensibly more congenitally determined than is asthma. Second, arthritis is primarily a condition of aging, and in general is most prevalent among the elderly (conditioned by overuse and abuse of the musculoskeletal system). Interestingly, the results here show that arthritis appears often among young people, and, for girls, is closely associated with income. For example, almost 6 percent of young girls in the low-income category have arthritis, compared with 1.9 percent in the high-income bracket. For some reason, low incomes expose girls to this risk. It may have

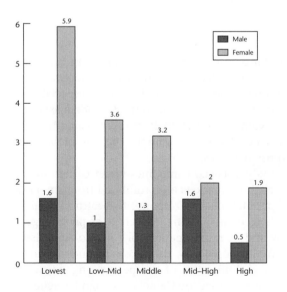

FIGURE 14.5
Percentage of Canadian Youth with Arthritis, by Income Level

Source: Based on Statistics Canada (1998).

something to do with diet, exercise, and prenatal and neonatal care. Even in a system of universal health care, access to adequate diets, lifestyles, and gynecological and pediatric care is determined by social standing (Mustard & Roos, 1994). This class phenomenon is not as apparent for boys, although boys in the high-income bracket have almost negligible rates of arthritis (0.5 percent). Lastly, it is significant that arthritis is much more common among girls than among boys, and although most clinical evidence suggests similar rates for boys and girls (Woo & Wedderburn, 1998), these self-report survey results suggest that possibly girls are more aware of their condition than boys are and have pursued medical intervention, in light of the conventional wisdom that suggests women of all ages pursue medical care more than men do.

Overall, the results from the first set of figures illustrate quite clearly that poverty places youth in medical jeopardy. Furthermore, the findings suggest that gender has an influence on levels of health and on how poverty affects health. The following discussions illustrate how many of the medical dangers that threaten the health of adolescents are the result of adult "business as usual." In effect, the health risks faced by youth are the result of the adult pursuit of profit or, at least, are the result of youth emulating adult behaviour. And startlingly, they are largely preventable.

DRUGS, ALCOHOL, AND TOBACCO: ADULT GRATIFICATION, ADOLESCENT DANGER

This discussion of high-risk substance abuse is significant for several reasons. First, it illustrates that many of the substances that place youth at extreme risk are manufactured legally by adults in the pursuit of profit — and youth are the calculated markets for many of these dangerous substances. Second, when youth ingest substances that endanger their health, they often do so in emulation of adults or as a response to abuse or neglect in an adult world; their use of chemicals is largely an attempt to normalize an unendurable existence.

Tobacco Use

Tobacco is likely the most addictive substance and, ironically, the one most accessible to young people. While rates of tobacco use have declined in the overall population in recent years, the rates of tobacco use among adolescents have increased, especially for female youth, despite the prohibitions surrounding selling cigarettes to underage youth. In Canada in 1994, 29 percent of young women aged 15 to 19 smoked regularly, compared with 26 percent of young men (Clark, 1996). Disturbingly, the rate of smoking among adolescent females continues to rise (Greaves, 1996).

Although smoking is a voluntary activity, tobacco companies target certain demographic markets regardless of the fact that those markets are prohibited from smoking. As smoking decreases among the adult population — in response to health campaigns and a general overall awareness of the dangers of smoking, especially as people age — children and adolescents provide a new and lucrative market for tobacco advertisers. Current tobacco advertisements that promise popularity, thinness, and independence are clearly targeted at young women. As an indication of the penetrating impact of advertising on the young, Greaves (1996) reports that the Camel campaign launched in the United States in 1988 (which features the cartoon camel Old Joe) increased Camel's share of the illegal children and youth market from 0.5 percent to 32.8 percent, and 94 percent of American high school students recognize the Old Joe trademark.

Given the widespread knowledge that cigarettes and other forms of tobacco are a proven health risk, what is it that compels children and youth, especially female youth, to smoke in increasing numbers? Greaves (1996) contends that the explanations lie somewhere in the contemporary ethos of gender equity and potential for equal opportunity for girls and boys and the structural barriers that continue to exist for girls and women. Smoking is emblematic of independence and choice. Tobacco companies foster this in ads that focus on being "your own person." The image of independence, coupled with girls' struggle to be equal to boys, fosters an adolescent world in which acceptance and maturity are equated with smoking. However, the opportunities for young men are much greater than they are for girls. Young women are faced with a reality of the struggle for equality in a structurally unequal world, and smoking becomes a part of their reality, in response to the alienation they feel from the work world and from the constraints of the domestic sphere. Smoking provides

> symbolic adult status at a time when access to the real thing is undermined both by the paradoxes of femininity, work and adulthood.... Once established, the smoking habit may be an important means of managing the inherent tensions between and within paid work, domesticity and constraining notions of appropriate sexual identity in young women's lives. (Kostash, 1989, quoted in Greaves, 1996, p. 113)

The notion that smoking is a way of establishing a psychosocial identity in a world that promises success, often without fulfillment, has implications for male smoking as well. Consistent with the overall theme of this chapter, it is easy to argue that children and youth are part of the marginalized classes. They do not vote, they have little policy impact on the world into which they are thrust, and most of the institutions that provide self- and social fulfillment (clubs, community organizations, and so on) are created by and for adults and are financially and constitutionally unavailable to youth. It is conceivable that both male and female youth — especially the most socioeconomically deprived youth (Conrad, Flay, & Hill, 1992) — smoke in an attempt to establish control and ultimately to access, at least symbolically, the democratic process. As Greaves (1996) and others have argued, however, for girls the double jeopardy of living on the margins and living in a patriarchal world dictates unusual vulnerability to the "culture of smoking."

Alcohol and Drug Use

As is discussed in a subsequent section, street youth use and abuse alcohol and drugs because it helps them normalize marginal and traumatic lives. The extent of the trauma faced by street youth is evidenced by the McCreary Centre Society (1994) study of youth in British Columbia in 1994. The shocking findings were that 98 percent of female youth on the street reported some form of prior abuse, as children or adolescents. The elevated levels of physical, psychological, and emotional harm — either through previous childhood experience or through immediate life circumstances — are linked to the abuse of alcohol and drugs (Centre for Addiction and Mental Health, 1999; Hagan &

McCarthy, 1998) and ultimately linked to high propensities to suicide and self-abuse, including **slashing**, and to poor levels of health (Schissel & Fedec, 1999; McCreary Centre Society, 1994). For example, Schissel and Fedec (2000), in their study of Saskatchewan children and youth involved in the sex trade, found relatively high levels of both alcohol and drug abuse among a young-offender population. However, among the young offenders who were involved in the sex trade, levels of substance abuse were extremely high: 100 percent of non-Aboriginal young offenders involved in the sex trade had severe alcohol problems, compared with 50 percent of young offenders not in the sex trade (the corresponding rates for Aboriginal youth were 86 percent and 65 percent, respectively).

The association of substance abuse with trauma is not only characteristic of street youth, however. Regardless of socioeconomic context, youth who have been victims of adult exploitation and abuse show elevated rates of alcohol and drug abuse. For example, the 1992 study *Rape in America* found that serious drinking problems were 12 times higher and serious drug problems were 25 times higher among rape victims than among non-victims (Males, 1996). It is significant that in the public discourse surrounding youth alcohol and drug abuse, issues of childhood and youth victimization by adults are rarely addressed, in lieu of the more politically expedient focus on dangerous kids. An additional contradiction is that most of the substances abused by children and youth are manufactured legitimately by adults, are often manufactured under the guise of medical care, and are "pushed" to youth by multinational corporations who work very hard to foster the connections between the use of their substances and success, especially in sports. Although this is especially true for tobacco manufacturers, companies like Labatt and Budweiser have so convincingly insinuated themselves into the culture of youth that underage drinking has become almost normative. And, of course, when youth are condemned for their potential criminality, drinking and drug use are cited as triggering factors. The therapeutic response, as a result, is to teach abstinence to youngsters, through law, education, or medicine. In a climate of tolerance for widespread drinking in North America, especially in the context of sports, as Males (1996) argues, "any effort to teach youngsters abstinence from these substances is a little like trying to promote chastity in a brothel" (1996, p. 215).

It is significant in these discussions to realize that many of the drugs produced for therapeutic reasons are harmful to children and youth. For example, in the United States, the drugs that send most teenagers to emergency rooms are Tylenol, Aspirin, and ibuprofen. Out of all the emergency room visits for substance abuse among youth, 71 percent were for pharmaceutical overdoses, 15 percent for alcohol, caffeine, and drugs combined, and only 14 percent for street drugs (Males, 1996). In Canada, the increasing use of Ritalin to control children and youth who are unable to fit into a regular classroom situation — diagnosed as attention deficit disorder, or ADD — results in much of the drug ending up on the street and being used in combination with other pharmaceuticals. An equally pressing problem is that Ritalin use on hyperactive or ADD children and youth has increased by 4.6 times in Canada since 1990 (Chisholm, 1996). The implications of this are staggering, given evidence to suggest that ADD is difficult to define, let alone diagnose. Some doctors regard Ritalin as a panacea for youth attention problems — and prescribe accordingly — while others regard it as a dangerous narcotic. In some communities, such as Vernon, B.C., 10 percent of 11-year-old boys were found to be on the drug (Rees, 1998). Significantly, Sweden banned Ritalin in 1968 because of heavy abuse (Diller, 1998).

The grim reality is that Ritalin has dangerous side effects, including drug dependence, headaches, eye and mouth tics, insomnia, and long-term risks from cancer and chronic depression (Diller, 1998). It is, however, an extremely lucrative amphetamine for Ciba-Geigy, the primary manufacturer. Social commentators, in response, have argued that in a climate of fiscal restraint and consequent larger classroom sizes, teachers are using Ritalin to manage inordinately large and diverse student contexts. More directly, it appears that Canadians have chosen, very unapologetically, to ignore the environment in which they place their children and youth and to focus on the more lucrative, more compelling world of individual sickness and deviance:

> In spite of the rhetoric in schools of education about the importance of taking into account the individual needs of the children in a classroom, the current system of public education is designed to make that nearly impossible.... Instead, it becomes necessary to find ways of making children able to perform in the environment as they find it. And, in late twentieth-century America, when it is difficult or inconvenient to change the environment, we don't think twice about changing the brain of the person who has to live in it. (Livingston, 1997, pp. 17–18)

The complicity of adults in pushing legitimate pharmaceuticals to youth is illustrated in the following section on sports, popular culture, and body image.

THE PATHOLOGY OF BODY IMAGES

Body weight has for decades been considered a diagnostic indicator of health, but only recently has it become a dominant concern for health care professionals and the focus of personal crusades for an increasing number of Canadians (Nichols, 1999). The medical argument is simple: insufficient and excess weight statuses are health risks, especially in light of the research on eating disorders and youth and on obesity and longevity. Health Canada's standard weight scale that shows acceptable weight per height has become an acceptable standard for judging whether a person is at risk. However, despite the medical validity of this diagnostic tool, the issue of body weight is politically charged. First, body weight and body image are social constructions that have evaluative power. One has to look no farther than advertisements for brand-name clothing or for cosmetics to see that the society places most value on lithe and youthful body types. This socially constructed image of the acceptable body serves industries like clothing and cosmetics. The image is an ideal that people strive to achieve, and the struggle is costly and never-ending. As Findlay argues:

> The media and advertising industries, for example, promote their products by suggesting that success and beauty will belong to every woman if she diets properly or purchases the latest stay thin formulas. The medical profession, for its part, advocates a thin build over a heavy one, thus reinforcing the dominant norms. Women equate the attainment of the normative appearance with social mobility.... Consistent exposure to impossible images of ideal beauty conveys a sense of perpetual deficiency to ordinary women.... The effort is often exhausting and painful. (Findlay, 1996, p. 176)

As we will come to see, the effort is not only exhausting and painful, but for young women and men also has the potential to create permanent physical damage. A fundamental aspect in understanding body weight and health jeopardy for youth is that the struggle to achieve the ideal body type, especially for youth, is often fostered by adults in contexts like athletics and art and in the business world of fashion. It is based on an ethos that achievement and success are closely tied to, or perhaps are equivalent to, maintenance of a certain body image. Cosmetics and clothing industries target youthful audiences and sports and artistic organizations exploit youth in the search for physical domination and victory. The final irony is that when governments proclaim eating disorders, especially obesity, as a national health problem, they target and blame individuals who are the most exploited and disadvantaged, and ultimately they lay blame on the victims for taxing an already heavily burdened health care system. (See also Chapter 10 of this book regarding the "medicalization" of appearance.)

Before expanding on these issues, however, it is worth illustrating how body weight is closely tied to gender and class. Figures 6 and 7 are based on the National Population Health Survey, and levels of both underweight and overweight are based on Health Canada standards of acceptable weight per height. The figures are important in illustrating how female and male youth differ in the effects of wealth on health. First, for male youth, insufficient weight is most common among those in the lowest-income category. For girls, the opposite is true, with those in the highest income categories experiencing the highest levels of inadequate weight. This finding for young females is consistent with the sociomedical literature, which documents the highest prevalence of eating disorders among populations in which the pressure toward thinness is the greatest, including young affluent women in Western societies (Dolan, 1991; Nasser, 1988). The findings for young men are more difficult to explain and, although perplexing to understand in an affluent country like Canada, maybe poor young males simply lack access to an adequate diet by virtue of their poverty, especially given how much, in

FIGURE 14.6

Percentage of Underweight Canadian Youth, by Income Level

Source: Based on Statistics Canada (1998).

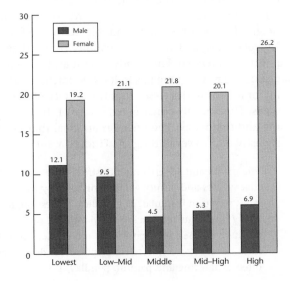

general, developing young males need to eat. Certainly, the National Organization on Poverty in Canada has argued that this is the case for children, and it is conceivable that poor young males, as well, suffer poor diets as a result of their privation.

Finally, in this figure it is apparent that the malady of insufficient weight is much more prevalent among young females than among males, and this finding is consistent with current research that analyzes **anorexia nervosa** and **bulimia** in the context of constructed images of femininity and social value (Showalter, 1997; Findlay, 1996).

Figure 7 illustrates the condition that would appear to be the corollary of anorexia and bulimia but is, at a very core level, a manifestation of the same types of social values placed on body type and size. Health Canada has declared obesity to be a national health problem and has essentially created a national stigma for those who are overweight. The results here indicate quite clearly that, if the two poorest-income levels of adolescents are isolated, young women are substantially more overweight than their male counterparts. At the high end of the income spectrum, however, the opposite is true; young men have higher rates of obesity than young women.

The explanations are explored in research conducted at McGill University that investigated obesity among children and youth in Montreal. The conclusions from this research direct attention at higher levels of fat intake and lower levels of micronutrient intake among poor families (Johnson-Down et al., 1997). The general sociomedical conclusion is that a general trend toward obesity in children and youth in Canada is more pronounced in more disadvantaged children than it is in their wealthier counterparts (Yip, Scanlon, & Trowbridge, 1993), and that the unhealthy dietary habits learned early in life tend to persist into adulthood (Clarke & Lauer, 1993). It is interesting that the findings from the National Population Health Study in Figure 7 show the low income–poverty effect for young females only. If the effect of poor diets in children is manifested in adolescents and adults, one would expect the class effect to apply to young males as well as females.

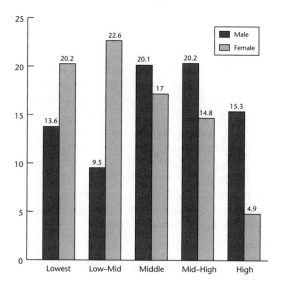

FIGURE 14.7
Percentage of Overweight Canadian Youth, by Income Level

Source: Based on Statistics Canada (1998).

In light of the foregoing discussions, the question arises as to how body image and body size come to preoccupy youth to a point where weight control leads to self-injurious behaviours like anorexia and bulimia at one extreme and obesity at the other. What is being investigated is how a generation of adolescents comes to orient themselves primarily to body image as a source of validation and identity. This **pathology of body image** filters down to children. The "sickness of body image" starts at a very early age, as confirmed by the Jacobs Institute of Women's Health in 1997: 40 percent of third-grade girls said they were dieting to lose weight. By the fifth grade, the figure had increased to 75 percent (Mosley, 1997).

EATING DISORDERS AND SEXUALITY

Despite the profusion of medical research based on the psychopathology of eating disorders — from research based primarily on the taxonomy of psychiatric disorders and eating disorders (Garfinkel et al., 1995) to the psychological search for connections between eating disorders and personality characteristics — the historical question remains: why are youth only now engaging in injurious eating behaviours? The first and most obvious response is that the social value we place on thinness and youth is so strong, and of course, so closely tied to the merchandising of "body image enhancing products," that youth grow up orienting their lives to "**beauty norms**." But, more importantly, modern society creates the equation between social and personal value and beauty; and children and youth are extremely vulnerable to the inadvertent and subliminal conveyors of this message. Feminist authors generally contend that thinness is a patriarchal and political–economic construction that sets tyrannical cultural expectations for girls and women. As is argued in the next section, the tyranny of body image is becoming as oppressive for young men as it is for young women.

Popular culture critic Naomi Wolf (1990) contends that diet, cosmetic, fashion, and plastic-surgery industries conspire to keep women unsure of themselves and their physicality and "in their place." Youth, more so than others, buy into the "beauty myth" and place themselves at risk by engaging in self-destructive behaviours such as anorexia nervosa and bulimia. Anorexia nervosa is characterized by extreme weight loss and a pathological fear of becoming fat, whereas bulimia is distinguished by binge eating and then purging by vomiting or laxative use. In either case, medical researchers argue that victims of the disorders are already troubled people who are unfortunately influenced by popular culture images of the ideal body. Current estimates in Canada suggest that 1.5 percent of young women have serious cases of bulimia and another 1 percent have anorexia nervosa. However, although medicine studies the relatively uncommon "pathological cases," there is increasing evidence that a large proportion of all youth, especially female youth, are preoccupied with weight to the point that they put themselves at risk through inadequate eating or purging or through the use of diet pills (Showalter, 1997). What is occurring, as a result, is less an eating disorder epidemic than a normative youth orientation based on popular culture body images. A harsh example of the influence of popular culture has been documented recently by Harvard Medical School anthropology professor Anne Becker (Shin, 1999), who has studied eating habits in Fiji in the wake of the introduction of television in 1995. Her findings, based on a

1998 survey and historical work on Fijian society, determined that a sudden increase in eating disorders among young girls in Fiji coincided with and may be linked to the introduction of television and access to American shows such as *Melrose Place, Xena, Warrior Princess*, and *ER*. In her survey, 74 percent of Fijian girls reported "being too fat," and 15 percent reported they had vomited to control weight. And, as Becker reports, this is in a historical and cultural context in which "robust, well-muscled" body types are the norm and in which dieting and purging are unknown. She concludes that television is a pathogen and that Western ideals of physicality and body image are like a plague.

In response to critics like Wolf, more psychologically oriented conspiracy theorists like Showalter (1997) and Shorter (1994) blame the media, clinics, doctors, and charismatic healers for constructing a public panic over a series of decades that culminated in a real epidemic of eating disorders as potential patients "bought into" the hype. Showalter, especially, argues that a mass publicity campaign spread the news of this modern condition to every young woman in the Western world. And these young women react accordingly in true psychosomatic fashion by manifesting the behaviours of the constructed disease (Showalter, 1997; Shorter, 1994).

Although theories of popular culture are important and intuitively interesting, they do make some rather broad leaps of faith regarding the immediate impact that the entertainment and advertising industries have on personal conduct. They also stop short of tying images of men and women to the broader historicocultural forces that shape the ways that society views men and women as distinct, sexualized beings.

Several decades ago, Michel Foucault (1980) argued that modern society is characterized by the "deployment of sexuality." In essence, he suggested that sex has become so sublimated and mysterious that a proliferation of discourses has resulted as a consequence of the uncertainty of sexuality. The more we repress sex, the more we crave to know about it, especially among the disciplines of medicine, science, and, of course, pop psychology. His work seems appropriate here because it helps explain the seemingly overwhelming concern with body image. Body image is about sexuality, about understanding the mystery of sex at an organizational and professional level and at a personal level. Adolescents, especially young women, are largely defined — and define themselves — as sexual beings. If sexuality is the fundamental defining characteristics of the "normal" (and abnormal) person, then a preoccupation with the trappings of sexuality is understandable. To appear conventional (i.e., attractive), young people fulfill the mandate of a sexualized society by engaging in "grooming conduct." While anthropologists might argue that this is normal sexual conduct for the human animal, a more insightful Foucaultian-based analysis would contend that repressed sexuality is a modern invention that has led us to explore, at length, the mysteries and deviances of sex.

The legitimate speakers in this discourse of sex are, of course, science and medicine, but more and more commonly they are popular culture, in the forms of pop psychology and fashion and stardom. And it is no surprise that young people engage in "body image activity" by using the inventions of science and medicine as legitimate techniques of self-development. Many of the substances that youth choose to control weight and to foster a certain body image are produced by pharmaceutical companies and the industry of medicine as legitimate means of corrective sexuality. The next section, on sports and legitimate drugs, is an apt example of how this strategy works.

THE PATHOLOGY OF ATHLETICS

A 1993 study of anabolic steroid use in sports in Canada indicated that 83 000 Canadians between the ages of 11 and 18 used steroids — 2.8 percent of all youth in this age category and 4.3 percent of all male youth (Melia, Pipe, & Greenberg, 1996). American research indicates higher incidences, ranging from 5 to 10 percent of adolescent boys (Eliot & Goldberg, 1996). The evidence regarding steroid use is overwhelming: anabolic steroid use can lead to heart problems, depression, severe aggressive behaviour, sex-organ problems in both men and women, and several forms of cancer. In short, continued steroid use can lead to premature death, as evidenced by several high-profile cases, including American football star Lyle Alzado and World Wrestling Federation star Rick Rude.

Steroid use among Western youth illustrates one of the fundamental dangers of contemporary athletics. The "succeed at all cost" mentality has become so pervasive in sports, especially among youth, that coaches instruct within this paradigm. So much of what coaches and other sports officials communicate to youth is an inadvertent expectation that athletic prowess and success is closely tied to body shape and body image. In essence, athletic prowess and attractiveness become conflated, and this has implications for muscle-enhancement and weight control. Male youth take steroids to emulate popular culture idols, mostly athletes, as evidenced by the overwhelming popularity of professional wrestling among young men. Female youth tend to fixate on weight control, especially in the subjectively judged sports that require a lean, youthful body for presentation, such as figure skating, gymnastics, and competitive dance. In these "aesthetic" sports, participants commonly reach their athletic prime before puberty, and obsessive weight control to keep the "child body form" among young female athletes has been linked unequivocally to gynecological risks such as **amenorrhea**, infertility, and osteoporosis (Fogelholm et al., 1996; Constantini, 1994).

The conflation of athletics and aesthetics results in double jeopardy for male and female youth. Most research on steroid use among young men suggests that at least 50 percent of steroid users are concerned with improving their body image. That young men buy into the "beefcake myth" suggests that they, in part, are as susceptible to the damaging effects of images of sex and gender in popular culture as are young women. Many young men are willing to risk the dangers of steroid use to avoid the stigma of being considered small and weak. The use of steroids, however, is more complex than the use of mere cosmetics. As Parks and Read argue, the increasing preoccupation with body image among young men (and the attendant use of muscle-enhancing substances) "may induce some adolescents to participate in athletics in general, while the individual's body type may provide the impetus for selection of a particular sport" (Parks & Read, 1997, p. 594). Their research is instructive in illustrating that the futile struggle to obtain the perfect physique is closely tied to perceived success in athletics, which in turn is closely tied to popularity and success in school. These connections are borne out by the popularity of school sports like football and the social popularity of elite high school athletes, especially males.

For young women, the connection between body obsession and sports is similar in its psychic implications but different in its physical manifestations. The traditional "female sports" are based on the aesthetics of the female body. Figure skating and gymnastics (especially rhythmic gymnastics) are typical athletics whose presentation and form are judged as closely as or more closely than athletic prowess. It is these aesthetic sports that create the undue pressure on young female athletes to control their weight. As is the case for young males, messages of body image and performance efficiency are often communicated to young females by coaches, either directly or inadvertently, in a competitive "winning" context. Geoff Gowan, president of the Coaching Association of Canada, argues that coaches at all levels have enormous influences on their athletes and that what coaches say in a casual way "may be perceived by the young athlete, particularly in a sport where body shape and weight is of immense importance, to have a significant impact. These athletes are just beginning to get conscious of the fact that there is a danger she is going to get too heavy or too big or whatever, but is also trying to please a coach" (Moser, 1994). Kevin Spink, a sport psychologist at the University of Saskatchewan, in interviews with young athletes in aesthetic sports, found that a majority were dieting and that their intense preoccupation with weight and body image is fostered by coaches, parents, and other competitors. The subtle pressure to attain a certain body size and shape is contained in a "discourse of competition" that is based on "body talk," as if the aesthetic body is paramount to participation (Moser, 1994).

This "gestalt of success" carries with it extraordinary risk, especially for female youth. Spink argues that "the idea that body image affects our self-esteem is just starting to emerge.... It's basically the anxiety a person feels when physique is being evaluated in any way."(Moser, 1994, p. B2). A growing body of research focuses on the actual physical risk that athletes face in organized sports. The overarching conclusion is that young athletes in sports in which leanness or weight gain are required are at substantially higher risk for eating disorders, to the extent that in one study in Norway, the researchers found that of the 522 young females athletes studied, 22.4 percent could be classified as at risk from eating disorders, and 89 percent of those at risk were diagnosed with anorexia nervosa or bulimia. They state that 75 percent of those young athletes who were told by coaches that they were too heavy used pathogenic weight control methods, including purging, dieting, water loss, extreme exercise, and amphetamine use (Sundgot-Borgen, 1994). The dangers that this poses for young female athletes especially include disordered eating, amenorrhea, and osteoporosis (precipitated by gradual loss of bone density) (DiPietro & Stachenfeld, 1997).

Although the connections between eating disorders and athletics have been discussed primarily in the context of young women, it is significant that recent research is uncovering a hidden epidemic of high-risk behaviours (including anorexia and bulimia) among male adolescents, especially those who participate in sports such as long-distance running (Parks & Read, 1997). Furthermore, weight classification sports such as wrestling, boxing, and rowing have an atypical associated risk that involves short-term weight loss and subsequent rapid weight gain. The athletes involved are primarily young men who use laxatives and diuretics, wear plastic heat suits, and ingest no water. In short, they do anything to rid the body of water in an attempt to make a certain weight class. The typical pattern is to lose several kilograms of weight and then to regain the weight loss through binge drinking and eating, a subtle form of bulimia. This technique — almost universally accepted in high school weight-class sports — is potentially lethal: in 1997, three U.S. college wrestlers died in the midst of strenuous **weight-loss workouts**, including rapid dehydration and starvation, which resulted in heart and kidney failure (Litsky, 1997).

Figures 8 and 9 give the reader some sense of the extent of the chemical control of body weight by teenagers in Canada. The data are based on the Saskatchewan Youth Attitude Survey of 1996, a representative sample of 2600 youth aged 13–19 in Saskatchewan. The data present the extent of diet pill use and steroid use for males and females within age categories.

Figure 8 illustrates several important phenomena regarding chemical weight control. First, it is clear that female youth use diet pills more than their male counterparts in all age groups. Second, the overall rates of use indicate a marked increase in use from the youngest to oldest age groups for girls, to the extent that over 11 percent of female adolescents 17–19 years of age use diet pills six or more times a year (6 percent + 5.2 percent). For male youth, the rates are significantly lower than for female youth, but importantly, as many young males use diet pills as do older male adolescents (especially those who use pills more than twelve times a year).

For steroid use (Figure 9), young males tend to be the primary users, to the extent that over 4 percent of 17–19-year-old males use steroids more than twelve times a year. Almost 7 percent of this group use steroids at least six times a year. Steroid use, although highest for oldest males, is relatively high for 12–14-year-old male youth (over 3 percent use steroids more than twelve times a year). As expected, the rates for female youth are substantially less than for males, but, steroid use for girls is highest in the youngest age group. Either steroid use for girls diminishes with age or there is a cohort increase in use for girls. These data are from 1996, and it may be that steroid use is becoming more common for girls, the youngest groups manifesting this cohort effect the most.

In light of this rather convincing data that youth are participating in the body image struggle, it is significant that the substances used by youth to their own detriment are manufactured, marketed, and advocated by adults. Again, the advocacy is not overt; the subtle pressure to appear "strong" and "beautiful" and to buy into the ethos of physical and occupational success allows legitimately produced drugs like amphetamines and

FIGURE 14.8

Percentage of Saskatchewan Youth Who Take Diet Pills, 1996

Source: Based on Saskatchewan Youth Attitude Survey (1996) (unpublished).

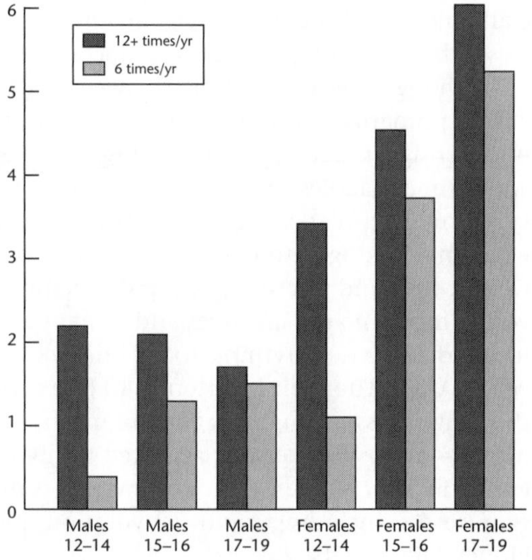

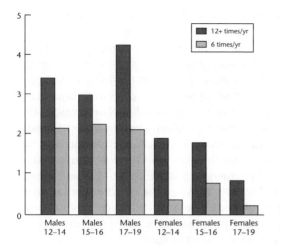

FIGURE 14.9

Percentage of Saskatchewan Youth Who Take Steroids, 1996

Source: Based on Saskatchewan Youth Attitude Survey (1996) (unpublished).

steroids to become part of youths' arsenal in the fight against their physicality. Although the use of steroids and diet pills has recently acquired the status of deviant activity, new ammunition for physical improvement is constantly on the horizon. Among the new quick fixes for "underdeveloped" athletes are the amino-acid–based compounds like **creatine** and male-hormone-based substances, including **androstenedione**. These new "safe" chemicals are touted as natural compounds that can enhance muscle growth and improve body image and physical efficiency. High school age youth are consumers of such products (primarily creatine) due to the ethos of sports and success in school, because the products are advertised as safe and natural, and because they are often used and endorsed by sports heroes.

Similar products are offered for weight control that are not narcotics-based but are based on the "natural" suppression of appetite. Although products like creatine are easy to access, there is little research regarding their long-term effects, especially on the developing adolescent body. The limited research does suggest, however, that androstenedione can cause premature closure of the growth plates in youth and that side effects typical of anabolic steroid use are more pronounced in youth than in adults (Schnirring, 1998a). Furthermore, creatine, the supplement of choice in high schools, may produce kidney failure and liver damage (Schnirring, 1998b). More importantly, such products encourage self-consciousness of being overweight or underweight and perpetuate the pathology of body image for youth, especially in the context of what is defined as athletic excellence.

YOUTH AND WORK: EXPLOITATION AND INEXPERIENCE

One of the basic human rights in Canada is to be able to work in a safe a secure environment for adequate wages. This right accrues to everyone, regardless of social characteristics. Although Canadians often violate the legislation, they do legislate protection from labour exploitation for children, as a result of their knowledge of how industries have historically exploited children for profit and how children and youth are still exploited throughout the world: despite the United Nations declaration on the rights of the child in 1989, 250 million children worldwide work long hours in hazardous conditions (Parker, 1997).

In general, however, adolescent labour in most countries is considered a normal part of the transition to adulthood. What is rarely acknowledged is that youth labour is highly exploitative; wages are generally low, benefits nonexistent, and on-the-job injuries common. In fact, young workers are more likely than their adult counterparts to be injured on the job, and their injuries are relatively serious (Dunn & Runyan, 1993). Furthermore, the industries that use youth labour (the fast food industry is typical) rarely provide the training and safety standards that are considered fundamental in the adult work world. In the United States, approximately 70 adolescents under the age of 18 die from work-related injuries per year, and about 64 000 are treated in emergency wards for on-the-job injuries. Approximately 40 percent of all work-related injuries for youth occurred in the fast food preparation industry. Federal child labour regulations in the United States prohibit anyone under 16 years of age from cooking or baking, yet one third of all injuries to youth in 1992 occurred among 14–15 year olds who were identified as cooks.

In Canada, the same 16-year-age regulation applies to youth who work in the general construction industry; yet, in July 1999, in Lashburn, Saskatchewan, a 15-year-old boy was killed when he was trapped between the cab and the box of a truck he was operating at a tire recycling plant. The boy was alone and unsupervised and was obviously in charge of operating heavy equipment. The negligence of management is distressing, and the family's trauma is unimaginable. What is equally distressing is the relative indifference to the incident evidenced by Occupational Health and Safety investigators whose initial comments focused on the applicability of the age restriction to this industry and their comments in the media that "when we hear about a very young worker, it causes us some concern" (Trifunov, 1999). It is certainly reasonable to expect that regulatory officials would take a more pro-active, advocacy stance. The reality in this situation is typical of many other workplaces: underage youth are employed at sometimes less than minimum wage, are often untrained, and are often unsupervised.

Many industries that employ youth as seasonal or "on-call" employees depend on exploited labour to maximize their profit (Reiter, 1996). The fast food industry, for example, is staffed largely by school-age employees and the turnover rate is deliberately high. In contexts like this, employers rarely spend time and money training employees in workplace safety. It is expensive to do so, and somewhat futile when the employee will only be on the job for a few months. Ironically, although the types of injuries that occur among youth in the food service industry are "soft-tissue" injuries, the government of Ontario is currently introducing legislation that would cut workers' compensation benefits for soft-tissue injuries by deducting from the worker's initial wage the amount of work that the injured person could still perform while injured. As Doug Pearault, president of the Ottawa and District Injured Workers' Group, argues, the most disadvantaged by this bill are young people, whose wages are already so low that the wage deduction from their assessment will leave no compensation (Bodnar, 1999).

The above arguments apply to adolescents working in legal conditions. The tragedy of adolescent health and labour, however, is most apparent in the research on hidden work, primarily youth working in illegal conditions. The employment of children and youth under illegal conditions is increasingly common in Canada and the United States (Basran, Gill, & MacLean, 1995). This trend is undoubtedly tied to increasing rates of poverty among children and the increasing exploitation of immigrant labour (Landrigan & Belville, 1993). In the United States, at least 70 percent of work-related injuries occur to children and youth who are employed illegally, and their injury rate is ten times that of children and youth employed legally. For example, in 1993, 1500 sweat shops in the garment industry in New York City employed children between the ages of 8 and 18, and these children were exposed to "unguarded machinery, no fire exits, boilers, wiring problems, egress problems, machines too close together" (Holloway, 1993, p. 16).

The most innocuous context for illegal child and youth exploitation in North America is agriculture. In most states in the United States, agriculture is not even covered by child labour laws. In Canada, agricultural labour is covered, but the ethos of the family farm virtually dictates that child and youth labour is expected. Despite the cultural orientation toward children and youth and farm work in agriculture-based communities, the implications for children and youth are severe, both in terms of the potential for immediate accidental injury and in terms of long-term exposure to dangerous environmental pathogens.

On the first point, because the labour of children and youth on farms is often unpaid or at least not part of the formal wage labour system, accidents largely go unreported unless they are fatal or extremely severe. Nonetheless, the evidence suggests that Canada has one of the highest accident mortality rates in the industrialized world and that in agriculture-based provinces like Saskatchewan, the accidental death rate for 15–19-year-olds is almost twice the Canadian rate (Glor, 1989).

On the second point, the work of Basran, Gill, & MacLean (1995) is most important. The researchers surveyed Indo-Canadian migrant farmworkers in the Fraser Valley in British Columbia. One of the central concerns of the study was to determine the degree of exposure to agricultural chemicals among workers and their children. Approximately 50 percent of the immigrant farmworkers reported bringing children with them to the fields, primarily as a consequence of lack of daycare facilities. Like the adults, the children were exposed to pesticides and herbicides, not primarily from direct spray contact but from next-day contact with treated plants and soil. The workers, while reluctant to report on the health effects on their own children, indicated a considerable and alarming effect on the children of other workers, to the extent that only 9 percent of all the workers surveyed suggested that children's ill health was not related to pesticide or herbicide exposure. The authors concluded that

> children in Surrey are being exposed to health risks, the implications of which may be quite severe, simply because there is a poverty of childcare resources in Surrey and there are simply no other options for the families of these children. (Basran, Gill, & MacLean, 1995, p. 87)

STREET KIDS: THROWAWAY ADOLESCENTS

One of the central arguments in this chapter is that poverty disposes youth to relatively high health risk. The introduction outlined the connections between poverty and certain illnesses. The two subsequent sections showed how substance abuse and low-end work both are related to the associations between poverty and ill health. This section will show how living on the margins of society dramatically endangers the health of society's most marginalized youth. Schissel and Fedec (1999) conducted a study of street youth by examining the *Young Offenders Act* (YOA) files of young offenders. A subset of the data was based on young offenders who had been charged with involvement in the sex trade. The adolescents in question were primarily street youth in Saskatoon and constituted a cross-section of youth who had been convicted under the YOA and who were involved in the sex trade in the inner city.

Figure 10 compares the health jeopardy for street youth involved in prostitution with that of young offenders who were not involved in the sex trade. As most of the literature on youth and street life suggests, prostitution is engaged in because of economic need, and the youth involved represent the most marginalized adolescents in society. The two most important phenomena in Figure 10 are the astonishing increase in health risk for youth involved in the sex trade and the absolute levels of health risk for both groups of youth. For example, 41.7 percent of female youth involved in the sex trade had been pregnant. Pregnancy not only poses a health risk for street youth as mothers, which also places the fetus at risk, but it is also an indicator of high-risk sexual activity. This subgroup of street youth is obviously engaging in unprotected sex: "Unprotected sex is a valuable commodity in the sex trade, and the highest profits are obtained from the prostitution of young girls who are willing to engage in unprotected sex" (Schissel & Fedec, 1999, p. 38). Female street youth not only run the risk of pregnancy, they obviously are exposed to sexually transmitted diseases (STDs) and run rather extreme risks from HIV, AIDS, and carcinogenic STDs.

Substance abuse poses an immediate risk for all youth, but is especially threatening for marginal youth. For example, for the "no involvement" in prostitution group, 42 percent used drugs and alcohol and 20 percent suffered severe alcohol abuse. For those youth in the sex trade, the figures increased dramatically to more than 80 percent using drugs and alcohol and over 40 percent with severe alcohol problems. For those who are living dangerous and unpleasant lives, substance abuse may be the only reasonable form for normalizing an otherwise intolerable life situation. This is further evidenced by the self-injury

FIGURE 14.10

Health Risks for Young Offenders, by Extent of Involvement in the Sex Trade: Saskatoon, 1996

Source: Based on Schissel and Fedec (1999), p. 48.

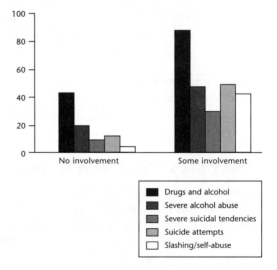

Drugs and alcohol
Severe alcohol abuse
Severe suicidal tendencies
Suicide attempts
Slashing/self-abuse

indicators. Ten percent of the no-involvement youth had severe suicidal tendencies, and over 10 percent had attempted suicide. For "involvement" youth, approximately 25 percent had severe suicidal tendencies and 25 percent attempted suicide. Finally, whereas a small percentage of all youth in the study engaged in slashing, over 40 percent of youth in the sex trade engaged in this form of self-abuse (Schissel & Fedec, 1999, p. 48).

The phenomenon of slashing is important in understanding the trauma of marginality. Research on slashing has argued that it is a form of emotion-masking behaviour typical of people who are in extremely traumatic life situations, exemplified by the high rates of slashing among women prisoners (Schissel, 1995). The alarmingly high rates of slashing among youth prostitutes display quite clearly the extreme psychic trauma under which they live. That even a small percentage of all the youth in this study engaged in slashing indicates the marginal and traumatic nature of life for many young offenders. Certainly, the expectation is that slashing would be nonexistent in a psychically and socially healthy adolescent population.

It is clear from these data that young offenders, as typically marginal youth, are exposed to rather severe medical trauma. The risks run from substance abuse to self-injury to **high-risk sexuality**. Importantly, for the most marginal in the society, the inner city street kid who sells herself or himself to survive, the medical jeopardy is startling.

The pathology of economic and social marginality for adolescents is further illustrated by focusing on the social and cultural genocide experienced by First Nations people in Canada. This protracted genocide has resulted in extreme physical and emotional jeopardy for Aboriginal youth. On January 26, 1993, six Innu youth in Davis Inlet, Labrador, tried to commit suicide together by sniffing gasoline. Their attempt at collective death was thwarted by an addictions counsellor who heard the youth declare that they wanted to die. Subsequently, fourteen youth from this small community were airlifted south for medical treatment, but the legacy of colonialization and government neglect remained. Ninety-five percent of the adult population were addicted to alcohol, 10 percent of the children and youth were chronic gasoline sniffers, and 25 percent of the adults had attempted suicide. Seven years later, the trauma for Davis Inlet had grown. In November 2000, twenty Innu children were again airlifted to the Goose Bay treatment centre as an interim reaction to another epidemic of gas sniffing among the children. Of the 169 children aged 10–19 living in Davis Inlet at the end of 2000, 154 had attempted gas sniffing and seventy of them were chronic sniffers. Davis Inlet is typical of Aboriginal communities in Canada that have been historically exploited and socially and economically neglected.

Geoffrey York, in his compelling book *The Dispossessed*, documents how, in a matter of 30 years, Aboriginal communities in Canada went from virtually no pathologies to levels of self-damage equivalent to those in Davis Inlet. His historical argument is an indictment of economic exploitation and community disruption in Canada's Aboriginal communities, and he describes how feelings of hopelessness and despair, coupled with the omnipresence of development, has led to what could be considered a type of protracted collective suicide among northern Aboriginal youth. For example, the Shamattawa Crees in northeastern Manitoba were relocated to reserves in the 1940s. Their trauma and cultural dislocation are described in a contemporary community scenario, which York describes as the rule and not the exception:

> Gasoline is the lifeblood of Shamattawa. It is the lifeblood of any northern Indian reserve. Without it, the Cree cannot run their skidoos or their motorboats. Without these vehicles, they cannot collect firewood to heat their homes, nor can they hunt or fish or trap to supplement their social assistance cheques.
>
> But gasoline is the deadliest poison at Shamattawa. Children and teenagers sniff to gain a quick escape, a cheap and immediate high — a few minutes of euphoria in a land of poverty and misery. Their attraction to gasoline becomes irresistible. The children of Shamattawa teach each other how to inhale it. At night, they break into snowmobile gas-tanks to steal more of the precious substance, until if finally dominates their existence.... Medical experts have concluded that gasoline sniffing is one of the most dangerous addictions in the world...a single inhalation can hook a child.... Gasoline sniffers often become convinced that they are invincible.... Once inhaled, gasoline harms the kidneys and liver, and inflicts permanent damage on the nervous system and the brain. (York, 1992, pp. 8–9)

It is clear from York's vivid description that when a people is shunted off to the margins of the society, either through sociopolitical neglect or through flagrant economic exploitation, the damages are extreme and filter down most dramatically to children and youth. Whether it is life on an inner city street or life in a socioeconomically damaged northern Aboriginal community, the reality is that children and youth are in extreme jeopardy and that their physical and emotional sufferings follow them to adulthood. A growing body of work on the long-term damage resulting from the sexual and physical exploitation of Aboriginal children in residential schools, for example, clearly shows how physical and mental injury to children and youth results in future generations of wounded and impaired adults (Miller, 1996).

CONCLUSION

The health of children and youth in Canada can be framed in the context of certain indisputable truths. First, although the United Nations has recently declared Canada to be the best country in the world in which to live, it chastised Canada for its deplorable record on child and youth poverty and for creating and sustaining Third World conditions for Aboriginal peoples. Second, in 1996 UNICEF reported that Canada's teenage suicide rate was alarmingly high compared with that of other industrial countries. From 1979 to 1991, suicides by young people aged 15–19 doubled to 13.5 percent per 100 000, ranking Canada third behind New Zealand and Finland. And, for every actual youth suicide in Canada in 1991, there were eighteen hospitalizations related to suicide (Beaulne, 1997). Further, the risk factors for suicide most often are those associated with political and economic exploitation and marginality: low family income, low education, losses due to divorce, family relocation, unemployment, loss of cultural and personal identity, and social isolation. Finally, Canada's child and youth poverty rate is the second highest in the industrialized world, next to that of the United States, and the problem is greatest for single mothers, over 50 percent of whom live below the poverty line. The Canadian Council on Social Development in 1998 cited the highlights of its study on youth and child poverty and concluded that child and youth poverty rates are rising, the gap between the rich and the poor is widening, and poor children and youth have fewer opportunities than before.

In light of the foregoing, Canadians need to inquire how a country as affluent as Canada arrives at a point at which children and youth are *de facto* disregarded. In fact, it is ill regard more than disregard, as evidenced by public demands to get tougher on youth crime, to make youth more accountable in school, and, in the interests of fiscal prudence, to implement work-for-welfare programs in many jurisdictions. This condemnation of youth is found in most media and is consistent and mostly unfounded (Schissel, 1997).

But Canadians need look no further than the way their society is structured. For the most part, Canada's success, internationally and internally, is based on a responsible balance of payments, low interest and inflation rates, a decreasing deficit, and a healthy dollar. None of these indicators has anything to do with the real health of the society and its people. Economic growth and vitality is an adult concern in a democratic, adult-based political economy. Children and youth do not vote; they are literally and figuratively disenfranchised from all levels of democratic input. Yet, as consumers of adult-produced goods — both legal and illicit — they are a fertile market. And, as cogs in the wheels of industry, they are an easily exploited reserve army of labour; at the extreme, they are **commodified** as the hottest commodities for sexual exploitation on the street and in residential schools. Children and youth do not count until they are needed. They, as the United Nations has implied, are not the benefactors of Canada's political and economic society, despite our collective but seemingly empty rhetoric that they are our most valuable resource.

ACKNOWLEDGEMENT

The author is indebted to the Social Sciences and Humanities Research Council of Canada (Grant Number 41-095-1532) for funding for the Saskatchewan Youth Attitudes Survey (1996).

STUDY QUESTIONS

1. *Smoking is a considerable and increasing health risk for female youth. Why is this so, in light of growing public concern about smoking as a major health problem?*
2. *Why do relatively poor youth tend to experience certain weight-related problems and wealthier youth experience others? What explains the persistent relationships between socioeconomic status and weight-related health problems among youth?*
3. *The popular perception is that athletics is very beneficial for children and youths because it contributes to both physical and emotional well-being. In this chapter, however, there is evidence that organized athletics may be a threat to the well-being of male and female youth. Explain the "pathology of athletics" and how adults may be held responsible for it.*
4. *Why is the basic human right to "work in a safe and secure environment" so easily and readily violated in terms of the employment of children and youth?*
5. *Many of the damaging things that happen to children and youth seem to be the result of an economic–corporate and political world engaging in "business as usual." Explain how this happens.*
6. *In an ethical world, health status should have nothing to do with the amount of wealth a person has. And, yet, socioeconomic status is often related to the health and well-being of children and youth. How does one make sense of this rather obvious social injustice?*

GLOSSARY

amenorrhea A delay in the onset of menstruation due, in part, to obsessive weight control in young women, especially in the context of organized athletics.

androstenedione An amino-acid–based compound that occurs naturally in the body but is produced artificially and used to enhance muscle growth and repair.

anorexia nervosa An eating disorder characterized by extreme weight loss and a pathological fear of becoming fat.

beauty norms The standards by which women and girls are judged on the basis of stereotypical images of thinness, youth, and beauty.

bulimia An eating disorder characterized by binge-eating and then purging by vomiting or by laxative use.

commodified Looked upon by greater society, in terms of economic value. Youth may be seen either as assets or liabilities, or as consumers, labourers, or sexual commodities and exploited as such by the labour market, politics, the marketplace, and the sex trade market.

creatine An amino-acid–based compound that occurs naturally in the body but is produced artificially and used to enhance muscle growth and repair.

high-risk sexuality A general reference to sexual conduct characterized by a lack of safe-sex practices, including sexual relations with unknown partners.

pathology of body image The obsession with body image (staying thin, young-looking, athletic, and sexually attractive), which creates the conditions under which many people, especially youth, engage in self-injurious behaviour while attempting to attain the ideal body image.

slashing The phenomenon of self-injury usually occurring as a result of knife or razor blade wounds that, in many cases, are attempts to mask the trauma of living in adverse life situations, such as being in jail or "on the street."

weight-loss workouts In weight-class sports, exercise done to reduce body weight to acceptable levels, engaged in by young male athletes in an attempt to lose weight through dehydration; accomplished by exercising in extreme conditions that generate excessive perspiration.

RECOMMENDED READINGS

Basran, G., Gill, C., & MacLean, B. (1995). *Farmworkers and their children.* Vancouver: Collective Press. An excellent empirical study of the effects of agricultural labour on Indo-Canadian migrant workers and their children in British Columbia's Fraser Valley. The authors document and discuss how, as new Canadians are employed as migrant farm workers, their children suffer from medical problems due to exposure to toxins in the agricultural work environment.

Canadian Institute of Child Health. (2000). *The health of Canada's children: A CICH profile* (3rd ed.). Ottawa: Author. A comprehensive and current empirical review of the state of health of Canada's children; includes a comprehensive bibliography.

Diller, L. (1998). *Running on Ritalin: A physician reflects on children, society, and performance in a pill.* New York: Bantam Books. A critical analysis of how Ritalin has become a panacea for all types of behavioural problems among children and youth. The author attacks medicine and education, which have become addicted to Ritalin as a form of crowd control of children and youth.

Greaves, L. (1996). *Smoke screen: Women's smoking and social control*. Halifax: Fernwood. An insightful account of the increasing phenomenon of smoking among Canadian women, with a specific focus on why young women begin to smoke and how the tobacco industry plays on issues of gender equality and success in a male world to convince young women that smoking is liberating.

Males, M. (1996). *The scapegoat generation: America's war on adolescents*. Monroe, ME: Common Courage Press. A comprehensive, empirically supported study of the sociopsychological and medical dangers that threaten youths and of how many of these dangers are deliberately created and perpetrated by adults against youths in the pursuit of profit and political success.

York, G. (1992). *The dispossessed: Life and death in native Canada*. Toronto: Little, Brown. A necessary study of the effect that a covert policy of economic and social genocide has had on First Nations communities in northern Canada. It describes, in important detail, how communities went from highly livable communities to places in which children and youth are extremely vulnerable as a result of unbridled economic development.

REFERENCES

Basran, G., Gill, C., & MacLean, B. (1995). *Farmworkers and their children*. Vancouver: Collective Press.

Baxter. S. (1993). *A child is not a toy: Voices of children in poverty*. Vancouver: New Star Books.

Beaulne, G. (1997). *For the safety of Canadian children and youth: From injury data to preventive measures*. Ottawa: Health Canada.

Bodnar, C. (1999, March 5). Students may hurt from new workers' comp bill. *Fulcrum Online*.

Canadian Institute of Child Health. (1998). *The air children breathe: The effects on their health*. Ottawa: Pollution Probe and Author.

Canadian Institute of Child Health. (2000). *The health of Canada's children: A CICH profile* (3rd ed.). Ottawa: Author.

Centre for Addiction and Mental Health. (1999). *Canadian profile: Alcohol, tobacco and other drugs*. Ottawa: Canadian Centre for Substance Abuse.

Chisholm, P. (1996, March 11). The ADD dilemma. *Maclean's,* pp. 42–44.

Clark, W. (1996, Winter). Youth smoking in Canada. *Canadian Social Trends,* 2–6.

Clarke, W.R., & Lauer, L.R. (1993). Does childhood obesity track into adulthood? *Critical Review of Food Science and Nutrition, 33,* 423–430.

Conrad, K.M., Flay, B.R., & Hill, D. (1992). Why children start smoking cigarettes: Predictors of onset. *British Journal of Addiction, 87*(12), 1171–1724.

Constantini, N.W. (1994). Clinical consequences of athletic amenorrhea. *Sports Medicine, 17,* 213–223.

Diller, L. (1998). *Running on Ritalin: A physician reflects on children, society, and performance in a pill*. New York: Bantam Books.

DiPietro, L., & Stachenfeld, N. (1997). The female athlete triad. *Medicine and Science in Sports and Exercise, 29,* 1669–1671.

Dolan, B. (1991). Cross-cultural aspects of anorexia nervosa and bulimia: A review. *International Journal of Eating Disorders, 10,* 67–68.

Dunn, K., & Runyan, C. (1993). Deaths at work among children and adolescents. *American Journal of Diseases in Children, 147,* 1044–1047.

Eliot, D., & Goldberg, L. (1996). Intervention and prevention of steroid use in adolescents. *American Journal of Sports Medicine, 24*(6), S46–S47.

Findlay, D. (1996). The body perfect: appearance norms, medical control, and women. In B. Schissel & L. Mahood (Eds.), *Social control in Canada: Issues in the social construction of deviance* (pp. 174–200). Don Mills, ON: Oxford University Press.

Fogelholm, M., Lichtenbelt, W., Ottenheijm, R., & Westerterp, K. (1996). Amenorrhea in ballet dancers in the Netherlands. *Medicine and Science in Sports and Exercise, 28*, 545–550.

Foucault, M. (1980). *The history of sexuality. Vol. 1. An introduction.* New York: Vintage Books.

Garfinkel, P., Lin, E., Georing, P., Spegg, C., Goldbloom, D., Kennedy, S., Kaplan, A., & Woodside, D.B. (1995). Bulimia nervosa in a Canadian community sample: Prevalence and comparison of subgroups. *American Journal of Psychiatry, 152*, 1052–1058.

Glor, E. (1989). A survey of comprehensive accident and injury experience of high school students in Saskatchewan. *Canadian Journal of Public Health, 80*, 435–440.

Greaves, L. (1996). *Smoke screen: Women's smoking and social control.* Halifax: Fernwood.

Hagan, J., & McCarthy, B. (1998). *Mean streets: Youth crime and homelessness.* Cambridge: Cambridge University Press.

Holloway, M. (1993). Hard times: Occupational injuries among children are increasing. *Scientific American, 269*, 14–16.

Johnson-Down, L., O'Loughlin, J., Koski, K., & Gray-Donald, K. (1997). High prevalence of obesity in low income and multi-ethnic schoolchildren: A diet and physical activity assessment. *Journal of Nutrition, 127*(12), 2310–2315.

Kostash, M. (1989). *No kidding: Inside the world of teenage girls.* Toronto: McClelland and Stewart.

Kutcher, S., Ward, B., Hayes, D., & Wheeler, K. (1996). Mental health concerns of Canadian adolescents: A consumer's perspective. *Canadian Journal of Psychiatry, 41*, 5–10.

Landrigan, P., & Belville, R. (1993). The dangers of illegal child labour. *American Journal of Diseases in Children, 147*, 1029–1030.

Litsky, F. (1997, December 19). Collegiate wrestling deaths raise fears about training. *New York Times,* p. C7.

Livingston, K. (1997, Spring). Ritalin: Miracle drug or cop-out. *The Public Interest,* pp. 3–18.

Males, M. (1996). *The scapegoat generation: America's war on adolescents.* Monroe, ME: Common Courage Press.

McCreary Centre Society. (1994). *Adolescent health survey: Street youth in Vancouver.* Burnaby: Author.

Melia, P., Pipe, A., & Greenberg, G. (1996). The use of anabolic-androgenic steroids by Canadian students. *Clinical Journal of Sport Medicine, 6*(1), 9–14.

Miller, J.R. (1996). *Shingwauk's vision: A history of native residential schools.* Toronto: University of Toronto Press.

Morbidity and Mortality Weekly Report. (1996, August). Asthma mortality and hospitalization among children and young adults — United States, 1980–1993. *American Family Physician, 54*, 777.

Moser, D. (1994, December 15). Eating disorders in sports. *Regina Leader Post,* p. A3.

Mosley, B. (1997). Striking the balance. *Women's Sports and Fitness, 19*, 29.

Mustard, C.A., & Roos, N.P. (1994). The relationship of prenatal care and pregnancy complications to birth weight in Winnipeg, Canada. *American Journal of Public Health, 84*(9), 1450–1457.

Muszynski, A. (1994). Gender inequality and life chances: Women's lives and health. In B.S. Bolaria & R. Bolaria (Eds.), *Women, medicine, and health* (pp. 57–72). Halifax: Fernwood.

Nasser, M. (1988). Culture and weight consciousness. *Journal of Psychosomatic Research, 32*, 573–577.

Nichols, M. (1999, January 11). The obesity epidemic. *Maclean's*, pp. 54–58.

Northcott, H.C. (1991). Health status and health care in Canada: Contemporary issues. In B.S. Bolaria (Ed.), *Social issues and contradictions in Canadian society* (pp. 178–195). Toronto: Harcourt Brace Jovanovich.

Oen, K., Fast, M., & Postl, B. (1995). Epidemiology of juvenile rheumatoid arthritis in Manitoba, Canada, 1975–1992: Cycles in incidence. *Journal of Rheumatology, 22*(4), 745–750.

Offord, D.R. (1989). Ontario child health study: Summary of selected results. *Canadian Journal of Psychiatry, 43*, 483–491.

Parks, P., & Read, M. (1997). Adolescent male athletes: Body image, diet, and exercise. *Adolescence, 32*(127), 593–602.

Parker, D.L. (1997). *Stolen dreams: Portraits of working children*. Minneapolis: Lerner.

Rees, A. (1998, June 30). Ritalin 25: North Okanagan hot spot. *Vancouver Province*. www.vancouverprovince.com/newsite/features/ritalin/1618154.html.

Reiter, E. (1996). *Making fast food: From the frying pan into the fryer*. Montreal: McGill–Queen's University Press.

Schissel, B. (1995) Degradation, social deprivation and violence: Health risks for women prisoners. In B.S. Bolaria & R. Bolaria (Eds.), W*omen, minorities and health* (pp. 287–300). Halifax: Fernwood.

Schissel, B. (1997). *Blaming children: Youth crime, moral panics, and the politics of hate*. Halifax: Fernwood.

Schissel, B., & Fedec, K. (1999). The selling of innocence: The gestalt of danger in the lives of youth prostitutes. *Canadian Journal of Criminology, 41*(1), 33–56.

Schnirring, L. (1998a). Androstenedione et al: Nonprescription steroids. *Physician and Sports Medicine, 26*(11), 15–18.

Schnirring, L. (1998b). Creatine supplements face scrutiny: Will users pay later? *Physician and Sports Medicine, 26*(6), 15–23.

Senthilselvan, A. (1998). Prevalence of physician-diagnosed asthma in Saskatchewan, 1981–1990. *Chest, 114*(2), 388–392.

Shin, L. (1999, May 20). Fiji TV: Wrong images? *Newsweek*. www.newsweek.com.

Shorter, E. (1994). *From the mind into the body: The cultural origins of psychosomatic symptoms*. New York: Free Press.

Showalter, E. (1997). *Hystories: Hysterical epidemics and modern media*. New York: Columbia University Press.

Statistics Canada. (1998). *National population health survey, 1996–1997*. Ottawa: Minister of Industry.

Sundgot-Borgen, J. (1994). Risk and trigger factors for the development of eating disorders in female elite athletes. *Medicine and Science in Sports and Exercise, 26*, 414–419.

Trifunov, D. (1999, July 13). Dead worker's family not interested in blame. *Saskatoon Star Phoenix*, p. A13.

Trypuc, J.M. (1994). Gender based mortality and morbidity patterns and health risk. In B.S. Bolaria & R. Bolaria (Eds.), *Women, medicine, and health* (pp. 73–88). Halifax: Fernwood.

Webber, M. (1992). *Street kids: The tragedy of Canada's runaways*. Toronto: University of Toronto Press.

Wolf, N. (1990). *The Beauty Myth*. Toronto: Vintage Books.

Woo, P., & Wedderburn, L.R. (1998). Juvenile chronic arthritis. *The Lancet, 351*, 969–973.

Yip, R., Scanlon, K., & Trowbridge, F. (1993). Trends and patterns in height and weight of low-income U.S. children. *Critical Review of Food Science and Nutrition, 33*, 409–421.

York, G. (1992). *The dispossessed: Life and death in native Canada*. Toronto: Little, Brown.

15

The Health of the Elderly: From Institutional Care to Home and Community Care

MARGARET J. PENNING University of Victoria

INTRODUCTION

Like the other industrialized nations, Canada has an "aged" population that is continuing to age.[1] At the beginning of the twentieth century, 5 percent of Canadians were aged 65 years and older (Norland, 1994). By 1996, the proportion had risen to over 12 percent (Bélanger & Dumas, 1998). It is estimated that by 2031, almost one quarter (23 percent) of the nation's population will be aged 65 and over and almost half of the older adult population will be aged 75 and over (Bélanger & Dumas, 1998).

Health and health care invariably emerge as major areas of concern when discussing an aging population, both from an individual and a social perspective. In particular, one often hears of concerns regarding the impact of population aging on health care utilization and costs. There is no doubt that an aging population will have a major influence on the health care needs of the population and the demands imposed on the Canadian health care system. However, aging, health, and illness are situated within given social, political, and economic contexts, and it is ultimately these factors and not demography that determine how health and old age are defined and dealt with in a society (see Gee, 2000; McDaniel, 1987).

This chapter focuses on the nature and implications of the social construction of health and aging in the Canadian health care context. It argues that these constructions tend to reflect the application of biomedical criteria, resulting in the **medicalization** of the health and health care issues associated with aging. This is consistent with the primary focus of the Canadian health care system on the treatment and cure of acute conditions by physicians, largely within acute-care hospital settings. Yet, in many ways, older adults and the health needs they present remain marginal to this system. Consequently, often they not only find themselves considered to be inappropriate and problematic users of the primary publicly funded health care system, but also among the primary recipients of a secondary, more privately focused system of health care.

THE SOCIAL CONSTRUCTION OF HEALTH AND AGING

It is frequently noted that the ways we perceive and define health and aging are socially constructed. Therefore, whether we view old age as a time of health or of illness and disease depends, to a large extent, on how these constructs are defined and assessed. In the not too distant past, many of the changes associated with old age (e.g., decreases in vision, hearing, and mobility) were considered natural and normal accompaniments of aging. However, with the ascendence of "scientific medicine" in the late nineteenth and early twentieth centuries, they were gradually redefined as diseases (Brown, 1996). Today, "health" tends to be defined by using biomedical criteria and, consequently, is generally equated with the absence of disease or pathology. Aging, in turn, tends to be constructed as a medical problem — thus, as a biological process involving inevitable and progressive physical and cognitive decline, disease, and ill health (see Estes & Binney, 1989; Stahl & Feller, 1990).

With its focus on the treatment and cure of disease, the **biomedical model** is oriented primarily toward acute rather than chronic disease. However, while acute conditions (those characterized by a specific onset and limited duration) tend to decline in later life, chronic conditions (or diseases that persist over time and tend not to be curable) become more prevalent (Brown, 1996). About 80 percent of older adults today report having one or more chronic conditions, with some of the most prevalent of these being arthritis and rheumatism, hypertension, heart disease, and diabetes (Lindsay, 1997). Importantly, having these conditions is related not only to age but also to such factors as gender, socioeconomic status, race, and ethnicity. For example, women and those with lower education and income report the greatest number of chronic conditions (Novak, 1997). These are not, however, necessarily the major causes of mortality. In Canada, the major causes of mortality in later life include cardiovascular disease, cancer, respiratory diseases, accidents, and diseases of the digestive system (Statistics Canada, 1998).

Whereas the biomedical perspective equates health with the absence of disease, other perspectives define health more broadly and in positive rather than negative terms. One of the most often-cited definitions is the one developed by the World Health Organization (WHO), which some years ago conceptualized health as "a state of complete physical, mental and social well-being and not merely the absence of disease or infirmity" (WHO, 1958, p. 459). Following from these broader definitions, health status has also been assessed in terms of levels of functioning and self-assessments of mental, physical, and social well-being that may or may not correspond with one another. For example, not all **chronic illnesses** necessarily or automatically result in reductions in functioning, as reflected in restrictions on people's abilities to engage in the major activities of daily living (i.e., at home, at work, at school, in social life, in sports and leisure).

The picture that emerges from a look at the health status of older adults more broadly differs from that developed solely on the basis of information regarding the presence or absence of disease. For example, although functional **disability** also increases with age, most older adults report relatively good health, are active, function autonomously, and feel good about themselves and their lives. Therefore, despite the fact that most report having one or more chronic conditions, research evidence indicates that less than half (46 percent) of older (aged 65+) people living in the community (i.e., not in institutional care) report experiencing any activity limitations or disability (including problems in such areas as mobility, agility, hearing, seeing, and speaking) as a result (Norland, 1994). Similarly, only about 39 percent report experiencing difficulties with basic personal care activities such as eating, bathing, dressing, and personal mobility (Lindsay, 1997). Even fewer (about 15 percent of those aged 65 and over) experience severe disabilities (Norland, 1994). It is therefore apparent that chronic conditions do not necessarily imply high levels of disability among older adults.

Self-assessments of physical and mental health tend to be even better. In general, research findings suggest that when older adults are asked to describe their health compared with that of other people their own age, approximately three quarters state that they are in good to excellent health (Norland, 1994). The vast majority (80 to 95 percent) also indicate being satisfied with their health and with their lives in general (Norland, 1994). Although self-reports and assessments of health are often discounted as not providing valid representations of health, research evidence also reveals that self-reports are often equal to or better than physician evaluations for predicting various outcomes, including mortality (see Ferraro & Farmer, 1999).

Overall, these findings suggest that while old age tends to be socially constructed as a time of illness and disability, with health conceptualized broadly, the older population as a whole tends to emerge as having relatively good health. Moreover, where health-related needs are evident, they tend to be in terms of chronic rather than acute conditions.

THE HEALTH CARE SOLUTION

The social construction of old age as a time of illness and disability has implications not only for attitudes regarding aging and old age but also, for the way people deal with the health-related needs of the older segments of the population — for the health policies and services we develop, how they are structured, where they are delivered, and by whom.

In general, biomedically defined problems are accompanied by biomedically oriented solutions. Therefore, as a nation, Canada has structured its health care system with a primary focus on the treatment and cure of acute conditions — on the delivery of health care services that are primarily medical in focus, physician-dominated, and centred in acute care hospital settings. In 1957, for example, the *Hospital Insurance and Diagnostic Services Act* was introduced, providing coverage for acute hospital care for the entire population. In 1968, a comparable national insurance plan for physician services (the *Medical Care Act*) was established. Together, these statutes provided universally available, publicly insured access to physician and acute hospital care. But other forms of care, corresponding with broader definitions of health and needs for chronic rather than acute care, are not similarly covered.

The distribution of public expenditures on health provides evidence of this focus. In 1996, for example, public expenditures on health care in Canada totalled $75.2 billion, of which over 70 percent went to cover the costs of physician, hospital, and pharmaceutical services (34 percent to hospital care, 23 percent to salaries for physicians and other health professionals, and 14 percent to drugs). Ten percent went to fund other health care institutions (e.g., nursing homes, psychiatric hospitals), while 18 percent went to all other expenditures, including **home care** as well as public health and other expenditures, such as administration (Health Canada, 1997).

Acute Physician and Hospital Care

Given the social construction of health and aging in biomedical terms and a health care system structured to provide biomedically focused services, it comes as no surprise that older adults are major consumers of physician and other medical services.[2] According to the 1996–97 Canadian National Population Health Survey (Statistics Canada, 1998), 89 percent of noninstitutionalized older adults living in Canada reported having contacted a physician at least once during the previous year. About the same proportion (87 percent) reported having used one or more medications (prescription and nonprescription) or other health products in the previous month. Overall, older adults appear to account for about one quarter of all physician billings for care and use about 40 percent of all prescription drugs (Barer, Evans, & Hertzman, 1995).

Acute-care hospitals also play a primary role in the biomedical approach to health; they serve as repositories for the latest medical technologies and places where health care professionals control the treatment process (Brown, 1996). Approximately one fifth of all older adults report having spent at least one night in hospital during the previous year and, as noted by Barer, Evans, and Hertzman (1995, p. 218), although people over 65 represent only about one eighth of the Canadian population, they account for more than half of all days spent in hospitals and undergo half of all surgical procedures.

Not only are hospitalization rates among the elderly population relatively high, they have also continued to increase since the introduction of nationally insured hospital services. For example, between 1961 and 1992, as per capita use of hospitals decreased for all other age groups, there was a 23 percent increase in use by those aged 75 and older (Bergman et al., 1997). In 1960, those aged 65 and over accounted for 13 percent of all hospital admissions and 29 percent of all days spent in hospital (Nair, Karim, & Nyers, 1992). This increased to 33 percent of admissions and 60 percent of days in hospital by 1995–96 (Health Canada, 1999).

These increases in hospital utilization do not appear to reflect increases in the proportion of older adults in the population (i.e., population aging). Instead, they appear to be due to changes in how older adults are treated by the health care system — more intensive servicing and an increasing concentration of hospital care on meeting the health care needs of a relatively small segment of the older adult population: those who are very old, those recovering from the effects of strokes, and those who are dying (see Barer, Evans, & Hertzman, 1995). A study conducted in British Columbia found that just 2 percent of hospital patients accounted for almost half (48.5 percent) of all days spent in hospital in 1985–86 (Barer, Evans, & Hertzman, 1995). Along similar lines, findings reported by Hertzman et al. (1990) indicate that 80 percent of the increase in hospital occupancy rates observed for older adults between 1969 and 1987 occurred in extended care and rehabilitation units (rather than in hospital units devoted to acute care), suggesting that older adults in hospital "were recovering from strokes and cardiac conditions, suffering from senile dementia or awaiting placement elsewhere" (Northcott & Milliken, 1998, p. 98).

Somewhat paradoxically, however, the biomedicalization of aging also appears to be accompanied by a lack of interest and expertise on the part of the medical community in dealing with the largely chronic health problems of an aging population (Forbes, Jackson, & Kraus, 1987). Whereas chronic conditions typically require a greater orientation toward care rather than cure, those trained in the biomedical model generally focus their attention on issues of cure. Research evidence suggests that physicians frequently have negative views of patients with conditions like arthritis, diabetes, emphysema, and chronic pain, which challenge their faith in the abilities of scientific medicine by offering little likelihood of cure while bringing their own abilities into question (Klein et al., 1982). Consequently, the amount of time spent by physicians in medical encounters with older patients is often less than that spent with younger patients, even though they present more problems. Physicians have also been found to be reluctant to treat those in institutional facilities, apparently viewing them as hopeless (Kane et al., 1980).

Older adults may also be considered inappropriate candidates for curative treatments. For example, some research evidence indicates that differential treatment options may be available for older and younger adults. A study conducted by Ganz (1992) reveals that older women with breast cancer (the vast majority of such patients) are less likely to be offered breast conserving surgery as a treatment option during the early stages of cancer than are younger women. As well, findings suggest that physicians tend to support the idea of rationing services and treatments for those considered too old to benefit from them (Kirkey, 1992).

Taken together, findings of this nature suggest that while we define old age as a time of disease and seek to treat it within the context of a biomedically oriented health care system, we also construct disease in old age as a problem not appropriate for biomedical intervention. In this way, the old would appear to occupy a unique (and marginal) position in the modern health care system. The fact that chronic rather than **acute illness** tends to prevail in later life suggests a mismatch between the health care needs of an aging population and the health care system developed to meet those needs.

Long-Term Institutional and Community-Based Care

Although the primary focus of the health care system has been on acute care, the major health-related needs of many older adults are for services that will enable them to cope with chronic conditions and the functional disabilities that result from them — thus, long-term rather than acute care. Prevailing approaches to long-term care range from chronic hospital and nursing home care at one end of the continuum through formal community-based care to informal and self-care at home at the other. However, while physician and acute hospital services are publicly funded and, in principle at least, universally available to those in need regardless of their ability to pay, no directly comparable system of national health insurance exists to cover nonhospital-based long-term care services (that is, either institutional or community-based care). Instead, long-term care remains much more heavily oriented toward the private sphere, with the responsibility and costs of care often borne directly by the recipients.

Like acute-care hospitals, chronic-care hospitals provide medical and nursing services and are therefore included in the provisions of Canada's public health insurance system. However, while care is free to patients if provided in acute-care hospitals, this is not necessarily the case in chronic-care hospitals. Many are privately owned and operated on a for-profit basis. For example, in 1990, while 365 Canadian hospitals (29.4 percent) were privately owned and operated, most of them were long-term care hospitals that collected fees from patients for the services provided (Lassey, Lassey, & Jinks, 1997). According to Deber & Williams (1995, p. 301), most provinces also require that patients contribute to the costs of their care through income-based co-payments (to cover room and board costs) in these institutions.[3] Interestingly, they note that some provinces have introduced similar charges for patients with long stays (e.g., 60 days or more) in acute-care hospitals.

However, most long-term care is not hospital-based but provided in other institutional settings (e.g., nursing homes, homes for the aged, special care or personal care homes) or in people's own homes in the community. These services do not come under the provisions of the public health insurance program. Instead, they are covered by two programs: the Canada Assistance Plan and the Extended Health Care Services Program.[4] As a result, they fall within the domain of social welfare programs rather than the health care system. This means that they are viewed quite differently by the state. As Deber and Williams note:

> At their best, Canada's social programs embody a principled social commitment to enrich the lives of Canadians who for some reason (e.g., aging, disability) need external support to maintain their dignity, independence and quality of life. At their worst, they embody the belief, descended from Victorian Poor Laws, that individuals and their families bear responsibility for their own welfare, and that those who require external support are, in most cases, the victims of their own misfortune. This policy framework would imply that the state should provide only the most minimal assistance, and provide that as a last resort. Accordingly, throughout most of the country's history, services for seniors and those with disabilities, to the extent they were available, were provided primarily on a local basis...as part of the "public welfare" system.... There was relatively little direct involvement by federal or provincial governments. (1995, p. 299)

Consequently, unlike physician and hospital-based programs, which are generally publicly funded (with private insurance prohibited for any services covered by provincial plans), formal long-term-care programs (including institutional, community, and home-based programs) have developed under the auspices not only of the public sector but also the private for-profit and private not-for-profit sectors, resulting in a diversity of systems and models of care across as well as within provinces (Greb et al., 1994). Guarantees of universality, comprehensiveness of services, portability, and so forth, as well as restrictions on private ownership, user fees, and extra-billing that apply to acute care services do not apply to long-term care.[5]

LONG-TERM INSTITUTIONAL CARE
In the early part of the nineteenth century, care of chronically ill older adults was in the hands of family or, for those with sufficient financial resources, also in the hands of privately hired help. In either case, it was generally provided at home. There was little alternative to the poorhouse for those without family or financial resources (Forbes, Jackson, & Kraus, 1987). In the dawn of the twenty-first century, much appears unchanged. The

long-term care of older chronically ill and disabled adults often remains in the hands of family. Those with sufficient financial resources are also able to access privately paid services, which now include both community-based and residential care. Currently, those lacking such resources may also be able to access some level of publicly funded community-based care. However, the vast majority of governmental funding for long-term care goes to support the care provided in nursing homes, homes for the aged, and other institutional facilities. Those without family and other resources are the most likely to find themselves in such facilities.

Like most other health services, institutional care is a provincial responsibility and, therefore, is subject to considerable variation across the country. No uniform or coherent policy exists in Canada to regulate standards of accommodation, funding arrangements, quality, and standards of care (Tarman, 1994). The same diversity is evident in terms of ownership. In 1988, almost half (48.7 percent) of all long-term-care facilities in Canada were privately owned and operated on a for-profit basis. This also varied considerably by province (see Table 15.1, based on data from Greb et al., 1994).[6] However, because for-profit institutions tend to be smaller in size than either nonprofit or public institutions, the greatest proportion (48.9 percent) of long-term-care beds (and thus, of residents as well) are in public institutions.[7]

While provincial governments provide some funding for the care of those assessed as eligible, because long-term care is not considered to be *medically necessary*, residents can also be charged user fees to cover the costs of their care (Jacobs, Mills, & Hollander, 1997). In each province, at least some residents of long-term-care institutions are required to contribute to the overall cost of their care, with the level of copayment often

TABLE 15.1 *Long-Term-Care Facilities for the Elderly, by Facility Ownership, Canada and the Provinces, 1988*

		Facility Ownership		
	Number of Facilities	Public (%)	Private For-Profit (%)	Private Not-For-Profit (%)
Canada	4082	35.8	48.7	15.5
British Columbia	551	18.0	56.4	25.6
Alberta	167	65.3	20.4	14.4
Saskatchewan	512	40.6	47.9	11.5
Manitoba	165	8.5	32.7	58.8
Ontario	960	30.5	57.2	12.3
Quebec	875	76.1	13.0	10.9
New Brunswick	552	2.5	87.1	10.3
Prince Edward Island	42	21.4	73.8	4.8
Nova Scotia	149	28.9	57.0	14.1
Newfoundland	109	8.4	75.2	18.3

Note: Long-term-care facilities include acute-care facilities with long-term-care beds; chronic-care facilities; psychiatric facilities; extended-care facilities; nursing homes; and residential-care facilities.

Source: Greb et al. (1994, p. 287).

dependent upon the level of care and personal ability to pay (based on income or assets). The nature and extent of the copayment varies. In the Atlantic provinces, residents are "income and asset tested and may have to pay up to the full cost of care, or an amount which is capped that is considerably more than the room and board costs of care" (Hollander & Walker, 1998). In other provinces, residents may pay up to a fixed cost to cover the costs of the room and board component of care. In British Columbia, for example, those with state-supported or public pension income only (i.e., OAS, GIS) are required to pay an amount equivalent to 85 percent of this income. Those with income beyond this level are required to contribute an amount up to the average board and room cost for the province (Hollander & Pallan, 1995).

Currently, a minority of older adults are in long-term institutional care at any time. In 1991, about 7 percent of Canada's population aged 65 and over (8.6 percent of older women and 4.9 percent of older men) were residents of various health care institutions (including chronic-care hospitals, psychiatric facilities, and special-care homes). The vast majority (90.2 percent) were residents of special-care homes, including nursing homes and homes for the elderly (Norland, 1994). This varies somewhat by province; it is highest in Prince Edward Island, Saskatchewan, and Quebec, and lowest in British Columbia, Alberta, Ontario, and Nova Scotia (Greb et al., 1994).

The likelihood of institutionalization also increases with age. In 1991, very few persons (1.6 percent) aged 65 to 74 were institutionalized in nursing homes and related settings. However, this increased to 8.2 percent of those aged 75 to 84 and 32.4 percent of those aged 85 and over (Norland, 1994). Consequently, it is estimated that about one in every four older adults can expect to spend some time in such facilities before they die (Chappell, 1995a). Institutional residence also varies by gender and socioeconomic status. For example, among those aged 85 and over, about a quarter (23.3 percent) of men but over a third (36.3 percent) of women were institutionalized in 1991 (see Figure 1, based on data from Norland, 1994), a differential reflecting the combined realities of age- and gender-based poverty, higher levels of chronic illness, and disability among women, as well as their lesser access to informal community-based supports. Research findings indicate that in addition to the influence of health problems, age, and gender,

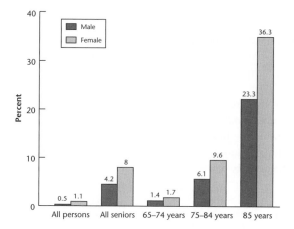

FIGURE 15.1

Residence in Special-Care Homes within Selected Age–Sex Groups, Canada, 1991

Source: Norland (1994, p. 33); based on data from the 1991 Census of Canada, special tabulations.

being without a spouse or other informal caregiver also influences the likelihood of being in long-term institutional care (Rockwood, Stolee, & McDowell, 1996).

Overall, these findings suggest that it is the very old, women, and those with lesser access to social and economic resources who are the most likely recipients of this more privately focused and market-driven form of long-term care.

COMMUNITY-BASED HOME CARE SERVICES

Home care services encompass personal health, supportive, and therapeutic services provided in the home setting and designed to enable those who are "incapacitated in whole or in part, to live at home, often with the effect of preventing, delaying or substituting for long-term care or acute care alternatives" (Health and Welfare Canada, 1992, p. 4). They were first introduced in Canada in the 1950s as pilot programs and, at that time, tended to offer medical services only, primarily as a means of shortening hospital stays. However, in the 1970s, home health care services were more formally introduced as a means of potentially limiting the number of people requiring long-term residential care (Chappell, 1994).

At that time, it was also argued that home care needed to be considered a basic form of health care in its own right (and not only as a substitute for institutional care) and that the types of services offered needed to be broad and include a wide range of personal health and supportive services necessary to maintain or help "persons with health and/or social needs related to physical or mental disability, personal or family crises or to illness of an acute or chronic nature" (Health and Welfare Canada, 1975, p. 13, cited in Chappell, 1994, p. 239). The types of services offered through these programs can include nursing care, social work, physiotherapy, occupational therapy, speech therapy, medical supplies, and equipment, as well as homemaker services, transportation, assistance with personal care, household repair, meal preparation, and other household tasks.

However, formal community-based home care has not yet emerged as a major component of Canada's health care system. Home care appears to be one of the fastest-growing programs in the health care system (Williams, 1996), particularly when percentage increases in funding (rather than actual dollars) are taken into account. It has also attained prominence in government policy documents and rhetoric, where it is seen as an inexpensive alternative to increasingly costly physician, hospital, and institutional care. The 1990s saw an extensive review and restructuring of the Canadian health care system, a process initiated in response to growing governmental concern over the current and future costs of health care as well as the system's effectiveness and efficiency. Home care, along with other community-based services, assumes a central role in the new health care system that is being envisioned. As noted by Chappell:

> The rhetoric provides a vision of a new health care system which is truly a health and not simply a medical care system.... [W]e would see a redistribution of dollars from medical and institutional care to a broader base of community health services.... [It] promises to bring care closer to home and to shift decision making and the power base from...professionals to the individual whose health is affected. (1995b, p. 25)

However, home care remains both politically and economically secondary and subordinate to the more medical components of the health care system. For example, in

1997–98, home care accounted for only a small proportion (4 percent) of total national public health care spending (Health Canada, 1998). According to Lesemann and Nahmiash (1993, p. 83), this is because social services, housing, transportation, and home care are still not considered to be health services in the strict sense of the term. Similarly, Schwenger (1987) asserts that while lip service is given to home care services, programs such as meals-on-wheels, friendly visiting, and homemakers are considered frills by many of those in departments of health; they are referred to as "soft services" and as less important than *harder* medical, nursing, and other therapeutic services. They tend to be equated with the kinds of things people do for themselves and with the kinds of help received from family members and friends (Chappell, 1994).

Although publicly funded home care programs currently exist in every province and territory, responsibility for these programs once again rests with the provinces and territories. Consequently, home care policies, services, and the ways in which they are delivered vary a great deal from one province or territory to the next. In some, home care services are administered and delivered as part of a provincial health care program. In others, they are regionally or locally administered. Some provinces (e.g., Newfoundland, Prince Edward Island, Ontario) require physician referral, especially for access to professional services (e.g., nursing, physiotherapy), thereby preserving the gate-keeping function of the physician as well as the dominance of the biomedical approach. Others also have age restrictions (e.g., limiting access to those aged 65 and over) and income restrictions.

Unlike physician and hospital services, home care services are not covered by national health insurance. Consequently, like long-term residential care, the private health care sector is more heavily involved. Across the country, home care services are delivered by both public and private sources and on both a proprietary and not-for-profit basis. Most provinces currently offer a mix of publicly and privately funded services. While professional and medically oriented services (e.g., medical, nursing, therapeutic services) are often delivered by publicly funded program staff, supportive health services (e.g., personal care, homemaking assistance, meal preparation, transportation services) are often contracted out. In British Columbia, for example, professional services (long-term care assessment, case management, nursing, and rehabilitation services) are provided directly by government. All other services are purchased from for-profit or not-for-profit agencies external to government (Hollander & Pallan, 1995). Most programs also involve user fees, usually assessed on a sliding scale depending upon income (Chappell, 1994).[8]

Figures for community care are difficult to access, particularly when it comes to privately paid services. However, according to the 1996–97 Canadian National Population Health Survey (Statistics Canada, 1998), about 10 percent of adults aged 65 and over and 24 percent of those aged 80 and older reported receiving publicly funded or subsidized formal home care services in the previous year. Approximately 5 percent received homemaker or home help services. Fewer received home nursing care (3.9 percent), help with personal care (e.g., bathing, dressing, getting in and out of bed — 3.2 percent), and meal preparation or meal delivery services (1.7 percent).

Once again, those most likely to rely on these services are those with high levels of chronic illness and disability, older elderly women, those without access to informal sources of support, and those with lower levels of income (Penning & Chappell, 1996).

COMMUNITY-BASED SELF AND INFORMAL CARE

Health and health care were largely individual and family responsibilities prior to the ascendence of the biomedical paradigm, and long-term institutional care was reserved for those with the misfortune to require care but who lacked the social and economic resources required to secure it from private sources. Today, the perception is that care is primarily vested in formal and largely state-supported bureaucratic structures, which have taken over the private roles and responsibilities of self, family, and community (with the latter all too willingly backing away from their traditional personal, familial, and community obligations). However, research evidence indicates that this is not the case. Instead, formal services, whether delivered in institutional or community settings, provide only a small fraction of the overall care that older adults and other people receive. Today, as in the past, the vast majority of long-term care continues to be either self-administered or provided by family members, friends, and others in the community — acting within the context of a largely "hidden health care system" (Levin & Idler, 1981).

Self-care includes the broad range of activities that individuals engage in to promote health, prevent disease, limit illness and disability, and restore health (Levin & Idler, 1983). Research on self-care in relation to chronic illness suggests that it, rather than either informal or formal care, represents the single most dominant mode of care (Stoller, 1998). For example, findings from the U.S. National Self-Care and Aging study indicate that the vast majority of older adults with functional disabilities practise some form of self-care, usually involving behavioural adaptations (75 percent), the use of various types of equipment or devices, or adaptations to their living environments. Similarly, a recent Canadian study of older adults with relatively high levels of chronic illness and disability found that most (89 percent) engaged in one or more self-care practices, primarily for assisting with personal-care tasks such as bathing, dressing, and mobility (Penning et al., 1998). Both studies also revealed that the likelihood of engaging in self-care increased as the severity of disability increased.

With regard to informal care, evidence amassed over more than two decades now confirms that informal resources, particularly family members, are major sources of care, providing an estimated 75–85 percent of all the long-term care received by older adults, including those with relatively high levels of chronic illness and disability (Chappell, 1993; Marshall, 1994). Typically, formal services are accessed only as a last resort and usually in conjunction with and secondary to informal care (Tennstedt, Harrow, & Crawford, 1996).

An emphasis on self-care locates the responsibility for long-term care among chronically ill older adults and, therefore, disproportionately among the very old, women, and those lacking social and economic resources, who are the most likely to have chronic illnesses. Similarly, an emphasis on informal care relies most heavily on the unpaid labour of women. The vast majority (70 percent or more) of informal caregivers are women, particularly older wives and middle-aged adult daughters (Brody, 1990; Chappell, Penning, & Sörenson, 1995). While older men frequently rely on their spouses for care and support, older women tend to rely on adult children, especially daughters. It has been estimated that informal caregivers provide an average of about 4 hours of care per day and that they often continue to provide care for many years

(Chappell, Penning, & Sörenson, 1995). Moreover, about a third of all informal caregivers, including about half of all adult child caregivers, are in the paid labour force (Stone, Cafferata, & Sangl, 1987). Therefore, the work-related and other costs of caregiving (e.g., lost career mobility, fewer retirement benefits, lost leisure, and financial, physical, social, and emotional stress) also accrue disproportionately to women.

CONCLUSION

This chapter has focused on the implications of the social construction of health and aging in accordance with the biomedical model. It was noted that while chronic rather than acute conditions tend to prevail in later life and require a focus on long-term *care* rather than short-term *cure*, the Canadian health care system has been structured with a primary focus on acute medical and hospital care. Long-term care remains secondary and continues to be structured more as a private responsibility, to be assumed by individuals and their families, than collectively in the context of public institutions.

The Canadian health care system is often cited as an example of an equitable if not ideal system, one that "embodies the collectivist principle that the community has responsibility for the welfare of its members" (Clark, 1998, p. 159). Yet, evidence indicating that it is the very old, women, and those with limited economic and social resources who are the least likely to have their needs met in this system and among those most likely to be required to assume private responsibilities for care (either by paying for it or by providing it themselves) would seem to challenge generalized claims regarding equity.

There are also indications that the emphasis on private responsibilities for care may well increase rather than decrease in the near future. As Canada and other industrialized countries seek ways to reform their health care systems, largely to cut costs, community-based services such as home care are being widely touted as inexpensive alternatives for acute and long-term hospital and institutional care (Taylor, 1990; Williams, 1996). Yet, there are concerns that while restructuring of health care has resulted in reduced funding for health care and, therefore, in hospital and hospital bed closures, declines in admission rates, and shortened hospital stays, sufficient additional resources are not being transferred to the community care sector (Chappell, 1995b). Consequently, care in the community threatens to become, increasingly, care by the community.

STUDY QUESTIONS

1. *Outline the biomedical model of health. What are the limitations of this model for an understanding of the health and health care issues faced by an aging population?*
2. *Who are the major beneficiaries of the biomedical approach to health and health care? Why?*
3. *Given evidence indicating a lack of interest by the biomedical community in dealing with the chronic health problems of older adults, how can evidence pointing to the increasing intensity of hospital care for older adults in recent years be explained?*
4. *Discuss the likely implications of changing the focus of Canada's health care system toward community-based (self, informal, and formal) care. Are they likely to differ depending upon such factors as age, gender, and social class?*

GLOSSARY

acute illness Illness characterized by sudden onset and limited duration (e.g., appendicitis, influenza).

adult daycare A program that typically provides personal care, health care, and recreational services in a group setting and on a half- or full-day basis.

biomedical model A model that regards health as being the absence of disease and therefore focuses on the biological determinants of disease (thereby ignoring broader social, environmental, and other influences).

chronic illnesses Illnesses that develop and persist over time and are unlikely to be cured (e.g., arthritis, cancer, diabetes, heart disease).

disability A restriction or lack of ability to perform the regular activities of daily life (e.g., work roles, housework, personal care).

home care An array of services provided to individuals who are incapacitated so as to enable them to live at home. Services vary but can include personal care (assistance with bathing, dressing, grooming), meal preparation, household cleaning, transportation, therapeutic care, the administering of medications and other treatments.

medicalization A social process that "consists of defining a problem in medical terms, using medical language to describe a problem, adopting a medical framework to understand a problem, or using a medical intervention to 'treat' it" (Conrad, 1996, p. 139).

RECOMMENDED READINGS

Béland, F., & Shapiro, E. (Eds.). (1995). Policy issues in care for the elderly in Canada [Special issue]. *Canadian Journal on Aging, 14*(2). A series of articles focusing on the cost and delivery of health care services for the older population in Canada. Issues covered range from the impact of population aging on the costs of health care to long-term-care reform.

Chappell, N.L. (1994). Health care in Canada. In D.G. Gill & S.R. Ingman (Eds.), *Eldercare, distributive justice and the welfare state* (pp. 233–254). Albany: State University of New York Press. A discussion of the development of the Canadian health care system and its limitations for meeting the needs of older chronically ill adults. It addresses issues of equity, appropriateness of care, and public accountability in the Canadian health care system.

Estes, C.L., & Binney, E.A. (1989). The biomedicalization of aging: Dangers and dilemmas. *Gerontologist, 29*(5), 587–596. A useful discussion (from a U.S. perspective) of the role of medicine in the definition and treatment of aging that argues that the biomedicalization of aging socially constructs old age as a process of physical decline and places aging under biomedical control. The implications for policy, public perceptions, and other areas are addressed.

Forbes, W.F., Jackson, J.A., & Kraus, A.S. (1987). *Institutionalization of the elderly in Canada*. Toronto: Butterworths. A monograph describing the care of older adults in long-term-care institutions in Canada; outlines the history of institutional care, discusses the different types of institutions, describes the characteristics of those who are institutionalized, and addresses some relevant policy issues in institutional care.

REFERENCES

Aronson, J. (1985). Family care of the elderly: Underlying assumptions and their consequences. *Canadian Journal on Aging, 4*(3), 115–125.

Barer, M.L., Evans, R.G., & Hertzman, C. (1995). Avalanche or glacier? Health care and the
demographic rhetoric. *Canadian Journal on Aging, 14*(2), 193–224.

Bélanger, A., & Dumas, J. (1998). *Report on the demographic situation in Canada, 1997.*
Ottawa: Minister of Industry. (Statistics Canada cat. no. 91-209-XPE.)

Bergman, H., Béland, F., Lebel, P., Contandriopoulos, A.P., Tousignant, P., Brunelle, Y.,
Kaufman, T., Rodriguez, R., & Clarfield, M. (1997). Care for Canada's frail elderly population: Fragmentation or integration? *Canadian Medical Association Journal, 157*(8),
1116–1121.

Brody, E.M. (1990). *Women in the middle: Their parent-care years.* New York: Springer.

Brown, A.S. (1996). *The social processes of aging and old age* (2nd ed.). Upper Saddle River, NJ:
Prentice-Hall.

Chappell, N.L. (1989). Health and helping among the elderly: Gender differences. *Journal of
Aging and Health, 1,* 102–120.

Chappell, N.L. (1993). Implications of shifting health care policy for caregiving in Canada.
Journal of Aging and Social Policy, 5(1/2), 39–55.

Chappell, N.L. (1994). Health care in Canada. In D.G. Gill & S.R. Ingman (Eds.), *Eldercare,
distributive justice and the welfare state* (pp. 233–254). Albany: State University of
New York Press.

Chappell, N.L. (1995a). Aging in Canada. In E. Sawyer & M. Stephenson (Eds.), *Issues and
challenges for the Canadian long-term care sector* (pp. 227–246). Ottawa: Canadian
Hospital Association Press.

Chappell, N.L. (1995b). Policies and programs for seniors in Canada. *World Review of
Sociology, 1,* 17–35.

Chappell, N.L., Penning, M.J., & Sörenson, S. (1995). *Informal caregivers to adults in British
Columbia.* Joint Report of the Centre on Aging and the Caregivers Association of British
Columbia.

Clark, P.G. (1998). Moral economy and the social construction of the crisis of aging and
health care: Differing Canadian and U.S. perspectives. In M.M. Minkler & C.L. Estes
(Eds.), *Critical gerontology: Perspectives from political and moral economy* (pp. 147–167).
Amityville, NY: Baywood.

Conrad, P. (1996). Medicalization and social control. In P. Brown (Ed.), *Perspectives in medical sociology* (2nd ed., pp. 137–162). Prospect Heights, IL: Waveland Press, Inc.

Crichton, A. (1997). Long-term care in Canada. *Health Care Management, 3*(1), 115–124.

Deber, R.B., & Williams, A.P. (1995). Policy, payment and participation: Long-term care
reform in Ontario. *Canadian Journal on Aging, 14*(2), 294–318.

Estes, C.L., & Binney, E.A. (1989). The biomedicalization of aging: Dangers and dilemmas.
Gerontologist, 29(5), 587–596.

Evans, R.G. (1984). *Strained mercy: The economics of Canadian health care.* Toronto:
Butterworths.

Ferraro, K.F., & Farmer, M.M. (1999). Utility of health data from social surveys: Is there a
gold standard for measuring morbidity? *American Sociological Review, 64*(2), 303–315.

Forbes, W.F., Jackson, J.A., & Kraus, A.S. (1987). *Institutionalization of the elderly in Canada.*
Toronto: Butterworths.

Freund, P.E., & McGuire, M.B. (1999). *Health, illness and the social body: A critical sociology* (3rd ed.). Upper Saddle River, NJ: Prentice-Hall.

Ganz, P.A. (1992). Treatment options for breast cancer: Beyond survival. *New England Journal of Medicine, 326*(17), 1147–1149.

Gee, E.M. (2000). Population and politics: Voodoo demography, population aging and Canadian social policy. In E.M. Gee & G.M. Gutman (Eds.), *The overselling of population aging: Apocalyptic demography, intergenerational challenges, and social policy* (pp. 5–25). Don Mills, ON: Oxford University Press.

Greb, J., Chambers, L.W., Gafni, A., Goeree, R., & LaBelle, R. (1994). Interprovincial comparisons of public and private sector long-term care facilities for the elderly in Canada. *Canadian Public Policy, 20*(3), 278–296.

Health and Welfare Canada. (1990). *Report on home care.* Prepared by the Working Group on Home Care for the Federal/Provincial/ Territorial Subcommittee on Long Term Care.

Health and Welfare Canada. (1992). *Future directions in continuing care.* Ottawa: Minister of Supply and Services Canada.

Health Canada. (1997). *Canada's health system.* Ottawa: Policy and Consultation Branch, Health Canada.

Health Canada. (1998). *Public home care expenditures in Canada, 1975–76 to 1997–98.* Ottawa: Minister of Public Works and Government Services.

Health Canada. (1999). *Statistical report on the health of Canadians.* Ottawa: Author.

Hertzman, C., Pulcins, I.R., Barer, M.L., Evans, R.G., Anderson, G.M., & Lomas, J. (1990). Flat on your back or back to your flat? Sources of increased hospital services utilization among the elderly in British Columbia. *Social Science and Medicine, 30*(7), 819–828.

Hollander, M.J., & Pallan, P. (1995). The British Columbia Continuing Care system: Service delivery and resource planning. *Aging: Clinical and Experimental Research, 7*(2), 94–109.

Hollander, M.J., & Walker, E.R. (1998). *Report of continuing care organization and terminology.* Ottawa: Minister of Public Works and Government Services Canada.

Jacobs, P., Mills, C., & Hollander, M. (1997). Financing long-term care in Canada. *Health Care Management, 3*(1), 101–115.

Kane, R.L., Solomon, D., Beck, J., Keeler, E., & Kane, R. (1980). The future need for geriatric manpower in the United States. *New England Journal of Medicine, 302,* 1327–1332.

Kirkey, S. (1992). MDs back rationing of care: Survey. *Saskatoon Star Phoenix,* p. A14.

Klein, D., Najman, J., Kohrman, A., & Munro, C. (1982). Patient characteristics that elicit negative responses from family physicians. *Journal of Family Practice, 14*(5), 881–888.

Lassey, M.L., Lassey, W.R., & Jinks, M.J. (1997). *Health care systems around the world.* Upper Saddle River, NJ: Prentice-Hall.

Lesemann, F., & Nahmiash, D. (1993). Home-based care in Canada and Quebec: Informal and formal services. In F. Lesemann & C. Martin (Eds.), *Home-based care, the elderly, the family and the welfare state: An international comparison* (pp. 81–99). Ottawa: University of Ottawa Press.

Levin, L.S., & Idler, E.L. (1981). *The hidden health care system: Mediating structures and medicine.* Cambridge, MA: Ballinger.

Levin, L.S., & Idler, E.L. (1983). Self-care in health. *Annual Review of Public Health, 4,* 181–201.

Lindsay, C. (1997). *A portrait of seniors in Canada* (2nd ed.). Ottawa: Statistics Canada (cat. no. 89-519-XPE).

Marshall, V.W. (1994). A critique of Canadian aging and health policy. In V.W. Marshall & B. McPherson (Eds.), *Aging: Canadian perspectives* (pp. 232–244). Peterborough, ON: Broadview.

McDaniel, S. (1987). Demographic aging as a guiding paradigm in Canada's welfare state. *Canadian Public Policy, 13*, 330–336.

Nair, C., Karim, R., & Nyers, C. (1992). Health care and health status: A Canada–United States statistical comparison. *Health Reports, 4*(2), 175–183.

Norland, J.A. (1994). *Profile of Canada's seniors*. Ottawa: Statistics Canada (cat. no. 96-312E).

Northcott, H.C., & Milliken, P.J. (1998). *Aging in British Columbia. Burden or benefit?* Calgary: Detselig Enterprises.

Novak, M. (1997). *Aging and society: A Canadian perspective* (3rd ed.). Scarborough, ON: International Thomson Publishing.

Penning, M.J., & Chappell, N.L. (1996). *Home support services in the Capital Regional District: Client survey*. Final report submitted to the Capital Regional District, Department of Health, Victoria, B.C.

Penning, M.J., Chappell, N.L., Stephenson, P.H., Rosenblood, L., & Tuokko, H.A. (1998). *Independence among older adults with disabilities*. Final report submitted to the National Health Research and Development Program, Health Canada, Ottawa.

Rockwood, K., Stolee, P., & McDowell, I. (1996). Factors associated with institutionalization of older people in Canada: Testing a multifactorial definition of frailty. *Journal of the American Geriatric Society, 44*, 578–582.

Schwenger, C.W. (1987). Health care for the elderly in Canada. *Journal of Public Health Policy, 8*(2), 222–241.

Sorochan, M. (1995). Home care in Canada. *Caring, 14*(1), 12–19.

Stahl, S.M., & Feller, J.R. (1990). Old equals sick: An ontogenetic fallacy. In S.M. Stahl (Ed.), *The legacy of longevity* (pp. 21–34). Newbury Park, CA: Sage.

Statistics Canada. (1998). National population health survey. Public use microdata files. Ottawa: Author.

Stoller, E.P. (1998). Dynamics and processes of self-care in old age. In M.G. Ory & G.H. DeFriese (Eds.), *Self-care in later life* (pp. 24–61). New York: Springer.

Stone, R., Cafferata, G.L., & Sangl, J. (1987). Caregivers of the frail elderly: A national profile. *The Gerontologist, 27*(5), 616–626.

Tarman, V.I. (1994). Institutional care and health policy for the elderly. In B.S. Bolaria & H.D. Dickinson (Eds.), *Health, illness, and health care in Canada* (2nd ed., pp. 424–439). Toronto: Harcourt Brace.

Taylor, M.G. (1990). *Insuring national health care: The Canadian experience*. Chapel Hill: University of North Carolina Press.

Tennstedt, S., Harrow, B., & Crawford, S. (1996). Informal care vs formal services: Changes in patterns of care over time. In M.E. Cowart & J. Quadagno (Eds.), *From nursing homes to home care* (pp. 71–91). New York: Haworth Press.

Wilkins, K., & Park, E. (1998). Home care in Canada. *Health Reports, 10*(1), 29–37. Ottawa: Statistics Canada (cat. no. 82-003).

Williams, A.M. (1996). The development of Ontario's home care program: A critical geographical analysis. *Social Science and Medicine, 42*(6), 937–948.

World Health Organization (WHO). (1958). *The first ten years of the WHO*. Geneva: World Health Organization.

NOTES

1. According to the United Nations, a country is considered "young" if less than 4 percent of its population is aged 60 or over; "youthful" if 4 to 6 percent is aged 60 and over; "mature" if 7 to 9 percent is aged 60 or over; and "aged" if 10 percent or more of its population is aged 60 and over.

2. As Chappell (1989) points out, the biomedical focus of Canada's health care system is perhaps best revealed by the central role of physicians within it. It has been estimated, for example, that physicians control about 80 percent of all public spending on health care (through their influence over fee-for-service payments, hospital admissions, drug prescriptions, laboratory testing, referrals to specialists, and so on; see Evans, 1984).

3. The rationale for this requirement for copayment in hospital settings appears to be that it will discourage patients from remaining in hospital settings (acute or chronic) when they could instead be moved to other (less costly) institutions such as nursing homes (see Forbes, Jackson, & Kraus, 1987).

4. The first was established in 1966 as a federal–provincial program to share the cost of developing social welfare programs and, therefore, providing limited resources to cover such things as homemakers and adult daycare services. The second was established in 1977 to provide provinces with some support for the development of nursing homes, home care, adult residential care, and ambulatory health care services.

5. Canada's public health care insurance program was founded on five principles: universality of coverage (i.e., coverage for all Canadians); accessibility of services; comprehensiveness of services; portability (from one province or region to another); and public administration (on a nonprofit basis and without the involvement of the private sector).

6. In Alberta and Quebec, long-term-care institutions tended to be publicly owned and operated (by municipal, provincial, or federal health authorities). However, in most other provinces (British Columbia, Ontario, New Brunswick, Newfoundland, Nova Scotia, and Prince Edward Island), the majority were privately owned and operated on a for-profit basis. In Manitoba, most were also privately operated but on a nonprofit basis.

7. In 1988, about a quarter (26.1 percent) of all older adults in long-term-care facilities were in private institutions (Greb et al., 1994). Again, this varied by province, ranging from a low of 8.8 percent in Quebec to highs of 40.3 percent in Ontario and 43 percent in Prince Edward Island.

8. In Prince Edward Island, there are user fees for medical supplies; in Quebec, for medication; and, in Ontario, for visiting nursing services. More often, however, the professional and medical services are provided at no cost to the user, while user fees are applied to supportive services. For example, Prince Edward Island charges for visiting homemaker services, Nova Scotia charges for all support services, Quebec for meals, Manitoba for meals and transportation, and Saskatchewan for all services (Chappell, 1994, p. 242). In British Columbia, clients receiving homemaker services contribute on a sliding scale, depending on their assessed ability to pay; those receiving meal services pay for the cost of food; and a daily charge is levied for the cost of adult daycare services.

PART 6

Environment, Work, and Health

It has long been known that health status is directly related to features of the physical and social environments. Current policy frameworks highlight these and other factors as determinants of health.

In Chapter 16, Samuel Abaidoo presents several debates currently raging over the environmental and health risks and benefits associated with the development and application of agricultural biotechnology. Drawing on the work of Schumacher, Abaidoo maintains that agriculture has three essential functions:

- to keep humans in touch with nature and to remind us that we are a very vulnerable part of it;
- to humanize and ennoble nature as part of our wider habitat; and
- to provide foodstuffs and other materials essential for life.

Abaidoo maintains that consequent on the capitalist modernization of society and the industrialization of agriculture, these three functions have all been subordinated to increased agricultural productivity. Although this is often justified as a means to feed an ever-increasing global population, Abaidoo notes that the greatest increases in agricultural productivity have been motivated by the search for profits; feeding the world's poor, to the extent that it happens, is subordinate to this.

He argues that agricultural biotechnology is the most recent and intrusive innovation in this regard. As such, it has the potential to generate massive private gain; but it also entails the potential for widespread environmental and health risks. Thus he counsels prudence in its further development and deployment.

Sullivan and Cole, in Chapter 17, turn to the relationships between work and health. The global hegemony of neoliberalism and the ascendancy of market capitalism has obliterated socialist alternatives for developing new work relations. The collapse of socialism leaves us facing the question, "What type of capitalist society do we wish to live in?" Set against this background, Sullivan and Cole provide a model of the pathways by which work and health are related. According to this model, workers' health is affected by three factors:

1. labour market conditions and employment patterns in general;
2. workplace-specific exposure to various risk factors; and
3. the nature and efficacy of available health care service.

The primary focus of the chapter is on the effects of labour markets and workplace specific exposures. Sullivan and Cole identify five factors in the changing labour market experience of Canadian workers that affect health outcomes:

- the rising participation of women and the growth of service sector jobs;
- the decline of manufacturing jobs;
- the implementation of the new high-performance, just-in-time management practices;
- the growth of precarious employment; and
- the regulatory retreat associated with global trade liberalization.

These factors are examined relative to issues of work organization, management practices, job structure, and their consequences for worker health and safety. Although there are clearly strong pressures to reform the Canadian workers' compensation system, since it is generally more efficient than the American system, Sullivan and Cole feel that its main features and advantages may be preserved.

16

Agricultural Biotechnology, the Environment, and Health

SAMUEL ABAIDOO Kennesaw State University

AGRICULTURE, BIOTECHNOLOGY, AND THE RISK SOCIETY

Human beings have a necessary interaction with the natural world. Advances in scientific know-how and the corresponding development of more sophisticated technologies have changed the sociocultural character of human beings, nature, and humans' relationship to it. Indeed, the process of civilization can be understood as the ongoing changes in these domains.

Some of the core areas of human transformative interaction with nature are mining, power generation, fishing, forestry, manufacturing, and, most importantly for present purposes, **agriculture**. The intensification of human and nature interactions and the various deleterious environmental and health effects of this intensification have caused contemporary modern society to be referred to as a **risk society** (Beck, 1992).

Of the various spheres of economic activity outlined above, agriculture — the deliberate tending of plants and animals through their life cycles for human use — has been the most fundamental, enduring, and widespread. As the system through which human beings secure the means of physical and sociocultural sustenance from the environment, agriculture has been, and still is, practised in most societies, both modern and traditional. Historically, agriculture has been viewed as a more benign "environmental" activity, compared with other forms of human–nature interaction. Thus, "farmers were thought to be the natural stewards of the environment. Their values, formed in the presence of nature, were emblematic of what all persons should believe" (Thompson, 1995, p. 12).

In the past several centuries, however, agriculture has undergone major transformations, especially since the beginning of the industrial revolution some 200 years ago. The industrial revolution ushered in the era of industrial or **green revolution** agriculture and accentuated the intrusiveness of human–nature interaction. As a result, industrial agriculture has become focused on three basic tasks. Schumacher (1973, p. 113) identified these three basic functions of agriculture:

1. to promote awareness that human survival depends upon a living nature;

311

2. to humanize and ennoble the wider habitat; and
3. to produce the food and other materials needed for life.

The first two functions support **accommodative interactions** between humans and the physical environment. Promoting an awareness of humanity's dependence on nature presumably influences people to develop and nurture sustainable relationships with nature. As a corollary of the first function, the second role of agriculture requires the extension of human attributes of respect to nature. The humanization, or enchantment, of nature represents an enlightened self-interest, since human survival is linked to the "well-being" of the "wider habitat."

Over the past couple of centuries, and particularly associated with the industrialization of agriculture, producing more food has risen to dominance. Associated with this increase in production is the marginalization or displacement of the first two functions. Rather than "ennobling" nature, aspects of it that are seen to impede the achievement of maximum productivity are defined as obstacles that need to be overcome. The growing obsession with increased productivity has resulted in sharp increases in the levels of food production, to the point where one North American farmer can feed between 100 and 120 other people (Agriculture and AgriFood Canada, 2000; Palen, 1997, p. 55). The focus on increased food production, however, has environmental costs, partly because of the growing dependence on agro-chemicals, such as pesticides and synthetic fertilizer (Newton & Dillingham, 1994, p. 48).

The growing focus on maximizing agricultural productivity has led some to suggest that not only is the environment put in jeopardy, but human survival is as well. Schumacher (1973, p. 113), for example, states that a civilization that pursues ever-increasing agricultural productivity "and which pursues it with such ruthlessness and violence that the two [other] tasks are not merely neglected but systematically counteracted, has [no] chance of a long-term survival." In other words, the introduction and use of more sophisticated technology, such as agro-chemicals and agricultural machinery, under industrial agriculture has undermined the fulfillment of two of the three essential tasks of agriculture. More importantly, it has contributed to the creation of the risk society.

Against this background, agricultural **biotechnology** is emerging as a major transformation in agriculture and, therefore, as a major change in how humans interact with the environment. Agricultural biotechnology refers to the "creation" of technological products and processes out of living organisms for use in agriculture (Conway, 2000; Ho, 1999; Grace, 1997). Currently most agricultural applications of biotechnology involve the genetic engineering of plants and animals. This entails the modification of genes to change the characteristics of a targeted organism. The modification may involve the isolation of genes governing desired traits, which are then extracted, copied, and sliced or inserted into another organism to produce **transgenic** organisms or products. Through this transgenic process, genetically modified (GM) crops, such as Bt corn and Bt potato, which contain a naturally occurring bacterium, have been developed and commercially cultivated. Besides these commonly known transgenic processes, biotechnology also includes cell culture technology, cell fusion technology, **enzyme technology**, and immobilization technology (Ho, 1999; Rifkin, 1998; Gottweis, 1997).

Agricultural biotechnology results in the intensification of human–nature interactions and the acceleration of the **commodification of nature**, which refers to the process by which components of nature, including genetic material and bacteria, are converted into commodities that can be exclusively controlled and marketed (Shulman, 1999, pp. 138–143). As well, agricultural biotechnology represents a further step in ongoing attempts to establish a scientific (technological) triumph over aspects of nature that human society finds constraining or impediments to the maximization of human welfare. As a new tool for manipulating and controlling nature, agricultural biotechnology has reinforced concerns about the state of human–nature interactions and the role of technology in the creation of the risk society. These concerns have generated a passionate public debate about the risks and benefits of agricultural biotechnology and whether its use should be encouraged, accelerated, slowed down, discouraged, or completely discontinued. There are many interrelated dimensions to this debate, including claims and counterclaims about the scientific, social, ethical, and economic rationales for introducing agricultural biotechnology. The debate also addresses the health and environmental implications for the widespread use of these technologies.[1]

This chapter focuses on two dimensions of the debate regarding the environmental and health impacts of agricultural biotechnology: claims of benefits by advocates, and counterclaims of risks by critics. The next section is a brief synopsis of the growth in the use of genetically modified crops since their commercial introduction in 1996. This is followed by an examination of the benefit–risk arguments with respect to the environment and to human health.

GROWTH OF AGRICULTURAL BIOTECHNOLOGY: THE WORLD AND CANADA

Since the first commercial cultivation of genetically modified (GM) crops in the mid-1990s, biotechnology applications in agriculture have mushroomed rapidly. Between 1996 and 1997, the cultivation of GM crops increased sharply, from 1.7 million hectares to 11 million hectares. Then it increased by more than 100 percent in 1998, to 27.8 million hectares worldwide (RAFI, 1999; Clive, 1998). Over 70 percent of this worldwide cultivation in 1998 was made up of herbicide-tolerant crops, with insect-resistant crops making up about 28 percent (Clive, 1998). About 40 million hectares of GM crops were planted worldwide during the 1999 planting season, an increase of over 11 million hectares above the cultivation levels for 1998 (Conway, 2000; James, 1999). During the 2000 season, about 43 million hectares were planted with GM crops (RAFI, 2000). Most of the commercial cultivation of GM crops has occurred in three countries: the United States, Canada, and Argentina (Clive, 1998; Nickson & McKee, 1998).

In Canada 50 000 acres (about 20 234 hectares) of Roundup Ready canola was planted in Western Canada in 1996 (*Saskatoon Star Phoenix*, 1999). By 1998, cultivation of GM canola had increased sharply to 3 million acres (over 1.2 million hectares). In 1998, about 240 000 acres (over 97 000 hectares) of GM corn was cultivated in Canada — about 20 percent of total corn acreage in the country. By 1999, about 35 percent of agricultural land was devoted to the cultivation of genetically modified corn. Overall, 9.7 million acres (about 3.9 million hectares) of GM crops were cultivated in Canada in 1999 (James, 1999). Canada's cultivation in 1999 amounted to approximately 10 percent of global GM acreage, which places Canada behind only the United States (74 percent) and Argentina (15 percent) in GM crop cultivation.

AGRICULTURAL BIOTECHNOLOGY AND THE ENVIRONMENT

Benefit Arguments

The overarching argument used by advocates in support of agricultural biotechnology has been the capacity of the new technology to counteract food insecurity around the world, particularly in developing countries. This proposed goal and primary benefit of agricultural biotechnology is consistent with the third task of agriculture identified by Schumacher (1973). Although this suggested overarching benefit has environmental implications, supporters also argue that agricultural biotechnology will have specific multiple benefits for environmental protection. Advocates suggest that the new technology will "enable farmers to produce food in a cost effective, socially acceptable and *environmentally sound manner*" (Nickson & McKee, 1998, p. 97; emphasis added). Supporters argue that agricultural biotechnology will contribute to environmental enhancement by helping farmers to reduce the use of agro-chemicals such as pesticides and herbicides (Carpenter & Gianessi, 2001; Robinson, 1998; Newton & Dillingham, 1994, p. 51).

Currently most cultivated arable land in industrial countries, as well as some land in developing countries, has been exposed to synthetic herbicides and pesticides. Apart from the fact that most synthetic herbicides stay in the environment for a long time, compared with organic herbicides, the intensive use of some herbicides is known to have resulted in the creation of chemical-tolerant weeds (Ammann, 1999). Agricultural biotechnology is expected to help correct these harmful environmental effects of industrial agro-chemical–based agriculture. In the case of pesticides, for example, genetic modification has been used to internalize pest control in seeds. In theory this makes it unnecessary to use chemical pesticides in large quantities, if at all (Carpenter & Gianessi, 2001). Examples of crops that have been genetically engineered in this way to fight pests include Bt corn, Bt potato, and boolgard cotton. The bacterium *Bacillus thuringiensis* (Bt), which has been used by organic farmers for a number of years, serves as the internalized biological pest control agent to fight against the European corn borer and the potato beetle.

Increased commercialization of agricultural biotechnology is also expected to result in reduced tillage, which in turn will improve the retention of soil nutrients and limit soil erosion. Improved retention of soil nutrients will also enhance the capacity of the soil to regenerate its fertility. This is expected to lead to a reduced dependence on synthetic chemical fertilizers and the overall reduction of harmful synthetic agro-chemicals in the environment.

Another environmental benefit cited by supporters and advocates of agricultural biotechnology is that the new technology will slow down the expansion of agriculture into fragile ecosystems (Avery, 1998; Fischer, 1998). The expansion of agriculture into fragile ecosystems is deemed to be a formidable threat in light of the increasing global population and the associated need to increase food production. It is argued that the uncontrolled expansion of agriculture into fragile ecosystems will be harmful to the environment, by compromising or destroying wildlife habitats. Besides the destruction of wildlife habitats and its wider implications for the environment, the expansion of agriculture into uncultivated land may also expose human populations to health hazards that have hitherto been unknown. Agricultural biotechnology is expected to help slow down the spatial expansion of agricultural production through the creation of crops that will significantly improve yield growth (Romanow, 2000; Pinstrup-Anderson, 1999; Nickson & Mckee, 1998). The new technology promises crops that have been genetically modified to be drought-resistant and others that can thrive under adverse conditions such as high soil salinity (Conway, 2000). Improving access to marginal lands, such as land with high salinity, is expected to discourage people from abandoning such lands for "unbroken" land or "virgin" forests. In light of these potential environmental as well as other benefits, advocates suggest that the adoption of agricultural biotechnology should be promoted and accelerated.

Agricultural biotechnology is also expected to contribute to the reduction of environmental pollution associated with large-scale farm animal operations, such as the new mega-sized hog operations. In that specific case, hogs produce manure with high levels of phosphorus, which has been identified as a serious water pollutant in the environment. High levels of phosphorus contribute to the fast growth of algae in rivers and lakes. The growth of algae, in turn, reduces the amount of oxygen available to support other life forms in the water, especially fish. Regarding this particular source of environmental pollution, agricultural biotechnologists promise to produce genetically engineered pigs that produce lower levels of phosphorus. Towards this end an *E. coli* gene and a fragment of mouse gene have been used by researchers at the University of Guelph to engineer the "Enviropig" (Honey, 1999). The enviropig, which is expected to be on the market by 2002, is expected to produce manure that has 20–50 percent less phosphorus content. The reduction in the phosphorus content is also expected to promote the use of manure as fertilizer, thus reducing the use of synthetic fertilizer, which has been linked to other environmental problems.

Risk Arguments

Environmental critics of agricultural biotechnologies reject the potential benefits identified above in favour of less environmentally disruptive, alternative forms of agriculture, which can address the issue of food insecurity (Kneen, 1999a; Shiva, 1997; Goldberg et al. 1990). These alternatives, such as organic and other forms of sustainable agriculture, support practices that are consistent with the three-functions agriculture model described by Schumacher (1973). In the first place, the idea that agricultural biotechnology will correct some of the environmental deficiencies associated with industrial agriculture, such as widespread use of agro-chemicals and its deleterious impacts, is seen by critics as a tacit admission that the previous intensification of technological use in agriculture has been problematic (Shiva, 1997). Resort to a "biotechnological fix" of environmental problems that have been partly created by a previous agricultural technology appears to be very characteristic of the technological treadmill in our "risk society."

According to critics, the introduction of biotechnological applications into human–nature interaction, via agriculture, can be expected to exacerbate the environmental problems of industrial agriculture (Kneen, 1999b; RAFI, 1999, 2000a). By proposing a biotechnological fix of environmental problems, advocates expect that society will come up with more and better technology to deal with the potential problems that may emerge from the new technology. In this regard, advocates suggest that risks associated with agricultural biotechnology should not be discussed in isolation but in relation to benefits accruing to society and especially to food-insecure people (Conway, 1999, 2000;

McGloughlin, 1999; Krattiger, 1998). In other words, the technology is expected to do more good than harm, and in the case of the latter, human ingenuity can be counted upon to fix any harmful effects. Critics, on the other hand, consider the risks to be serious enough to warrant a slowing down of the deployment of the new technology or an outright ban (Kneen, 1999b; Ho, Ryan, & Cummins, 1999; Marsden & Drummond, 1999; Marsden et al., 1999). Some critics consider the potential and known risks serious enough to warrant a global invocation of the **precautionary principle** or global moratorium on the commercialization of GM crops. This will allow for long-term comprehensive tests of the risks associated with agricultural biotechnology.

Critics have suggested that genetic material from GM crops can be transferred to wild varieties of these crops and pose an environmental threat. Specifically, crops engineered to be resistant to herbicides, such as Roundup Ready canola, can transfer the herbicide resistance trait to their wild "cousins" such as wild oilseed rape. The risk of cross-pollination will vary by geographical region because of variations in the presence of wild varieties of GM crops. There have already been reported cases of this happening, especially between GM canola and wild oilseed rape (Paulson, 2000; Highfield, 1998). According to critics, the wild plant species that are cross-pollinated by GM crops will be transformed into "super weeds," which will require more potent herbicides to control them (Highfield, 1998). So, rather than reducing agro-chemical use, agricultural biotechnology will end up encouraging the use of more potent synthetic chemicals in the environment.

The fact that some GM crops have been made resistant to herbicides is also considered problematic because it may encourage the liberal use of herbicides (Altieri, 1994, 1995). Since some of these herbicides will kill all plants except for the resistant GM crop, the environmental impact of increased use can be very harmful indeed. Similarly, the genetic manipulation of crops to make them pest resistant, as in the case of Bt corn and Bt potato, is also considered to be a potential long-term threat to the environment. This is because pests could mutate and develop resistance to Bt, thus rendering it ineffective — a problem that is reported to have already occurred (RAFI, 2000b). The mutation of pests to develop resistance to GM crops will represent the short-circuiting of the evolutionary paths for pests. Such mutations will in turn set in motion another technological treadmill as we seek more powerful technology to deal with mutant pests.

The capacity of GM crops to harm wild plants and wild animals has also been cited as an environmental problem. It is argued that the deliberately designed harmful effects of GM crops will not be limited to pests or the "nonbeneficial" insects, but will also harm "beneficial" insects, natural fauna, and flora (Suzuki, 1999). The study involving the use of pollen from Bt corn and monarch butterfly has been cited as a case in point. This study found that pollen from Bt corn is very harmful to the monarch butterfly because exposure of the monarch's larvae to the pollen increased mortality (Losey et al., 1999). A disproportionate destruction of "beneficial" insects is estimated to have negative implications for bird populations and to be disruptive to the entire food chain.

Agricultural biotechnology is also supposed to pose a serious risk to the genetic diversity of plants in general and crops in particular. This is because the new agricultural technology will intensify the practice of monoculture production by adding another twist — the genetic uniformity of crops (Altieri, 1995). The direct environmental implication of this is a further reduction of genetic diversity of plants and crops, which has already experienced major declines in the past century. The United Nations Food and

Agricultural Organization (FAO) estimates that about 75 percent of plant and crop genetic diversity has been lost since the beginning of the twentieth century, due mostly to human activity (FAO, 1996). The threat to plant biodiversity has been identified as a serious problem in cases where farmers increase the use of glyphosate (Roundup) pesticide as a direct result of adopting Roundup Ready crops, such as canola and soybean (Von Weizsacker & Tappeser, 1999).

Considering the identified risks, the need for caution in the widespread establishment of an agricultural biotechnology regime becomes very important, more so when the primary justification for accelerating the agricultural biotechnology transition is not fully supported by current evidence and practices. The primary justification is the need to improve food security around the world, especially for food-insecure people in developing countries. Current evidence indicates that food insecurity is not necessarily a function of food supply. Rather, it is a function of the lack of access to land and resources to produce food, as well as lack of ability to buy food that is already available (Bolaria & Wotherspoon, 2000; FAO, 1996; Busch & Lacy, 1984). Second, current practices clearly indicate that the selection of crops for genetic modification is market-driven not need-driven. With the exception of corn, all the major GM crops in commercial cultivation will not improve food security. Even in the case of corn, over 60 percent of U.S. production is devoted to feeding livestock and other industrial uses (Carpenter & Gianessi, 2001). Thus the reference to famine or food insecurity as primary justifications for agricultural biotechnology is untenable. Obviously GM soybean, canola, cotton, and corn fed to livestock or used in making sweeteners will not contribute to hunger alleviation in food-insecure countries.

Current attempts to introduce agricultural biotechnology to food-insecure regions are not likely to make significant improvements in food security. This is because adoption of agricultural biotechnology, like its green revolution predecessor, is both resource and scale sensitive. This means that farmers with better access to financial resources and sizable holdings of arable land will be the likely beneficiaries of agricultural biotechnology. Large-scale farmers in developing countries, however, tend to cultivate cash crops for the external market, not food to meet the needs of rural and urban food-insecure people.

AGRICULTURAL BIOTECHNOLOGY AND HEALTH

A significant body of biotechnology research and applications focuses more directly on human health, including pharmaceutical and medical biotechnology. This line of research accounts for about 70 percent of R&D investments in biotechnology but has generated less controversy than agricultural biotechnology (Buttel, 1998; Krimsky & Wrubel, 1996). Besides the direct applications of biotechnology in medicine and pharmacy, there are innovations in agricultural biotechnology that blur the boundaries between agriculture, medicine, and pharmacy. The examination of health benefit–risk arguments in this section focuses primarily on biotechnological applications that attempt to blend agriculture with pharmacy and medicine.

Benefit Arguments

Advocates of agricultural biotechnology point to a series of realized and potential health benefits of the new technology. The benefits are associated with the genetic modification of crops as well as farm animals. Under the agricultural biotechnology regime, farmers are generally expected to "produce new crop products of greater nutritional value," which will enhance health (Conway, 2000, p. 6). Toward this end, genetic engineering has spawned a new branch of agricultural practice known as **biopharming** or **molecular farming** (Pollack, 2000). Molecular farming represents the convergence of farming, pharmacy, and medicine and is being pursued by about 20 life science companies worldwide. Through molecular farming, agricultural biotechnology promises to convert crops and animals into what have been described as **biofactories**. This means that plants and animals will be genetically modified to produce vitamins and other minerals that will promote healthy living and combat diseases such as Crohn's disease and hepatitis B (Romanow, 2000). As part of molecular farming, farm animals such as sheep and goats are undergoing genetic modification to enable them to produce human proteins (Pollack, 2000; King & Stabinsky, 1999a, 1999b). Plants are also being modified to produce edible vaccines. A case in point is the genetic enhancement of the iron and vitamin A content of rice (Romanow, 2000; Potrykus, 2000; McGloughlin, 1999). The enriched rice is expected to prevent blindness among poor consumers in developing countries, especially in Asia. Proponents argue that the coupling of agriculture with pharmacy and medicine will increase the supply of much-needed drugs and vaccines. This will result in better health care for patients as well as reduction in cost to patients and to health systems in general (Romanow, 2000; Pollack, 2000).

Besides the biofactory strategy involving molecular farming, farm animals are also undergoing genetic engineering with the view of producing leaner meat, as has been the case with a patented pig in New Zealand (*Western Producer*, 1993). As well, efforts are underway to genetically modify farm animals to grow organs that can be harvested for human use. Human genetic material may be incorporated into the genetic modification of donor animals to improve organ receptivity by the human recipients. Research into animal–human organ transfers, commonly described as **xenotransplantation**, is currently focusing on pigs and baboons. The process has been celebrated as a major breakthrough for medical practice because of perennial shortages of human-donated organs. It has been projected that the current Canadian transplant gap of about 5441 organs will reach about 16 250 by the year 2020 (Kennedy, 2000). This 200 percent increase in donated organs shortfall will have perilous consequences for an aging population. It is hoped that a successful xenotransplantation project based on agriculture–pharmaceutical biotechnology will create a stable supply of organs required for surgery.

Risk Arguments

On May 17, 1999, the British Medical Association (BMA) joined a growing number of groups and individuals who expressed doubts about the health safety of genetically modified foods (Weiss, 1999). Like other bodies, the BMA pointed to a number of potential health risks relating to toxicity and antibiotic resistance, among others that have not been adequately investigated. The organization thus called for a moratorium in commercial cultivation of GM crops in the United Kingdom and the labelling of food items that contain GM ingredients (Weiss, 1999). In general, critics of the more "basic" agricultural biotechnology, which is not blended with pharmacy and medicine, point to three main sources of health risks: the risks associated with the inputs or genetic "raw material" used in genetic modification; risks associated with the modification process; and, ultimately, risks associated with modified crops themselves (Ho, 1998, 1999).

Regarding inputs or "raw materials," genetic engineers use "parasitic genetic elements as vectors to carry or smuggle genes into cells" (Ho, 1999). Disease-causing viruses are routinely used as vectors or carriers of desired genes, essentially because of their proven capacity to infest. The vectors and the accompanying desired genes are usually shot with specially made gene guns at very high speeds into the cells of a targeted seed. Apart from the vectors, genetic engineers also use viruses as the triggers or promoters to activate or turn on foreign genes inserted into GM crops. Genetic modification also routinely involves the use of antibiotic resistance markers that allow scientists to verify if the inserted gene sequence has been attached to an active segment of DNA as desired (Ho, 1999).

Despite assurances to the contrary, the use of viral vectors, viral promoters, and antibiotic resistance markers as inputs in genetic modification is deemed to be inherently risky to human health. The use of antibiotic resistance genes as markers, for example, can exacerbate the problem of antibiotic resistance, which is already a serious public health concern. Critics also suggest that artificially constructed and natural genetic "inputs" used in genetic modification can contribute to the suppression of immune systems and also create allergic reactions (Cunningham, 2000; Ho, 1998).

Regarding the modification process and the use of disease-causing viruses, genetic engineers and supporters of agricultural biotechnology argue that the disease-causing components of the viruses used as **vectors and promoters** are deactivated or rendered sterile before use. They are therefore not supposed to pose health risks. Supporters also argue that there has not been any evidence of risks, as critics contend. Critics, however, suggest that the genetic modification process is not foolproof (Ho, 1996, 1999). The deactivation of the capacity of disease-causing viruses to infect host cells, and eventually consumers, may be an incomplete process. Nontarget genes in the host crop may reactivate the harmful aspects of so-called sterile vectors and viral promoters. Critics also suggest that other foreign genes may recombine with other virus particles to generate new harmful viruses. The possibility of reactivating dormant viruses has been observed to be very high in Cauliflower Mosaic Virus (CaMV), which is widely used as a viral promoter (Ho, 1999; Ho, Ryan, & Cummins, 1999).

Although supporters of agricultural biotechnology consider the talk about environmental and health risks to be nothing more than fear-mongering, the unpredictability of the genetic modification process has been confirmed on a number of occasions. For example, 8 years after passing safety assessments in the United States and 4 years after commercial cultivation, it has now been found that GM soybeans contain two extra gene fragments (Meikle, 2000). These extra gene fragments were apparently inserted accidentally during genetic modification processes. In 1997, about 60 000 bags of GM canola seeds that were "seriously contaminated" were sold to Canadian farmers just before the planting season (Scoffield, 2000). In September 2000, the United States Department of Agriculture (USDA) recalled over 300 maize products because GM maize that had been approved for animal feed found its way into a number of consumer products (RAFI, 2000b).

In the case of the extra gene fragments, the biotechnology industry maintains that they are inactive and do not make the GM soybean riskier than conventional varieties. Industry also argues that the discovery of the gene fragments means that there is improved capacity to "see" genes. In the case of the so-called "rogue" GM canola, Health Canada's testing found no significant health risks. It was further suggested that the fact that Monsanto detected the error and that industry and government officials were able to recall or plough the contaminated seeds under proves that the production and regulatory systems are effective (Scoffield, 2000). The USDA-recalled maize products are supposed to cause "minor" allergic reactions. Despite the attempts at damage control to allay public concerns, these three incidents indicate that genetic engineering and its regulation are fraught with potentially damaging slip-ups. The call for caution in the market deployment of agricultural biotechnology is therefore a legitimate one.

It has been further argued that the breaching of species barriers through genetic engineering can lead to unprecedented intra-genomic interactions with unknown long-term health effects (Ho, 1998, 1999). Species barriers are breached when genetic material is transferred from one species to another. An example is the transfer of the gene that protects arctic fish from the cold to tomatoes or strawberries to make them cold resistant (Cunningham, 2000). When species barriers are breached, the foreign genetic material can interact with the genome of the host in ways that are not fully known or understood. Genetic materials used in the genetic modification of crops cannot be confined to a particular cell, but can actually move between cells and move genes around in the process. The health implications of such inter- and intra-cell genomic interactions associated with the breaching of species barriers are not fully understood, partly because they do not occur in nature or in traditional breeding. As a result, there is no existing cumulative experiential knowledge of what the interactions may entail and what their effects may be. Contrary to the perception of precision assumed by genetic engineers, critics suggest that specific intra-genomic interactions cannot be completely predetermined or predicted prior to the genetic modification (Ho, Ryan, & Cummins, 1999; Ho, 1998). The effects of such an interaction on the crops so modified and, subsequently, on human health can be very harmful.

Regarding biopharming or molecular agriculture, it has been suggested that the drugs inserted into plants may end up in the general food supply. This can occur either because of the misrouting of crops or seeds, or because pollen from a drug-containing crop in an open field fertilizes a nearby food crop (Pollack, 2000, p. 1). To reduce the risk of cross-pollination between drug-bearing GM crops and other crops, the USDA estimated that the separation distance between the two crops should be double the usual distance for regular GM crops and non-GM crops (Pollack, 2000).

Apart from the risks of environmental exposure for noncrop plants in the buffer zone, the increased distance requirement undermines the promise that agriculture biotechnology will help contain the expansion of acreage devoted to agricultural production. Besides, the distance requirement may be difficult to maintain in regions where crops are grown very close together, out of necessity (Conway, 2000). To combat these potential problems, some companies are planning either to undertake molecular farming on a much smaller scale in greenhouses or to harvest drug-bearing crops before they reach sexual maturity, thus pre-empting any potential cross-pollination. Despite these assurances, critics remain unconvinced, because no one knows for sure how, or if, pharmaceutical proteins produced by drug-bearing plants will undergo significant changes during plant growth, harvesting, and storage (Pollack, 2000).

Opponents of agricultural biotechnology contradict health benefits claims and argue that the new technology overall is more risky than beneficial. Xenotransplantation, for example, has come under severe criticism as a serious health risk. Specifically, critics argue that the crossing of species boundaries through xenotransplantation can expose human populations to diseases that so far are limited to animals. The dangerous chain effects of such a potential genetic contamination of the human population have not been lost on policymakers. As a result, policymakers, particularly in the United Kingdom, have been creating legislation that restricts some liberties of xenotransplantation patients. Specifically, it has been proposed that people who undergo xenotransplantation should agree to a strict regime of controls and monitoring of their lives and to permanent postoperation celibacy. The expectation is that a life of celibacy will curtail the spread of any potential health risks that might have crossed over from animals to humans through xenotransplantation.

Besides the problem of enforceability, however, coerced celibacy raises a number of ethical issues. It assumes that the massive intrusion and invasion of personal privacy that will be engendered by perpetual monitoring of clients of xenotransplantation is unproblematic. While improved health may result from the procedure, the trade-off of compulsory celibacy with its multiple implications may not be desirable, and indeed may be considered a repression of quality of life. Besides, the leap from the use of xenotransplanation as a tool for alleviating ill health to its use in the service of **eugenics** is a small one. The prospect of resurrecting or reinforcing eugenic aspirations (i.e., trying to create "perfect humans") should cause us to pause and rethink the entire enterprise.

In cases where genetic engineering has produced products that are beneficial to health, it has been shown that such benefits have not fully accrued to society but primarily to those holding patents on such products. A case in point is the increased production of insulin as a result of genetic engineering. It has been suggested that one plant of the biotechnology company Eli Lilly can produce enough insulin to meet the needs of most U.S. diabetics (King & Stabinsky, 1999a, 1999b). Despite this potentially huge capacity, insulin "prices have not dropped significantly to reflect the new abundance" (King & Stabinsky, 1999a, 1999b, p. 77). This suggests that any benefits of the new technology will more likely accrue to private companies than to the general society.

CONCLUSION

The debate about agricultural biotechnology appears to involve two polarized groups, proponents and opponents. In reality, there are internal variations among both proponents and opponents. The internal variations reflect differences in motivations and rationales for either supporting or opposing biotechnology. Some proponents support an unbridled push for rapid commercialization of the technology because of perceived benefits. Others are generally supportive but want the technology to be introduced with care. Similarly, there are those who oppose the technology outright as a dangerous development, motivated by greed and a desire for corporate control over food, with little cognizance of its environmental and health implications. Other critics oppose what they consider to be a rapid introduction of agricultural biotechnology to the market despite many unanswered questions and the lack of well-established regulatory protocols that will ensure public safety.

While some proponents limit the basis of their support to what they consider to be proven science, some opponents broaden the criteria for evaluating the usefulness of agricultural biotechnology to include ethical and moral questions and the broad issue of social justice. A comprehensive analysis of the multifaceted dimensions of support and opposition to agricultural biotechnology and their underlying assumptions and beliefs and of how that informs the definition of benefits versus risks is beyond the scope of this chapter. It is however, worth pointing out that the criteria for assessing benefits and risks of the new transition in agricultural practice and its combination with medicine are not the same for the participants in the debate.

There is a strong case for a cautious approach to the introduction of this new technology in agriculture. This is especially so since the primary food insecurity rationale for agricultural biotechnology is not supported by the market imperatives driving agricultural biotechnology R&D, crop selection, and adoption. Proceeding with caution, which means taking adequate time to undertake a thorough empirical investigation of the long-term environmental, health, and social effects of agricultural biotechnology, will not worsen the problem of food insecurity. It will rather give society the opportunity to deal carefully with the risks and assess whether they can be reasonably overcome, or whether the risks are justified in light of the benefits. Proceeding with caution will also afford society the opportunity to assess less risky alternatives and determine whether they can be enhanced to fulfill the same goals set for agricultural biotechnology. Rather than seeing advocates of caution in the biotechnology debate as obstacles to progress, it is useful to interpret such calls as a reflection of a growing weariness with the accentuation of conditions that make our contemporary world a risk society.

STUDY QUESTIONS

1. *How has agriculture changed the way humans interact with the environment? What have been the advantages and disadvantages of these changes?*
2. *What are the possibilities for achieving a balance in fulfilling the three essential functions of agriculture, as described by Schumacher?*
3. *How does the risk–benefit debate about agricultural biotechnology differentiate between human health impacts and environmental impacts?*
4. *What are the main dimensions of risks associated with the inputs, processes, and products of agricultural biotechnology for human health and the environment?*
5. *Identify the benefits expected to result from molecular farming. Do these benefits justify an accelerated or cautious development of molecular farming?*

GLOSSARY

accommodative interactions Forms of human interactions with nature that are not exclusively predicated on serving very narrow human interests.

agriculture The intentional tending of plants and animals by humans through all the stages of their development, with the aim of having some control over food supply.

biofactories Biotechnology-based farms that serve primarily as quasi-factories for producing pharmaceuticals.

biopharming/molecular farming An evolving practice that involves the genetic manipulation of plants to produce pharmaceutical or medical products; it literally integrates farming with pharmacy and medicine.

biotechnology A relatively new technology that uses living organisms or parts thereof to "create" commercial products and processes; involves very specific practices based on molecular biology and genetics.

commodification of nature A process through which parts of nature are treated as commodities to be traded through the market.

eugenics The practice of using genetic manipulations and other associated practices to "produce" a "perfect human being" who has desirable physical and physiological characteristics.

enzyme technology The manipulation of proteins that control the steps in chemical reactions to achieve desired results.

green revolution The drive during the 1960s and 1970s to introduce high yielding varieties (HYVs) of crops, along with irrigation, synthetic fertilizers, and pesticides, into developing countries to help alleviate hunger.

precautionary principle A public policy approach involving anticipatory action to reduce potential harm to human health and the environment, even in the absence of complete proof of harm; usually called for when there is scientific uncertainty about the effects of a new technology.

risk society A transition in societal evolution from a stage in which naturally occurring hazards are predominant to one in which risks are deliberately produced through the technological control of nature for the sake of some benefits (see Beck, 1992).

transgenic Of specific products of biotechnology, created by isolating genes governing desired traits in one organism and extracting, copying, and inserting of such genes into another organism.

vectors and promoters Vectors: parasitic genetic elements that serve as carriers of desired genes into the cell of organisms targeted for modification. Promoters: viruses used to trigger or turn on foreign genes inserted into targeted crops or organisms.

xenotransplantation Animal-to-human organ transfers; may involve the incorporation of human genetic material into donor animals to improve organ receptivity by human recipients.

RECOMMENDED READINGS

Conway, G.R. (1999). *The doubly green revolution: Food for all in the 21st century*. Ithaca: Cornell University Press. A celebration of agricultural biotechnology as the new green revolution that will expand and accelerate the benefits of the "old" green revolution for the developing world.

Doyle, J. (1985). *Altered harvest: Agriculture, genetics and the fate of the world food supply.* New York: Viking Penguin. A critical review of changes introduced to agriculture through genetic manipulation; it contends that the changes will undermine global food security.

Grace, E.S. (1997). *Biotechnology unzipped. Promises and realities.* Toronto: Trifolium Books. A succinct and useful overview of what biotechnology entails; also highlights overblown claims about the potential benefits of biotechnology.

Krimsky, S. (1991). *Biotechnics and society: The rise of industrial genetics.* New York: Praeger. A discussion of the evolution of biotechnology in a sociohistorical context, highlighting facilitating factors, underlying motivations, and their implications.

Krimsky, S., & Wrubel, R. (1996). *Agricultural biotechnology and the environment.* Chicago: University of Illinois Press. A comprehensive review of the effects and implications of agricultural biotechnology for the environment; the effects are deemed to be detrimental.

REFERENCES

Abaidoo, S. (in press). Agricultural biotechnology, developing countries and the hunger problematic. A critical review. In E. Einsiedel (Ed.), *Governing the gene: The social landscape of biotechnology.* Amsterdam: Kluwer.

Adam, B. (1998). *Timescapes of modernity: The environment and invisible hazards.* London: Routledge.

Agriculture and AgriFood Canada. (2000). Canada agricultural facts. www.agr.ca/fact_e.phtml.

Altieri, M.A. (1994). *Biodiversity and pest management in agroecosystems.* New York: Haworth Press.

Altieri, M.A. (1995). *Agroecology: The science of sustainable agriculture.* Boulder, CO: Westview Press.

Ammann, K. (1999, August 15). Environmental benefits of biotechnology. In *Viewpoints on biotechnology.* Boston: Centre for International Development (CID), Harvard University.

Avery, D.T. (1998, Summer). The promise of high-yield agriculture. *Forum for Applied Research and Public Policy, 70–76.*

Beck, U. (1992). *Risk society: Toward a new modernity.* (M. Ritter, trans.). London: Sage.

Bolaria, S., & Wotherspoon, T. (2000). Income inequality, poverty, and hunger. In S. Bolaria (Ed.), *Social issues and contradictions in Canadian society.* Toronto: Harcourt.

Busch, L., & Lacy, W. (1984). *Food security in the U.S.* Boulder, CO: Westview Press.

Buttel, F.H. (1998). Assessing the environmental implications of agricultural biotechnologies: A sociological perspective. *National Agricultural Biotechnology Council (NABC) Report 10,* 45–57.

Carpenter, J.E., & Gianessi, L.P. (2001). Agricultural biotechnology: Updated benefits estimates. National Center for Food and Agricultural Policy. www.ncfap.org.

Clive, J. (1998). *Global review of commercialised transgenic crops.* International Service for the Acquisition of Agri-biotech Applications Briefs.

Conway, G.R. (1999). *The doubly green revolution: Food for all in the 21st century.* Ithaca: Cornell University Press.

Conway, G.R. (2000, March 28). Crop biotechnology: Benefits, risks and ownership. Speech delivered at GM Food Safety: Facts, Uncertainties, and Assessment Conference, Edinburgh, Scotland.

Conway, G.R., & Toenniessen, G. (1999). Feeding the world in the 21st century. *Nature 402,* C55–C58.

Cunningham, J. (2000, June 9). GMOs: Potentially disastrous or farmer's ally? From Arctic strawberries to a patent on life. *Sherbrooke Record*, p. 8.

Food and Agriculture Organization (FAO). (1996). *State of the world report. Genetic diversity*. Presented at World Food Summit.

Food and Agriculture Organization (FAO). (1999a). *Lessons from the green revolution: Towards a new green revolution*. Technical background document, presented at World Food Summit.

Food and Agriculture Organization (FAO). (1999b). *Biotechnology: Fifteenth session of the Committee on Agriculture*. Technical background document, item 7 of provincial agenda.

Fischer, J.R. (1998). An overview. *National Agricultural Biotechnology Council (NABC) Report 10*, 3–7.

Fowler, C., & Mooney, P. (1990). *Shattering: Food, politics and loss of genetic diversity*. Tucson: University of Arizona Press.

Friedland, W.H. (1994). The new globalisation: The case of fresh produce. In A. Bonanno et al. (Eds.), *From Columbus to ConAgra's: The globalisation of agriculture and food*. Lawrence: University of Kansas Press.

Goldberg, R.J. (1992). Environmental concerns with the development of herbicide-tolerant plants. *Weed Technology, 6*, 647–652.

Goldberg, R.J., Rissler, I., Shand, H., & Hassebrook, C. (1990). *Biotechnology's bitter harvest: Herbicide-tolerant crops and the threat to sustainable agriculture*. Biotechnology Working Group, Washington.

Gottweis, H. (1997). Genetic engineering, discourses of deficiency and the new politics of population. In P.J. Taylor, S.E. Halfon, & P.N. Edwards (Eds.), *Changing life: Genomes, ecologies and commodities*. Minneapolis: University of Minnesota Press.

Grace, E.S. (1997). *Biotechnology unzipped. Promises and realities*. Toronto: Trifolium Books.

Highfield, R. (1998, August 7). Researchers reveal risks of creating super weeds. *Electronic Telegraph, 1169*.

Ho, M.-W. (1996, March 22). The hazards of genetically-engineered food. Presentation to the National Council of Women of Great Britain Symposium on Food: Facts, Fallacies and Fears.

Ho, M.-W. (1998). Genetic engineering — Dream or nightmare? In M.W. Ho (Ed.), *The brave new world of bad science and big business*. Bath, UK: Gateway Books.

Ho, M.-W. (1999, September 11). Civil society vs. corporate empire. Talk presented in Progressive Farm Leaders Summit on Genetic Manipulation and Agriculture, Coalition of Family Farmers, Manassas, Virginia.

Ho, M.-W., Ryan, A., & Cummins, J. (1999). Cauliflower mosaic viral promoter — A recipe for disaster? *Microbial Ecology in Health and Disease, 4*.

Honey, K. (1999, June 23). These little piggies are a scientific marvel: Canadian scientists' "Enviropigs" cause less pollution. *The Globe and Mail*.

James, C. (1999). Global review of commercialised transgenic crops: 1999. *ISAAA Briefs, 8*.

Kennedy, M. (2000, June 21). Organ donor shortfall forecast to worsen as population ages. *Saskatoon Star Phoenix*, p. A10.

King, J., & Stabinsky, D. (1999a). Biotechnology under globalisation: The corporate expropriation of plant, animal and microbial species. *Race and Class, 40*(2/3), 73–89.

King, J., & Stabinsky, D. (1999b, February 5). Patents on cells, genes, and organisms undermine the exchange of scientific ideas. *The Chronicle of Higher Education, Opinion & Arts*, pp. B6–B8.

Kneen, B. (1999a, Winter). Death science creeps onto the farm. *Alternatives Journal, 25*(1).

Kneen, B. (1999b). *Farmageddon: Food and the culture of biotechnology*. Gabriola Island, BC: New Society.

Krattiger, P. (1998, June 12). Agricultural biotechnology is critical to third world. *Saskatoon Star Phoenix*, p. D12.

Krimsky, S., & Wrubel, R. (1996). *Agricultural biotechnology and the environment*. Chicago: University of Illinois Press.

Losey, J.E., Rayor, L.S., & Carter, M.E. (1999). Transgenic pollen harms monarch larvae. *Nature, 399*, 214.

Marsden, T., & Drummond, I. (1999). *The condition of sustainability*. London: Routledge.

Marsden, T., Flynn, A., & Harrison, M. (1999). *Consuming Interests: The social provision of foods*. United Kingdom: UCL Press.

McGloughlin, M. (1999). Ten reasons why biotechnology will be important to the developing world. *AgBioForum, 2*(3&4), pp. 163–174.

Meikle, J. (2000, May 31). Soya gene find fuels doubts on GM crops. *The Guardian*.

Mikesell, L. (1999, February 19). Biotechnology Industry Organization — BIO response to Bt lawsuit. Posted on BIOWeb.

Newton, L.H., & Dillingham, C.K. (1994). *Classic cases in environmental ethics*. Belmont, CA: Wadsworth.

Nickson, T.E., & McKee, M.J. (1998). Ecological aspects of genetically modified crops. *National Agricultural Biotechnology Council (NABC) Report, 10*, 95–104.

Palen, J.J. (1997). *The urban world* (5th ed.). New York: McGraw-Hill.

Paulson, J. (2000, February 23). Super-resistant canola confirms fears. *Saskatoon Star Phoenix*.

Perlas, N. (1994). *Overcoming illusions about biotechnology*. London: Zed Books.

Pinstrup-Anderson, P. (1999). Commentary: Modern biotechnology and small farmers in developing countries. *Research Perspectives, 21*(2).

Pollack, A. (2000, May 14). New ventures aim to put farms in vanguard of drug production. *New York Times*.

Potrykus, I. (2000). Vitamin-A and iron-enriched rice may hold key to combating blindness and malnutrition: A biotechnology advance. *Nature Biotechnology, 17*, 37.

RAFI. (1998, July–August). Seed industry consolidation: Who owns whom? *Communiqué*.

RAFI. (1999, January–February). Traitor technology: The terminator's wider implications. *Communiqué*.

RAFI. (2000a, November–December). Biotech's generation 3. *Communiqué*.

RAFI. (2000b, December 13). Calendar of calamities — 2000. Biotech's "Generation 1" — Travails of misspent youth. *Genotypes*.

Rifkin, J. (1998). *The biotech century*. New York: Putnam Books.

Robinson, M. (1998). The seed industry and agricultural biotechnology. *National Agricultural Biotechnology Council (NABC) Report, 10,* 143–148.

Romanow, R. (2000, May 30). Frankenfood's critics are hard to swallow: The public should fear scaremongers, not genetically altered crops. *The Globe and Mail*.

Saskatoon Star Phoenix. (1999, May 1). Mighty Monsanto claims seed piracy, p. A10.

Schumacher, E.F. (1973). *Small is beautiful: Economics as if people mattered*. New York: Harper & Row.

Scoffield, H. (2000, January 4). Contaminated farm seed sold in genetic mixup. *The Globe and Mail*.

Shulman, S. (1999). *Owning the future*. Boston: Houghton Mifflin.

Shiva, V. (1997). *Biopiracy: The plunder of nature and knowledge*. Toronto: Between the Lines.

Suzuki, D. (1999, November 4). We are all guinea pigs. *Moncton Times and Transcript.*

Thompson, P.B. (1995). *The spirit of the soil: Agriculture and environmental ethics*. London: Routledge.

Von Weizsacker, C., & Tappeser, B. (1999). Possible human health impacts of Monsanto's transgenic glyphosate-resistant soybean. Posted on Third World Network, www.twnside.org.

Vasil, I.K. (1998). Plant biotechnology: Achievements and opportunities at the threshold of the 21st century. Paper presented at the IX International Congress on Plant Tissues and Cell Culture, Jerusalem.

Weiss, R. (1999, May 18). Call by U.K. doctors group adds to trade tensions with U.S., brings strong reaction from hill. *Washington Post.*

Western Producer. (1993, April 15). Genetically engineered pig gets patented.

NOTE

1. The scope of this chapter does not allow for an analysis of other aspects of the agricultural biotechnology debate, including scientific legitimacy, the privileging of scientific knowledge, the ethics of knowledge production, appropriation and use, the implications for agrarian communities, and the implications for trade, among others. For a discussion of these issues, see Abaidoo (in press).

17

Work, Safety, Health, and Compensation

TERRENCE SULLIVAN AND DONALD COLE Institute for Work & Health

INTRODUCTION

This chapter outlines the current Canadian social and institutional arrangements for dealing with and preventing the adverse health consequences of work. It explores the effects of labour market changes in the workforce as a consequence of globalization and technological change and investigates the changing nature of the workplace as well as the kinds of exposure workers face in their daily work. It concludes by examining some of the changes in social arrangements in "regulatory reform" and potential future developments in institutional arrangements that are required by changing state and market conditions.

More than 300 years ago, Bernardino Ramazzini, an Italian physician in Modena, first characterized the unique disease conditions associated with particular occupations in *The Diseases of Workers*. Friedrich Engels concluded in 1845 in *The Condition of the Working Class in England* that the incidence and distribution of typhoid and tuberculosis in the population developed in direct association with the production process of capitalism. The key to eradicating disease was altering the relations of production under capitalism. Almost 300 years since Ramazzini's first publication and more than 150 years after Engels, we have a better understanding of how work is essential to our health and how income and occupation link social structure and health (Brunner, Blane, & Wilkinson, 1996). Although our understanding may be improved, workers in Canada continue to struggle for the recognition of occupational health problems (Reasons, Ross, & Paterson, 1981).

With the triumph of neoliberalism, market ideas, trade, and market mechanisms have been declared victorious over state-based solutions to the social health problems associated with capitalism (Boyer & Drache, 1996). The modern question has become, in what kind of capitalist state would people most like to live and work (Hutton, 1995). Indeed, the changing political economy of health has shifted from a focus exclusively on alternatives to capitalist methods of production to the forms of social arrangements in capitalist labour market conditions that are optimally associated with the production of health in the population (Drache & Sullivan, 1999; Sullivan, 2000). Exemplary work by Ross et al. (2000) suggests, for example, that while income disparity and overall health in the population are linked, Canada does a better job than the United States does of buffering this disparity through social transfers in health and education.

A more complete understanding of the effects of work on health now exists, and it can be linked to at least three distinct pathways, as illustrated in Figure 1. The health of workers is affected through the broad effects of labour markets on employment patterns — overemployment, insecure employment, wage and labour market change, and polarization within an overall regulatory framework for labour. Second, the health of workers is also affected by workplace-specific exposure effects, including the traditional concerns with adverse biological exposures on the job (Law Reform Commission of Canada [LRCC], 1986) and the rise of job stress and strain (Sullivan & Adler, 1999). Third, the health of workers is influenced by the availability, nature, and efficacy of health care services provided for injured workers and the extent to which these services encourage labour market attachment. This third factor in Canada is well integrated in the public payer system (Sullivan, 1998). This chapter will not detail these services further but concentrates on the "upstream" factors of labour markets and workplace-specific exposure factors. Each of the three pathways identified in Figure 1 is affected by different social actors, and each poses special challenges and problems for workers struggling to limit their risks of injury, ill health, and disability at work.

Historically in Canada, recognition of the relationship between work and health was given social prominence in the establishment of workers' compensation systems and industrial safety regulations. Since the turn of the century, ongoing changes in the workforce and labour market have altered the health problems that workers experience. These changes have been driven by the growth and the international migration of capital, goods, and services by new workplace technologies and labour processes, as well as by the kinds of work tasks and associated exposures.

FIGURE 17.1

Conceptual Map of How Work Affects Health

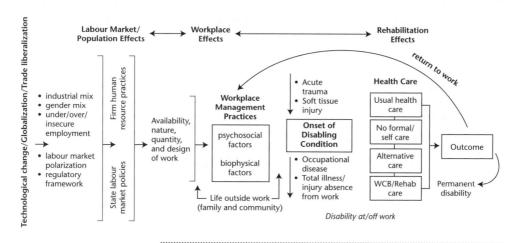

Source: © Institute for Work & Health 1998.

WORKERS' COMPENSATION

The regulation of work-related injury in Canada is tied to the history of workers' compensation in this country, beginning with the report of the inquiry by Justice William Meredith in Ontario in 1913 and the establishment of the first workers' compensation statute in 1914. Workers' compensation in Canada was adapted from the social insurance model developed in Bismarck's Germany. This social insurance altered the common law liability of the employer to provide damages to an employee injured by the negligence of the employer. Until that time, the common law recognized that the employment contract was one in which the worker assumed the risks incidental to employment and the risks associated with injury at the hands of co-workers. Meredith declared the common law assumptions — properly called the assumption of risk rule or the doctrine of common employment — "unfair and inequitable" (Meredith, 1913). Taken together with the third common law rule of contributory negligence (the worker's role in the injury), this "unholy trinity" of defences by employers was swept aside by Meredith in what is now termed a historic compromise.

Meredith sketched out the key principles underlying workers' compensation schemes. They encompassed the notion of compensation based on work-related injury rather than fault. Workers were to be paid benefits related to their earnings through a scheme financed by industry as long as the work injury disability lasted. These benefits would be in lieu of damages under a common law **tort** system. In this way, workers would not be left "indigent" following an injury, and companies would not be brought to the brink of bankruptcy through tort actions. These principles have been applied across Canadian provinces and territories, with the inclusion of federal workforces within each jurisdiction, and have endured largely unchanged to this day. Although some variation exists in the institutional arrangements, as in British Columbia (Rest & Ashford, 1992), Canada enjoys comparable workers' compensation structures and health and safety arrangement from province to province (Gunderson & Hyatt, 2000).

Workers' compensation claims provide one of the few sources on work-related conditions in Canada. Figure 2 demonstrates a steady fall in the rate of occupational fatalities in recent years. Figure 3 plots the incidence of compensated injuries per 100 workers in Canada over the last 26 years (Human Resources Development Canada [HRDC], 1998). Unlike the case 50 years ago, when traumatic injuries were still domi-

FIGURE 17.2

Occupational Fatality Rate per 100 000 Workers, Canada, 1970–1996

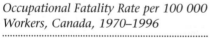

Source: Human Resources Development Canada (1998).

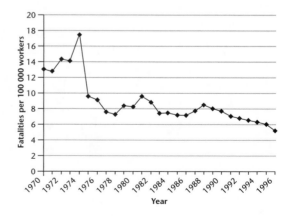

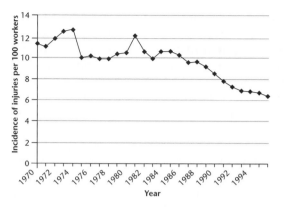

FIGURE 17.3
Rate of Incidence of Injuries per 100 Workers, Canada, 1970–1996

Source: Human Resources Development Canada (1998).

nant, disabling injuries of the lower back and of the upper extremities, known as **repetitive strain injuries**, associated with overexertion and overuse, now constitute more than half of all work injuries and more than three quarters of all costs.

These soft-tissue injuries, strains, and sprains are called **work-related musculoskeletal disorders (WMSD)**. Yet, in the adjudication of claims to workers' compensation authorities, not all WMSD claims are accepted as being work-related. Claims for occupational disease, particularly for non–skin disease claims, are even more likely to not be recognized, and the continuous struggle for their recognition in Canada is well documented (Reasons, Ross, & Paterson, 1981). Such filtering through the administrative apparatus of workers' compensation schemes constrains researchers' knowledge of the burden of work-related injury and occupational diseases across the country. Canada does not have a national occupational health and safety hazard **surveillance** system that independently ascertains the risks and dangers to which workers are exposed in workplaces.

OCCUPATIONAL HEALTH AND SAFETY

Virtually all advanced economies have developed some form of more direct regulation of occupational health and safety in workplaces (Yates & Burton, 1998). These attempts date from the early *Factories Acts* to reduce safety hazards and *Mining Acts* to combat dust exposures and have extended to a long list of statutes covering a variety of workplaces. In Canada, attempts to promote health and safety in workplaces can now be characterized by five key mechanisms:

1. the levying of **premiums** and the experience rating of firms and sectors based on injury experience;
2. direct regulation of hazardous conditions, equipment, and exposures;
3. participation in **joint health and safety committees**;
4. workers' right to refuse unsafe work; and
5. health and safety training in the workplace, including access to information.

The first is carried out by workers' compensation authorities and the second by either integrated workers' compensation boards or ministries of labour at the provincial or federal level. The latter three are based on the "Ham" principles established by the 1976 Ontario Report of the Royal Commission on the Health and Safety of Workers in Mines. Ham (1976) called for an **internal responsibility system** of joint health and safety committees that would have the power to inspect, investigate, and make decisions respecting health and safety; the right to refuse unsafe work for individual workers; and the right to be informed of substances in the workplace that could be harmful. Table 1 provides a snapshot of the application of the role of joint health and safety committees in Canadian jurisdictions.

There are important distinctions in how the above principles are applied from province to province, including the operation of joint committees, their powers, and their responsibilities. An underlying issue in their application is the extent of workers' knowledge of their rights and obligations with respect to such committees. Walters and Haynes (1993) have argued, on the basis of extensive interviews, that workers may have a limited awareness or understanding of these rights.

LABOUR MARKETS

Workers' experiences in the labour market may influence both their health and the trajectory of their working lives. An extensive body of social research has demonstrated the health impacts of unemployment, low wages, blue collar compared with white collar work, and other such factors (Amick & Lavis, 1999). At least five important structural changes in the labour force currently underway are likely affecting the health of workers and the patterns of ill health among Canadian working women and men:

1. the increased participation of women in the labour force;
2. the rise of service and emotional work and the decline of resource and manufacturing jobs;
3. the implementation of new management practices and the changing employment "contract";
4. the growth of nonstandard employment (contingent, contract, and home work) and the associated wage polarization; and
5. the changes in labour regulations associated with trade liberalization.

Tables 2 and 3 provide a picture of accepted lost-time injuries by the nature of injury, organized by gender and by most severely affected body part. With women making up just under 50 percent of the labour force in Canada, differences are occurring in the nature and types of injury experienced by women and men. Although overall women report fewer injuries than men do, a larger proportion of those injuries reported by working women are strain and sprain injuries, particularly of the upper extremity and back. These differences between men and women are explained at least to some degree by the different nature of work that they do (occupational segregation) as well as by the double burden that women still face in their work and family life (Messing, 1998). Although these numbers may provide a reasonable picture of the change in time, they do not properly reflect the suppression of reporting that can be one of the perverse incentives associated with rating the workers' compensation premiums of companies on the basis of their experience with injury (Thomason, 2000).

TABLE 17.1 *Comparison of Role, Powers, and Functions of Health and Safety Committees and Committee Members as Set out in Legislation*

	Role in Complaints	JHSC Inspections	Government Inspections	Maintain Records	Role in Right to Refuse Cases	Recommendations	Access to Information	Develop Programs
Newfoundland	✔		✔	✔	✔	✔	qualified	✔
Nova Scotia	✔		✔	✔	✔	✔		
Prince Edward Island	✔	✔	✔	✔		✔	✔	✔
New Brunswick	✔	✔	✔	✔	✔	✔	✔	✔
Quebec	✔		✔	✔	✔	✔	✔	✔
Ontario	✔	✔	✔	✔	✔	✔	✔	
Manitoba	✔		✔	✔				✔
Saskatchewan	✔		✔	✔	✔	✔	✔	✔
Alberta		✔	qualified			✔		✔
British Columbia		✔	✔	✔	✔	✔	✔	
Northwest Territories			✔	✔	✔	✔	✔	
Yukon	✔	✔	✔	✔	✔	✔	✔	✔
Federal	✔		✔	✔		✔	✔	✔

Source: O'Grady (2000, p. 171).

TABLE 17.2 *Accepted Lost-Time Compensated Injuries, by Nature of Injury and Gender, Canada, 1996*

Nature of Injury	Within Genders (Column %)		Across Genders (Row %)		
	Women	Men	Women	Men	Total
Sprains, strains	46.8	40.2	12.4	29.6	42.0
Contusion, crushing, bruises	13.5	15.1	3.5	11.0	14.5
Cut, laceration, puncture	6.4	10.2	1.7	7.5	9.2
Fracture	4.1	6.4	1.1	4.7	5.8
Inflammation or irritation	7.8	4.9	2.1	3.6	5.7
Occupational injury, n.e.c.	5.5	4.5	1.5	3.3	4.8
Other occupational injury or illness	3.8	2.6	1.0	1.9	2.9
Scratches, abrasions (superficial wounds)	1.1	3.5	0.3	2.6	2.9
Others	11.0	12.6	2.9	9.3	12.2
Total	100	100	26.5	73.5	100

Note: These percentages exclude "unknown" and "not-coded" claims.

Source: Chung, Cole, & Clarke (2000, p. 73); Association of Workers' Compensation Boards of Canada (AWCBC).

TABLE 17.3 *Accepted Lost-Time Compensated Injuries, by Part of Body and Gender, Canada, 1996*

Part of Body	Within Genders (Column %)		Across Genders (Row %)		
	Women	Men	Women	Men	Total
Back	29.7	26.6	7.8	19.6	27.4
Finger(s)	9.3	12.5	2.5	9.2	11.7
Leg(s)	6.2	8.5	1.6	6.3	7.9
Shoulder(s)	7.9	5.6	2.1	4.1	6.2
Multiple parts	8.0	4.9	2.1	3.6	5.7
Arm(s)	5.7	4.8	1.5	3.6	5.1
Ankle(s)	4.6	5.0	1.2	3.7	4.9
Hand(s)	4.1	4.7	1.1	3.5	4.6
Wrist(s)	5.6	3.4	1.5	2.5	4.0
Foot(feet)	2.8	3.8	0.7	2.7	3.4
Others	16.1	20.2	4.3	14.8	19.1
Total	100	100	27.3	76.1	100

Note: These percentages exclude "unknown" and "not-coded" claims.

Source: Chung, Cole, & Clarke (2000, p. 74); Association of Workers' Compensation Boards of Canada (AWCBC).

Along with the rise of women in the labour force has been a dramatic shift in the structure of employment and the growth of service sector work, and what Hochschild calls emotional work (Hochschild, 1983). Although manufacturing jobs and resource sector jobs on which the Canadian economy has historically been dependent have not disappeared, they have declined dramatically in the last 30 years. The service sector is now the most common employment sector, and is dominated by women. The new and dramatic growth of service sector employment and low-wage jobs, "McJobs," has created its own unique set of emotional pressures and strains. These include the false sympathy, warmth, and "bounce" demanded by many service sector outlets in restaurants and retail jobs.

In addition, both the service sector and the manufacturing sector have been characterized by the intensification of work, including the reduction of cycle time and management pressures to reduce "non–value-added" activity. The McDonald's adage of "time enough to lean — time enough to clean" has become the watchword of service sector employment in this country. These new management practices have been characterized as "lean production" in manufacturing sectors. They include the use of a core group of employees to deliver on core business lines, with contingent and contract employment to meet changes in work volumes; the adoption of "high performance" management practices requiring performance-based contracts with all employees; the implementation of just-in-time methods of supply and production to eliminate waste; and attempts to promote "wellness" as a means of limiting exposure and expense in employee health benefits in order to meet the demands of competitive wage costs.

The growth of contingent and nonstandard work, including part-time contract and home work, in contrast to "regular" employment, has at least three kinds of adverse health consequences (Mayhew, Quinlan, & Ferris, 1997). The first risk is that a contingent workforce is likely less well trained to cope with particular health and safety circumstances in changing employment situations. Contingent workers are often given the more difficult kinds of work and are often poorly trained to contend with such work. Second, contingent workers face high levels of insecurity in their work, a problem known to be associated with a range of ill-health outcomes (Stansfeld, Head, & Ferrie, 1999). Third and not least, the growth of contingent and nonstandard employment alongside the segregation of the labour market into relatively secure knowledge-oriented jobs and less well paying and less secure service sector jobs has resulted in wage polarization in Canada. This wage polarization, and the associated increases in the dispersion of income, have been shown by Richard Wilkinson and others to be associated with overall poorer health in the working population — jurisdictions that may have comparable median life expectancy and have greater income dispersion will show overall poorer health (Wilkinson, 1996). Increased inequality appears to have an independent effect on population health, giving some confirmation to Engels's early commentary on the political economy of health.

In Sennet's (1998) view, the "flexibilization of work in the late 20th century is creating a world of work in which attachments and social supports are 'corroded' by the shifting utilitarian calculus of the electronic age. Jobs are replaced by 'projects' and fields of work. Employees are replaced with contractors and 'e-lancers'."

The transnational imperatives of trade liberalization are affecting Canada's approach to health and safety regulation, as they have the regulation of health and safety in

Europe. It has been argued that the European directive has provided some basis for "upwards harmonization" toward the highest standard of occupational health and safety, although it appears that the European directive has had only some small effects in its early stages and that those are largely limited to Northern Europe (Walters, 1997). It has been argued, conversely, that the North American Free Trade Agreement (NAFTA) has created downward pressures as a function of free trade (Canadian Labour Congress, 1993). In spite of the employment adjustments that have occurred in conjunction with the NAFTA, including the flight of small suppliers in the auto sector to low-wage, low-regulation sun belt locations in the United States, a large-scale degeneration of Canadian health and safety practices is not immediately apparent, and any large-scale harmonization of labour standards with Mexico would require very unusual preconditions (Gunderson, 1998).

WORKPLACE ORGANIZATION

Industrial sociology has a tradition of documenting careful study of changes in power, control, resistance, and conflict at work (Grayson, 1989; Reinhardt, Hurley, & Robertson, 1997). As a function of the changes in management practices, regulatory liberalization, and the triumph of markets, representation by workers on behalf of workers' health may be more constrained. Although the overall rate of unionization in Canada has declined remarkably little, a dramatic decline has occurred in private-sector unionization alongside the growth of public-sector unionization (O'Grady, 2000). Unions have played an important role in bargaining for job redesign, rationalizing and humanizing work practices, and refusing unsafe work. In the "new competitive order," it is unclear how Canada will fare with respect to the important buffering role of trade unions in representing worker interests in combating ill health at work.

Much of the management literature is focused on the importance of management leadership in occupational health and safety. A number of recent Canadian studies highlight the role of organizational factors and management practices in occupational health and safety outcomes. Shannon and colleagues at McMaster University surveyed over 1000 firms in Ontario manufacturing and retail sectors to explore the relationship between work organizational factors and safety. The targeted respondents at the company level were the senior manager for human resources and the management co-chair of the joint health and safety committee. On the worker side, the question was directed to the worker co-chair of the joint health and safety committee. Among the variables associated with lower claim rates were the delegation of authority, a high degree of worker autonomy and participation, and the encouragement of career commitment. Lower claim rates were associated with health and safety being defined in each manager's job description, health and safety constituting an important component of managers' performance appraisals, the participation of the workforce in health and safety decisions, and the provision of group safety incentives. By contrast, factors associated with higher rates of injury included high employee turnover and industrial relations conflicts, measured by the number of grievances by union members.

Regarding the internal responsibility system, several variables were related to higher claim rates, including little training for joint health and safety committee members, labour threats to take issues outside of the health and safety committee, management threats of sanctions, and work refusals in the previous 3 years. More cooperative workplaces, not surprisingly, had lower rates of injury. In further reviews of organizational factors at work and a systematic review of existing literature, Shannon and colleagues concluded that several primary factors were important and that firm-level performance was related to health and safety. Perhaps most important and consistent among the factors was the commitment of top management to safety regardless of the nature of the study (Shannon, Robson, & Guastello, 1999). The role of joint committees, including adequate delegation of authority to them, was also identified as an important factor in this review, perhaps demonstrating that supervisors and workers can quickly determine where the real priorities for safety improvements in production lie. The challenge, of course, is to obtain management commitment, a task that is more easily said than done, given the number of managers who have actually taken Dupont-like training[1] to improve leadership in safety culture within their firms. This challenge is ever greater with the rise in small business, which has generated many of the new jobs lost to structural adjustment (Eakin, 1992).

The question of management commitment leads logically back to the five major mechanisms for fostering health and safety at work and the question whether government should "punish or persuade" firms to engage in healthy and safe management practices. The generous assessment would be that firms that do well will endure and survive in the competitive world, particularly one where health and safety regulations and workers' compensation help shape the context in which firms operate. A less generous assessment would be that firms can still compete on the basis of low wages and expendable workers. However, it is worth noting that the general trend in both fatalities and injuries in Canada has been steadily downward, tending to support a Darwinian view that safer firms will endure. The extent to which such a position also holds for long-latency occupational diseases like silicosis and cancers is dubious, given that costs are borne long after exposures occur, in the order of decades. This fact may argue for the continued strong regulation of exposure limits, particularly for toxic chemicals in the workplace.

JOB STRUCTURE

Linked to organizational factors are a range of studies documenting the relationship between job strain and ill health. The extent to which workers have a measure of discretion, control, and social support in their workplace (as measured by a set of instruments developed by Karasek and Theorell, 1990), will be predictive of a range of ill health outcomes, including cardiovascular disease and depression (see Figure 4). More recently, medical sociologist Johannes Siegrist has developed an effort–reward imbalance model that measures the perceived imbalance between the efforts that workers make and the rewards they receive in connection with their work (Siegrist, 1996). Such imbalances are also associated with heart disease risk factors (see Figure 5).

The importance of these two models for studying the ill-health effects of job structure on workers cannot be overestimated. Both models have linked job structure with cardiovascular disease, providing a compelling case for what workers have been struggling for many years to achieve: a higher quality of working life. A clear articulation of job stress into a set of workable models linking decision structures, job demands, and

FIGURE 17.4
*The Karasek-Theorell Demand/Control/
Support Model*
....
See Karasek and Theorell (1990) for a more
thorough discussion of this model.
....
Source: Karasek & Theorell (1990). Copyright ©
1990 by Robert Karasek. Reprinted by permission
of Basic Books, a member of Perseus Books, L.L.C.

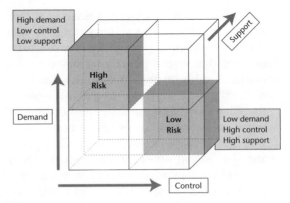

job rewards with a range of unequivocal health outcomes is potentially an important
tool in equipping workers with something other than fuzzy complaints about job stress.
Indeed, as workers have long known, jobs low on the occupational hierarchy have the
highest job stress and strain, not those at the top. The risks and dangers associated with
the social environment at work can be clearly linked with structural differences in the
nature and organization of work, both at the level of the job and at the level of the firm.
In many respects, these new models represent tools to combat the increased demands
on workers associated with global competitiveness and new management practices.

INSTITUTIONAL CHANGES AND OPTIONS

There is little doubt that Engels was correct in his assertion 150 years ago regarding the
roots of ill health in the methods of production. Workers at the bottom of the occupational hierarchy have the worst health and die earlier of all causes of death (Johnson &
Hall, 1995). We have increasingly robust empirical data linking the conditions of work
to organizational and management practices and the structure of jobs. However, what
Engels did not anticipate was the triumph of global capitalism and the constraining
effects of market forces on state actions in the late twentieth century.

The Organisation for Economic Co-operation and Development (OECD), the United
States, and the Canadian government have all been involved in processes to reduce the
regulatory burden and promote firm competitiveness in a global market. A recent OECD
consensus document on regulatory reform (OECD, 1997) notes a retreat from "com-

FIGURE 17.5
*Measuring the Perceived Imbalance
Between the Efforts and Rewards
Associated with Work*
....
Source: Siegrist (1996, pp. 27–41). Copyright © 1996
by the Educational Publishing Foundation. Reprinted
with permission.

The Effort–Reward Imbalance Model also addresses several other key
points, including "intrinsic" efforts (e.g., competitiveness, irritability)
and status control (e.g., security, prospects).

mand" style approaches to the regulation of occupational health and safety toward a more flexible internal responsibility process at firm levels. OECD argues, on the basis of an Australian example, that such reforms have resulted in both the reduction of injuries and the reduction of costs for firms. It is certainly right to question why such "official discourse" is championing the language of market liberalization and regulatory retreat in occupational health and safety.

The introduction of experience rating has resulted in a number of perverse incentives for workers' compensation in Canada, including promotion of litigious and conflictual approaches to claims adjudication for workers' compensation boards. As well, claims do not likely reflect the full burden of WMSD in the Canadian workforce. A recent study of a large newspaper in Ontario (Polanyi et al., 1997) made apparent that a large proportion of workers were routinely operating with various kinds of pain or discomfort, which were often aggravated by their work and affected their ability to carry out their job duties (see Figure 6).

Based on qualitative work, the extent to which such pain or discomfort was acceptable or considered to be disabling varied across individuals and sections of the organization. The social threshold for disability varies not only within a workplace but also seems to vary from workplace to workplace within a given sector. As Deb Stone points out in *The Disabled State* (1984), every jurisdiction must draw the precarious line between a needs-driven economy based on justice and fairness and a work-driven economy based on prosperity, merit, and the distribution of wealth. Ongoing discussion among all stakeholders on the set point for such thresholds must occur for both public and private insurance schemes. This is especially important given the challenging conditions of mental stress, job strain, and musculoskeletal disorders facing workers in the modern world of work.

Evidence on the effectiveness of traditional mechanisms for promoting the health and safety of workers also needs to be increased. The systematic evaluation of policy changes and workplace interventions remains limited despite the high stakes involved (Goldenhar & Schulte, 1994). Despite considerable economic and social research, the extent to which experience rating actually improves the conditions of work, rather than merely reducing less serious claims, continues to be debated. Viscusi (1986) has

Lost days at work — 15%

Pain > 12 times or > 7 days in last year, > moderate intensity — 20%

Reported to workplace — 22%

Saw health practitioner — 29%

Work aggravates pain to some extent — 51%

Any neck or upper limb pain — 60%

FIGURE 17.6

The Upper-Extremity Work-Related Musculoskeletal Disorders Iceberg, 1-Year Prevalence, 1996

Source: Institute for Work & Health, STAR/SONG/IWH office study (1998).

noted some evidence for the role of workplace inspections in reducing injury frequency rates. Similarly, work reorganization experiences have tended to improve health but have not been accompanied by the kinds of rigorous assessments that would be helpful (Polanyi et al., 1998).

There are three ways in which workplace organizations might consider improving the health of their workforce (Institute for Work & Health, 1998). First, organizations may be most motivated by the costs of sickness benefits and, therefore, seek to reduce those benefits or improve value for money. Since a growing proportion of non-**compensable sickness** benefits are for mental health problems, taking into account the two models of job structure–health relationships assumes even greater importance. Second, they may be interested in improving the health of their workforce through wellness programs, employee assistance programs, and fitness programs at work. Sometimes the hope is that such individualized risk-reduction programs will limit the costs of health benefits, although the evidence for such cost reductions are slim in the Canadian context. Finally, firms could do a better job for the health of their employees by maintaining a people-friendly culture that promotes labour force attachment, accommodation, and a safe and rapid return to work. The latter focus on disability management and a safe return to work is growing in importance, as firms experience the pressures of growing long-term disability claims and as the Canadian workforce ages and human rights legislation promotes work for all, including those with disabilities.

Perhaps the pessimistic view of increased cycle time pressure, job intensification, and downward wage pressure must be met with a more optimistic vision of the adoption of benchmarking and best practices for health and safety. The historical focus on the quality of working life laid the basis for modern attempts to provide scorecards on healthy workplaces (Lewchuk & Robertson, 1996). Although many of these scorecards will be focused on cost and benefit management, some approaches are now focused on the actual measurement of health status and the measurement of risks for ill health in the workplace (Shannon, Robson, & Guastello, 1999). Healthy workplace indicators are being looked at carefully by the National Institute of Occupational Safety and Health in the United States and elsewhere, as potentially important new tools in the struggle to maintain a focus on worker health.

At the macro level, workers' compensation and occupational health and safety regulatory schemes have a relatively robust tradition in Canada. Indeed, recent studies of competitiveness in workers' compensation schemes indicate that the Canadian schemes fare very well in comparison to American counterparts (Thomason & Burton, 2000). Relatively low administrative costs (less than 15 percent of overall workers' compensation costs) and a relatively manageable price of health services and benefits are associated with single-payer structures in Canada. The United States, in contrast, suffers from the inflated rates that are being paid for medical care in a multi-payer structure. More than half of a workers' compensation dollar is allocated for health care benefits for injured workers. Although there are increasing pressures to privatize work injury insurance in Canada, the benefits that may accrue from such a move would likely be modest. The uniquely Canadian arrangement of twelve provincial monopoly insurance systems for workers' compensation has been a stable feature for more than 85 years. State-mediated concessions to global capital arising from trade liberalization appear to take the form of downward pressure on replacement wages, benefits, and entitlements to appease the wishes of foreign direct investors who are looking for domains of low regulatory burden (OECD, 1997). The challenge for Canada in the coming years will be to keep the performance of our systems front and centre in harmonization and **privatization** debates.

Likewise with respect to occupational health and safety — the shift away from command and control regulatory schemes toward firm-level imperatives to better manage overall health and safety practices is likely to be the way forward in the new millennium (O'Grady, 1999). Only time will tell if delegated authority and responsibility would have prevented the Westray mining disaster in Nova Scotia and the regulatory failure of occupational health and safety (Richard, 1997). Governments will continuously be challenged to maintain a precarious balance between internal responsibility coupled with incentive schemes and the direct regulation of exposure limits for toxic substances or ergonomic risk, a debate that has so far concluded only in British Columbia. In striking a new balance in Canada, the state will need to maintain mechanisms to hold accountable footloose multinationals that are doing their best to avoid both the regulatory sweep of the state and financial accountability for harm, as Engels anticipated they would.

CONCLUSION

This chapter reviewed briefly the origins of workers' compensation and the history of occupational health and safety performance in Canada in recent decades. It explored key mechanisms associated with the prevention of occupational injuries and diseases in the workplace and the institutional arrangements for enabling these mechanisms in legislation across Canada.

The chapter then explored the manner in which the changing labour market experience of workers in Canada effects a range of health outcomes. These include the rising participation of women in the labour force, the growth of service jobs, the decline of research in manufacturing jobs, the implementation of new high-performance, just-in-time management practices, the growth of precarious employment, and the regulatory retreat associated with trade liberalization. Each of these is explored in relation to its consequences for the health of the workforce, with special emphasis on workplace organization, management practices, and job structure. These latter two concerns provide a fruitful ground for research in looking at the factors that mediate the effects of occupational and class hierarchy on a range of ill-health outcomes and injury. The job-strain model and effort–reward imbalance models are highlighted for their value in measuring job stress and its effects on cardiovascular disease in particular.

How Canadian occupational health and safety and workers' compensation arrangements will fare in the global marketplace remains to be seen. Up until now, they have withstood many of the pressures of downward competitive pressure. Canada maintains reasonably high benefit arrangements in workers' compensation (Sullivan, 1998) and a competitively priced workers' compensation scheme, as well as many key elements of a progressive occupational health and safety system (Gunderson & Hyatt, 2000).

Canada, like other advanced jurisdictions, faces continuous pressure to demonstrate outcomes. This will require more careful evaluation research on occupational health and safety practices and the use of firm-level benchmarking and measurement tools to give indications of effective workplace health and safety efforts.

Given that Canada's largest **harmonization** pressure is concerned with the United States, perhaps Canadians can take some comfort in the fact that their workers' compensation systems appear relatively efficient in relation to those of Canada's major competitive trading partner. One thing is clear: Canadian provinces need to continue to play a role in mediating the interests of workers and in holding accountable multinationals doing business in Canada. This is the only way that the nation can ensure some accountability for the health of its workforce.

STUDY QUESTIONS

1. *What are the key mechanisms in Canada to promote occupational health and safety?*
2. *What are the principles of workers' compensation in Canada?*
3. *Which aspects of labour force change affect the health of workers?*
4. *Which management practices and job features are associated with higher rates of injury at work?*
5. *What are the future challenges for workers' compensation and occupational health and safety in Canada?*

GLOSSARY

compensable sickness One recognized by a workers' compensation board.

harmonization The tendency toward convergence in tax, social, and industrial policy associated with trade liberalization. Upward harmonization typically involves raising standards, whereas downward harmonization typically involves reducing standards in order to be more competitive.

internal responsibility system An approach to joint health and safety at the firm level, underscored by the work of James Ham in the 1976 report of the Royal Commission on Health and Safety regarding workers in mines in Ontario. Joint committees are provided with the power to inspect, investigate, and make decisions relating to occupational health and safety, the right to refuse unsafe work for injured workers, and the right to be informed of substances in the workplace that could be harmful.

joint health and safety committee A workplace committee composed of equal numbers of management and employee representatives.

premiums Specified sums of money collected by a payroll tax on employers to provide work injury insurance.

privatization Part of the "new management practices," a trend that includes outsourcing, contracting out, and divesting whole subsidiaries; these practices typically involve labour shedding and de-unionization.

repetitive strain injuries Injuries to the soft tissues, muscles, bone, joints, and ligaments associated with the repetitive motion typically involved in manufacturing and service work and frequently in keyboarding.

surveillance The systematic collection, evaluation, and dissemination of health-related data.

tort Legal action arising from a breach of contract law and the harms associated with such a breach.

work-related attribution The statistical attribution or portion of work injury or disease that can be linked to workplace exposures.

work-related musculoskeletal disorders (WMSD) Injuries involving strains and sprains to the muscles, bones, joints, and ligaments.

RECOMMENDED READINGS

Gunderson, M., & Hyatt, D. (Eds.). (2000). *Workers compensation: Foundations for reform.* Toronto: University of Toronto Press. An excellent collection of papers, bringing together a range of topical issues in the reform of workers' compensation and occupational health and safety. Although it has a strong economic focus, it includes a range of contributions from scholars in law and social science as well.

Richard, K.P. (1997). *Report of the Westray Mine public inquiry. The Westray story: A predictable path to disaster.* Westray Mine was the site of the most recent large-scale occupational health disaster in Canada. Following a full-scale special inquiry in the province of Nova Scotia, Justice Richard explores the failure at the political level, at the administrative level, at the regulatory level, and at the level of the workplace parties to prevent this avoidable disaster in the coal mining industry in Nova Scotia. The inquiry raises serious accountability questions about occupational health and safety and the challenges of the constitutional mechanisms in Canada to ensure that such occupational disasters do not happen.

Shenk, C., & Anderson, J. (Eds.). (1995). *Reshaping work: Union responses to technological change.* Toronto: Ontario Federation of Labour. A collection that highlights the challenges faced by labour in responding to the effects of new technology on work organization and underscores the important changes associated with the introduction of free trade in Canada, the benefits and challenges of labour adjustment programs, and the rise of new management practices.

Sullivan, T. (Ed.). (2000). *Injury and the new world of work.* Vancouver: UBC Press. A collection of papers highlighting four broad challenges in dealing with the problems of work injuries in the new world of work: the changing nature of work and the changing nature of injury and disability associated with this work; the effects of joint health and safety committees on injury experience, the interaction of psychosocial and biomechanical factors in the prevention of work related injury, and the all-important role of organizational and management practices at the firm level in giving rise to the variation in work-related injury; the challenges of treating and managing the highest burden of injury conditions associated with modern disability — soft-tissue injuries of the lower back and upper extremities; and finally, the challenges of reconciling **work-related attribution** for a range of health conditions with a need to maintain competitive benefits and regulatory regimes in the face of globalization.

REFERENCES

Amick, B., & Lavis, J. (1999). Labour markets and health: A framework and set of applications. (Working Paper). Toronto: Institute for Work & Health.

Boyer, P., & Drache, D. (1996). *States against markets*. London: Routledge.

Brunner, E., Blane, D., & Wilkinson, R. (1996). *Health and social organization*. London: Routledge.

Canadian Labour Congress (CLC). (1993). Two years under free trade: An assessment. In G. Lowe & H. Krahn (Eds.), *Work in Canada*. Toronto: Nelson.

Chung, J., Cole, D., & Clarke, J. (2000). In T. Sullivan (Ed.), *Injury and the new world of work*. Vancouver: UBC Press.

Drache, D., & Sullivan, T. (Eds.). (1999). *Health reform: Public success, private failure*. London: Routledge.

Eakin, J. (1992). Leaving it up to the workers: Sociological perspective on the management of health and safety in small workplaces. *International Journal of Health Services, 22*, 689–704.

Engels, F. (1993 [1845]). *The condition of the working class in England*. Oxford: Oxford University Press.

Goldenhar L., & Schulte, P. (1994). Intervention research in occupational health and safety. *Journal of Occupational Medicine, 36*, 763–775.

Grayson, P. (1989). Reported illness from a CGE closure. *Canadian Journal of Public Health, 80*, 16–19.

Gunderson, M. (1998). Harmonization of labour practices under trade liberalization. *Relation Industrielle, 53*(1), 24–54.

Gunderson, M., & Hyatt, D. (Eds.). (2000). *Workers compensation: Foundations for reform*. Toronto: University of Toronto Press.

Ham, J. (1976). *Report of the Royal Commission on the Health and Safety of Workers in Mines*. Toronto: Ministry of the Attorney-General, Province of Ontario.

Hochschild, A. (1983). *The managed heart*. Berkeley: University of California Press.

Human Resources Development Canada (HRDC). (1998). *Occupational injuries and their cost in Canada*. Work Injury in Canada.
http://info.load-otea.hrdc-drhc.gc.ca/~oshweb/oicc9296/lt022_e.htm.

Hutton, W. (1995). *The state we are in*. London: Jonathan Cape.

Institute for Work & Health. (1998, Summer). National roundtable on employee health. *Employee Health and Productivity*.

Johnson, J., & Hall, E. (1995). Class, work and health. In B. Amick, S. Levine, A. Tarlov, & D. Chapman Walsh, *Society and health* (pp. 247–271). New York: Oxford University Press.

Karasek, R., & Theorell, T. (1990). *Healthy work: Stress, productivity and the reconstruction of working life*. New York: Basic Books.

Law Reform Commission of Canada (LRCC). (1986). Workplace pollution — working paper no. 53. Ottawa: LRCC.

Lewchuk, W., & Robertson, D. (1996). Working conditions under lean production: A worker-based benchmarking study. *Asia Pacific Review, 2*(4), 60–81.

Mayhew, C., Quinlan, M., & Ferris, R. (1997). The effects of subcontracting/outsourcing on occupational health and safety: Survey evidence from four Australian industries. *Safety Science, 25*(1–3), 163–178.

Meredith, W.R. (1913). Final report on laws relating to the liability of employers. Toronto: Legislative Assembly of Ontario.

Messing, K. (1998). *One-eyed science: Occupational health and women workers*. Philadelphia: Temple University Press.

O'Grady, J. (2000). Joint health and safety committees: Finding a balance. In T. Sullivan (Ed.), *Injury and the new world of work*. Vancouver: UBC Press.

Organisation for Economic Co-operation and Development (OECD). (1997). *The OECD report on regulatory reform.* http://www.oecd.org/subject/regreform/report.htm.

Polanyi, M., Cole, D., Beaton, B., Chung, J., Wells, R., Abdolell, M., Beech-Hawley, L., Ferrier, S., Mondloch, M., Shields, S., Smith, J., & Shannon, H. (1997). Upper limb work-related musculoskeletal disorders among newspaper employees: Cross-sectional survey results. *American Journal of Industrial Medicine, 32,* 620–628.

Polanyi, M., Frank, J., Eakin, J., Shannon, H., & Sullivan T. (1998). Creating healthier work environments: A critical review of health enhancing organizational changes at various companies. In *Determinants of health: Settings and issues, Canada Health Action: Building on the legacy* (Vol. 3), Papers Commissioned by the National Forum on Health. Pointe-Claire, QC: National Forum on Health and Edition Multimondes.

Ramazzini, B. (1964 [1713]). *The diseases of workers.* (W.C. Wright, Trans.). New York: Hafner.

Reasons, C., Ross, L., & Paterson, C. (1981). *Assault on the worker: Occupational health and safety in Canada.* Toronto: Butterworths.

Reinhardt, J., Hurley, C., & Robertson, W. (1997). *Just another car factory.* Ithaca, NY: Cornell–ILR Press.

Rest, K., & Ashford, N. (1992). *Occupational safety and health in British Columbia: An administrative inventory.* Vancouver: Workers Compensation Board of British Columbia.

Richard, K.P. (1997). *Report of the Westray Mine public inquiry: The Westray story: A predictable path to disaster.*

Ross, N.A., Wolfson, M.C., Dunn, J.R., Berthelot, J.M., Kaplan, G.A., & Lynch, J.W. (2000). Relation between income inequality and mortality in Canada and in the United States: Cross sectional assessment using census data and vital statistics. *British Medical Journal, 320,* 898–902.

Sennet, R. (1998). *The corrosion of character: The personal consequences of work in the new capitalism.* New York: Norton.

Shannon, H. (2000). Firm level organizational practice and work injury. In T. Sullivan (Ed.), *Injury and the new world of work.* Vancouver: UBC Press.

Shannon, H., Robson, L., & Guastello, S. (1999). Criteria for evaluating occupational safety interventions. *Safety Science, 31,* 161–179.

Siegrist, J. (1996). Adverse health effects of high effort/low reward conditions. *Journal of Occupational Health Psychology, 1,* 27–41.

Stansfeld, S., Head, J., & Ferrie, J. (1999). Sickness absence in the Whitehall II study. A comparison of periods of job security and insecurity. In T. Sullivan & S. Adler (Eds.), *Job stress and health. International Journal of Law and Psychiatry, 22*(5–6), 425–440.

Stone, D. (1984). *The disabled state.* Philadelphia, PA: Temple University Press.

Sullivan, T. (1998). Outcomes research: Payer and provider applications in Canada and the United States. In J. Harris & R. Loeppke (Eds.), *Integrated health management: The key role of occupational medicine in managed care, disability management, productivity, prevention, and integrated delivery systems.* Beverly Farms, MA: OEM Press.

Sullivan, T. (Ed.). (2000). *Injury and the new world of work.* Vancouver: UBC Press.

Sullivan, T., & Adler, S. (Eds.). (1999). Work stress and disability in the new millenium. *International Journal of Law and Psychiatry, 22,* (5,6).

Sullivan, T., & Frank, J. (2000). Restating disability or disabling the state: Four challenges. In T. Sullivan (Ed.), *Injury and the new world of work* (p. 7). Vancouver: UBC Press.

Thomason, T. (2000). Fatality benefits: Rationale and practice. In T. Sullivan (Ed.), *Injury and the new world of work* (pp. 284–304). Vancouver: UBC Press.

Thomason, T., & Burton, J. (2000). The costs of workers compensation in Ontario and British Columbia vs. the United States. In M. Gunderson & D. Hyatt (Eds.), *Workers compensation: Foundations for reform.* Toronto: University of Toronto Press.

Viscusi, K. (1986). The structure and enforcement of job safety regulation. *Law and Contemporary Problems, 49*(4), 127–150.

Walters, D. (1997). Preventive services in occupational health and safety in Europe: Development and trends in the 1990s. *International Journal of Health Services, 27*(2), 247–271.

Walters, V., & Haynes, T. (1993). Workers' use and knowledge of the internal responsibility system: Limits to participation and occupational health and safety. In G. Lowe & H. Krahn (Eds.), *Work in Canada* (pp. 339–350). Toronto: Nelson.

Wilkinson, R. (1996). Unhealthy societies: The afflictions of inequality. London: Routledge.

Yates, E., & Burton, J. (Eds.). (1998). *International examinations of medical-legal aspects of work injuries.* London: Scarecrow Press.

NOTE

1. Dupont is a corporation with a long tradition of management-led organizational safety practices. They offer their experience in health and safety management to other firms on a consulting basis.

PART 7

Current Issues and Public Policy

The health care system, like all social institutions, is constantly in a state of flux. The source of this flux is changing social needs and political and economic interests. Policymakers attempt to anticipate and respond to these changing needs and interests; the chapters in this part of the book examine ways in which evolving needs and interests are reflected in current policy debates and health care practices.

Dickinson begins the section in Chapter 18 with a look at the policy debates and reforms associated with current health care reforms. He maintains that contemporary reform initiatives are rooted either in efforts to contain costs and reduce government expenditures or in efforts to shift the focus of health care from treatment and cure to health promotion and injury and illness prevention. He describes the development of medicare and shows how rising costs were built into the system as a result of compromises made between the federal and provincial governments and the medical profession when medicare was first established. Dickinson then turns to the main ways in which governments have attempted to control rising costs. He argues that many of these cost control initiatives undermine the principles upon which medicare is based and thereby erode Canada's system of comprehensive, universal, portable, and publicly administered health care.

Related to, but not reducible to, these cost control strategies are a number of policy initiatives known as health promotion. The goal of health promotion is to improve the overall health status of the population. The population health promotion framework is based on the assumption that health status is determined by a number of factors, including the nature and organization of the health care system, but also including human biology, lifestyle choices, and the nature of the social and physical environments. Dickinson outlines the main dimensions of policy and reform initiatives from the health promotion policy framework. He then examines the regionalization of health care policymaking and service delivery. He argues that this institutional development has the potential both to increase the democratic participation in and control of the health care system and to result in greater privatization of health care service delivery and the erosion of medicare. He concludes that it is too early to tell which of these tendencies is likely to predominate.

Mental health is a perennial policy problem. In Chapter 19, Dickinson argues that this is so because debate in this area is characterized by disagreement over the nature of the problem to be solved, and as a result there is disagreement about how best to solve it. Dickinson shows, through a review of the literature, that the mental health domain is populated by a number of distinct groups with distinct and irreconcilable understandings of the nature of mental disorders and of how best to deal with them. Medical professionals and others maintain that mental disorders are mental illnesses that should be treated like other illnesses. Nonmedical health professionals, such as psychologists and social workers, maintain that mental disorders are really reflections of underlying psychosocial problems of living, not illnesses. Finally, members of the psychiatric consumer or psychiatric survivor movement maintain that whatever the true nature of the problem, its treatment and management are the prerogative of those with the problem, not some professional group. Dickinson concludes that although current mental health policy initiatives recognize at least some of these contending approaches to the problem, their resolution is by no means assured.

Drug therapies are an essential and growing part of Canada's health care system. Joel Lexchin, in Chapter 20, highlights the contradiction between the public good and private profit, especially in the pharmaceutical industry. He shows that the unusually high profits of the pharmaceutical industry are the result of industry–state relations, the research activities of drug companies, the price of drugs, and the industry-promoting activities of physicians in their prescribing behaviours. Lexchin argues that when the drive for profits and the needs of health care consumers conflict, the pursuit of profits prevails.

Lexchin's paper raises profound ethical problems. Storch, Rodney, and Starzomski pick up on this theme in Chapter 21. They maintain that ethical issues are inherent in all health care decisions, whether the issue is clinical decisions, institutional decisions, or policy-level decisions. At the level of clinical decisionmaking, the common ethical question concerns quality of life. Quality of life issues are particularly thorny due to the fact that the concept is rather vague and relative to people's positions and preferences. The issue is further complicated by the question of who should make quality-of-life assessments and who should pay for them.

Some of the contemporary clinical decisions that Storch and her colleagues address are end-of-life decisions, transplantation and organ donation decisions, and genetics and genetic testing. Institutional-level decision, particularly resource allocation decisions, are also inherently ethical decisions. Whether resources are made available for a kidney dialysis program or a mental health program for the elderly directly affects the quality of life of those involved and raises the question of equity.

The authors go on to describe the ways in which ethical issues, both clinical and institutional, are currently addressed in Canada. This discussion is followed by speculation regarding future ethical concerns and issues in the context of Canadian health care. The authors conclude that the challenge is to develop the motivational, institutional, and procedural means to enable ethical decisionmaking at all levels of the health care system.

Bolaria and Bolaria in Chapter 22 provide an overview of the debate on the relative importance of personal and structural determinants of health and illness. Specifically, their focus is on lifestyles and life chances. They argue that both the biomedical–clinical paradigm and the lifestyles approach tend to neglect the social-structural context of individuals' lives and that the singular focus on lifestyles ignores the social and material bases of lifestyles and health and illness. The literature indicates that lifestyles are shaped by life chances and socioeconomic inequalities produce social variability in health status.

Chapter 22 concludes with a discussion of policy implications of the individualistic and structural perspectives concerning health promotion. Whether the policies and programs target individuals and their harmful lifestyles or target social conditions and inequalities depends upon the analysis of the sources of health problems. In conclusion, the authors emphasize the importance of research on social behaviour and lifestyle choices individuals make within the social-structural constraints of their lives, because such an investigation would make a significant contribution to the structure–agency debate in sociology.

In Chapter 23, Northcott addresses the issue of alternative health care services and their relationship to the conventional, medically dominated health care system. Northcott shows how medicine and the conventional health care system are based on the biomedical model of health and illness, which discounts or marginalizes alternative conceptions of the causes and treatment of illness. The emerging biopsychosocial model of health and illness provides both conceptual and practical space for alternative theories and modes of treatment. It is in this context that more alternative approaches to health care develop.

Northcott examines selected alternative treatments. He argues that as alternative practitioners pursue legitimation, validation, and professionalization, there is a tendency toward a convergence between alternative and conventional medicine. Patient eclecticism is another factor identified by Northcott as supporting integration and giving rise to a pluralistic health care system.

The final chapter in this section looks at the evolving nature and organization of health care in the context of a growing societal pluralism. Ujimoto points out in Chapter 24 that multiculturalism creates a need for policymakers to know a number of things:

- ethnic cultures, so as to have insight into how various ethnic groups understand and adjust to aging;
- attitudes and behaviours regarding aging among various ethnic groups, to facilitate effective health care and social supports.

Canadians need this understanding in order to effectively address gaps in their health care systems.

18

Health Care, Health Promotion, and Health Reforms

HARLEY D. DICKINSON   University of Saskatchewan

INTRODUCTION

Canadians take for granted that they have access to medical care without direct out-of-pocket costs at the point of service delivery. The system of **universal**, **comprehensive**, and **portable** health care insurance, publicly administered on a nonprofit basis — commonly known as **medicare** — is consistently identified as one of the most popular government programs. Consequently, policymakers have been hesitant to publicly advocate making changes to it.

In recent years, however, concern about the growing crisis in health care has become common. The two main dimensions of this crisis are rising costs and the growing gap between the health needs of the population and the capacity of the existing health care system to satisfy them. The first of these problems has resulted in the introduction of cost containment strategies. The first part of this chapter examines a number of these strategies. The second problem has resulted in the development of population **health promotion** as a new health policy framework. The second part of this chapter examines aspects of this development.

HEALTH CARE COSTS: CRISIS AND CONTROL

Rising costs are a structural feature of the Canadian health care system. Between 1960 and 1996, total health expenditures, including both public and private sector expenditures, rose from $2.14 billion to an estimated $75.2 billion. Since the introduction of state hospitalization insurance in 1957 and medical care insurance in 1968, public sector health expenditures have increased from approximately 43 percent of total health expenditures in 1960 to about 74.6 percent in 1991. Since that time, however, they have decreased to under 70 percent (Health Canada, 1990, p. 22; Health Canada, 1997, p. 2).

Although Canada supposedly has a universal, comprehensive, and publicly financed health care insurance system, over 30 percent of health care expenditures currently are paid for privately. This proportion has grown in recent years, partly as a result of government cutbacks and cost containment efforts. Indeed, some maintain that cutbacks are really a means of dismantling medicare by stealth and moving toward a private for-profit American style health care system (Fuller, 1998).

The greatest proportion, by far, of health care expenditures is for personal health care, that is, expenditures related directly to the care of individuals. Personal health care consists of various services, such as "institutional and related services," "professional services," "drugs and appliances," and a number of services provided as entitlements under various government programs such as welfare, workers' compensation, and veterans' services. In combination, personal health care services account for about 88 percent of total health care expenditures. The remaining 12 percent is accounted for by things not primarily related to the care of individuals (Health Canada, 1990, p. 184), such as "prepayment administration," "public health," "capital expenditure," "health research," and "miscellaneous health costs." Table 1 shows the actual dollar figures expended on personal health care in selected years between 1975 and 1996.

Medicare: Financing and Cost Containment

Because medicare is considered by many to be a right of citizenship, it is often assumed that it will continue to exist in its present form, more or less, indefinitely. This need not be the case. Medicare is of relatively recent origin, being established in stages in the post–World War II period.

The first stage corresponded to the introduction of the federal government's hospital construction grants program in 1948. The second step was marked by the introduction of the *Hospitalization Insurance and Diagnostic Services Act* by the federal government in 1958. This piece of legislation established a national system of hospitalization insurance on a cost-shared basis between the federal and the provincial and territorial governments. The next step occurred with the passage of the 1966 *Medical Care Services Act* by

TABLE 18.1 *Total Health Expenditures, by Category, Canada, Selected Years, 1975–1996 ($ millions)*

Category	1975	1985	1995	1996
Total health expenditures	12 260.9	40 058.1	74 306.4	75 224.7
Personal health expenditures	10 503.3	33 680.5	61 024.2	61 551.0
Institutions	6 518.7	20 023.2	33 196.6	33 218.5
• Hospitals	5 396.8	15 957.9	25 944.1	25 714.6
• Other institutions	1 121.9	4 065.3	7 252.5	7 503.9
Professional services	2 737.5	9 356.4	17 267.5	17 487.2
• Physicians	1 838.1	6 040.7	10 799.8	10 867.5
• Other professionals	899.4	3 315.7	6 467.7	6 619.7
Drugs	1 247.1	4 300.9	10 560.2	10 845.2
Other health care costs	1 757.6	6 377.6	13 282.2	13 673.7
• Capital	536.9	1 839.0	1 901.9	1 850.0
• Public health	468.5	1 708.4	3 671.0	3 798.6
• Other expenditures	752.2	2 830.2	7 709.3	8 025.1

Source: Health Canada (1997).

the federal government. The passage of the *Canada Health Act* in 1984 consolidated the provisions and principles of the two previous health insurance acts (Vance, 1988 [1991]).

Under the Canadian constitution, health is a provincial responsibility; consequently, the federal government is able to act in this area only with the consent and cooperation of the provinces. The necessary consent and cooperation is generally achieved through financial incentives or disincentives. In the case of hospitalization and medical care insurance, for example, the federal government was able to persuade recalcitrant provinces to institute a health care insurance program by sharing the costs.

Under the terms of the first cost sharing arrangement, federal contributions were directly tied to, and determined by, provincial expenditures on hospital and medical care services. As a result, the federal government had no control over its health care expenditures. Naturally this was an undesirable situation. The provincial governments too came to be dissatisfied with that arrangement because it discouraged innovation and experimentation with alternative forms of health care service delivery. Nonphysician and nonhospital forms of care and treatment were ineligible for federal funds. The original cost sharing agreement also discouraged attempts to increase the efficiency of hospital and medical care services, at least insofar as every reduction by the provinces in the costs of those services resulted in a corresponding reduction in the amount of federal money transferred to them. Thus, both federal and provincial governments were interested in changing the terms and conditions of the original cost sharing arrangement (Soderstrom, 1978).

The *Federal–Provincial Arrangements and Established Programs Financing Act* (EPF) of 1977 was the first substantial revision of health insurance cost sharing arrangements. The EPF reduced federal contributions to health care from approximately 50 to 25 percent. It also uncoupled them from provincial expenditures and limited future direct federal increases to the rate of growth in the gross national product (GNP). Provincial expenditures exceeding that were ineligible for federal matching funds. The intent of the EPF was to provide the provinces with an incentive to contain costs (Vayda, Evans, & Mindell, 1979). These changes were made attractive to the provinces by the transfer of federal "tax points," which enabled them to increase their levels of income taxation to make up for reduced federal cash transfer payments.

Further cost control incentives were provided to the provinces by the federal government in the mid-1980s. Revisions to the cost sharing arrangements at that time limited federal transfers to the provinces to an annual rate of growth that was 2 percentage points *below* the rate of increase in the GNP. Following that, the federal government further reduced the level of transfer payments to the provinces by freezing them for 2 years at the 1989–90 levels. In 1992–93, federal transfers were allowed to increase at the rate of growth in GNP *less* 3 percent. In 1999, increased federal government health expenditures were announced. Although total health care expenditures continued to increase, various federal government cutbacks dramatically slowed the rate of increase and resulted in a shift in the area of expenditure at the provincial level.

The most dramatic effects are relative to hospital expenditures, which decreased from about 41 percent of total health expenditures in 1985 to 37.3 percent in 1994. Over that same period, expenditures on drugs increased from 9.5 to 12.7 percent of health expenditures. Most other categories of expenditure either decreased, or stabilized, during that period.

Thus, the main shift in the area of expenditure has been away from hospital and other forms of institutional care and toward home care and various forms of community-based treatment. This structural shift in the location of care has been heralded by many as an important step forward. It is maintained that hospital-based treatment is often unnecessary, alienating, and isolating for patients who are often far from family and friends. A health care system that enables people to stay in their homes and communities is seen as a way to overcome the alienation and isolation of the sick, speed the healing process, and cut costs, all at the same time.

Critics point out, however, that in many cases, providing care in the home and community increases the burden for unpaid care providers, usually women. It is also the case that increased reliance on home care and other forms of community-based care is associated with increased use of drugs. Canada does not have a universal drug insurance plan. Thus, for most people, the cost of drugs is either a direct out-of-pocket expense or it is covered in whole or in part through supplementary, personal, or workplace-provided health insurance. Whatever the case, this contributes to the increased proportion of private health care expenditures. Another factor contributing to the privatization of health care costs is the fact that in many provinces the costs of home care and other types of community-based care are not covered by medicare. It is for this reason that government cost control strategies and health care reforms are seen as indirect ways of dismantling medicare.

In addition to restructuring the health care system, particularly its institutional component, provincial governments have responded to the intensified fiscal crisis they face as a result of federal government cutbacks in a number of ways:

- They have attempted to develop new forms of revenue.
- They have cut back or rationed the number and types of services provided.
- They have reduced the costs of the services provided.

Not surprisingly, there is a growing concern that these efforts will erode the principles upon which the health care insurance system rests.

ALTERNATIVE SOURCES OF FINANCING

Although federal cash transfers to the provinces have been reduced, the provincial governments' powers of taxation have increased. In practice, increasing taxes might be a difficult course of action to pursue insofar as many Canadians feel that they are already being unfairly taxed and may not, therefore, support any government or party that imposes additional tax burdens.

User fees (sometimes refereed to as deterrent fees) are another possible source of revenue. User fees can take several forms, including direct out-of-pocket charges to patients for each visit to the doctor or for a range of medical and hospital services considered nonessential. In the hospital, these include such things as semi-private and private rooms, and some drugs and prostheses. With regard to medical care, various services have been **deinsured** or are being considered for exclusion. In Saskatchewan, for example, optometrists' services were deinsured, and there is support for deinsuring other services and even for making certain categories of individuals ineligible for selected health care services.

Another form of user fee that has been used in the past and that is being considered again is an annual premium. This would be charged to individuals or families but would not constitute a direct out-of-pocket charge at the time of service use.

Extra billing, or the practice of allowing doctors to charge patients a fee in addition to the amount they receive from the health care insurance system, is another way to privatize some of the cost of medical care services. Doctors were willing to negotiate lower fee schedules when extra billing was allowed. Extra billing creates a financial barrier to health care for those with low incomes and, therefore, is antithetical to the principles upon which medicare was founded. Consequently, in 1984, the federal government attempted to eliminate extra billing when it imposed a dollar-for-dollar reduction in transfer payments to provinces that allowed it. Although there was considerable resistance on the part of the medical profession, it was ineffective and may well have had negative public relations consequences for them.

In an attempt to minimize the political liability of imposed tax increases or various user fees, governments are increasingly turning to other types of voluntary taxation in the form of lotteries and other forms of gambling. In some jurisdictions, health care services have been specifically identified as beneficiaries of gambling revenues.

Critics of these developments point out that gambling revenues are an unreliable basis from which to finance essential services like health care. Another criticism relates to the fact that gambling is often associated with social problems and increased crime rates. Additionally, it is suggested that gambling tends to be seen as an attractive option for the already poor, who see the possibility of a "big win" as a "quick fix" to their financial problems but who frequently find themselves losing and intensifying their financial woes. In general, state-sponsored gambling is seen to be a tax on the poor that contributes to the perpetuation and intensification of the problems of poverty, including poor health.

REDUCING THE NUMBER OF CONTACTS WITH THE HEALTH CARE SYSTEM

Generally there are three mechanisms for reducing the number of contacts with the health care system: first, improving the health status of the population so that need is reduced; second, modifying help-seeking and illness behaviours; and third, modifying caregivers' behaviours. The last two strategies do not necessarily presuppose improvements in health status. This chapter will consider attempts to improve the health of the population in the section on health promotion. This section looks at certain efforts to modify help-seeking and caregiver behaviours that are intended to reduce service utilization rates.

An obvious way to reduce the number of contacts with the health care system is to reduce the number and types of services that are eligible for coverage under medicare. This, of course, is a form of rationing. Clearly one of the consequences of such a cost containment strategy is that the comprehensiveness of medicare is eroded.

Despite that drawback, this strategy has some important proponents. A survey of Canadian physicians,[1] for example, showed that 81 percent of those who responded supported rationing some services and treatments for those too old to benefit from them or for those who "persist in unhealthy lifestyles or habits" (Kirky, 1992, p. A14). A majority of the doctors who responded also supported ending medicare coverage for all cosmetic surgery, making reproductive technologies available only to those who could afford to pay for them, and charging $5 user fees to everybody who uses hospital emergency wards (Kirky, 1992, p. A14).

These types of "solutions" are based on the premise that some people don't deserve health care services because of their status or behaviours. Such a position violates the principle of universality — that all Canadians, regardless of age, sex, race, religion, income, or place of residence, are eligible for necessary health care services as a right of citizenship. The notion that some people are undeserving of public health care insurance also is a form of "victim-blaming."

Although most doctors responding to the survey supported rationing and deinsuring services in order to contain costs, they were opposed to controlling costs through the imposition of caps on doctors' incomes. Despite medical opposition, however, a number of provincial governments have imposed caps on the amount budgeted for physician services and/or restructured the fee-setting procedures. The organized medical profession, of course, resists attempts to limit doctors' incomes or otherwise undermine their interests (Badgley & Wolfe, 1967). Over the past few years, doctors in a number of provinces have taken various forms of job action to protest threats to their earnings. In the summer of 1992, for example, British Columbia doctors responded to provincial government attempts to cap their incomes and alter the fee bargaining process with a series of walkouts, which resulted in the cancellation of appointments, lab tests, and elective surgery (*Saskatoon Star Phoenix*, 1992, p. A12).

Withdrawal of medical services is always an undesirable event. Therefore, the medical profession and policymakers have agreed that reducing the number of physicians is a more acceptable way to control rising costs. This marks a reversal of opinion. Traditionally, a shortage of physicians was seen as one of the main problems of the health care system. As a result, vigorous efforts were made to increase their numbers. Between 1968 and 1992, for example, the number of physicians in Canada increased from approximately 22 965 to 61 649, with the most recent figures including interns and residents (Blishen, 1991, p. 45, Table 3.7; Health Canada, 1993).

Reductions in the number of physicians will reduce costs by imposing an absolute limit on the number of medical services that can be provided. Because of the unequal geographical distribution of physicians, this form of rationing will not affect all Canadians equally. It seems inevitable that unless other changes to the nature and organization of health care services also take place, those who live in rural, remote, and other underserviced areas will find their situation worsened.

Elimination of the fee-for-service system of remuneration for physician services is often discussed as a cost control strategy (Wright, 1991). In a 1992 government policy document, for example, the Saskatchewan government noted that "under the current payment structure, some health care providers are rewarded (receive larger incomes) for high use of their services. This may encourage user dependency and is inconsistent with the goal of people taking more responsibility for their own health and relying less on the service system" (Simard, 1992, p. 9). These comments refer to the existing fee-for-service physician payment system.

Two alternatives are generally considered: a **capitation payment system** and a salaried payment system. Capitation payment schemes can assume a number of different forms, but generally they involve establishing health districts with a certain population density. On the basis of an estimate of medical care needs of the population, the physician is paid an agreed-upon amount per person in the district, regardless of whether the individuals actually use physician services. This remuneration system eliminates the structural pressure produced by the fee-for-service system of payment because the physician receives a predetermined income regardless of the level of services provided. It is generally agreed that the capitation form of remuneration greatly reduces the tendency to overprescribe and overtreat patients. It is also agreed that there is a greater incentive for physicians to spend a greater proportion of their time in patient education and other health promotion activities.

Physicians, especially their professional organizations, have traditionally opposed the salary system of payment and they have been strong advocates of the fee-for-service system. The main concerns of the medical profession are the potential loss of professional autonomy and incomes that a salaried system of remuneration entails. It is precisely these reasons, however, that make the salary system of remuneration an attractive policy alternative for those interested in reducing the costs and level of service utilization.

Successful physician resistance to working for salaries has had a profound influence on the nature and organization of health care throughout Canada. In the first place, it was one of the reasons that hospitalization insurance and medicare incorporated the fee-for-service payment system, despite the fact that its many limitations and inflationary effects were well known. It also accounts, in part, for the general failure to develop an integrated, coordinated, and holistic approach to health and illness care.

The attenuated development of the community clinic and community health centre approach to providing a comprehensive range of coordinated health and social welfare services in this country is partly the result of physician resistance to the salaried system of remuneration. The recent cost crisis and efforts to respond to it in constructive ways, however, have resulted in increased interest in, and commitment to, the development of regionalized systems of health care planning and service delivery (Dickinson & Bolaria, Chapter 2, this volume).

In this context, the community health centre concept, or some variant of it, is being advocated as an alternative to the private practice fee-for-service doctor's office and as a means of integrating the illness care and health promotion aspects of health care. Many envision salaried doctors working in these new settings as part of a team of health care professionals. Thus, the role and autonomy of the physician is likely to be reduced, if not in absolute terms, at least relative to an expansion of the roles and functions of other health care professionals, particularly primary care nurses.

From the point of view of service recipients, these anticipated changes are hoped to have positive consequences. The fee-for-service physician payment system militates against doctors spending more time with patients, providing health education or counselling services or basic human care and compassion. This in turn is thought to contribute to the alienation and frustration experienced by many patients, both in hospitals and in doctors' offices.

Increasing dissatisfaction with the nature of medical care is contributing to a burgeoning legitimation crisis, which assumes many forms. The most dramatic and disturbing are the increasing number of allegations of sexual abuse (Gray, 1992; Sears, 1992) and the growing number of malpractice suits. Both developments suggest a growing problem, or at least a growing awareness of the issue of iatrogenic injury and illness caused by inappropriate forms of treatment and drug prescription (Illich, 1976).

Other issues that are forcing a re-examination of the nature and organization of medicine are related to the development of new knowledge about human genetics and the application of new reproductive and life-sustaining technologies. This knowledge and its associated technologies have created an unprecedented capacity for control over life and death. Associated with this potential power, however, are awesome ethical and legal responsibilities. Available knowledge and technology forces the society to confront questions about who is to live, who is to die, and who is to decide. Historical experience with eugenics shows that the answers to these questions will not necessarily be benevolent or even benign.

In combination with the intensifying fiscal crisis, this multidimensional legitimation crisis is contributing to a growing interest in the reorganization of the health care system. This often assumes the form of patients' rights and various self-help movements as well as expanded responsibilities for nonphysicians. These developments are related to, and encouraged by, the rise to dominance in the policy arena of the health promotion initiative.

MODIFYING HELP-SEEKING AND ILLNESS BEHAVIOUR

The previous section outlined some of the initiatives that have been taken to alter the behaviour of health service providers. The other main focus for reducing service utilization is the help-seeking behaviour of service consumers (Barale, 1991; Webb, 1991). This basically involves efforts at public education intended to make people less reliant on the formal health care system and more self-reliant in terms of health care needs. As will be shown below, these efforts are a major part of health promotion policy. As laudable as the goal of increasing self-reliance may be, in some cases it may also contradict other well-established health promotion behaviour patterns. In particular, efforts to reduce service utilization may discourage people from having regular diagnostic check-ups or from seeking medical assistance when symptoms first appear. This may have unintended negative health consequences because, for example, as we are constantly told, the best way to cure cancer is to prevent it through the choice of low-risk lifestyles and to have regular medical check-ups and early treatment when symptoms have been identified.

It is increasingly common to hear the argument that universal access to diagnostic services for early detection purposes is a wasteful and ineffective use of scarce resources. It is suggested that only those known to be at high risk or likely to benefit from early detection and treatment should be eligible for insured diagnostic testing. The current debate with regard to mammography screening of women for breast cancer provides a good example. Some researchers maintain that only women 50 years and over should be screened on a regular basis because it is only women in this age group who benefit from early diagnosis and treatment. Others claim that all women, regardless of age, should regularly receive mammography screening to aid in early detection and treatment. It has been suggested that those who support universality with regard to this issue tend to be those who have a direct, often economic, interest in expanded service delivery. This includes the medical technology corporations, who benefit from increased demand for mammography machines, those professionals who benefit from providing the service, and others who have an interest in sustaining a cancer hysteria for fundraising purposes. Proponents of targeted screening maintain that universal mammography is an irrational and ineffective waste of scarce health care resources.

CONTROLLING COSTS IN THE HOSPITAL SECTOR

Table 1 (p. 352) clearly shows two things; first, the largest category of health resources is expended on institutional care; second, of the amount spent on the provision of institutional care, the largest proportion is spent on hospitals. In 1996, for example, it is estimated that more than $25.7 billion was spent on hospital services in Canada.

Cost control efforts in the hospital sector are of two general types: efforts to reduce hospital use, and efforts to reduce the duration and cost of each hospital service provided. Reducing hospital use takes several forms. One of the most obvious and, at the same time, least acceptable, is the common practice of leaving available hospital beds empty.

Another strategy involves reducing the number of hospital beds. This is usually associated with the expansion of alternative forms of community-based institutional care and home care. In 1996, hospital expenditures decreased by 0.9 percent while expenditures on other forms of institutional care increased by 3.5 percent (Health Canada, 1997). In 1997–98, home care expenditures increased by 4.8 percent over 1996 expenditures. At $2 billion, home care expenditures in 1997–98 were double the 1990–91 expenditures. The average annual rate of growth for home care expenditures in that period was 11 percent (Health Canada, 1998).

Other efforts to reduce the number and duration of hospitalizations include early release and delayed admission programs. An increasingly common example is early maternity discharge programs. Under these programs, mothers who have had healthy pregnancies and who meet other criteria may choose to go home from hospital with their newborn babies from a few hours to a few days after delivery. Expectant mothers are made aware of the program in Saskatchewan through their doctors and at prenatal classes. Once a mother has decided to participate, she is visited in hospital by a community health nurse, who provides information and makes arrangements for the new mother and baby to go home. The nurse also visits the mother and baby at home within the first 24 hours and then daily for 3 to 5 days. During these visits, the nurse does complete examinations and assessments of mother and baby and provides additional information on infant care and feeding as well as on self-care for the mother.

As part of the home-based service, the community nurse provides various services including the collection of lab specimens and the removal of sutures. The community nurse works in cooperation with both the mother and her doctor. Participating women also have access to nursing services through a special telephone number 24 hours a day, 7 days a week. Women also have the option of contacting their physician should an emergency arise (Staff of Saskatoon Community Health Unit, 1992, p. 34).

An extension of this early-discharge program is the extramural hospital developed in New Brunswick (Adams, 1987; Ferguson, 1987). The two main functions of the extramural hospital are to facilitate the early discharge of a wide range of patients and to delay or prevent the need for hospitalization through the provision of community-based services and treatments that enable people to remain in their homes. About half the admissions to the extramural hospital are early-discharge patients, and the other half are admitted directly from the community, thus delaying or preventing the need for their admission to the much more expensive acute-care hospitals.

The budget for extramural hospitals is additional to that of existing acute-care hospitals. Consequently, there are no immediate savings. It is thought, however, that savings will be realized in the long run, especially if a more integrated and coordinated social welfare and health care system can be established. Some believe that making the extramural hospital the master institution of a coordinated health care and social services system will result in more effective and efficient use of health care and social services dollars and that this will also result in improved population health status. The "hospital without walls" marks an important organizational innovation in health care delivery. The main structural reform of the health care system since its inception, however, has been **regionalization** of policy planning and service delivery. This is discussed in Chapter 2 of this volume.

It is expected that the anticipated savings realized as a result of increased efficiency in the health care system will be redirected toward various health promotion and injury and illness prevention programs. Included are such programs as home care, family planning, smoking cessation initiatives, anti-drug campaigns, efforts to encourage healthy eating habits, and efforts aimed at reducing family violence and increasing positive capacities to cope with uncertainty and stress.

These and other efforts to reduce the utilization of medical and hospital services are related to other efforts to reduce the costs of health care services. A key element in reducing the costs of services is changing the nature of the services provided.

REDUCING THE COSTS PER HOSPITALIZATION

The largest proportion of hospital expenditures goes to salaries and wages. As a result, some of the most vigorous cost containment efforts are directed toward increasing hospital worker productivity and reducing the costs per service provided.

Labour costs can be reduced in absolute or relative terms. Absolute reductions in labour costs can be achieved in two ways: by reducing wages, and by reducing the number of workers or the number of hours worked without reducing the number of services provided. Relative cost reductions can be achieved by increasing the level of productivity at a rate higher than the increase in wages. Relative cost reductions often are accomplished through either organizational or technological means. Organizational strategies usually involve extensions to the occupational division of labour. Technological means of reducing costs entail the development and application of labour-replacing and productivity-enhancing technologies.

Various factors, including government policy, influence the capacity to use and the effectiveness of different managerial strategies. It is not possible to examine them in detail here. With reference to absolute wage reductions in the hospital sector, however, it is important to note that the imposition of wage controls in the mid-1970s, as part of a more general anti-inflation policy, had the effect of real wage reductions for nurses and other hospital workers (White, 1990). Subsequent government policy has resulted in real income reductions for many categories of workers in both the private and public sectors of the economy (Myles, Picot, & Wannell, 1988). This contributes to increased poverty, which in turn is related to lower health status (see Dickinson & Kosteniuk, Chapter 3 in this volume).

Besides simply reducing wages, absolute reductions have been achieved by transforming the nature and organization of hospital work processes. The most dramatic example of this is the replacement of full-time with part-time workers. Part-time workers are less expensive than those who work full-time, for a number of reasons. First, part-time workers' wage rates tend to be lower than those of full-time workers. This is because part-time workers tend not to be unionized; therefore, they have not achieved the benefits of collective bargaining. Another reason part-time workers are less expensive than full-time workers is related to the fact that part-time workers often are not covered by the full range of employment-related benefits, such as pension and unemployment insurance. Employers are not required to make contributions to these on behalf of part-time employees. It is estimated that this saves employers about 10 percent of employment-related expenses.

The use of part-time workers can also reduce costs by increasing productivity. Because part-time workers are only called upon to work at times of peak demand — when there is work to be done — they are paid only for the time that they are actually working. The amount of slow time, when there is little work to be performed, is reduced, and consequently productivity is increased.

The intensity of work and, hence, productivity, are also increased by the use of labour-replacing technologies. These technologies tend to be developed to replace workers who perform routine, standardized, and repetitive tasks. In the hospital setting, for example, robots are being developed and used to perform a growing array of tasks, including picking up and delivering linens, meals, lab specimens, and medical supplies (Robertson, 1985). Although this is more common in the United States, where hospitals are generally run for profit, the Toronto Hospital for Sick Children uses a robot for lab specimen preparation (Robertson, 1985).

Although labour-replacing technologies tend to replace living labour with machines, other forms of technology directly increase the intensity of the workers who remain on the job. A good example of this is the development of various kinds of monitoring equipment. Because patients are connected through these technologies to a central observation station, all patients on a ward, in principle, can be monitored by a single person. This means that fewer nurses are required to observe and monitor patients. As a result, fewer nurses are on a ward during any given shift; consequently, those who are on duty find their responsibilities intensified: each nurse is responsible for monitoring more patients and for collecting and interpreting more information about each patient and his or her health care needs.

In principle, more information is a good thing, at least insofar as it can result in more appropriate and effective care. In the context of cost reduction strategies, however, it often has the opposite effect. There are two reasons for this. First, intensifying nurses' work can contribute to information overload, fatigue, stress, and burnout, which in turn can be associated with reduced proficiency in judgement and decisionmaking abilities. Second, reduced staffing levels enabled by new technologies can result in patients' requirements exceeding the capacity of staff to satisfy them. For example, in an acute-care unit, if more than one patient is in need of intensive care at the same time, the required number of nurses to provide it may be unavailable.

For many nurses, these and other cost containment and productivity enhancing management strategies result in a deterioration of working conditions and in a reduced capacity to provide the personal care considered to be the hallmark of good quality nursing (Warburton & Carroll, 1988; Armstrong et al., 1997). From the patient's perspective, the rationalization of nursing work is often experienced as a lack of caring, compassion, or understanding of their experiences, concerns, and needs. These conditions are part of the current crisis in nursing (Hewa & Hetherington, 1990). The crisis is manifested in a number of ways, many of which contribute to the deepening of the crisis itself. Central to the crisis is the problem of recruiting and retaining nurses. Many nurses experience high levels of job dissatisfaction, stress, frustration, and disappointment because of the disjuncture between expectations generated in the professional socialization process and the realities of the alienating, oppressive, and exploitative conditions under which they work (Armstrong, 1988; Armstrong, Choiniere, & Day, 1993; Campbell, 1988; Stroud, 1983).

These problems are intensified in the general hospital setting at least to the extent that the nature of health problems has changed over the past few decades. Increasingly, major health problems are of a chronic, long-term nature. This results in different care requirements, which in turn necessitate changes in the traditional caregiver–patient relationship away from one characterized by professional dominance of passive patients to one based upon a more egalitarian and collaborative relationship.

In her study of chronically ill patients' perceptions of nursing care, for example, Kirk (1990) commented on the changing nature of the nurse–patient relationship necessitated by the management of chronicity. A dimension of this changing relationship "involves recognizing the patient as an expert who has already developed effective means of assessing and managing illness" (Kirk, 1990, pp. 138–139). She goes on to note that relating to the "chronically ill patient as a collaborator in care rather than a [passive] recipient of care may be instrumental in bridging the gap between illness management at home and in the institution" (Kirk, 1990, p. 138).

This bridging function and the management of illness and disability at home — or more generally in the community, rather than on an in-patient basis in hospital — is a central element of the new health promotion initiative.

HEALTH PROMOTION: HEALTH AS A RESOURCE

This section outlines the main dimensions of the framework for current health promotion policy in Canada. This includes an overview of the concept of health underpinning health promotion initiatives, along with a brief description of the main goals of health promotion and the strategies and mechanisms proposed for achieving them.

When the principal sources of morbidity were infectious diseases, health was defined in negative terms: as the absence of disease. In the post–World War II period, however, as the primary forms of morbidity came to be chronic, degenerative, and largely incurable, given the state of medical science and technology, the definition of health changed. Currently, health is defined in positive terms as a resource. Maximum health is achieved when individuals are able to attain and sustain a state of complete physical, emotional, and social well-being. Health promotion, therefore, entails the creation of conditions that enable, or empower, individuals to cope with, or change, those factors that influence their health. Four general factors have been identified as important in this regard: human biology, lifestyles, the social and physical environments within which people live, and the nature and organization of the health care system (Lalonde, 1974). Effective health promotion policy and practice, therefore, must address each of these areas.

Given this conceptual framework, three main obstacles to the achievement of health have been identified. First are continued inequities in the distribution of health and illness among the Canadian population. This is related to the second impediment, unhealthy lifestyles among those with poor health. The third impediment is the inability or unwillingness of people to cope with their illnesses and disabilities without undue reliance on expensive and, in many cases, unnecessary and ineffective modes of professional treatment and care. Overcoming these immediate barriers to health is seen as the main challenge to, and the primary means for, achieving health for all.

The health promotion framework proposes three strategies and three mechanisms for meeting the challenges and achieving the goal. The three strategies are 1. fostering public participation in the definition of health needs, 2. strengthening community health services as the most appropriate means of achieving health, and 3. coordinating healthy public policy.

These three strategies are to be realized in the form of three health promotion mechanisms: self-care, mutual aid, and the creation of healthy environments. These mechanisms are not simply viewed as means to an end; rather, the means are the end. Thus, self-care, mutual aid, and the capacity to achieve healthy environments are equivalent to the achievement of health, which is defined as "the ability to manage or even change [one's] surroundings" (Epp, 1986, p. 3).

This section will look briefly at these three strategies before examining the three mechanisms of self-care, mutual aid, and creation of healthy environments.

Strategy 1: Fostering Public Participation

Fostering public participation in, and as a means of, promoting the achievement of health and the adoption of healthy lifestyles, is achieved by "helping people to assert control over the factors which affect their health" (Epp, 1986, p. 9). At a more concrete level, it is achieved through the two mechanisms of self-help and mutual aid. Fostering public participation also involves the regionalization of health care planning and service delivery. This is to allow and encourage greater involvement on the part of those who have traditionally been excluded from, or marginalized in, the determination of health needs and the most appropriate means of satisfying them (Simard, 1992, p. 17). The regionalization of health care is often seen as a necessary aspect of the second health promotion strategy, strengthening community health services.

Strategy 2: Strengthening Community Health Services

A commitment to strengthening community health services entails a commitment to reforming the existing health care system, which is medically dominated and hospital oriented. Strengthening community health services then clearly implies enhancing their role and function in relation to the existing health care system. This point was explicitly made in the Epp Report, which stated that "adjusting the present health care system in such a way as to assign more responsibility to community-based services means allocating a greater share of resources to such services" (Epp, 1986, p. 10). In this regard, the federal government has taken a number of initiatives in the areas of health promotion to encourage healthy lifestyles, including the allocation of "$30 million annually to improve the quality of life of the elderly through self-care projects and education" (Vance, 1988 [1991], p. 14).

Within this commitment it is taken for granted that "communities will become more involved in planning their own services, and that the links between communities and their services and institutions will be strengthened" (Epp, 1986, p. 10). In principle, this commitment to increased participation and democratization of health needs definition and provision seems both desirable and necessary. Fundamentally altering the structural framework within which health care needs are defined and satisfied, however, promises to be difficult (Dickinson & Torgerson, 1998–99).

Past experience with increasing public participation through altered budgeting procedures in the Regina Community Clinic, for example, leads one to expect that the medical profession will resist any changes it sees as detrimental to its professional autonomy and dominance (Young, 1975). Times and circumstances have changed, however, since the 1970s, and the necessity and willingness of the medical profession to constructively adapt to a changed role in the health system may be greater. The health promotion plan for the transformation of the Saskatchewan health care system, for example, states that:

> The medical profession is receptive to innovation and to reviewing its role in the health system, including working as team members with other health professionals. Major consultation has begun and a new dialogue is emerging. Alternative methods of payment for physicians and the lack of physicians in rural areas will be explored. (Simard, 1992, p. 21)

Although the medical profession may be receptive to innovation, the outcomes of these consultations remain to be seen.

It seems inevitable that different structures of service delivery and modes of payment will emerge, depending on local conditions and factors. Indeed, the capacity to respond to the circumstances and needs of different communities is identified as one of the main advantages of the health promotion initiatives. A potential problem associated with the decentralization of needs determination and service delivery is the erosion of standards and fragmentation of services. Cutbacks in the level of federal government support for health care services has led some to express concern over the continued capacity of the federal government to ensure the maintenance of uniform standards in terms of the quality and extent of health care services across the country.

The decentralization of needs assessment and service delivery envisioned by health promotion policy, of course, is consistent with the definition of health that underpins this policy initiative. It is also consistent with the relativistic definition of health upon which the entire health promotion edifice rests. The Epp Report, for example, states that "this view of health...emphasizes the role of individuals and communities in defining what health means to them" (Epp, 1986, p. 3). Thus, it is clear that health is not absolute or universal. Rather, it is relative to one's social, economic, political, and cultural roles and functions. Although this conceptualization is generally seen as a progressive advance over purely medical and reductionist conceptions of health and illness, it too is characterized by its own contradictions (Bolaria, Chapter 1, this volume).

The contradictions emerge most clearly in relation to the main challenges identified by health promotion policy and the concrete mechanisms proposed for meeting those challenges. For example, the first challenge identified is the reduction of inequities. The Epp Report states in this regard that health promotion policy "assumes that there will be a greater emphasis on providing services to groups that are disadvantaged. It further takes for granted that communities will become more involved in planning their own services, and that the links between communities and their services and institutions will be strengthened" (Epp, 1986, p. 10).

At first glance, these assumptions seem unproblematic. The assumption that greater emphasis, presumably in the form of greater resources, will be put on providing services to the disadvantaged raises the possibility of fewer resources being devoted to providing necessary services to groups that are not defined as disadvantaged. This suggests the possibility that those deemed not to be disadvantaged will be required either to do without services or to pay for them in one way or another by themselves. It also raises the spectre of further privatization of health care delivery and the erosion of medicare. In addition it suggests the possibility of different rights and entitlements for different categories of the Canadian population, and in this way it may contribute to the amplification of jealousies and hostilities between different segments of the nation or community.

It is a fact of life in Canada that national unity is an elusive and, in some quarters, undesirable goal. The greater involvement of communities in needs assessment and service delivery decisions assumed and encouraged by health promotion policy may also be contradictory. Increased participation in defining problems and solutions politicizes those processes. Politicized decision making, of course, can have either positive or negative consequences. Positive consequences ensue when previously marginalized and disempowered groups are empowered and integrated into all aspects of community life. The negative effects of politicization are related to the fact that power, and other resources, are not equally distributed throughout society or within communities. Thus, existing inequities may be further entrenched and exacerbated through the political process. Thus, if politicizing health care policy and practice does not result in democratization, it may contribute to an entrenchment or extension of existing inequities. The form that this negative effect is most likely to take is the abandonment of the marginalized and disempowered to their own resources in the name of self-care and mutual aid.

Strategy 3: Coordinating Healthy Public Policy

This strategy is a direct extension of the broadened and context-sensitive definition of health underpinning health promotion policy. It is essentially a recognition that a broad spectrum of policy decisions can and do affect people's behaviours and hence have effects on population health status. Some of those specifically identified in the Epp Report are income security, employment, education, housing, business, agriculture, transportation, justice, and technology (Epp, 1986, p. 10).

The problem is that health concerns, in many cases, are not priority items in these other policy areas. Indeed, it may even be the case that priority objectives in some policy areas are in direct opposition to health promotion objectives. Economic development and business policies, for example, may create conditions that are detrimental to environmental, worker, and consumer health and safety (Bolaria, 1991; Dickinson & Stobbe, 1988; Harding, 1988).

Reconciling contradictory policy objectives may not be possible and, in many cases, even if it is possible it won't be easy. The health promotion policy recognizes this difficulty but has little to offer in the way of concrete suggestions about how to solve it. The only specific comment is the platitudinous observation that "we have to make health attractive to other sectors in much the same way that we try to make healthy choices attractive to people" (Epp, 1986, p. 10). How this is to be done remains a mystery.

The three health promotion strategies are linked to three mechanisms for achieving health: self-care, mutual aid, and the creation of healthy environments.

Mechanism 1: Self-Care

Self-care is defined as "the decisions and actions individuals take in the interest of their own health" (Epp, 1986, p. 7). As conceptualized in health promotion policy, it largely refers to individual lifestyle decisions and practices. Some examples of self-care are choosing a healthy diet, exercising regularly, limiting alcohol consumption, not smoking, and using a seat belt when driving.

For effective self-care, people must be both willing and able to make healthy choices. Consequently, individuals must possess the information, abilities, and capacities required to make healthy lifestyle choices. A key means of providing these resources is through the mechanism of mutual aid.

Mechanism 2: Mutual Aid

Mutual aid is seen as a primary way to enable self-care: "It implies people helping each other, supporting each other emotionally, and sharing ideas, information and experiences" (Epp, 1986, p. 7). Ideally, from the health promotion perspective, it takes place in the family, voluntary organizations, and self-help groups.

Mutual aid is seen as an informal complement to professionally provided care and services available in the formal health care system. It has been pointed out, however, that as health promotion mechanisms, self-care and mutual aid may also be seen as alternatives to professional services from the formal health care system (Bolaria, 1984). Thus, both these health promotion mechanisms have contradictory potential; they can enhance independence and control over the factors affecting one's health, and they can be considered as inexpensive, and possibly less effective, alternatives to professionally provided health care services.

Conceived of in the most positive way, mutual aid refers to the enhancement of community interdependence so as to increase the capacity for individual independence. There are many examples of this form of mutual aid, including Alcoholics Anonymous, One Voice for Seniors, Block Parents, and the Coalition of Provincial Organizations of the Handicapped (COPOH), as well as rape crisis centres and other types of crisis counselling services (Epp, 1986, p. 7). On the negative side, there is concern that community-based caregivers, particularly women, may potentially be expected to carry even greater burdens of caring in the name of mutual aid. The third mechanism, the creation of healthy environments, is intended, among other things, to ensure that the potentially negative effects of health promotion policy and practice are minimized or eliminated.

Mechanism 3: Creating Healthy Environments

The creation of healthy environments as a mechanism for the achievement of health is the most amorphous and ill-defined of the three health promotion mechanisms. It is defined as "altering or adapting our social, economic, or physical surroundings in ways that will help not only to preserve but also to enhance our health" (Epp, 1986, p. 9). This is understood to entail "ensuring that policies and practices are in place to provide Canadians with a healthy environment at home, school, work or wherever else they may be" (Epp, 1986, p. 9). In many respects, it is little more than a restatement of the health promotion strategy of coordinating healthy public policy.

The difficulties inherent in this health promotion mechanism are clearly evident. The practical definition and activation of this mechanism in many instances is being left to the initiative of specific special-needs groups and local communities.

CONCLUSION

This chapter has examined two aspects of current health policy: the cost containment efforts characteristic of the medically dominated and hospital-based illness care system, and the various dimensions of an emergent health promotion and illness and injury prevention policy. Although analytically and in many respects institutionally and functionally distinct, these two dimensions of health policy and practice are interrelated. Indeed, health promotion policy as it is currently conceived is not only intended to facilitate the achievement and preservation of health, in the long run it is also seen as a way to reduce health costs, or at least to slow the rate of growth (Epp, 1986, p. 13).

Health promotion policy is also seen as a means to integrate and more effectively coordinate the organization and delivery of health and illness care services. As such, it promises major changes in the distribution of resources and power within the health care arena. Change in the nature and organization of health care services has traditionally been a conflictual and often traumatic experience for Canadians. Despite an apparent consensus concerning the need for cost control and the principles of health promotion, there is likely to be much struggle over the specific ways in which current health care goals and priorities are implemented.

STUDY QUESTIONS

1. *Outline and discuss the main forms of cost control currently being applied to the illness care system in Canada.*
2. *What are the main mechanisms proposed for implementing health promotion objectives?*
3. *The primary goal of health promotion is the achievement of health for all. What is the definition of health used in this policy initiative? What are the main impediments to the realization of that goal?*
4. *The achievement of health and the containment of costs cannot be achieved without first limiting the power and autonomy of the medical profession. Discuss.*

GLOSSARY

capitation payment system   A system of payment for physician services in which physicians are paid a sum of money based upon an estimate of the medical services needs of the population in a defined catchment area. The amount paid to the physician is the same, regardless of the actual level of services delivered.

comprehensive coverage A core principle of medicare related to the fact that all services deemed medically necessary are covered.

deinsured services Services that have been removed from medicare coverage.

extra billing The practice of allowing doctors to charge patients a direct fee in addition to the agreed-upon fee paid to them by medicare. In principle, this practice has been disallowed by the 1984 *Canada Health Act*.

health promotion A health policy framework intended to result in improved population health status and consisting of three main strategies: increased public participation in the definition of health needs, the strengthening of community-based services relative to acute-care hospitals, and the coordination of health policy across policy sectors.

medicare A system of universal, comprehensive, tax-financed, portable hospitalization and medical care insurance publicly administered on a nonprofit basis.

portable coverage Medicare coverage that is available regardless of the province in which Canadians receive treatment.

regionalization A system of health system governance designed to increase local citizen involvement in health care planning and service delivery, to facilitate greater integration and coordination of the health care system, and to increase the efficiency and effectiveness of the health care system.

universal coverage One of the core principles of medicare: all citizens are entitled to coverage by medicare as a right of citizenship.

user fees Fees charged directly to patients for health care services at the point of delivery.

RECOMMENDED READINGS

Blishen, B.R. (1991). *Doctors in Canada: The changing world of medical practice*. Toronto: University of Toronto Press, in association with Statistics Canada. A look at the various factors changing the nature and organization of medical work. The main thesis is that there has been a shift from a system in which the medical profession was homogeneous and dominant vis-à-vis other health care professions and patients to one in which medical autonomy and dominance is being reduced.

Crichton, A., Robertson, A., Gordon, C., & Farant, W. (1997). *Health care a community concern? Developments in the organization of Canadian health services*. Calgary: University of Calgary Press. A comprehensive overview of changes to Canadian health care policy since World War II; argues that the Canadian health system evolved through three stages: from an individualistic, market-based model, to a collectivist model, to a social model that stresses health promotion and illness prevention, rather than simply crisis-oriented medical care.

Epp, J. (1986). *Achieving health for all: A framework for health promotion*. Ottawa: Health and Welfare Canada. A concise outline of health promotion as a policy objective that suggests a number of means by which the policy can be implemented.

Fuller, C. (1998). *Caring for profit: How corporations are taking over Canada's health care system*. Vancouver: New Star Books and Canadian Centre for Policy Alternatives. A look at the array of national and international interest groups committed to transforming Canada's multibillion-dollar nonprofit system of health care delivery into a for-profit system.

Lomas, J. (1997). Devolving authority for health care in Canada's provinces: 4. Emerging issues and prospects. *Canadian Medical Association Journal, 156*(6), 817–823. An examination of regionalization as a means to alter the "Medicare Pact" that entrenched the dominance of the medical profession in health care decision making and also built cost inflation into the health care system.

Taylor, M.G. (1978). *Health insurance and Canadian public policy: The seven decisions that created the Canadian health insurance system.* Kingston & Montreal: McGill–Queen's University Press. A classic and comprehensive study of the historical development of medicare and case study of the complexity of policymaking in the Canadian context. The historical lessons provide a useful backdrop for understanding some of the forces currently working to transform health care in Canada.

REFERENCES

Adams, O. (1987, April 15). Hospital without walls: Is New Brunswick's extra-mural hospital the way of the future? Interview with Gordon Ferguson. *Canadian Medical Association Journal, 136,* 861–864.

Armstrong, P. (1988, Summer). Where have all the nurses gone? *Healthsharing,* 17–19.

Armstrong, P., Armstrong, H., Choiniere, J., Mykhalovskiy, E., & White, J. (1997). *Medical alert: New work organizations in health care.* Toronto: Garamond Press.

Armstrong, P., Choiniere, J., & Day, E. (1993). *Vital signs: Nursing in transition.* Toronto: Garamond Press.

Badgley, R., & Wolfe, S. (1967). *Doctors' strike: Medical care and conflict in Saskatchewan.* Toronto: Macmillan.

Barale, A.E. (1991, September 16). Patients have unrealistic expectations of the system. *Saskatoon Star Phoenix,* p. A5.

B.C. doctors escalate dispute with government. (1992, July 3). *Saskatoon Star Phoenix,* p. A12.

Blishen, B.R. (1991). *Doctors in Canada: The changing world of medical practice.* Toronto: University of Toronto Press in association with Statistics Canada.

Bolaria, B.S. (1984). Self-care and lifestyles: Ideological and policy implications. In J.A. Fry (Ed.), *Contradictions in Canadian society.* Toronto: Butterworths.

Bolaria, B.S. (1991). Environment, work and illness. In B.S. Bolaria (Ed.), *Social issues and contradictions in Canadian society.* Toronto: Harcourt Brace Jovanovich.

Campbell, M.L. (1988). The structure of stress in nurse's work. In B.S. Bolaria & H.D. Dickinson (Eds.), *Sociology of health care in Canada.* Toronto: Harcourt Brace Jovanovich.

Carroll, W.K., & Warburton, R. (1988). Class and gender in nursing. In B.S. Bolaria & H.D. Dickinson (Eds.), *Sociology of health care in Canada.* Toronto: Harcourt Brace Jovanovich.

Crichton, A., Robertson, A., Gordon, C., & Farant, W. (1997). *Health care a community concern? Developments in the organization of Canadian health services.* Calgary: University of Calgary Press.

Dickinson, H.D., & Stobbe, M. (1988). Occupational health and safety in Canada. In B.S. Bolaria & H.D. Dickinson (Eds.), *Sociology of health care in Canada.* Toronto: Harcourt Brace Jovanovich.

Dickinson, H.D., & Torgerson, R. (1998–99). Health reform, empowerment and community sustainability: Findings from the PECOS study. *Health and Canadian Society, 5*(2), 203–223.

Epp, J. (1986). *Achieving health for all: A framework for health promotion*. Ottawa: Health and Welfare Canada.

Ferguson, G. (1987). The New Brunswick extra-mural hospital: A Canadian hospital at home. *Journal of Public Health Policy, 8*(4), 561–570.

Fuller, C. (1998). *Caring for profit: How corporations are taking over Canada's health care system*. Vancouver: New Star Books and Canadian Centre for Policy Alternatives.

Gray, C. (1992). Ontario's task force on sexual abuse: McPhedran fights back. *Canadian Medical Association Journal, 146*(4), 555–558.

Harding, J. (1988). Environmental degradation and rising cancer rates: Exploring the links in Canada. In B.S. Bolaria & H.D. Dickinson (Eds.), *Sociology of health care in Canada* (pp. 411–425). Toronto: Harcourt Brace Jovanovich.

Health Canada. (1990). *National health expenditures in Canada, 1975–1987*. Ottawa: Health and Welfare Canada.

Health Canada. (1993). *Health personnel in Canada, 1992*. Ottawa: Health Information Division.

Health Canada. (1997). *National health expenditures in Canada, 1975–1996*. Ottawa: Policy and Consultation Branch, Health Canada.

Health Canada. (1998). *Public home care expenditures in Canada, 1975–76 to 1997–98*. Ottawa: Policy and Consultation Branch, Health Canada.

Hewa, S., & Hetherington, R.W. (1990). Specialists without spirit: Crisis in the nursing profession. *Journal of Medical Ethics, 16*, 179–184.

Illich, I. (1976). *Limits to medicine, medical nemesis: The expropriation of health*. Toronto & London: McClelland & Stewart in association with Marion Boyers.

Kirk, K. (1990). Chronically ill patient's perceptions of nursing care. Unpublished M.Sc. Thesis, College of Nursing, University of Saskatchewan, Saskatoon.

Kirky, S. (1992, October 23). MDs back rationing of care: Survey. *Saskatoon Star Phoenix*, p. A14.

Lalonde, M. (1974). *A new perspective on the health of Canadians: A working document*. Ottawa: Health and Welfare Canada.

Lomas, J. (1997). Devolving authority for health care in Canada's provinces: 4. Emerging issues and prospects. *Canadian Medical Association Journal, 156*(6), 817–823.

Myles, J., Picot, G., & Wannell, T. (1988). The changing wages distribution of jobs, 1981–1986. *The Labour Force, October 1988* (pp. 85–129). Ottawa: Supply and Services Canada.

Robertson, S. (1985, November 25). Check-up. *Saskatoon Star Phoenix*, p. A11.

Sears, W.L. (1992). Alberta college latest to tackle issue of physician related sexual abuse. *Canadian Medical Association Journal, 146*(4), 567–568.

Simard, L. (1992). *A Saskatchewan vision for health: Working together for change*. Regina: Saskatchewan Health.

Soderstrom, L. (1978). *The Canadian health system*. London: Croom Helm.

Staff of Saskatoon Community Health Unit. (1992, June 28). Early maternity discharge program begins Thursday. *Saskatoon Sun*, p. 34.

Stroud, C. (1983, March). Silent nightingales. *Quest*, pp. 62–68.

Tuohy, C.H. (1995). What drives change in health care policy: A comparative perspective. *Timlin Lecture*, University of Saskatchewan, January 30.

Vance, J. (1988). Health policy in Canada. *Current Issue Review* [revised 1991].

Vayda, E., Evans, R.G., & Mindell, W.R. (1979). Universal health insurance in Canada: History, problems, trends. *Journal of Community Health, 4*, 217–231.

Warburton, R., & Carroll, W.K. (1988). Class and gender in nursing. In B.S. Bolaria & H.D. Dickinson (Eds.), *Sociology of health care in Canada* (pp. 364–374). Toronto: Harcourt Brace Jovanovich.

Webb, J. (1991, September 6). Education, not political interference will fix medicare. *Saskatoon Star Phoenix*, p. A5.

White, J.P. (1990). *Hospital strike: Women, unions and public sector conflict.* Toronto: Thomson Educational.

Wright, C.J. (1991). The fee-for-service system should be replaced. *Canadian Medical Association Journal, 144*(7), 900–903.

Young, T.K. (1975). Lay–professional conflict in a Canadian community health centre: A case report. *Medical Care, 13*, 897–904.

NOTE

1. About 12 000 surveys were mailed to Canadian doctors in May 1992, and approximately 3400 replies were received. This is about a 28 percent response rate; therefore, caution must be exercised in interpreting the results (*Saskatoon Star Phoenix*, 1992, p. A14).

19

Mental Health Policy in Canada: What's the Problem?

HARLEY D. DICKINSON   University of Saskatchewan

INTRODUCTION

There is a growing recognition that despite its many strengths, Canada's health care system has a number of weaknesses. One of the most significant weaknesses is that it is not primarily a health care system at all; rather, it is an illness care system. As such, it is a more or less effective means for dealing with acute injuries and illnesses, but it is less adequate as a solution to the chronic and degenerative health problems that predominate in Canada. Among the "new" health problems, mental health ranks high (Epp, 1986). As a consequence, considerable attention has been devoted to developing mental health policy in Canada (Epp, 1988).

The scope of the problem is substantial. It has been estimated that 20 percent of the Canadian population suffer from mental health problems; of these, 2 percent suffer from severe **mental illnesses** (Cochrane, Durbin, & Goering, 1997, p. 1). In addition, both the number of persons and the proportion of the population receiving treatment have increased over time, and the nature and location of treatment has changed dramatically (Randhawa & Riley, 1996).

The number of mental hospitals and the number of patients treated in them has decreased. At the same time, the number of persons receiving in-patient psychiatric services in general hospitals has increased. Between 1960 and 1976, for example, the number of beds in mental hospitals was reduced from 47 633 to 15 011. At the same time, the number of beds in psychiatric wards in general hospitals increased from 844 to 5836 (Cochrane, Durbin, & Goering, 1997, p. 1). Between the late 1960s and the early 1980s, mental disorder rose from the fifth most common to the leading cause of in-patient treatment in general hospitals (Blishen, 1991, pp. 36–38).

Many people, however, are never admitted to hospital for treatment of their mental health problems. In Ontario, more than half of all psychiatric patients are treated in primary care settings, and the family physician is most often the source of help (Lin & Goering, 2000). Across Canada, it is estimated that family physicians manage 80 percent of all mental health problems (Health Edition on Line, 2001). In addition, in Ontario, about 30 percent of all family physicians' patients experience some psychosocial or psychiatric problem. Other studies show that 50 to 75 percent of persons who could benefit from mental health services never seek help (Lin & Goering, 2000).

In addition to people who do seek help from physicians for mental health problems, there are those who only seek help from various nonmedical mental health professionals, or who receive informal help from family, friends, or other volunteers, or who receive no help or services. This last category of people contributes to the growing homeless populations that characterize contemporary urban societies (Hardin, 1993).

It is difficult to know the total cost of mental health problems. American estimates place them at more than $136 billion (Health Beat, 1992, p. 20). It has been estimated that in Canada in 1978, the cost of the hospital days alone exceeded $1 billion. Since then, hospital costs for mental disorders have increased (Bland, 1988, p. 1). The costs associated with noninstitutional treatment are additional to these costs. It is also estimated that direct hospital costs are at least matched by various indirect costs, including the costs associated with lost productivity, unemployment, and the personal suffering and reduced quality of life experienced by the mentally disordered and their families (Bland, 1988, p. 1). The mental health care system seems to be overwhelmed and incapable of effectively dealing with these problems. The reasons for this are the subject of debate.

This chapter briefly reviews some of the main dimensions of disagreement. It consists of two main sections. The first briefly describes how various solutions to the problem of mental disorders follow from the different ways in which the problem is defined. The second section briefly outlines a number of common themes and trends in current mental health policy debates. The central argument is that current policy initiatives undertaken within a health promotion policy framework reflect an attempt to establish an accommodation between differing and potentially incompatible definitions of the problem while at the same time containing costs.

THE SOCIOLOGY OF MENTAL ILLNESS AND MENTAL HEALTH

One problem that all societies must solve is what to do with individuals who engage in socially disruptive forms of deviant behaviour. The first and, arguably, the most important step is to define the problem. The way in which a problem is defined determines the type of solution that is implemented. If, for example, troublesome behaviours are defined as criminal, legal solutions will be devised; if a problem is seen as biological in origin, medical solutions will be developed; and if the problem is seen to be spiritual in origin, a religious solution will be developed. If there is uncertainty about the nature of the problem, there will also be uncertainty about the nature of the solution. This is the situation in the area of mental disorder.

In Western societies, the solution to the problem of what to do with individuals labelled deviant has evolved through a series of steps, from religious, to legal, to medical forms of management and control (Conrad & Schneider, 1980; Freidson, 1970; Kittrie, 1972; Manning, 1989; Scull, 1982, 1983). The medicalization of social control is generally thought to have taken place between the ends of the eighteenth and nineteenth centuries.

During that period, the form of deviance previously known as madness or insanity came increasingly to be understood as mental illness, and the asylum, later renamed the mental hospital, came to be the principal source and form of treatment (Conrad & Schneider, 1980; Foucault, 1973; Scull, 1982, 1983, 1991). The confinement of the mentally ill in mental hospitals remained the dominant solution to the problem until the 1960s. Since then, there has been a marked decline in the mental hospital as the principal means and location for managing mental illness and a corresponding rise of various community-based alternatives, including treatment in general hospitals. Although there is general agreement that this transformation heralded a major change in the nature and organization of **psychiatry**, there is little agreement about either the causes or the consequences of those changes.

A number of differing accounts of this transformation have been proposed (Busfield, 1986; Cohen, 1985; Dickinson, 1989; Ralph, 1983; Scull, 1983). Although it is not possible here to review them all, what follows is a brief sketch of the main aspects of the differing descriptions and explanations of the transition from asylum to community psychiatry.

The first, and probably most popular, account of the transformation is the "march of medical science" story (Cohen, 1985). According to this account, advances in modern medical science resulted in the discovery of new and true knowledge about the nature and causes of mental illness. The new scientific understanding of mental illness replaced the ignorance, superstition, and myths of previous generations and led to new forms of medical treatment that replaced the old treatment regimes that were discredited as ineffective at best and brutally inhumane at worst.

Central to this account is the claim that modern medical science demonstrated that "madness" and "insanity" were really "mental illnesses." Given this claim, it followed that mental illness should be treated in the same way, and in the same locations, as all other illnesses. In this regard, the mental hospital was considered an obstacle to the humane and effective medical management of the mentally ill (Goffman, 1961). The mental hospital was more like a prison than a hospital and its radical reform was seen as imperative. From this point of view, the transition from mental hospital to community psychiatry was essentially a triumph of science and humanitarian concern, the final realization of which was made possible by the discovery of powerful psychotropic drugs in the 1950s. To the extent that proponents of this rather celebrationist history acknowledge that there are problems with community psychiatry, these problems are generally thought to be the result of inadequate resources; therefore, the solution is more of the same.

Another, more critical, explanation argues that the decline of the mental hospital and the rise of community psychiatry is best understood as the substitution of one form of social control with another that was neither more humane nor scientifically justified than that which preceded it (Scull, 1983; Ralph, 1983). From this perspective, the transition from mental hospital to community psychiatry is best understood in political and economic terms. Scull (1983), for example, claims that in the post–World War II period a growing fiscal crisis of the state resulted in efforts to reduce costs. As a result, the state began to divest itself of responsibility for the institutional care or control of various deviant populations, especially the mentally ill. Thus, the emptying of the mental hospitals, a process Scull termed **decarceration**, and the abandonment of the mentally ill were driven by economic and political imperatives, not by the progressive and humanitarian advances of medical science.

Despite the differences between the "march of medicine" and the critical "fiscal crisis" perspectives for understanding the development of community psychiatry, both perspectives share the view that the object of treatment (or mistreatment) is the same: mental illness and the mentally ill.

The claim that the domain of psychiatry is mental illness, however, has not gone unchallenged. Indeed, Szasz (1972, p. 12) has proclaimed that mental illness is a myth and that psychiatric "treatment," especially involuntary treatment, is best understood not as the application of medical science to the treatment of mental illness, but rather as a form of torture. This view, variously expressed, is termed **anti-psychiatry**.

Anti-psychiatry shares with the critical "fiscal crisis" perspective the belief that the primary function of psychiatric diagnosis and treatment is the social identification, classification, and control of deviance. Anti-psychiatrists agree that persons diagnosed and treated as mentally ill have problems, but they disagree about the nature of those problems. Szasz (1972), for example, argues that the problems being diagnosed and treated as medical problems by psychiatry are really **psychosocial problems with living**. Conceived of in this fashion, it follows that individuals suffering from such problems should not be labelled as mentally ill, nor should they be treated by psychiatrists. Rather, they should be helped to solve their problems in living by those more suited to doing so, namely social workers, psychologists, or other, nonmedical, psychotherapists.

Another branch of the anti-psychiatry movement argues that even this position is wrong. Laing and Esterson (1964), for example, argue that persons labelled as mentally ill are not ill, nor are their putative problems in living the primary problem. Rather, the "mentally ill" are responding to an insane and maddening social reality in a sane and rational fashion. From this perspective, the problem is not the individuals who refuse to conform to social demands and expectations, but rather the health-destroying and soul-deforming demands of modern social institutions, particularly the bourgeois family and the capitalist economy. Those who are diagnosed as mentally ill are really reacting against the demands of family and economy by embarking on a journey of individual growth and personal development. Thus, from this perspective, madness is an act of resistance and psychiatrists are the storm troopers of society's reaction. The role of the radical, anti-psychiatric therapist in this rebellion against conformity and oppression is to aid and abet the rebels in their emancipatory journey through madness.

Despite the obvious and substantial differences between these two versions of anti-psychiatry, the versions do share a common component: a privileged position for the professional, nonmedical therapist. An alternative perspective on the appropriate role of professionals in the definition of mental health problems and their solutions is provided by the mental patient's–consumer's rights movement.

The mental patient's–consumer's rights movement emerged in its contemporary forms concomitant with the rise of community psychiatry. The culmination of efforts to medicalize psychiatry resulted in many mentally ill people being given the same rights as other patients, including the right to informed consent, the right to receive adequate treatment in the least restrictive environment, the right to refuse treatment, and various other protections against involuntary detention and treatment.

The extension of these rights to the mentally ill fundamentally altered the nature of the doctor–patient relationship. In most cases, psychiatric patients were empowered relative to psychiatrists and came to have a greater say in the definition of their problems and the determination of solutions. The empowerment of patients was further advanced in the context of the anti-psychiatry movement. This rejection of medical dominance was encouraged by various nonmedical mental health professions as part of their own struggles to achieve professional autonomy in the context of a newly emerging community psychiatry (Dickinson, 1989). One consequence of the competing claims concerning the nature of the problem and the most appropriate solution to it was that clients came to have a choice of treatments available to them and consequently came to act more as consumers than patients.

The presumed sovereignty of the consumer, however, is frequently limited by a number of factors, including the fact that the consumerist ethic is often mediated through advocacy–support groups that are not controlled by those with mental health problems. Many mental health advocacy groups, for example, are dominated by the families of those with mental health problems and/or various professional interests. This creates a potential for a conflict of interests between those who propose to speak for the service consumers and to define their needs and the service consumers themselves.

Recognition of this conflict of interests has contributed to the emergence of another branch of the anti-psychiatry movement, generally referred to as the **mental patients' liberation movement** or **psychiatric survivors movement** (Burstow & Weitz, 1988; Chamberlin, 1990; Olsen, 1993). This movement maintains that professionally provided mental health services, whether medical in nature or not, are oppressive forms of social control. Having said that, it must be pointed out that the psychiatric survivors movement, at least as it has evolved in Canada since the 1970s, is not homogeneous in terms of either membership or ideologies (Olsen, 1993; Trainor et al., 1997).

Chamberlin (1990, p. 323) notes that despite the lack of organizational and ideological unity, the movement is held together by its common commitment to a twofold mission, namely, the development of self-help alternatives to professionally provided treatment, and the securing of full citizenship rights for individuals labelled mentally ill. In practical terms, proponents of the anti-psychiatry perspective endorse the empowerment of service consumers in defining and resolving their problems.

Sociologists have contributed to these debates in a number of ways. Sociological analyses have focused on class and gender differences in the prevalence and incidence of mental disorders as well as class and gender differences in forms of treatment. There is an inverse relation between social class and the probability of being diagnosed with a mental disorder (Faris & Dunham, 1939; Hollingshead & Redlich, 1958; Leighton et al., 1963; Srole et al., 1962). In terms of gender differences, women are more likely to be diagnosed with mental disorders than are men (Chesler, 1972; Dohrenwend & Dohrenwend, 1976; Gove & Tudor, 1973; Showalter, 1985). The correlations between gender and mental disorder and social class and mental disorder are well established (Randhawa & Riley, 1996). There is some debate, however, over the explanation of these relationships.

Social selection theories have been developed specifically to explain the inverse relationship between social class and mental disorder. They maintain that low class position is a consequence of mental disorder, not a cause. There are two variants of this approach. The "downward drift hypothesis" suggests that people with mental disorders are unable to function effectively in occupational and other social roles. Over time, this results in a downward drift into the lower social classes. A variant on this view, the **social drift theory**, suggests that it is not so much that mentally disordered people drift down into the lower social classes; rather, their mental disorders limit their ability to achieve upward social mobility. As a result, in each generation, the mentally disordered are left behind and over time tend to be overrepresented in the lower classes. Both types of social selection theories accept the validity of psychiatric diagnoses.

Social causation theories, on the other hand, to a greater or lesser extent, reject medical explanations of mental disorder and deny that mental illness, as illness, exists. Rather, like Szasz, these theorists tend to understand mental disorder in terms of various psychosocial problems with living.

The social stress theory, for example, explains the correlation of class and gender with diagnosed mental disorder in terms of differential exposure to, and experiences of, stress. It is suggested that women and members of other marginalized groups experience greater stress in their lives, and this, in turn, is manifested as higher rates of mental disorders. The higher levels of stress are related to a general condition of social powerlessness that is experienced more concretely as overcrowded housing, broken homes, poverty, boring and dangerous work, and frequent and prolonged periods of unemployment.

Langer and Michael (1963) were among the first to demonstrate that members of the lower classes experienced greater stress than did members of the higher social classes. They, and others (Kessler, 1979) found, however, that at any given level of stress, members of the lower classes also cope less well than do members of the higher classes. This has given rise to the notion that class differences in the rate of mental disorders are not a result of the sheer magnitude of stress experienced, but rather that these differences reflect inequalities in the resources and coping skills available to members of the lower classes compared with others.

Kohn (1977) has argued that this is at least partly the result of class-based differences in the form and content of socialization. He maintains that the structural conditions of lower-class life and the marginalization and disempowerment that characterize it are reflected in a lower-class consciousness that is expressed as a form of passive fatalism and deference to authority.

In contrast, individuals in the higher classes occupy social positions that enable them to make consequential decisions. Occupying positions that provide at least relative degrees of power and autonomy gives rise to individuals who become more skilled and competent in terms of identifying and mobilizing the resources and supports needed to help them solve problems or to change the circumstances that give rise to problems. This relative resource richness helps explain why higher-class persons are less often diagnosed with mental disorders.

The societal reaction approach, or **labelling theory**, focuses on the reaction of society to the behaviour of individuals, not on the individual's behaviour itself. Thus, rather than seeing mental disorder as an illness that has causes within the mind or body of the individual, labelling theory understands the diagnosis of mental illness to be a social label attached to individuals who exhibit deviant behaviour or communication patterns. According to labelling theory, these labels come to be accepted by individuals as core elements of their identities and ultimately as important determinants of their social status (Scheff, 1984).

The class and gender patterns are explained by labelling theorists as a reflection of the fact that psychiatry tends to be a profession made up mostly of middle-class white males. The associated cultural characteristics and biases of psychiatrists, it is thought, predispose them to evaluate the mental health of members of the lower classes, racial minorities, and women unfavourably. This is because the normal behaviours of women and of members of the lower classes and racial minority groups are understood to be deviant from the point of view of middle-class white male professionals.

It is obvious from the foregoing that there is much disagreement concerning the nature and causes of the problem of mental disorder. It is, consequently, also the case that there is much disagreement and uncertainty about how to solve the problem. To briefly summarize, the mental health field is characterized by a number of distinct groups, each with different conceptions of the nature of the problem and the most appropriate solution to it. These groups are:

- medical professionals and others who maintain that the problem is really mental illness, which should be treated like every other illness;
- nonmedical professionals such as social workers, psychologists, and other types of psychotherapists who maintain the problem is really various types of psychosocial problems in living that require their therapeutic assistance for correct identification and solution; and
- psychiatric consumers–survivors who maintain that whatever the true nature of the problem, those suffering from it should be primarily responsible for its definition and solution.

The brief overview of some of the relevant sociological literature reveals that available research findings are also ambiguous, providing support for all the various positions. The following section shows that current policy initiatives can be understood as efforts to accommodate these incompatible perspectives and interests while at the same time responding to demands for cost containment.

CURRENT POLICY PROPOSALS AND DEVELOPMENTS

In Canada, mental health, like health in general, is a provincial responsibility. Each province, therefore, is developing its response to the problems of mental health relative to its own circumstances. Despite this, mental health policy in all jurisdictions is developing within the health promotion framework and consequently is characterized by a number of common themes and trends. These include an increased emphasis on mental health promotion and the prevention of mental disorders; the protection of human rights and freedoms; a greater emphasis on community care; and concern for the coordination of service planning and delivery (Epp, 1986, 1988; Health and Welfare Canada, 1990, p. 169; Macnaughton, 1992; Nelson et al., 1996). The balance of this chapter examines these themes and some of the contradictions embedded within and between them.

Mental Health Promotion and the Prevention of Mental Disorders

The promotion of mental health as a policy objective presupposes a definition of mental health. There is, however, no widely accepted definition. For that reason, Health and Welfare Canada proposed the following:

Mental health is the capacity of the individual, the group and the environment to interact in ways that promote subjective well-being, the optimal development and use of mental abilities (cognitive, affective and relational), the achievement of individual and collective goals consistent with justice and the attainment and preservation of conditions of fundamental equality. (Epp, 1988, p. 7)

An important aspect of this definition is that mental health is not defined as the absence of mental illness. Thus, mental health and mental illness are not seen as lying at opposite poles on a single continuum. Rather, it is suggested that they lie on separate continuums. Thus, mental disorders are conceptualized as existing on a continuum, with maximal mental disorder at one pole, characterized by the greatest severity, frequency, and range of psychiatric symptoms, and with the absence of mental disorder at the other pole, characterized by freedom from psychiatric symptoms (Epp, 1988, p. 9).

Mental health, on the other hand, is seen as lying on a continuum that has optimal mental health at one pole and minimal mental health at the other. Optimal mental health exists where individual, group, and environmental factors work together effectively to ensure subjective well-being, the optimal development and use of mental abilities, the achievement of goals consistent with justice, and conditions of fundamental equality. Minimal mental health, at the other pole, is characterized by subjective distress, an impairment or underdevelopment of mental abilities, a failure to achieve goals, destructive behaviours, and the entrenchment of inequalities caused by contradictory interactions between individual, group, and environmental factors (Epp, 1988, p. 8, Figure 2).

Given this conceptualization, the absence of psychiatric symptoms in itself does not imply optimal mental health. Similarly, the presence of mental disorders, or psychiatric symptoms, does not preclude the possibility of mental health. Rather, "mental disorder may be regarded as one of several possible obstacles" to the achievement of mental health (Epp, 1988, p. 8).

The promotion of mental health, therefore, is the same for all individuals regardless of whether they suffer from mental disorders. It involves minimizing or eliminating barriers to the achievement of empowering interactions between individuals, groups, and the environment (Epp, 1988, p. 9). These interventions can be aimed at individuals, or they can be directed toward altering social and organizational structures and policies.

Conceptually and practically, the prevention and treatment of mental disorders is distinct from the promotion of mental health, although in a number of aspects they intersect (Nelson et al., 1996). Although there is much debate about the underlying causes of many of the major mental illnesses and disorders, there is also an emerging consensus that they result from the interaction between biological, developmental, and psychosocial factors and "can — in principle, at least — be managed using approaches comparable to those applied to physical disease (that is, prevention, diagnosis, treatment and rehabilitation)" (Epp, 1988, p. 8).

Despite this emerging consensus about the multifactoral causes of mental disorders and illnesses, little is being done in the way of primary prevention, that is, the prevention of the onset of mental disorders (Nelson et al., 1996). Secondary prevention, or the prevention of relapse through the management of symptoms, has been facilitated by "pharmacological and other modalities" (Epp, 1988, p. 8), although there is still considerable controversy about both the effectiveness and the appropriateness of chemotherapy and other forms of treatment directed toward symptom management. Currently, therefore, attention is being given to tertiary prevention — the prevention or minimization of the degree of disability associated with mental disorders. In more concrete terms, tertiary prevention is directed toward minimizing the need for expensive inpatient and residential forms of treatment. Tertiary prevention efforts, whatever their focus, attempt to identify and mobilize resources in the form of self-help or mutual aid and to minimize a reliance on expensive professional services whenever possible.

Like current efforts to prevent mental disorders, mental health promotion practices are premised on the ideal of consumer involvement and empowerment. Not all stakeholders understand the nature of the problem, however, and thus do not approach its solution in the same way. This has led to the two "blind alleys" of mental health policy debate: "exclusive reliance on medical treatment technologies on the one hand, and anti-professionalism and exclusive reliance on individual initiative or volunteer action on the other" (Epp, 1988, p. 10).

Problem recognition is a first step toward its resolution. In the above quote it is clear that policymakers recognize the existence of two approaches to the problem of mental health and mental illness, namely, the medical and the anti-professional, anti-psychiatric approach. The distinctions and potential conflicts between the medical and the nonmedical professional models, however, are not as clearly recognized. Without concrete proposals for ways in which proponents of the contending positions are to cooperate, calls for various stakeholders to work together may be dismissed as hopelessly naive or, even worse, as an effort to obscure continued forms of psychiatric oppression or professional dominance behind an ideological facade of cooperative partnership (Boudreau, 1991b). The current emphasis on human rights and freedoms in mental health policy deliberations may be intended to forestall the latter interpretation.

Protecting Human Rights and Freedoms

The protection of human rights and freedoms has been a perennial concern relative to the social management and control of madness and mental illness. Over the past two centuries, the power to define and treat the mad or mentally ill has alternated between the state delegation of power to the medical profession and to the legal profession. The rationale for a medically dominated system is that early diagnosis and treatment are necessary for effective cures. The rationale for a legally structured system is twofold. In the first instance, it is intended to be a means to protect society from the mentally ill and the mentally ill from themselves. In the second instance, it is a means to protect the mentally ill from unjust and inappropriate confinement and treatment (Hardin, 1993).

This second objective rose to prominence in the face of recent attempts to demonstrate the truth of the claim that mental illness is really an illness that should be treated like every other illness. As a result of the successful medicalization of psychiatry, a growing recognition emerged of the right of mental patients to exercise informed consent, to refuse treatment, and to be treated in the least restrictive setting and manner possible. This support for mental patients' rights also, paradoxically, received impetus from the anti-psychiatry movement, which maintains that mental illness is a myth and that the system of medically dominated diagnosis and treatment was itself a violation of human rights.

These general factors contributed to a growing consensus that patients–consumers should have a significant say, if not a veto, in defining the nature of their problems and the nature of the most appropriate solution(s) to them. Consumer participation in these processes is currently seen as an effective means to protect their rights and freedoms (Health and Welfare Canada, 1990, pp. 173–174).

The forces that contributed to an emphasis on consumer participation as a means of ensuring the protection of individual rights and freedoms was given further impetus with the adoption of the *Canadian Charter of Rights and Freedoms* in 1982. In 1987, a draft *Uniform Mental Health Act* was prepared (Uniform Law Conference, 1987). The draft act, although it has no legal status, was intended to serve as a guide for the legislative incorporation of the requirements of the Charter into provincial and territorial legislation.

Despite the fact that there is an increasingly explicit commitment to consumer empowerment and participation in the mental health field, a contradiction remains. It resides in the fact that mental health policy and practice has a dual function: it is intended both to provide care and treatment to those in need, and to protect others from mentally disordered individuals who may be dangerous. Indeed, in the 1987 model mental health act, the protection of society and the terms and conditions for providing involuntary treatment to those considered dangerous are the dominant concerns (Health and Welfare Canada, 1990, pp. 173–174).

The provision of involuntary examination, custody, care, treatment, and restraint is inevitably in conflict with the principle of consumer control and voluntary participation. In legal terms, this contradiction can be expressed as a conflict between society's right to provide involuntary treatment to protect its members and the individual's right to refuse unwanted treatment.

Recent efforts to resolve this contradiction have resulted in the introduction of mandatory community treatment orders. These orders enable the courts to require individuals to take their medications and to appoint someone, often a physician, to ensure that they do so. It is generally thought that many individuals caught in the revolving door of hospitalization–release–hospitalization could have that cycle broken if they would stay on their medications while remaining in the community. Community treatment orders are an attempt to prevent re-hospitalization. Thus, they are part of the tertiary prevention efforts mentioned above.

Community Care

The emphasis on community care is often interpreted to mean the establishment of a more "balanced" configuration of institutional (i.e., in-patient and other residential treatment services) and community-based (i.e., out-patient and nonresidential) services and supports. More specifically, it refers to a further reduction in the use of long-term residential care facilities and expensive in-patient services in general hospitals.

The fact that the majority of mental health care costs are associated with the provision of general hospital-based treatment and care is considered indicative of the failure of the 1960s and 1970s **deinstitutionalization** movement (Lurie, 1984; Simmons, 1990; Trainor et al., 1992). It is important to note, however, that during the first phase of the development of community psychiatry, the substitution of general hospital-based in-patient treatment services for mental hospital services was seen as a major advance toward community psychiatry (Dickinson, 1989; Tyhurst et al., 1963).

The current commitment to reduced in-patient services is accompanied by the recognition that a range of housing alternatives are required "in order to provide for people at various levels of individual functioning, while allowing the appropriate degrees of professional supervision and personal autonomy" (Health and Welfare Canada, 1990, p. 170).

It is explicitly stated that the service users are to have a central role in developing and coordinating community psychiatric services (Health and Welfare Canada, 1990, p. 170). It is also made explicit that the satisfaction of those needs will involve the coordinated identification, use, and development of "informal and natural support networks with respect to care and rehabilitation efforts" (Health and Welfare Canada, 1990, p. 170).

The identification and mobilization of these informal community-based resources for the provision of care and rehabilitation services, in addition to being indicative of a respect for patient rights, also signals a commitment to least-cost solutions and constitutes a mainstay in mental health policy. Assuming that no new resources will be made available, this goal can only be achieved by reallocating resources from the medically dominated hospital sector to the nonmedical community mental health care system. Thus, it seems likely that putting community care into practice will not be easy or conflict-free. Recognition of this potential underpins a commitment to coordination in service planning and delivery.

COORDINATION OF SERVICE PLANNING AND DELIVERY

An accurate identification of needs is the foundation of service planning and delivery. It is generally believed that once needs are accurately identified, rational decisions can be made concerning the (re)allocation of mental health resources, both financial and human. Related to this is the proposition that an accurate assessment of needs, especially at the individual level, allows for the development of individualized service-delivery plans. This is deemed essential, both to minimize the possibility of unnecessarily institutionalizing individuals and inadvertently creating dependence, and to reduce the risks that individuals fall between the cracks in an uncoordinated system.

The priority currently given to coordination in policy planning and service delivery is at least partly a response to these general concerns. More specifically, it is a response to widespread criticism of the initial phase of the deinstitutionalization movement of the 1960s and 1970s. A problem with that first phase of community psychiatry was that it overemphasized efforts at deinstitutionalization, which in practice often amounted to little more than the depopulation of old asylums. This depopulation, which was made possible by the successful medicalization of psychiatry (Dickinson, 1989; Dickinson & Andre, 1988), was roundly criticized because it failed to adequately establish community-based services and resources. This failure had a number of consequences, all of which are considered to be bad. These consequences are referred to in various ways, but they generally include ghettoization and transinstitutionalization.

Ghettoization of the mentally ill is considered a result of the abandonment of discharged patients into a community setting that is not equipped or willing to provide the services and supports for them (Dear & Wolch, 1987; Scull, 1983). A consequence of this lack of adequate community mental health services is that discharged mental patients, who usually have few resources or money, tend to drift toward low-rent, inner-city neighbourhoods. Increasingly, those with mental disorders contribute to the growing population of homeless that is a ubiquitous and distressing feature of contemporary societies.

The problems associated with ghettoization, magnified by cutbacks to welfare and social services and by increasing levels of apparently permanent unemployment and underemployment, form a crucible for crime. The mentally ill are both victims and offenders. As a result, many discharged mental patients are caught up in the criminal justice system. This is often referred to as the criminalization of mental illness, and it is an aspect of **transinstitutionalization**.

Transinstitutionalization is the process of shifting individuals with mental disorders from one institutional setting to another without solving the problem that motivated their discharge from mental hospitals in the first place. Indeed, most analysts agree that transinstitutionalization exacerbates the problem because individuals end up in institutional settings that are even less well equipped to provide appropriate services and support than were the old mental hospitals. A recent report by British Columbia mental health advocate Nancy Hall estimated that 32 percent of inmates in B.C. correctional facilities have some type of mental disorder (*Saskatoon Star Phoenix*, 2000). This is also seen to be a problem for the aged mentally disordered, who, it is frequently maintained, are often simply drugged and warehoused in long-term-care facilities.

In an effort to avoid and correct these problems, decentralization and regionalization have been enthusiastically embraced as a means for coordinating mental health program planning and development. The anticipated advantages of decentralization and regionalization are twofold: it is hoped that they will enable the identification of location-specific service delivery needs, and that they will facilitate the creation of local commitment to the mobilization and reallocation of resources in the communities most directly affected. This last point is particularly important in light of the commitment to self-care and mutual aid as essential elements in the health promotion framework (Epp, 1986, 1988).

The commitment to decentralization and regionalization is expressed in varying degrees in various provinces, but generally it entails a transfer of at least some executive and fiscal responsibility to new administrative structures. This transfer of power is considered to have both positive and negative effects. On the positive side, it is argued to be an extension of democratic decision making into new areas of community life. On the negative side, it is argued that it simply results in the transfer of difficult and divisive resource-allocation decisions to local communities. Both of these have the consequence of politicizing decisions at the community level and thereby intensifying the struggle for control of available resources.

The nature of the membership of the regional planning and administrative bodies that are proposed and emerging in various forms and with various degrees of autonomy across the country is important if hopes for increased democratization are to be achieved. There are a number of "stakeholders" or vested interests in the mental health field. They do not all share a common definition of the nature of the problems to be solved, nor do they share a common vision of the most appropriate solutions to be applied (Boudreau, 1987, 1991a, 1991b; Dickinson, 1989; Dickinson & Andre, 1988;

White & Mercier, 1991). Furthermore, it is not apparent that any consensus can be reached on these issues.

Attempts to skirt these issues by selective participation in the planning and administration of mental health services will undermine the legitimacy of these new initiatives and, consequently, their likelihood of success. Sensitivity to this potential problem is crucial, given the importance to the health promotion framework of securing individual, family, and community participation in the planning and provision of services and support for those with mental health problems and mental disorders.

CONCLUSION

This chapter has focused on the problem-definition components of current policy initiatives in the mental health field and their relationship to the proposed reforms of mental health service systems. It argues that lack of consensus about the nature of mental health problems contributes to the institutionalization of contradictions at the level of service delivery.

More specifically, it argues that current policy initiatives appear to be directed toward establishing a compromise among three conceptions of the problem to be solved and the best way to solve it. Despite the laudable intentions behind these policy proposals, it is not clear that they can be effectively put into practice in the form of a comprehensive and integrated mental health care services system. The problem is that the various stakeholders, representing both medical and nonmedical professional interests and the nonprofessional interests of service users and their advocates, don't necessarily agree on the nature of the problem; nor do they agree on the best solution to it. Current policy initiatives, therefore, may have the unintended consequence of locking proponents of conflicting and possibly irreconcilable positions into a system of perpetual conflict. Thus, rather than being the solution to existing problems, current initiatives may simply be creating new ones.

STUDY QUESTIONS

1. *Identify and discuss the relationships between the three main approaches to defining the problem of mental disorders–mental health presented in this chapter.*
2. *What are the four main issues common to mental health policy debates and reforms currently taking place in Canada?*
3. *Outline and discuss the relationship between the anti-psychiatry movement and the psychiatric consumers–survivors movement.*
4. *The distinction between mental disorders and mental health problems is intended to avoid the two "blind alleys" of mental health policy debate. Outline and discuss.*

GLOSSARY

anti-psychiatry The view that psychiatry is a form of social control, not a medical specialty.

decarceration The thesis that the emptying of the mental hospitals was motivated more by economic and political interests of the dominant classes than by the interests of the mentally ill.

deinstitutionalization The process of shifting the treatment of mental illness from mental hospitals to the community in order to avoid the learned dependency and chronicity associated with long-term residence in bureaucratically organized institutions.

labelling theory The theory that mental illness is a social role assumed by individuals as a result of a social labelling process, particularly the process of psychiatric diagnosis.

mental illnesses Emotional, ideational, and behavioural abnormalities thought primarily to be caused by biochemical or neurological disorders.

mental patients' liberation–psychiatric survivors movement The most radical branch of the anti-psychiatry movement, which advocates for full citizenship rights for the mentally ill and emancipation from professional domination and control.

psychiatry The medical subspecialty that deals with the definition, classification, and treatment of mental illness.

psychosocial problems with living Emotional, ideational, and behavioural abnormalities thought to be primarily the result of traumatic experiences, faulty socialization, or stressful social and personal life experiences.

social drift theory The theory that the inverse relationship between social class and rates of mental illness is a result of intergenerational downward social drift, caused by the fact that the mentally ill are incapable of effectively performing social roles.

transinstitutionalization The process of shifting the mentally ill from one institution to another, particularly from mental hospitals to prisons and other long-term-care facilities where they receive little or no treatment.

RECOMMENDED READINGS

Cochrane, J., Durbin, J., & Goering, P. (1997). *Best practices in mental health reform.* Discussion paper prepared for the Federal/Provincial/Territorial Advisory Network on Mental Health. Ottawa: Health Canada. A summary of the common features of mental health reforms that have occurred since the 1980s and of the "best practices" to ensure successful reforms.

Dickinson, H.D. (1989). *The two psychiatries: The transformation of psychiatric work in Saskatchewan, 1905–1984.* Regina: Canadian Plains Research Centre. A case study of the ways in which the care and treatment of mental illness were transformed in Saskatchewan during the first three quarters of the twentieth century. The main argument is that psychiatry bifurcated into a medically dominated system of care and a system of care dominated by psychology and social work based upon different conceptions of the nature of mental disorders.

Epp, J. (1988). *Mental health for Canadians: Striking a balance.* Ottawa: Health and Welfare Canada. An attempt to apply the health promotion framework to the field of mental health; proposes concepts and strategies for finding a balance between a professionally dominated system of mental health care and a system premised on the rejection of professional dominance.

Scull, A. (1983). *Decarceration: Community treatment and the deviant — A radical view* (2nd ed.). Cambridge: Polity Press. A classic statement of the view that the emptying of the mental hospitals in the 1970s is best understood as the politically and economically motivated abandonment of the mentally ill and the substitution of one form of social control with another.

Szasz, T.S. (1972). *The myth of mental illness: Foundations of a theory of personal conduct.* Frogmore, UK: Paladin. An elucidation of the anti-psychiatry position that argues that "mental illness" is not really illness at all, but rather various psychosocial problems with living; thus, in this context, psychiatric treatment is more like torture than help.

REFERENCES

Bland, R.C. (1988). Prevalence of mental illness. *Annals of the Royal College of Physicians and Surgeons of Canada, 21,* 89–93.

Blishen, B.R. (1991). *Doctors in Canada: The changing world of medical practice.* Toronto: University of Toronto Press in association with Statistics Canada.

Boudreau, F. (1987). The vicissitudes of psychiatric intervention in Quebec. In E.M. Bennett (Ed.), *Social intervention, theory and practice* (pp. 295–323). Lewiston & Queenston: Edwin Mellen Press.

Boudreau, F. (1991a). Stakeholders as partners? The challenges of partnership in Quebec mental health policy. *Canadian Journal of Community Mental Health, 10,* 7–28.

Boudreau, F. (1991b). Partnership as a new strategy in mental health policy: The case of Quebec. *Journal of Health Politics, Policy and Law, 16,* 307–329.

Burstow, B., & Weitz, D. (Eds.). (1988). *Shrink resistant: The struggle against psychiatry in Canada.* Vancouver: New Star Books.

Busfield, J. (1986). *Managing madness: Changing ideas and practices.* London: Unwin Hyman.

Canadian Mental Health Association (CMHA). (1978). *Women and mental health in Canada: Strategies for change.* Toronto: Author.

Chamberlin, J. (1990). The ex-patient's movement: Where we've been and where we're going. In D. Cohen (Ed.), *Challenging the therapeutic state: Critical perspectives on psychiatry and the mental health system,* special issue of *The Journal of Mind and Behavior, 11*(3 & 4), 323–336.

Chesler, P. (1972). *Women and madness.* New York: Avon Books.

Cochrane, J., Durbin, J., & Goering, P. (1997). *Best practices in mental health reform.* Discussion paper prepared for the Federal/Provincial/Territorial Advisory Network on Mental Health. Ottawa: Health Canada.

Cohen S. (1985). *Visions of social control: Crime, punishment and classification.* Cambridge: Polity Press.

Conrad, P., & Schneider, J. (1980). *Deviance and medicalization: From badness to madness.* St. Louis: Mosby.

Dear, M., & Wolch, J. (1987). *Landscapes of despair: From deinstitutionalization to homelessness.* Princeton, NJ: Princeton University Press.

Dickinson, H.D. (1989). *The two psychiatries: The transformation of psychiatric work in Saskatchewan, 1905–1984.* Regina: Canadian Plains Research Centre.

Dickinson, H.D., & Andre, G. (1988). Community psychiatry: The institutional transformation of psychiatric practice. In B.S. Bolaria & H.D. Dickinson (Eds.), *The sociology of health care in Canada* (pp. 295–308). Toronto: Harcourt Brace Jovanovich.

Dohrenwend, D.P., & Dohrenwend, B.S. (1976). Sex differences in psychiatric disorder. *American Journal of Sociology, 81,* 1447–1454.

Epp, J. (1986). *Achieving health for all: A framework for health promotion.* Ottawa: Health and Welfare Canada.

Epp, J. (1988). *Mental health for Canadians: Striking a balance.* Ottawa: Health and Welfare Canada.

Faris, R., & Dunham, W. (1939). *Mental disorders in urban areas*. Chicago: University of Chicago Press.

Foucault, M. (1973). *Madness and civilization: A history of insanity in the age of reason*. New York: Vintage Books.

Freidson, E. (1970). *Profession of medicine: A study in the sociology of applied knowledge*. New York: Harper & Row.

Goffman, E. (1961). *Asylums: Essays on the social situation of mental patients and other inmates*. New York: Anchor Books.

Gove, W.R., & Tudor, J. (1973). Adult sex roles and mental illness. *American Journal of Sociology, 77*, 812–835.

Hardin, H. (1993, July 22). Uncivil liberties. *Vancouver Sun*, p. A15.

Health and Welfare Canada. (1990). *Mental health services in Canada, 1990*. Ottawa: Health and Welfare Canada.

Health Beat. (1992, May/June). Research for mental disorders gets shortchanged. *Natural Health: The Guide to Well-Being*, p. 20.

Health Edition on Line. (2001, February 23). Psychotherapy. *Miscellany*. http://www.healthedition.com/home.cfm.

Hollingshead, A., & Redlich, F. (1958). *Social class and mental illness*. New York: John Wiley & Sons.

Kessler, R. (1979). Stress, social status and psychological distress. *Journal of Health and Social Behavior, 20*, 259–272.

Kittrie, N. (1972). *The right to be different*. Baltimore: Penguin.

Kohn, M. (1977). *Class and conformity: A study in values* (2nd ed.). Chicago: University of Chicago Press.

Laing, R.D., & Esterson, A. (1964). *Sanity, madness and the family*. Vol. 1. *Families of schizo-phrenics*. London: Tavistock.

Langer, T., & Michael, S. (1963). *Life stress and mental health: The midtown Manhattan study*. London: Free Press Glencoe.

Leighton, D.C., Harding, J., Macklin, D., MacMillan, A., & Leighton, A. (1963). *The character of danger: Psychiatric symptoms in selected communities*. New York: Basic Books.

Lin, E., & Goering, P. (2000). *Fiscal changes for core mental health services delivered by fee-for-service physicians*. Institute for Clinical Evaluative Sciences (ICES), Atlas Reports, Uses of Health Services, Report 2. Toronto: ICES.

Lurie, S. (1984). More for the mind, have we got less? In M.D. Nair, R.C. Hain, & J.A. Draper (Eds.), *Issues in Canadian social services* (pp. 166–185). Toronto: Canadian Council on Social Development.

Macnaughton, E. (1992). Canadian mental health policy: The emergent picture. *Canada's Mental Health, 40*, 3–10.

Manning, N. (1989). *The therapeutic community movement: Charisma and routinization*. London: Routledge.

Nelson, G., Prilleltensky, I., Laurendeau, M.-C., & Powell, B. (1996). The prevention of mental health problems in Canada: A survey of provincial policies, structures, and pro-grams. *Canadian Psychology, 37*(3), 161–172.

Olsen, D. (1993). The movement. Unpublished paper, Department of Sociology and Anthropology, Carleton University.

Ralph, D. (1983). *Work and madness: The rise of community psychiatry*. Montreal: Black Rose Books.

Randhawa, J., & Riley, R. (1996, Spring). Mental health statistics, 1982–83 to 1993–94. *Health Reports, 7*(4), 55–61.

Scheff, T. (1984). *Being mentally ill: A sociological theory* (2nd ed.). New York: Aldine.

Scull, A. (1982). *Museums of madness: The social organization of insanity in nineteenth-century England.* Harmondsworth: Penguin.

Scull, A. (1983). *Decarceration: Community treatment and the deviant — A radical view* (2nd ed.). Cambridge: Polity Press.

Scull, A. (1991). Psychiatry and social control in the nineteenth and twentieth centuries. *History of Psychiatry, 2,* 149–169.

Showalter, E. (1985). *The female malady: Women, madness and English culture, 1830–1980.* New York: Pantheon Press.

Simmons, H. (1990). *Unbalanced: Mental health policy in Ontario, 1930–1989.* Toronto: Wall & Thompson.

Srole, L., Langer, T., Michael, S., Opler, M., & Rennie, T. (1962). *Mental health in the metropolis.* New York: McGraw-Hill.

System fails mentally ill offenders, say advocates. *Saskatoon Star Phoenix,* (2000, May 10). p. B6.

Szasz, T.S. (1972). *The myth of mental illness: Foundations of a theory of personal conduct.* Frogmore, UK: Paladin.

Trainor, J., Church, K., Pape, B., Pomeroy, E., Reville, D., Teft, B., Lakaski, C., & Renaud, L. (1992). Building a framework for support: Developing a sector-based model for people with serious mental illness. *Canada's Mental Health, 40,* 25–29.

Trainor, J., Shepherd, M., Boyle, K.M., Leff, A., & Crawford, E. (1997). Beyond the service paradigm: The impact and implications of consumer/survivor initiatives. *Psychiatric Rehabilitation Journal, 21*(2), 132–140.

Tyhurst, J.S., Chalke, F.C., Lawson, F.S., McNeel, B.H., Roberts, C.A., Taylor, G.C., Weil, R.J., & Griffin, J.D. (1963). *More for the mind: A study in psychiatric services in Canada.* Toronto: Canadian Mental Health Association.

Uniform Law Conference of Canada. (1987). *Proceedings of the sixty-ninth annual meeting: Appendix F — Uniform Mental Health Act.* Victoria, BC: Uniform Law Conference.

White, D., & Mercier, C. (1991). Reorienting mental health systems: The dynamics of policy and planning. *International Journal of Mental Health, 19,* 3–24.

20

Profits First: The Pharmaceutical Industry in Canada

JOEL LEXCHIN University Health Network

INTRODUCTION

The pharmaceutical industry is no different from any other enterprise in a capitalist economy; the primary motivation for making drugs is profit. The Code of Marketing Practice of the **Pharmaceutical Manufacturers Association of Canada** (PMAC), now called Canada's Research-Based Pharmaceutical Companies[1] states that "the Canadian innovative pharmaceutical industry is conscious of its unique position as a partner in the provision of prescription medications and services to the public" (1997, p. 1). The practical ethics of the industry are summed up in a quote from the president of PMAC: "The pharmaceutical industry has never claimed to be motivated by altruism, but rather by profit for survival" (Garton, May 26, 1980, personal communication).

This chapter will begin by exploring the contradiction between public good and private profits and examine, in depth, the profitability of the pharmaceutical industry. The next four sections will analyze some of the most significant factors contributing to the profits of the industry: the relationship between the state and the industry, the research efforts of the drug companies, the prices of drugs, and, finally, how industry promotion influences prescribing.

PRIVATE PROFIT VERSUS PUBLIC GOOD

Eli Lilly and Benoxaprofen

The incompatibility between public service and private profit becomes evident when the stated ethics of the industry clash with the realities of turning a profit. One example of how drug companies put profit above health involved Eli Lilly's anti-arthritis drug benoxaprofen. In 1980, this drug was marketed in Britain under the trade name Opren.[2] Lilly organized an aggressive promotional program for Opren, and very quickly the drug was enjoying large sales. However, shortly after the drug appeared on the shelves of British pharmacies, Lilly's British subsidiary informed British health officials of the first of eight deaths resulting from suspected adverse reactions to Opren that occurred between May 1, 1981, and January 1982.

In February 1982, nine months after the first known British death, benoxaprofen was evaluated by the Canadian Health Protection Branch (HPB) as safe for use in Canada.[3] In its submission to the HPB,[4] Lilly did not mention the eight deaths in Britain connected to benoxaprofen and omitted other information about other studies indicating potential problems with the drug. Lilly officials did not give any of this critical information about their product to the HPB until just before reports of the deaths in Britain were going to appear in the *British Medical Journal* (Regush, 1982, pp. A-1, A-6).

Bristol-Myers Squibb and Pravastatin

A more recent example of industry values is the lawsuit that Bristol-Myers Squibb (BMS) launched against the Canadian Coordinating Office for Health Technology Assessment (CCOHTA) in 1997. CCOHTA is an independent, nonprofit body that conducts evaluations of pharmaceuticals and medical technologies. In this case, CCOHTA was assessing a group of drugs called "statins," which are used to lower cholesterol. CCOHTA's position, backed up by an extensive review of the literature and by other medical bodies, was that all of the statins were equivalent and all would reduce complications associated with heart disease. BMS was concerned that such a conclusion would have negative financial implications for its statin Pravachol (pravastatin)[5] and went to court to block the publication of CCOHTA's report. The implications of this case went beyond the one report involved. What BMS was trying to do in defence of its profits was to stop the free flow of scientific information (Connection, 1998).

PROFITS IN THE PHARMACEUTICAL INDUSTRY

The Canadian subsidiaries of multinational drug companies, and the industry in general, have been extremely profitable. A 1983 report by the investment firm of Walwyn Stodgell Cochrane Murray Ltd. of Toronto called the pharmaceutical industry "a particularly attractive area for long-term investment. The field is characterized by high profitability and consistent growth. Favorable demographics assure that this growth will continue well into the foreseeable future" (1983, p. 142). This opinion is reinforced by Kenneth R. Kulju, senior health care analyst with Fahnestock & Co. in New York, who considers pharmaceutical stocks to be the premier investment group in the market (Livingston, 1988, p. 61). Table 1 shows the accuracy of this statement. From 1988 to 1995, the average pretax profit margin on equity was 29.6 percent for the pharmaceutical industry, compared with 10.7 percent for all manufacturing industries.

Profits as an Accounting Illusion?

The figures in Table 1 make it difficult to deny that there are huge profits to be derived from manufacturing pharmaceuticals. But the PMAC repeatedly claims that the high profits are an accounting illusion created by the standard accounting practice of treating **research and development (R&D)** expenditures as expenses against current income rather than capitalizing these outlays as an investment item (1975, p. 18). However, as

TABLE 20.1 *Rate of Return on Shareholders' Equity, Before Taxes, 1988–1995 (Percent)*

Year	Pharmaceutical Industry	All Manufacturing
1988	54.1	21.7
1989	40.1	15.5
1990	26.6	5.8
1991	31.7	0*
1992	24.6	2.6
1993	20.8	7.1
1994	21.5	14.4
1995	17.2	18.2
Average	29.6	10.7

*There was no return on shareholders' equity.

Source: Special run by Statistics Canada.

Gary Gereffi, professor of sociology at Duke University, makes clear, the accounting explanation of high profitability is inadequate, for several reasons (1983, p. 192).

First, the accounting bias is not just confined to the pharmaceutical industry but is present in all "discovery-intensive" industries, such as oil and gas, and in industries with high levels of research and development expenditures. Under certain circumstances, the accounting rate of return could actually understate rather than overstate the "real" or economic rate of return. Second, by allowing pharmaceutical companies to treat research and development costs as a current accounting expense, the government, in effect, is granting them an indirect fiscal subsidy to encourage their risk-taking efforts. This accounting method thus serves to raise the drug firm's profitability in fact as well as on paper.

Temin showed that even after "correcting" profits by treating research and development expenditures as an investment, the drug industry was still one of the most profitable industries around (1979, p. 445). More recent data from the United States came to the same conclusion. Even after making adjustments for differences among various industries, over the period 1976–87 returns in the pharmaceutical industry were 2–3 percent higher than in nonpharmaceutical firms (Office of Technology Assessment, 1993).

The High Cost of Research as a Justification for High Profits

As well as using accounting methodology as an explanation for high profits, the industry uses the high cost of research as a justification. Currently, spokespeople for the industry claim that it costs more than US $500 million[6] to discover and bring a new drug to market and state that they only recover their R&D costs in one third of new products. These claims are based on the results of two studies (DiMasi et al., 1991; Grabowski & Vernon, 1990). However, both of these analyses rest on a shared set of major limitations that are never articulated by PMAC and its member companies. These articles only consider R&D costs for **new chemical entities** (NCEs), which have been researched and developed "in house" by American-owned companies. The sample leaves out new drugs that were developed conjointly with, or entirely by, government, non-profit institutions, and universities; drugs licensed from other companies; and newly marketed drugs that are not NCEs, such as long-acting versions of a drug, combination products, or other new formulations of existing products. In fact, according to the DiMasi paper, R&D outlays for licensed or acquired NCEs were only one quarter of those for self-originated NCEs. Only about 40 percent of all the NCEs introduced by American-owned companies are self-originated (DiMasi et al., 1991).

The United States Office of Technology Assessment (OTA) has recalculated the figures on the costs of bringing a new drug to market, including the tax write-offs[7] that companies acquire by virtue of doing research (1993). Based on its analysis, the OTA concluded that the total cost to the point of market introduction was between $140 million and $194 million, substantially lower than the figure DeMasi produced. Furthermore, according to the OTA, new products bring in, on average, $230 million, or at least $36 million more than the R&D investment.

THE PHARMACEUTICAL INDUSTRY AND THE STATE

Compulsory Licensing and Patents

During the 1960s, a series of three reports all pointed out that drug prices in Canada were among the highest in the world. All three reports identified **patent protection** as one of the major reasons for this situation (Canada, House of Commons, 1967; Restrictive Trade Practices Commission, 1963; Royal Commission on Health Services, 1964).[8] The decision of the Liberal government of the time was to extend **compulsory licensing**[9] and allow companies to receive a licence to import a drug into Canada, rather than having to manufacture it here.

BILL C-102

The Pharmaceutical Manufacturers Association of Canada (PMAC) mounted a campaign against the legislation, Bill C-102, which cost $200 000 to $250 000 annually (Lang, 1974). Each PMAC official was given a list of the top 100 companies in Canada, along with the names and curricula vitae of their chief executive officers, and urged to contact these people with the message that Bill C-102 was bad for Canadian business. When the bill was in the committee stage, PMAC supplied the opposition Progressive Conservatives with ammunition to use against anti-industry witnesses (Lang, 1974). However, despite this intensive lobbying and propaganda effort, Bill C-102 was passed by the House of Commons.

Despite the multinational companies' strong and deeply rooted opposition to compulsory licensing, there is no good evidence that their economic position was adversely affected by it. Based on figures in the Report of the Commission of Inquiry into the Pharmaceutical Industry (the Eastman Report), in 1983 the multinationals had lost only 3.1 percent of the Canadian market to **generic competition** (1985, p. 158).

BILL C-22

The industry continued its vigorous lobbying efforts against compulsory licensing, and with the election of Brian Mulroney and the Progressive Conservatives as a government in 1984 it found an ally. The Conservatives wanted a free trade deal with the United States, and the multinationals were able to get the American government to apply pressure in their favour (Sawatsky & Cashore, 1986).

The Conservatives continually and vigorously denied any connection between the free trade agreement and changes in compulsory licensing (Crane, 1986, p. B1; Andre, 1986; Howard, 1987, p. A13), but the facts make their denials hard to credit. Bill Merkin, the U.S. deputy chief negotiator in the free trade talks, said:

> Ottawa didn't want it [intellectual property] to be in the free trade negotiations. They didn't want to *appear* to be negotiating that away as part of the free trade agreement. Whatever changes they were going to make, they wanted them to be viewed as, quote, 'in Canada's interest.'... It was a high priority issue for us. We were not above flagging the importance of resolving the issue [to the Canadian negotiators] for the success of the overall negotiations." (quoted in McQuaig, 1991, p. 136)

The Americans gave the final proof of the linkage between the two issues the day after the successful conclusion of the free trade talks. A U.S. summary of the agreement said the accord contained a clause "to make progress toward establishing adequate and effective protection of pharmaceuticals in Canada by liberalizing compulsory licensing provisions" (quoted in Auerbach, 1987, p. G2). It was only after Conservative politicians demanded the removal of that section that it was dropped from the final text of the agreement.

In return for free trade with the Americans, the Conservatives produced Bill C-22 and eventually passed it in December 1987. The essence of the bill was that it gave companies introducing new drugs a minimum of 7 years, and usually 10 years, of protection from compulsory licensing.

BILL C-91

Bill C-22 was not all that the Americans wanted. One senior official in the U.S. Administration said, "We want better than that [bill] in a free-trade agreement," while to another senior official it was "barely acceptable." The U.S. Pharmaceutical Manufacturers Association was willing to support the bill but said that the U.S. industry "would like to see a similar level of protection as in Western Europe and the U.S.... Canada's out of synch" (quoted in Lewington, 1987, p. A1).

The final demise for compulsory licensing came with the passage of Bill C-91 in 1993.[10] In this case, it was the Canadian eagerness to sign the NAFTA and GATT agreements that coincided with the interests of the drug industry. Although there is an argument that compulsory licensing would be theoretically possible under these agreements (Dillon, 1997), the Canadian government used them as the grounds for completely eliminating compulsory licensing.

While they were in opposition, the Liberals vehemently opposed Bill C-91. During the debate, David Dingwall said: "The Tory agenda is clear, one primary objective, which is to put money in the multinational corporations at any cost. Consumers be damned, research and development be damned, the health care system be damned, the objective is the bottom dollar of the multinational corporations who happen to be driving the agenda of the neo-Conservatives who are opposite this House [of Parliament]" (CBC Radio, 1997). When the Liberals were elected in 1993, Dingwall became minister of health, and by 1997 his attitude was, "we are now part and parcel of the international community in terms of our commitments to NAFTA. And I don't want to raise a false expectation that with the review of Bill C-91, which is coming up in 1997, that we are going to flush the intellectual property rights which Canada has supported from day one and will continue to support" (CBC Radio, 1997).

Examples of the Liberal reluctance to tamper with the new patent regimen are not hard to find. One section of Bill C-22 mandated a 10-year review of its effects. This review, which also incorporated a review of Bill C-91, took place in the late winter of 1997. The initial draft of the report from the Standing Committee on Industry, which conducted the review, contained a recommendation that the government "ask the World Trade Organization [set up after the conclusion of the GATT negotiations] to re-evaluate 20 year patents for drugs" (Standing Committee on Industry, 1997). By the time the final report was issued a few weeks later, that recommendation had been dropped.

The Pharmaceutical Industry and the Health Protection Branch

CLIENTELE PLURALISM

The industry has exercised its influence in the HPB through a method of interaction, a policy network, termed **clientele pluralism** (Atkinson and Coleman, 1989). This is a situation in which the state has a high degree of concentration of power in one agency (the HPB), but a low degree of autonomy. With respect to pharmaceuticals, in Canada, government regulation of drug safety, quality, and efficacy is almost solely the responsibility of the HPB. But the state does not possess the wherewithal to undertake the elaborate clinical and preclinical trials required to meet the objective of providing safe and effective medications. Nor is the state willing or able to mobilize the resources that would be necessary to undertake these tasks. Therefore, a tacit political decision is made to relinquish some authority to the drug manufacturers, especially with respect to information that forms the basis on which regulatory decisions are made.

On the other hand, the PMAC, the association representing nearly all of the multinational companies operating in Canada, is highly mobilized to assume a role in making and implementing drug policy through an elaborate committee structure, the ability to act on behalf of its members, and the capacity to bind member firms to agreements. In clientele pluralism, the state relinquishes some of its authority to private sector actors, who, in turn, pursue objectives with which officials are in broad agreement (Atkinson & Coleman, 1989).

Not only does the state turn over some of its authority, but the objectives being pursued are often jointly developed between PMAC and the relevant state bureaucracy, in this case the HPB. One example of delegation of government authority to the industry is control of promotional practices. This area has had a long and contentious history, but also a long history of cooperation between government and industry. Governments in nearly all industrialized countries, including Canada, have ceded day-to-day control over some or all aspects of pharmaceutical promotion to voluntary national industry associations. In turn, these associations have developed codes of marketing which their member companies are expected to adhere to. In Canada, promotion is regulated by two codes: one has been developed and is administered by an independent organization, the

Pharmaceutical Advertising Advisory Board (PAAB), and the second is the Code of Marketing Practices from PMAC. Despite reasonable-sounding provisions, both codes suffer from serious enforcement problems (Lexchin, 1997a; Mintzes, 1998), which results in a significant amount of deceptive promotion (Lexchin, 1994).

UNDERFUNDING AND COST RECOVERY

In recent years, there has been a fundamental change in the relationship between the HPB and the multinational pharmaceutical industry. Not only does the state still relinquish some of its authority to private sector actors, but the private sector (the drug companies) is now the major funder of the branch of the HPB, the Therapeutic Products Programme (TPP), that regulates the industry.

Downsizing the role of government played into the obsession with the federal deficit. The government saw nothing wrong with decreasing funding to the HPB from $237 million in 1993–94 to $136 million in 1996–97, with a projection for 1999–2000 of just $118 million (Kennedy, 1997). As resources for the HPB were progressively cut, the agency turned to the drug companies themselves for funds to keep operating, a process termed **cost recovery**. Companies pay an annual fee for each drug they market and fees for the evaluation of drug submissions, for licensing manufacturing establishments, and for a number of other services. Industry now contributes 70 percent of the $49 million in revenue that the TPP expects to receive in 1997–98 (Therapeutic Products Programme, 1997).

INCREASING INDUSTRY INFLUENCE

There are signs in a couple of areas that this combination of industry funding and a civil service with a bias for uncritical cooperation with industry is leading to a reorientation of HPB policy that is even more favourable to industry than in the past. Until March 1997, government controlled advertising of over-the-counter products to consumers. All promotion through radio or television had to be precleared by HPB staff, and print advertisements were reviewed if there were complaints about them. In April 1997, those functions were turned over to a private sector agency, Advertising Standards Canada, a move that will probably lead to a loosening of standards for promotion of this set of products.

Government is not just weakening the controls over OTC promotion. Currently, regulations ban direct-to-consumer advertising (DTCA) of prescription drugs, but for the past few years industry has been pushing the HPB to give up that restriction. Merck Frosst, one of the largest multinationals operating in Canada, has gone so far as to assert that the industry has a legal right to advertise prescription drugs directly to the public (Merck Frosst Canada, 1996). There are strong grounds for believing that DTCA would lead to inappropriate prescribing, greater overall expenditures on prescription drugs, and adverse health outcomes for consumers (Lexchin, 1997b). In 1996, the HPB held a workshop on the topic of DTCA, and apparently the only thing that is stalling further moves in this direction is the provinces' concern that DTCA would drive up the cost of provincial drug programs.

Perhaps the most revealing statement about this reorientation of the relationship between the HPB and the industry came from Dann Michols, director general of the TPP. In an internal bulletin distributed to HPB staff in February 1997, he discussed the question of who is the HPB's client. In the context of cost recovery, he advised staff that "the client is the direct recipient of your services. In many cases this is the person or company who pays for the service." The one-page document focused on service to industry, relegating the public to the secondary status of "stakeholder" or "beneficiary" (Michols, 1997).

Research And Development

As part of the trade-off for Bills C-22 and C-91, the industry — mostly the multinational sector — has increased its investment in R&D from 6.1 percent of sales in 1988 to 11.5 percent in 1997, so that by the end of 1997 the industry was spending $679.2 million (Cdn) in this area (Patented Medicine Prices Review Board, 1998). One point that both the industry and the government neglect to mention is that these are only 60-cent dollars, owing to a 40 percent tax write-off on R&D (Department of Foreign Affairs and International Trade and Industry Canada, 1996). Therefore, the actual cost to the pharmaceutical companies is only about $407 million. The question that has yet to be answered is the value of that R&D to the scientific community and to the Canadian public.

Scientific Value of Increased R&D

An early attempt to explore the first part of the question was a 1990 survey of 40 key medical figures engaged in pharmaceutical research in Canada. They were happy about the availability of funding, but they also expressed a number of misgivings about drug industry funding: 90 percent foresaw a likely conflict of interest; 80 percent deemed pharmaceutical clinical research "me too" research; while 75 percent saw it as "might as well" research; and 40 percent were worried about a potential delay in the publication of unfavourable results (Taylor, 1991).

Is the Canadian public getting value from the increase in R&D spending? From a review of the products that the industry has introduced since Bill C-22 passed in 1987, the answer may be no. From January 1991 to December 1997, a total of 577 new patented drug products were marketed in Canada for human use. Out of that number, only 50, or just under 9 percent, were felt to be either "breakthrough" medications or substantial improvements over existing therapies, with the rest being line extensions (50 percent) or moderate, little, or no therapeutic improvements (41 percent) (Patented Medicine Prices Review Board, 1998, Figure 16).

Moreover, since the therapeutically important drugs were not developed just for the Canadian market, they would have become available in Canada with or without the new R&D money that has been invested in Canada. Whether the Canadian research community was involved in the development of these drugs and whether that involvement may have speeded up their arrival on the market are questions that bear investigating. The answers will affect the assessment of the value of the increased R&D.

Does Industry R&D Reflect Societal Goals?

On a more fundamental level, the value of pharmaceutical R&D to Canadian society cannot be answered by counting the number of new important drugs. Are seven new drugs per year better than a government policy aimed at increasing R&D to improve agricultural output or to develop better mining technology? In what direction does Canadian society want to direct R&D? These issues were never publicly debated before Bills C-22 and C-91 were passed.

In an article in the *New England Journal of Medicine,* VanWoert stated that a representative of the United States Pharmaceutical Manufacturers Association confirmed that, in general, drug companies do not undertake research on relatively uncommon diseases, because drugs for them would generate insufficient profits (1978, p. 904). The same sentiments were echoed in 1980 by Joseph Williams, president of Warner Lambert, who was quoted by Gray as saying that "Our [Warner Lambert's] focus is to develop major drugs for major markets" (1981, p. 791).

Research funded by the pharmaceutical industry may leave many questions untouched. In a recent article, Dr. Patricia Baird, former chair of the Royal Commission on New Reproductive Technologies, noted that in the area of infertility, drug companies were only likely to fund research that would lead to a new patentable drug, ignoring topics such as behavioural factors involved in the cause and prevention of infertility (Baird, 1996). Do we want most of the money available for pharmaceutical research to be just narrowly directed into the development of new patentable medications, the main priority of the pharmaceutical industry, or do we also want to prioritize areas such as improving patient compliance with medications or reasons for inappropriate physician-prescribing practices?

DRUG PRICES

Effect of Generic Competition on Prices

The first generic competitor in the Canadian market typically enters at a price discount of about 25–30 percent, compared with the original product; when there are four or five generic competitors, there is a difference of 50–60 percent between the brand name product and the least expensive generic version (Lexchin, 1993) (see Figure 1). Before Bill C-22, these generic equivalents of best-selling drugs would appear within 5 or 6 years after the brand name drug was marketed. Now companies have a monopoly for about 12 years.[11] Not only is the entry of generic products delayed by about 7 years, but also, by the time they appear, sales of the brand name drug are usually starting to decline and therefore the saving from the generic product is less.[12]

According to figures in the Eastman Report, in 1982 generic competition had resulted in estimated savings to the Canadian public of at least $211 million; in other words, in the absence of generic competition, Canada's drug bill would have increased from $1.53 billion to almost $1.74 billion (Commission of Inquiry on the Pharmaceutical Industry, 1985). A report produced for the Canadian Drug Manufacturers Association, the organization representing Canadian-owned generic companies, estimated that the cumulative costs of Bill C-91 from 1993 to 2000 would be $1.7 billion, and by 2010 the cumulative costs from 1993 would be $4.0 billion (Schondelmeyer, 1993).

FIGURE 20.1

Relationship between Number of Companies Marketing a Drug and Price Spread between Least Expensive and Most Expensive Versions of a Drug (number of drug preparations in parentheses)

....

Source: Lexchin (1993).

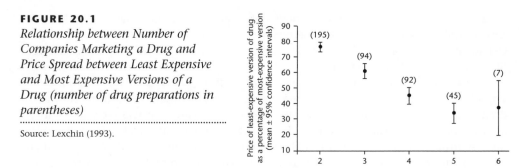

Patented Medicine Prices Review Board

Bill C-22 established the **Patented Medicine Prices Review Board** (PMPRB), which had a mandate to set the introductory price for new patented drugs and to limit the rate of rise in the price of patented medicines to the rate of inflation. According to reports from the PMPRB, since Bill C-22 passed in 1987, the rise in the price of patented drugs at the manufacturers' level has dropped below the rate of inflation, and since 1994 the price of patented drugs has actually deflated (Patented Medicine Prices Review Board, 1998, Figure 2).

DEDICATING PATENTS

The industry has been quick to seize on these changes as proof that it is keeping down drug prices, but these figures do not necessarily give a completely accurate picture. Since January 1, 1988, when Bill C-22 was proclaimed, multinational pharmaceutical companies dedicated 449 patents on a total of 136 drug products.[13] By virtue of these dedications, the prices of the products were no longer subject to the jurisdiction of the PMPRB. A recent report from the PMPRB revealed that following patent dedication, at least 43 of the 136 drug products were priced above the level allowed by the PMPRB. The estimated cost to Canadian consumers for the period January 1, 1989, to July 1, 1995, as a result of these dedications is almost $40 million (Patented Medicine Prices Review Board, 1995). (The PMPRB changed its practice after January 30, 1995, and its pricing guidelines now apply to products with patents dedicated.)

INTERNATIONAL COMPARISONS

The PMPRB compares Canadian prices with those in seven other countries (France, Germany, Italy, Sweden, Switzerland, the United Kingdom, and the United States) to arrive at an acceptable introductory price for new products. Comparing Canadian prices with those in the seven selected countries might not tell the complete story about the cost of drugs in Canada relative to other industrialized countries. It is interesting to speculate how the comparator group of countries was chosen. None of the documents examined by the author mention the criteria used to select this specific group of seven countries; it is common knowledge, however, that prices in Germany, Switzerland, and the United States tend to be among the highest in the industrialized world.

Choosing a different group of countries could dramatically alter the Canadian introductory price. A recent survey by Consumers International gives some hints of the magnitude of the differences between countries. Prices for 13 common brand name products were gathered from a group of developed countries. The average price in France, Germany, Italy, Switzerland, the United Kingdom, and the United States (six of the seven countries that the PMPRB uses) was more than 50 percent greater than in another group of six developed countries — Australia, Belgium, Finland, Greece, the Netherlands, and New Zealand (Balasubramaniam, 1995). Although the survey covered only a small number of products and has other methodological flaws, it does suggest that perhaps the comparator group of countries used by the PMPRB was chosen specifically to allow relatively high introductory Canadian prices.

High Introductory Prices

These high introductory prices are one reason that the cost of a prescription in Canada has risen dramatically since 1987. Although the PMPRB regulates the price of patented medicines, it has no power over the cost of a prescription. The average price per prescription (excluding the dispensing fee) in Ontario has gone from $24.58 in 1993 to $27.74 in 1997, an annual rise of 3.1 percent, compared with an increase in the consumers price index of 1.4 percent. Over half of the rise in prescription costs is due to the introduction of new drugs, specifically new (since 1987) patented medications. Prices for prescriptions containing new patented medications rose at a rate of 20.9 percent per annum between 1993–97, compared with 6.6 percent for prices for prescriptions of existing patented drugs and 4.1 percent for unpatented drugs (Green Shield Canada, 1998) (see Table 2). Physicians have been substituting these newer, more expensive drugs for older, less costly ones, leading to the rise in the cost of the average prescription.

TABLE 20.2 *Increase in Prescription Prices, 1993–1997**

	Cost per Prescription ($)		
	New Patented Drugs	Existing Patented Drugs	Unpatented Drugs
1993	36.03	49.43	17.12
1994	39.98	52.45	17.94
1995	46.76	56.83	18.28
1996	61.18	59.15	18.83
1997	76.88	63.70	20.10
Average annual increase 1993–97	20.9%	6.6%	4.1%

*Includes manufacturer and wholesale distribution costs; excludes dispensing fee.

Source: Green Shield Canada (1998).

The Value of New Drugs

If the new, more expensive medications were also more effective, then perhaps their prices could be justified, and similarly it would be understandable why they were replacing older, less expensive drugs. Elsewhere I have shown that for anti-hypertensives, anti-ulcer medications, and nonsteroidal anti-inflammatories (drugs used in the treatment of arthritis), the therapeutic gain from newly introduced drugs in these categories is marginal, but they are priced at a premium compared with older drugs (Lexchin, 1992). The adoption of these products by physicians, in the absence of a strong clinical rationale for doing so, makes a compelling case for the need to promote cost-effective therapy not only for health reasons, but also to restrain the rise in prescription prices.

THE PHARMACEUTICAL INDUSTRY AND THE MEDICAL PROFESSION

Doctors, their associations, and their journals are all prime objects of attention for the drug companies. Drugs with high introductory prices and 12 years of patent protection are no good to the companies if they are not being prescribed. Doctors are the ones who prescribe, and it is these prescriptions that translate into sales for the pharmaceutical houses. Nearly every doctor engaged in clinical medicine will prescribe, but a simple willingness to prescribe is not enough for the drug companies. In order to increase sales, and profits, the industry wants, and needs, more from doctors. Prominent among the strategies it uses for expanding sales and profits is to encourage the medical profession to look first to drug therapy for medical problems. The industry tries to present an image that will make the medical profession sympathetic to the claims the industry makes for its products and willing to take the industry's side against legislation the industry sees as hostile to its interests. In short, the pharmaceutical industry needs a medical profession as an ally; a medical profession that sees the industry's goals as being harmonious with its own.

In order to achieve this alliance, the industry literally wines and dines doctors: evening seminars are run by drug companies accompanied by a free bar and a free meal. Drug companies underwrite the cost of medical meetings, limiting physicians' out-of-pocket expenses. They fly doctors to meetings in expensive resorts and pay for their food and rooms. Although both the medical profession and the pharmaceutical industry have codes prohibiting paying for travel and accommodation, the companies knowingly violate these codes (Lexchin, 1999). All of these activities are sponsored by individual companies, and although the gifts almost always bear the name of one of the company's products, the aim of all this largesse is not solely to sell a particular drug. The companies, and by extension the industry as a whole, are after the goodwill of the doctors. They want to establish a positive view of the industry in the doctors' minds, to build and maintain the needed alliance with the medical profession.

It is eminently obvious why the drug industry wants an alliance with physicians; it is less clear why doctors should be willing to enter into such an alliance. The various gifts that doctors receive from the industry are certainly one factor, but probably a very minor one. It may be possible to buy the favour of some doctors, but not the vast majority. More important is the industry's support for various projects backed by physicians, such as the organ donation program and the research funding that comes from the drug companies;

but once again these activities directly affect only a relatively small number of doctors. There are, however, interactions with the drug companies that affect, and are appreciated by, the majority of doctors. Drug company funding of **continuing medical education** is one, and the personal visits from **detailers** are another (Woods, 1986).

Continuing Medical Education

Continuing medical education (CME) is the general term used for medical education that takes place after physicians start to practise. Although it can take many forms, meetings and conferences are the mainstays of CME. Nearly all forms of CME in Canada are partially or fully funded either directly or indirectly by the pharmaceutical industry. Even at conferences run by organizations such as the College of Family Physicians of Canada, the money that drug companies spend to rent booths covers a large portion of the cost of such events. Physicians have come to expect to pay relatively low costs for attending CME events because of such sponsorship.

Meetings and conferences run by universities and hospitals will almost always have rules that are supposed to ensure that the proceedings are insulated against influence by the pharmaceutical industry. Topics and speakers should be at the discretion of the individuals or groups organizing the event, not the company paying for it. Despite these precautions, there is evidence that biases still exist.

An analysis was performed to compare the content of two CME courses funded by two different drug companies. In both courses, the clinical effects noted for the company drug were more likely to be positive than for the noncompany drugs. The few statements directly comparing the drugs usually indicated that the company drug was the better drug (Bowman, 1986). A second study looked at prescribing immediately before and 6 months after doctors attended three separate CME courses. In each case, prescriptions for the drugs made by the sponsoring companies went up significantly more than did prescriptions for similar drugs that were not manufactured by the sponsoring company (Bowman & Pearle, 1988).

Pharmaceutical Promotion

Doctors are prime objects of attention for the multinational subsidiaries.[14] These companies spend 16–17 percent of sales on promoting drugs to doctors, compared with about 12 percent on research. Multinationals account for 83 percent of annual sales of $7.5 billion (*Scrip*, 1999); thus, spending on promotion is probably just over $1 billion per year. The companies would not spend so lavishly on promotion unless the tactic worked, and it does. The more intensively a product is advertised in journals, the greater its market share (Montgomery & Silk, 1972; Leffler, 1981; Krupka & Vener, 1985). The more physicians remember a journal ad, the more likely they are to prescribe the product (Walton, 1980; Healthcare Communications Inc., 1989).

DETAILERS

Promotion takes many forms, including journal advertising, direct mailings to doctors, posters, and sponsoring dinner meetings, but the most effective method is the use of sales representatives, or detailers — men and women who go from office to office to try to convince doctors to use their companies' products. Over 50 percent of the promotion budget is spent on salaries and expenses related to detailing. As might be expected, detailers are not objective sources of information.

Studies analyzing the quality of the information that they give have been conducted in Australia, Finland, and the United States either by audiotaping detailers' presentations (with their consent) or by having doctors fill out surveys immediately after seeing detailers. Although detailers usually mentioned the indications for their drugs, the vast majority of the time they did not spontaneously bring up prices, side effects, or contraindications. The American study found that more than 10 percent of the information given out by detailers was inaccurate (Lexchin, 1997c).

Eighty-five to 90 percent of doctors in Canada (Williams & Cockerill, 1990; Shin, Haynes, & Johnston, 1993) see detailers, on average about once every second week, and sales representatives are family physicians' second most frequently used source for drug information (Angus Reid Group, 1991).

The faculty at McMaster University became so concerned about possible adverse educational effects of contacts between detailers and residents in the internal medicine program that these interactions were essentially prohibited during working hours in the hospital (Education Council, Residency Training Programme in Internal Medicine, 1993).

OVERRELIANCE ON PROMOTION

Canadian physicians frequently use various sorts of promotion as a source for drug information, even though they don't always perceive it as credible (Angus Reid Group, 1991). The problem is that studies have consistently shown that the more that doctors rely on promotion, the less rational is their prescribing (Haayer, 1982; Ferry et al., 1985; Berings et al., 1994; Caudill et al., 1996). Even prescribers who think that they rely on scientific literature for their knowledge can be influenced by promotional sources without being aware of it (Avorn, Chen, & Hartley, 1982).

CONCLUSION

The thesis of this chapter has been that the driving force behind the pharmaceutical industry is the profit motive.

When profit and health considerations come into conflict with profit, as they did with Lilly and benoxaprofen or Bristol-Myers Squibb and pravastatin, then profit wins.

Making drugs is a very profitable venture in Canada. Profit levels in the pharmaceutical industry are double those in manufacturing in general, and this level is not due to an accounting "illusion," nor is it justified by research and development costs. Profits remain high even after considering differences in accounting practices, and the high R&D costs only apply to a subset of all the new drugs that are marketed.

The high level of profits is the result of a combination of five factors: the patent system, the relationship between the industry and the HPB, the type of R&D that the industry undertakes, drug prices, and finally, promotion to doctors.

Canada used to control drug costs through compulsory licensing, but that system was destroyed as a result of free trade deals with the United States and later because of GATT and NAFTA. Because the HPB traditionally had few resources, it existed in a clientele pluralist relationship with the industry, whereby certain functions, such as control over promotion, were turned over to the industry. In the past few years, the HPB has had its funding cut back even further and has turned to cost recovery to fund its operations. This development has created a situation in which the industry can exercise even more control over the functions of the HPB.

Although more pharmaceutical R&D is being done in Canada since Bill C-22 was passed, the scientific value of that research has never been systematically evaluated, and most of the products the industry brings to market do not represent major therapeutic gains. Instead, the industry directs its research efforts into areas that promise the greatest financial gain. Allowing industry goals to guide medical research is not always in the public interest.

The PMPRB has had a moderating influence on the price of patented medications, but its powers are limited, and despite the levelling off of prices, the cost of a prescription has continued to climb. Prescription prices are rising because doctors substitute newer, more expensive products for older, less costly ones. In many cases, this substitution cannot be justified, because the newer drugs are not more effective or any safer.

The pharmaceutical industry depends on physicians to prescribe its products, and as a result tries to form a close alliance with doctors in a variety of ways, including funding continuing medical education and spending heavily on promotion. Although there are rules in place to try to ensure that the information given out at meetings and conferences is not influenced by company sponsorship, biases still appear to exist.

One of the main reasons why doctors are switching from older, less costly products to newer and more expensive ones is because of the $1 billion per year that the multinational industry spends on promotion. Canadian physicians use promotion as a source of information about drugs, and the more they rely on promotion, the less rational they are as prescribers.

STUDY QUESTIONS

1. *How can the contradictions between the profit motive and the public interest be reconciled in the area of research and development?*
2. *What are the ethical implications when the interests of the public and private corporations are in competition, as may be the case with new drug approvals?*
3. *Should drug companies continue to fund the majority of the costs of continuing medical education? What would be the consequences for medical care if drug company funding were restricted and, as a result, doctors' attendance at these events declined?*
4. *Assuming that pharmaceutical promotion will continue to exist, what mechanisms could be used to ensure that it is accurate and unbiased?*
5. *Discuss whether the increase in research and development in Canada justifies the abolition of compulsory licensing.*

GLOSSARY

clientele pluralism A situation in which the state has a high degree of concentration of power in one agency, but a low degree of autonomy.

compulsory licensing   Granting a permit that effectively negates a patent. Theoretically, the company owning the patent on a drug would be a monopoly seller until the patent expired. However, if other companies apply for and are granted a compulsory licence against a drug, they can then market their own version of that drug before the patent has expired.

continuing medical education Activities that doctors undertake to keep their medical knowledge up to date.

cost recovery An annual fee paid by companies to the Therapeutic Products Programme for each drug that they market and for the evaluation of new drug submissions. This money is used to fund the majority of the operating costs of the TPP.

detailers Sales representatives for drug companies who visit doctors in their offices and attempt to convince physicians to prescribe their companies' products.

generic competition Competition with brand name products by generics that are usually priced at least 25 percent lower.

new chemical entities A class of new drugs, consisting of entirely new molecules that have not previously existed.

patent protection Protection from competition for a period of 20 years from the date that the patent was filed.

Patented Medicine Prices Review Board An independent, quasi-judicial body created by Parliament in 1987, when Bill C-22 was passed. The PMPRB regulates the introductory price of new patented medications and the rate of rise in the price of patented medicines.

Pharmaceutical Manufacturers Association of Canada An association that represents almost all of the multinational pharmaceutical companies operating in Canada, as well as some Canadian-owned biotechnology companies.

research and development/R&D The process of discovering a new drug and doing the testing necessary to bring it to market.

RECOMMENDED READINGS

Inquiry on the pharmaceutical industry. (1985). Ottawa: Minister of Supply and Services Canada. A comprehensive look into the economic aspects of the pharmaceutical industry and a discussion of all of the major issues regarding profits, compulsory licensing, and drug prices.

Mintzes, B. (1998, July). *Paper tiger or toothless tabby? Regulation of prescription drug promotion in Canada.* Health Policy Research Unit Discussion Paper Series (HPRU 98:6D), University of British Columbia. An up-to-date examination of how prescription drug promotion is controlled in Canada, including a critical analysis of the weakness of the codes of the Pharmaceutical Advertising Advisory Board and the Pharmaceutical Manufacturers Association of Canada.

Morgan, S.A. (1998). Issues for Canadian pharmaceutical policy. In *Striking a balance: Health care systems in Canada and elsewhere. Papers commissioned by the National Forum on Health.* Sainte-Foy, QC: Editions MultiMondes. Broad directions for the pharmaceutical policy in Canada, based on the structure and dynamics of the pharmaceutical industry; brings to light some of the economic and political incentives and constraints faced by major players in the industry.

Patented Medicine Prices Review Board. (1998). *Tenth annual report: For the year ended December 31, 1997*. Ottawa: Supply and Services Canada. A concise compilation of trends in the prices of patented medicines and the volume of research and development undertaken by the pharmaceutical industry.

Pharmaceutical Inquiry of Ontario. (1990). *Prescriptions for health*. Toronto: Author. A report commissioned because of the steep rise in the cost of the Ontario government drug program; examines the effectiveness of the drugs listed on the government formulary and the role of physicians and pharmacists in delivering cost-effective care.

REFERENCES

Andre, H. (1986, December 16). Notes for opening remarks to legislative committee on Bill C-22 by the Honourable Harvie Andre, Minister of Consumer and Corporate Affairs Canada, House of Commons.

Angus Reid Group. (1991, April). *Credibility and the marketing mix*. Toronto: Angus Reid Group.

Atkinson, M.M., & Coleman, W.D. (1989). *The state, business, and industrial change in Canada*. Toronto: University of Toronto Press.

Auerbach, S. (1987, October 17). U.S. bowed to Canadian demands to change pact. *Washington Post*, p. G2.

Avorn, J., Chen, M., & Hartley, R. (1982). Scientific versus commercial sources of influence on the prescribing behavior of physicians. *American Journal of Medicine, 73*, 4–8.

Baird, P.A. (1996). Funding medical and health-related research in the public interest. *Canadian Medical Association Journal, 155*, 299–301.

Balasubramaniam, K. (1995, December). Retail drug prices in the Asia-Pacific region. *HAI News, 86*, supplemental tables.

Berings, D., Blondeel, L., & Habraken, H. (1994). The effect of industry-independent drug information on the prescribing of benzodiazepines in general practice. *European Journal of Clinical Pharmacology, 46*, 501–505.

Bowman, M.A. (1986). The impact of drug company funding on the content of continuing medical education. *Mobius, 6*, 66–69.

Bowman, M.A., & Pearle, D.L. (1988). Changes in drug prescribing patterns related to commercial company funding of continuing medical education. *Journal of Continuing Education, 8*, 13–20.

Canada, House of Commons. (1967). *Second (final) report of the special committee of the House of Commons on drug costs and prices*. Ottawa: Queen's Printer.

CBC Radio. (1997, January 25). Drug patent law. *The House*.

Caudill, T.S., Johnson, M.S., Rich, E.C., & McKinney, W.P. (1996). Physicians, pharmaceutical sales representatives, and the cost of prescribing. *Archives of Family Medicine, 5*, 201–206.

Commission of Inquiry on the Pharmaceutical Industry. (1985). Report. Ottawa: Supply and Services Canada.

Connection. (1998). Spotlight: BMS vs CCOHTA. *Connection, 1*.

Crane, D. (1986, December 7). Drug bill concessions seem tied to trade talks. *Toronto Star*, p. B1.

Department of Foreign Affairs and International Trade and Industry Canada. (1996). *The case for investing in Canada: Assessing excellence in Canadian pharmaceutical research and development*. Ottawa: Author.

Dillon, J. (1997, March 4). *On feeding sharks: Patent protection, compulsory licensing, and international trade law*. A study prepared for the Canadian Health Coalition.

DiMasi, J.A., Hansen, R.W., Grabowski, H.G., & Lasagna, L. (1991). Cost of innovation in the pharmaceutical industry. *Journal of Health Economics, 10*, 107–142.

Education Council, Residency Training Programme in Internal Medicine. (1993). Development of residency program guidelines for interaction with the pharmaceutical industry. *Canadian Medical Association Journal, 149*, 403–404.

Ferry, M.E., Lamy, P.P., & Becker, L.A. (1985). Physicians' knowledge of prescribing for the elderly: A study of primary care physicians in Pennsylvania. *Journal of the American Geriatric Society, 33*, 616–621.

Gereffi, G. (1983). *The pharmaceutical industry and dependency in the third world*. Princeton: Princeton University Press.

Grabowski, H., & Vernon, J. (1990). A new look at the returns and risks to pharmaceutical R&D. *Management Science, 36*, 804–821.

Gray, C. (1981). The pharmaceutical industry: Promoting research in the 80's. *Canadian Medical Association Journal, 124*, 787–792.

Green Shield Canada. (1998, October). *Analysis of drug claim costs 1993–1997*. Toronto.

Haayer, F. (1982). Rational prescribing and sources of information. *Social Science and Medicine, 16*, 2017–2023.

Healthcare Communications Inc. (1989). *The effect of journal advertising on market shares of new prescriptions*. New York: Association of Independent Medical Publications.

Howard, R. (1987, October 16). MPs say Tories made deal on drug bill. *The Globe and Mail*, p. A13.

Kennedy, M. (1997, September 15). Fears raised over cuts to health protection. *Montreal Gazette*, p. A1.

Krupka, L., & Vener, A. (1985). Prescription drug advertising: Trends and implications. *Social Science and Medicine, 20*, 191–197.

Lang, R.W. (1974). *The Politics of Drugs*. Westmead: Saxon House.

Leffler, K. (1981). Persuasion or information? The economics of prescription drug advertising. *Journal of Law and Economics, 24*, 45–74.

Lewington, J. (1987, August 13). Drug-patent bill not enough to satisfy U.S. on free trade. *The Globe and Mail*, p. A1.

Lexchin, J. (1992). Prescribing and drug costs in the province of Ontario. *International Journal of Health Services, 22*, 471–487.

Lexchin, J. (1993). The effect of generic competition on the price of prescription drugs in the province of Ontario. *Canadian Medical Association Journal, 148*(1), 35–38.

Lexchin, J. (1994). Canadian marketing codes: How well are they controlling pharmaceutical promotion? *International Journal of Health Services, 24*, 91–104.

Lexchin, J. (1997a). Enforcement of codes governing pharmaceutical promotion: What happens when companies breach advertising guidelines? *Canadian Medical Association Journal, 156*, 351–357.

Lexchin, J. (1997b). Consequences of direct-to-consumer advertising of prescription drugs. *Canadian Family Physician, 43*, 594–596.

Lexchin, J. (1997c). What information do physicians receive from pharmaceutical representatives? *Canadian Family Physician, 43*, 941–945.

Lexchin, J. (1999). Following the rules in marketing. *Canadian Medical Association Journal, 161*, 685–686.

Livingston, M. (1988, January). Pharmaceutical stocks: Prescription for financial health. *Physician's Management Manuals*, pp. 57–61.

McQuaig, L. (1991). *The quick and the dead*. Toronto: Viking.

Merck Frosst Canada Inc. (1996, July 17). Direct-to-consumer advertising of prescription pharmaceuticals: A Merck Frosst position paper on how to use comprehensive patient information to deliver improved, cost-effective health outcomes.

Michols, D. (1997, February). Drugs and medical devices. *Programme Quality Initiative Bulletin, 2*. Ottawa: Health Protection Branch.

Mintzes, B. (1998, July). *Paper tiger or toothless tabby? Regulation of prescription drug promotion in Canada.* Health Policy Research Unit Discussion Paper Series (HPRU 98:6D), University of British Columbia, Vancouver.

Montgomery, D., & Silk, A. (1972). Estimating dynamic effects of market communications expenditures. *Management Science, 18,* B485–B501.

Office of Technology Assessment. (1993). *Pharmaceutical R&D: Costs, risks and rewards.* U.S. Government Printing Office, Washington, D.C. (cat. no. OTA-H-522).

Patented Medicine Prices Review Board. (1995, October). Decision on patent dedication. *Bulletin, 17.*

Patented Medicine Prices Review Board. (1998). *Tenth annual report: For the year ended December 31, 1997.* Ottawa: Supply and Services Canada.

Pharmaceutical Manufacturers Association of Canada. (1975). *The performance of the Canadian pharmaceutical manufacturing industry.* Ottawa: Author.

Pharmaceutical Manufacturers Association of Canada. (1997). *Code of marketing practice.* Ottawa: Author.

Regush, N. (1982, October 25). How a suspect arthritis drug evaded government checks. *Montreal Gazette,* pp. A1, A6.

Restrictive Trade Practices Commission. (1963). *Report concerning the manufacture, distribution and sale of drugs.* Ottawa: Queen's Printer.

Royal Commission on Health Services. (1964). *Report.* Ottawa: Queen's Printer.

Sawatsky, J., & Cashore, H. (1986, August–September). Inside dope: The multi-million-dollar sellout of Canada's generic drug industry. *This Magazine, 20,* 4–12.

Schondelmeyer, S.W. (1993, January). *The cost of Bill C-91: An economic impact analysis of the elimination of compulsory licensing of pharmaceutical in Canada.* Ottawa: Canadian Drug Manufacturers Association.

Scrip. (1999, April 14). Canadian pharma sales rise 12.7 percent. *Scrip, 2428,* 16–17.

Shin, J.H., Haynes, R.B., & Johnston, M.E. (1993). Effect of problem-based, self-directed undergraduate education on life-long learning. *Canadian Medical Association Journal, 148,* 969–976.

Standing Committee on Industry. (1997, April). *Draft Report. Review of Section 14 of the Patent Act Amendment 1992.*

Taylor, K.M. (1991). The impact of the pharmaceutical industry's clinical research programs on medical education, practice and researchers in Canada: A discussion paper. In *Canadian pharmaceutical research and development: Four short-term studies.* Ottawa: Industry, Science & Technology Canada.

Temin, P. (1979). Technology, regulation, and market structure in the modern pharmaceutical industry. *Bell Journal of Economics, 10,* 429–446.

Therapeutic Products Programme. (1997, September). *Overview of Product Licensing Framework II.*

VanWoert, M.H. (1978). Profitable and nonprofitable drugs. *New England Journal of Medicine, 298,* 903–905.

Walton, H. (1980, June). Ad recognition and prescribing by physicians. *Journal of Advertising Research, 20,* 39–48.

Walwyn Stodgell Cochran Murray Ltd. (1983, May 10). For pill, like to try one from the U.K.? *Investor's Digest,* p. 142.

Williams, A.P., & Cockerill, R. (1990). *Report on the 1989 survey of the prescribing experiences and attitudes toward prescription drugs of Ontario physicians.* Research report, Pharmaceutical Inquiry of Ontario.

Woods, D. (1986). PMAC to spend almost $1 million annually to reach "stakeholders." *Canadian Medical Association Journal, 134,* 1387–1389.

NOTES

1. The Pharmaceutical Manufacturers Association of Canada currently has 63 member companies, including almost all the large multinationals operating in Canada. Fewer than 20 of its members are Canadian-owned companies, and these are generally small biotechnology companies. The Canadian Drug Manufacturers Association represents 14 Canadian-owned generic companies, the largest of which are Apotex and Novopharm.
2. In Canada and the United States the drug was called Oraflex.
3. The Health Protection Branch is the division of Health Canada charged with monitoring the safety and efficacy of prescription drugs. Before the HPB allows a drug to enter the Canadian market, the manufacturer has to present evidence to it that the product is safe and effective for human use and that the manufacturing process meets appropriate standards.
4. The branch of the HPB that regulates drugs was then the Drugs Directorate and has since been renamed the Therapeutic Products Programme.
5. In 1998, Pravachol had sales of $121 million, making it the sixth-leading drug in Canada in terms of dollar sales (*Scrip*, 1999).
6. The $500 million amount is an extrapolation, based on inflation and other factors, from a figure of $194 million in 1990.
7. DeMasi did not factor in tax savings from R&D.
8. At that time, companies had a monopoly on their product for 17 years from the time that the patent was granted. In the late 1960s, it took about 4 years to get a drug to market, so the effective monopoly period was about 13 years. The patent term is now 20 years from the date that the application for a patent is filed.
9. A compulsory licence is essentially a permit that effectively negates a patent. Theoretically, the company owning the patent on a drug would be a monopoly seller until the patent expired. However, if other companies apply for, and are granted, a compulsory licence against a drug, they can then market their own version of that drug before the patent has expired. The compulsory aspect means that the company owning the patent cannot block the licence from being granted. Since 1923, companies in Canada had been able to get a compulsory licence allowing them to manufacture the drug in Canada, but because of the small size of the market few licences were issued.
10. Although C-91 was passed in 1993, it was made retroactive to December 1991. Some people claim that this was a favour to Merck, the largest multinational subsidiary operating in Canada, because it disallowed a compulsory licence on one of Merck's best-selling products.
11. It takes about 8 years from the time a patent application is filed until a drug appears on the market.
12. As an example, 5 years after a drug appears, it may have sales of $100 million. Therefore, a generic that costs 25 percent less could lead to savings of up to $25 million. By 12 years, sales of the drug may be down to $50 million, and therefore generic savings would only be $12.5 million.
13. Patent dedication is essentially a voluntary surrender of the patent for public use.
14. By and large, generic companies do not promote to doctors.

21

Ethics in Health Care in Canada

JANET STORCH, PATRICIA RODNEY, AND ROSALIE STARZOMSKI

University of Victoria

INTRODUCTION

Over the past four decades, advances in the science and technology of medicine and health care have brought a plethora of societal challenges, particularly for those at the end of their lives. Early sociological studies portrayed some of these challenges (e.g., Fagerhaugh et al., 1980; Glaser & Strauss, 1965; Mauksch, 1975; Sudnow, 1967). For instance, they showed the distress of patients, families, and providers when terminal diagnoses were not disclosed.

At the same time that sociologists were studying the challenges for medicine and health care at the end of life, bioethics was becoming established as a discipline. Indeed, the widespread application of ethical theory to health care is a recent phenomenon. The term "bioethics" appeared about 30 years ago, with the publication of a text about bio-logical knowledge and human values (Roy, Williams, & Dickens, 1994, pp. 3–4). Fuelled by the post–World War II Nuremberg trials of the 1940s and advances in hemodialysis, kidney transplantation, and mechanical ventilation in the 1960s (Jonsen, 1997), bioethics quickly encompassed the efforts to address value-based questions posed by developments in science and technology and their application to health care (Roy, Williams, & Dickens, 1994, p. 4). With roots in medical ethics, philosophical ethics, and religious ethics, bioethics flourished and diversified (Fox, 1990; Roy, Williams, & Dickens, 1994, pp. 4–13). Concomitant societal changes contributed to this growth, par-ticularly "moral pluralism, the human rights movement, and attitudes towards death" (Roy, Williams, & Dickens, 1994, p. 12).

This chapter provides a social critique of contemporary ethics issues in health care in Canada. Although there is a rich literature of ethical analyses of these issues in the Canadian context (e.g., Baylis et al., 1995a; Kluge, 1999; Roy, Williams, & Dickens, 1994; Sherwin, 1992; Yeo & Moorhouse, 1996), these types of in-depth analyses will not be the focus of this account. Instead, this chapter provides an overview of selected eth-ical issues related to clinical practice, to the context of health care, and to health poli-cy, at the macro, meso, and micro levels of analyses. The first of these levels is the level of societal responsibilities for the health of the total population (the macro level); the second is the level of institutional responsibilities for programs of care (the meso level), and the third is the level of individual professional responsibilities for patients and families receiving health care (the micro level). In so doing, we draw on theory and research from ethics and the health care professions. We also draw on a growing body of social science literature that critiques health care as well as health care ethics (e.g., Churchill, 1997; Coward & Ratanakul, 1999; Fox & Swazey, 1992a, 1992b; Weisz, 1990).

Clinical health ethics issues are discussed in the first main section of the chapter. These issues are often featured in the popular press and occupy a substantial portion of health ethics literature. Frequently referred to as the spectacular or quandary issues of health ethics, the ones addressed here include end of life issues, transplantation and organ donation, and genetics and genetics testing. This is not an exhaustive list, but it does represent the issues in the field. A common thread in these ethical issues is the matter of quality of life. The second main section of the chapter focuses on contextual issues in the delivery of health care, including resource allocation and the moral climate of health care agencies. These issues are often regarded as less spectacular or nonspectacular issues in health ethics. They rarely grab the headlines, yet they are the issues of everyday ethics and system ethics that affect *all* individuals involved in health care. The third main section provides an overview of how clinical and contextual ethical issues are being addressed in Canada. The fourth and final main section deals with ethical matters pertaining to health policy, including new reproductive technologies and the broadening scope of research ethics issues. Finally, the chapter discusses some major themes emerging in health ethics issues and some predictions about health ethics issues in the next decade.

CLINICAL HEALTH ETHICS ISSUES

Quality of Life

Underpinning most clinical health ethics issues are concerns about the quality of life. What constitutes quality of life? Who can and should make a quality of life assessment? There are many definitions of quality of life, and there are major methodological problems in determining the dimensions of quality of life. Molzahn (1998, p. 58) suggests that quality of life is an assessment of life overall, as perceived by the individual. In many instances, health professionals may take a position that a particular patient's quality of life is poor, leading to the conclusion that death is preferable. But perceptions of quality of life can be highly individual. For instance, for someone who has been disabled since birth, that individual's assessment of a life worth living is likely to have a different meaning from an assessment by an individual who was formerly robust and healthy but who is now incapacitated. The implementation of poorly defined quality of life assessments has the potential to be particularly detrimental to the disabled and the elderly — groups already devalued in Western society — by providing an excuse to limit treatment to less expensive types of care or to shorten life by withholding treatment.

The same concern about quality of life assessment is at the heart of the debate about sustaining the life of very **low birth weight** babies (whose assessment counts — the parents' or the physicians'?), and the debate about treatment of patients on dialysis for renal failure. In their study of nurses and physicians in a neonatal intensive care unit and of the parents of the children in the neonatal unit, for example, Lee, Penner, and Cox (1991) reported major attitudinal differences among parents and health care professionals about the outcomes for babies treated in the neonatal unit. Health professionals made more dismal assessments of the quality of life of the children. This observation led investigators to propose that nurses who have more contact with the babies in an intensive care (ICU) setting and who do not see the babies after they leave the ICU and are well, may have more negative attitudes about the prognosis of these infants. This led to a belief that there was a need for more education of health care professionals about neonatal outcomes and a greater recognition of the wishes of parents. Similar findings were reported by Molzahn (1989), who found that nurses, physicians, and dialysis patients had different perspectives about the patients' quality of life, with physicians ranking the quality of life higher than patients did, and nurses ranking the quality of life lower. She speculated that this may have been a result of the amount of time nurses spent with patients in the dialysis unit and the fact that they did not see them managing well in their home environment.

Quality of life judgements creep into the abortion controversy as well, when, for instance, a woman believes that she would be unable to provide a good quality of life for her child. In a different manner, quality of life has been used as the impetus for developing new ways in which previously infertile individuals and others desiring offspring can conceive children. In this case, the argument is in favour of broadening the definition of health care to include services that enhance reproductive capacity because, from the perspective of some, having children is seen to be important to health, happiness, and quality of life. As it addresses various clinical health ethics issues, this chapter therefore includes some commentary on quality of life.

End of Life Issues

Not surprisingly, some of the most significant and pervasive issues in bioethics arise at the end of life. In other words, the societal challenges chronicled by early sociological studies have become articulated in terms of ethics. The following sections review some of the subsequent work on euthanasia, **withholding and withdrawing treatment**, the concept of **futility**, and the concepts of trust and compassion. Inherent in every one of these issues is a deep concern about the quality of living while dying.

EUTHANASIA

> Every discussion of euthanasia is bedevilled by the many different understandings of the term, as used in popular, academic, and professional discourse. It is very difficult for opponents and proponents of euthanasia to agree on a definition of the term. (Roy, Williams, & Dickens, 1994, p. 410)

Given the psychological, social, and spiritual significance of death, it is no wonder that discussions of euthanasia are difficult. To facilitate clarity, this chapter uses the definition posited by Roy, Williams, and Dickens, and widely (though not universally) accepted by ethicists and health care professionals. That is, euthanasia is considered to be the "deliberate, rapid, and painless termination of a life of a person afflicted with incurable and progressive disease" (1994, p. 411). **Assisted euthanasia** refers to advancing one's own death by requesting help from others either to provide lethal dosages of drugs with instructions about how to use them effectively, or requesting others to administer drugs or other mechanisms to bring about one's death (p. 412).

It is essential to understand how euthanasia differs from withholding and withdrawing treatment. Euthanasia (which used to be called "active" euthanasia) entails a deliberate act with the intent of terminating life. Withholding and withdrawing treatment (which used to be [misleadingly] called passive euthanasia), on the other hand, entail reasoned clinical judgements identifying the treatments that are or are not in the patient's best interest. That best interest is determined on the basis of an assessment of the patient's personal, cultural, and spiritual values, as well as an assessment of the patient's prognosis, treatment options, and so forth (Kuhl & Wilensky, 1999; Moreno, 1995, Storch, 1999).

The issue of euthanasia is not new. Debates about euthanasia in Western society appeared in the literature as early as 1873 and were revisited in the 1920s, 1930s, and 1940s. The revelations at the military and medical crimes trials held at Nuremberg shortly after World War II "produced widespread revulsion against euthanasia, even when voluntary and for the purpose of relieving suffering" (Roy, Williams, & Dickens, 1994, p. 417). With few exceptions (e.g., the Netherlands), contemporary Western societies since then have continued to reject euthanasia as a policy option. However, several U.S. states along the Pacific coast, notably California, Washington, and Oregon, moved beyond discussion to a "series of ballot initiatives." In 1994, Oregon became the first state to pass an assisted suicide law (Moreno, 1995, pp. 120–167).

In Canada, the Law Reform Commission of Canada (1983) recommended against decriminalizing euthanasia in any form. In 1995, the Special Senate Committee on Euthanasia and Assisted Suicide upheld that recommendation. The findings of the committee were that public requests for euthanasia often arose out of a confusion between euthanasia and the withholding and withdrawal of treatment. Moreover, the Special Senate Committee (1995) and a Special Subcommittee (2000) recommended that programs of palliative care be made more available so that all patients and families could be supported in the dying process. Concerns were raised in the Special Senate Committee report (1995) and were echoed again by the Special Subcommittee (2000) about inadequate pain relief for dying patients and institutional structures and workloads that made it difficult to provide appropriate care (see also Bernabei et al., 1998; Hunter, 2000). Two of the authors of this chapter have argued elsewhere that a policy permitting euthanasia would be particularly dangerous in the current era of cost constraints (Ericksen, Rodney, & Starzomski, 1995). There is significant risk that vulnerable patients and family members would opt for euthanasia "because of inadequate resources for care rather than because of well-informed, autonomous decision making" (p. 32).

Nonetheless, this is not the end of the debate.[1] Many members of the public — some of whom are part of "Right to Die" groups — argue compellingly for dignity and control at the end of life. While most health care professionals as well as the Canadian Medical Association and the Canadian Nurses' Association believe that such dignity and control can be furnished through programs of palliative care, questions about euthanasia will continue to appear in the press and in government chambers. This is particularly likely as poignant cases of euthanasia arise, such as the Rodriguez case and the Latimer case (Sneiderman, 1994, 1997).

WITHHOLDING AND WITHDRAWING TREATMENT

Fortunately, questions about the ethics and legality of withholding and withdrawing treatment have become more clearly answered in recent years. In 1983, the Law Reform Commission of Canada recommended that nothing in the various sections of the Criminal Code should be interpreted as requiring a physician "to continue to administer to or undertake medical treatment against the clearly expressed wishes of the person for whom the treatment is intended" or "to continue to administer or to undertake medical treatment, when such treatment is medically useless and is not in the best interests of the person for whom it is intended, except in accordance with the clearly expressed wishes of this person for whom it is intended" (p. 32). Furthermore, the Law Reform Commission of Canada (1983) also addressed the problem of pain relief in palliative care by recommending that nothing in the Criminal Code should be "interpreted as preventing a physician from undertaking or obliging him to cease administering appropriate palliative care intended to eliminate or to relieve the suffering of a person, for the sole reason that such care or measures are likely to shorten the life expectancy of this person" (p. 35).

Meanwhile, several hospitals began the development of "Do Not Resuscitate" (DNR) policies in an attempt to protect patients from the loss of dignity occasioned by prolongation of life and to protect health care professionals from potential legal liability should they determine that further treatment by resuscitation would be medically useless. This action eventually led to an agreement to a common Canadian guideline (1984) by four major professional bodies in Canada: the Canadian Medical Association, the Canadian Hospital Association, the Canadian Nurses' Association, and the Canadian Bar Association. Since then, the Canadian Healthcare Association, the Canadian Medical Association, the Canadian Nurses' Association, and the Catholic Health Association of Canada, in cooperation with the Canadian Bar Association, have developed a Joint Statement on Resuscitative Interventions (1995). In general, this latest statement is consistent with the 1983 Law Reform Commission of Canada recommendations. Moreover, it provides directions to facilitate communication between patients, families, and members of the health care team.

In the late 1990s, initiatives to formalize the use of advance directives, also known as personal directives made in advance, were widespread in Canada (Dossetor & Cain, 1997, p.101; Wilson et al., 1996). An advance directive is "a written document containing a person's wishes about life-sustaining treatment" that "extend[s] the autonomy of competent patients to future situations in which the patient is incompetent" (Singer, 1994, p. 111). **Advance directives** are best when they are accompanied by the appointment of a proxy (surrogate) decision maker who knows the patient and can represent his or her best interest (Dossetor & Cain, 1997; Singer, 1994). Advance directives and proxy decision makers are meant to assist with decisions about the withholding and withdrawal of treatment including, but not limited to, resuscitation.[2] Currently, the standards of professional practice, professional codes of ethics, and DNR policies indicate that health care professionals should obtain information about what a patient who is no longer competent would want. Advance directives, such as living wills and consultation with a proxy decision maker who knows the patient well and speaks for his or her best interest, can greatly facilitate communication about the withholding and withdrawal of treatment, even though these directives are not yet codified in law in every Canadian province (Blondeau et al., 2000).

THE CONCEPT OF FUTILITY

An important concept that has emerged in contemporary debates about end-of-life decision making is the concept of futility. To say that treatment is futile is to say that it is impossible or unlikely to achieve its therapeutic goal, or that there is something problematic about the goal (Browne, 2000, p. 2). Sneiderman, Jecker, and Jonsen (1990) believe that futility has two distinct components, physiological effect and benefit. From their point of view, some treatments can be futile because they do not produce a desired physiological effect or the anticipated goal of treatment.

More specifically, *quantitative* futility occurs when physicians conclude from empirical data that they are not obligated to offer medical treatment to a patient. *Qualitative* futility occurs when physicians will not offer treatment because it will not result in a return to consciousness or the ability to leave a critical care hospital unit (Sneiderman, Jecker, & Jonsen, 1990; Taylor, 1995). As Taylor explains:

> These [futility] proposals are generally grounded in the conviction that patients should be protected from decisions that are not in their best interest. Moreover, there ought to be a way to deter patients from making decisions that violate the best interests of society. (1995, p. 302)

However, there are a number of concerns about the ways in which the concept of futility can be employed as a seemingly "objective" tool to limit patient autonomy. Futility determinations are difficult to apply in many cases because of individual variation and because there is not sufficient outcome data with which to determine the potential physiological effect (Starzomski, 1994, 1998). A diagnosis of "medical futility" can be used to limit the ability of patients and families to request treatment that the physician feels is inappropriate. But what percentage of success is considered adequate to consider a treatment beneficial? Even with outcome data, each case should be evaluated in terms of the potential benefits as seen through the eyes of the patient. The patient or his or her guardian should be the one, when presented with the information about the benefits and burdens of treatment, to make a choice based on his or her own individual interpretation of quality of life. Yet, in some situations, patients or their guardians are not given accurate information or it is presented in an overly optimistic manner, thus affecting their ability to make a truly informed decision. For instance, Degner and Beaton (1987), when studying whether people with cancer were interested in making decisions about their health care, found that in many cases people wanted to participate but were hindered in doing so by a lack of information about and interpretation of what was happening to them. This observation has been supported by the extensive research on patient choice by Wennberg (1990), whose results showed that patient choice is enhanced when people have appropriate information and understanding (Starzomski, 1994, 1998).

Furthermore, saying no to patients and families is not necessarily implemented in an equitable manner. Some patients and family members have difficulty in discussions about futility because of value conflicts with physicians and other health care professionals, particularly when they are of a sociocultural background different from the professionals' (Burgess et al., 1999; Rodney, 1997; Taylor, 1995; Wolf, 1994).

Although some have suggested that people faced with decisions about continued or new treatments to sustain life would be inclined to ask for too much, it has been the authors' experience in dealing with many hundreds of patients and families that very few choose to pursue a treatment of questionable benefit when information about what is known is presented fairly and honestly, with the risks and benefits accurately presented. Clearly, this information disclosure must occur in a supportive and caring environment where patients, families, and health care providers work in a collaborative manner (Blondeau et al., 2000; Kuhl & Wilenski, 1999; Rodney, 1994, 1997; Roy, 1994; Roy, Williams, & Dickens, 1994; Starzomski, 1994, 1998; Taylor, 1995; Tilden et al., 1999; Wilson, 2000). Taylor (1995) warns that the "debate about futility determinations underscores the urgent need for some professional to bring to ethical discourse about treatment decisions a sense of who the patient is and the values that underlie the patient's and surrogates' demands for treatment" (p. 303). The ability of family and team members to focus on *who the patient is as a person* must become central in major treatment decisions (Kuhl & Wilenski, 1999; Nisker, 2001; Rodney, 1994, 1997; Solomon et al., 1990). Negotiating these decisions will require trust and compassion between all who are involved (Rodney, 1997; Taylor, 1995, p. 303).

A growing number of ethicists and health care professionals are calling for a more compassionate approach to decision making and care at the end of life (Kuhl, 1994; Roy, 1994; Roy, Williams, & Dickens, 1994). They want to take the principles and goals of palliative care and apply them more broadly to *all* patients who are, or might be, dying (Subcommittee, 2000). In the words of David Kuhl, who is a palliative care physician and the former chair of a hospital ethics committee:

> Those who provide care for the dying seek to address issues of pain and suffering in the context of the psychological, spiritual, mental, and physical complexities of the individual experiencing a terminal illness. People who are dying are still living and have the right to be in control of their lives. The individual must be heard with regard to decisions about care, about withholding or withdrawing treatment, and about working toward healing prior to their death. (Kuhl & Wilenski, 1999, p. 83)

Organ Transplantation and Organ Donation

Since the first successful kidney transplant, performed in Boston in 1954 between identical twins, transplantation has been considered an extremely controversial area, generating significant discussion in the health care arena and highlighting many of the issues that are central in the resource allocation debate (Murray, 1992; Sells, 1992; Hauptman & O'Connor, 1997; Starzomski, 1997, 1998). Transplantation has been viewed as a microcosm within which some of the most difficult ethical issues related to the evolution of technology and allocation of scarce resources is occurring (Bailey, 1990; Fox & Swazey, 1992a, 1992b; Midgley, 2000; Starzomski, 1994, 1997).

DISTRIBUTIVE JUSTICE

Organ transplantation has been declared one of the greatest achievements of the twentieth century, moving from the impossible to the commonplace, offering people with end-stage organ failure "a gift of life" (Murray, 1992). A successful transplant offers some people virtually complete physical rehabilitation and improvement in overall quality of life (Laupacis et al., 1996; Molzahn, 1991). However, others are not so fortunate. Some die while on transplant waiting lists; others reject their organs after transplantation and/or succumb to the many complications of the treatment (Fox & Swazey, 1992a, 1992b; Murray, 1992; Starzomski, 1994, 1997, 1998).

Although success rates are improving, they are still low for transplantation of some organs (for example, bowel and multiple organs). Some have raised concerns about transplantation, particularly when the success rates are low or the procedures are considered experimental, pointing out that transplantation consumes a large proportion of health care resources and benefits only a few. Might these resources be used more effectively elsewhere in the health care system? Should society be wary of the "technological imperative," that is, the tendency to feel that the ability to develop extraordinary interventions automatically justifies their use (Fox & Swazey, 1992a, 1992b; Starzomski, 1994, 1997)?

As a result of the shortage of donor organs and of the human and financial resources required for transplantation, distributive justice questions analogous to those posed in the early years of transplantation are resurfacing: who will make the decisions about the resource commitment for transplantation, and who should be treated when all cannot be treated? (Fox & Swazey, 1992a, 1992b). Fox and Swazey describe transplantation as epitomizing many of the issues that are part of the health care reform debate. They note, however, that with few exceptions, there has been a reluctance to deal the question of distributive justice. Much of the debate about resource allocation in transplantation has focused narrowly on the methods required to procure organs sufficient to meet the demand rather than on discussions about the level of resources allocated for transplantation or on the views of the public and health care providers about how they think resources ought to be allocated (Starzomski, 1994, 1997, 1998).

LEVELS OF RESPONSIBILITY

The community at large is faced with fundamental questions at the macro or societal level about the level of resources to be allocated to life-saving technology such as organ transplantation (Benjamin, 1992; Brooks, 1993; Evans, 1992). Also at the macro level, a major worldwide organ shortage crisis has raised questions about changing the procedure to gain consent to use human tissue, in various ways: examining strategies for presumed consent (Sadler, 1992), using fetal tissue for transplantation (Martin, 1992), offering financial incentives for organ donation (Dickens, 1991; Warren, 1993), engaging in buying and selling organs (Kazim et al., 1992), using anencephalic infant donors (Dickens, 1988; Roy, Williams, & Dickens, 1994), considering the use of xenografts (transplanting from one species to another) (Nicholson, 1996; Singer, 1992), and considering cloning to solve the problem of shortage of organs for human transplantation.

As research in the area of xenografting continues, questions about the level of regulation for this new technology are being discussed with the goal that the appropriate level of research and clinical application of xenograft technology will be identified prior to human trials in Canada. Given the potential risks of transmitting animal pathogens into humans (xenozoonosis), as well as the many ethical concerns about raising animals for transplant purposes, the need to proceed with caution and appropriate regulation is imperative.

At the meso or institutional level of the health care system, questions are raised about the type of patients who should be the recipients of organ transplantation, and how selection criteria should be developed (Kilner, 1990; Kluge, 1993). In addition, as transplant waiting lists grow, a question arises about the number of waiting lists on which a recipient should be listed. Another difficult question at the meso level arises when determining how decisions should be made about the proportion of an institutional budget devoted to transplantation compared with other programs (Balk, 1990; Starzomski, 1994, 1998).

Decisions at the micro level of the health care system are evident in questions about how health care providers decide whether a transplant is in a given patient's best interest. For example, health care providers make decisions about removing kidneys and parts of livers and lungs from individual living donors to be transplanted into specific recipients (Sieglar, 1992). In addition, organs from unrelated donors are considered more frequently in transplant centres around the world (Spital, 1992, 1993). Finally, there is the question of how many re-transplants one individual is entitled to receive (Evans et al., 1993).

Although the above list is not exhaustive, it provides an overview of some of the most perplexing problems in transplantation today. The problems highlight concerns about autonomy and informed consent. Importantly, the critical principle of justice is embedded in many of the ethical issues about organ transplantation, exposing deep tensions about the societal sense of what is true or just (Kjellstrand & Dossetor, 1992).

Problems related to transplantation and organ donation raise a need for a collaborative approach among health care providers and the public to define and determine legitimate and just applications of organ transplantation technology. In Canada, there has been wide discussion about the need to reduce the gap between the supply of donor organs and the increasing demand for organ transplants (Federal–Provincial Advisory Committee on Health Services, 1996; Standing Committee on Health, 1999). A Parliamentary committee on health, after several months of hearing from expert witnesses, released a report that outlined a comprehensive strategy for the reorganization of organ and tissue transplant services in Canada, including recommendations to develop a national organ-donation management network with federal and provincial cooperation (Standing Committee on Health, 1999). This model includes a multifaceted approach, including an acknowledgement that at all levels of the system there needs to be a collaborative approach among consumers, health care providers, and government to increase the number of organs available for transplantation and to ensure a high-quality Canadian organ and tissue donation program.

Genetics and Genetic Testing

THE HUMAN GENOME PROJECT

New genetic knowledge and techniques are changing the way in which many people think about health and illness, personal risk, and familial responsibility (Beardsley,

1996; Cox, McKellin, & Burgess, 1995; Halsey-Lea, Jenkins, & Francomano, 1998; Midgley, 2000; Nisker & Gore-Langton, 1995). Knowledge is being developed rapidly, due in large part to the **human genome project**.

The human genome project is considered one of the most significant research endeavours of the twentieth century. The purpose of the project is to coordinate scientific discoveries, data, and methods related to genetic research with the goal of understanding the structure, function, and outcome of hereditary instructions within the human genome (Halsey-Lea, Jenkins, & Froncomano, 1998; Hoffman, 1994). As a result of the project, which involves researchers in a number of centres worldwide, large numbers of genes have been identified and new commercial tests are becoming available for genetic screening purposes. These discoveries raise a series of ethical questions for health research and for health care delivery. Should researchers be setting some boundaries in this search for new genetic knowledge and the applications of this knowledge? To be able to effectively answer this question requires discussion about genetic research, policy development, regulation, testing, and caring for persons with genetic disorders (Kerr, Cunningham-Burley, & Amos, 1998).

SOCIAL, ETHICAL, AND MORAL ISSUES

The availability of genetic testing raises a host of difficult social and ethical issues for at-risk individuals and families, health care professionals, and society as a whole. Questions related to the confidentiality and privacy of genetic information, to informed consent and voluntary decision making by patients and families, and to the potential for abuse of genetic information are emerging. When is the knowledge derived from such testing likely to be an appropriate social intervention? Who should know the results? How and when should information about hereditary risk be provided to other members of the family? This will, in turn, have important implications for the clinical management and support of families affected by genetic disorders.

A variety of other ethical issues and moral experiences (e.g., perceived responsibility in marital and reproductive planning, duty to provide caregiving) present themselves. In particular, it is important to understand from the perspective of individuals and families at risk for genetic disorders what the issues are and how they intersect with and present new challenges for the clinical management of the conditions. As studies of the social and ethical experiences of offering predictive genetic testing for other adult onset disorders (such as Huntington's chorea) have shown, one of the most prominent aspects of the experience is the profound importance of family and family dynamics (Cox, McKellin, & Burgess, 1995; Hayes, 1992; Kessler, 1994; Wexler, 1996). The impact of predictive testing on families is discussed in genetic counselling sessions, but there are significant moral dimensions of this that are not typically the responsibility of counsellors or other service providers (e.g., future caregiving responsibilities for family members with Huntington's chorea). Moreover, it is often the case that participants' perceived responsibilities are not explicitly recognized as moral issues that have a significant bearing on the shape and outcome of predictive genetic testing (Cox & McKellin, 1999). There is a need for continued research to better understand the social, ethical, and legal ramifications of new genetic knowledge. Broad societal dialogue must occur to determine the appropriate application of that knowledge today and in the future. The ethical quandaries described in this section occur in the wider context of resource allocation and health reform.

CONTEXTUAL HEALTH ETHICS ISSUES

Resource Allocation

The growth in the size and complexity of health systems in the Western world is seen to present significant problems for economic viability. From a language of health management that focused primarily on expansion of services with no limits to the possibilities for medical advance, examining the appropriate limits of medicine gradually became the norm in the 1990s (Callahan, 1990; see also Rodney & Varcoe (in press), and Chapter 6 of this book for a critique).

Economic needs to sustain the current system in Canada paved the way for profound debate about sensible approaches to the provision of health services, for numerous government studies of provincial systems of care, and for suggestions to reduce benefits in Canadian medicare, with the all too convenient allegations of patients' abuse of the system to justify removal of services (Evans, Barer, & Hertzman, 1991). The scope and magnitude of the subsequent changes in health care delivery have been unparalleled in Canadian history (Storch & Meilicke, 1999). Voices reminding the health establishment that it is responsible for encouraging patients to use the system and that it has accepted few limits to its modes of practice (Jecker, 1991) are not often heard or acknowledged. Nor are the voices reminding the health establishment that disparities and inequities that have long existed may be worsened by the outcomes of the current debates (Blue et al., 1999).

Beginning in the mid-1940s, Canadians gradually developed a framework for a Canadian health care system based upon values of equity. Although the explicit commitment to equity in health care was new at that time, the commitment was based on egalitarian principles that had shaped Canada as a nation since its inception (Saul, 1997). The belief that all persons should have access to required medical care and hospital services was enshrined in the legislation introducing hospital insurance and medical care in Canada in 1957 and 1968 respectively. The right to health care was further emphasized in the *Canada Health Act* of 1984 amid bitter disputes about the physician's right to independence versus the citizen's rights to access to care (Taylor, 1987). Despite its relative equity and effectiveness over the past 40 years, the just allocation of health care resources is currently subject to serious political challenges (Douglas, 1993; Taft & Steward, 2000).

REFORM INITIATIVES

By the late 1990s, most members of the Organisation for Economic Co-operation and Development (OECD), composed of countries in Europe, North America, and the South Pacific, had launched a major reform of their health care systems (Evans, 1993, p. 35; National Forum on Health, 1997). The focus of the reform was to address issues and concerns about the allocation of health care resources, many of which have arisen as a result of the "spare no expense" philosophy in health care (Lomas, 1996; Starzomski, 1997; Thorne, 1993). Therefore, determining the optimal methods for allocation of health care resources has become one of the most critical issues facing the system in the twenty-first century.

Fundamental questions of distributive justice have led to some of the most widely debated questions at all political levels in Canada. There is increasing discussion about the need to determine what Canadians wish to spend on health care, how resources should be allocated within federal and provincial health care budgets to meet the health care needs of citizens, how priorities should be determined within these budgets, and who will make the decisions about how resources will be allocated (National Forum on Health, 1997; Starzomski, 1997). It is believed that resolving these allocation dilemmas requires a partnership of consumers, providers, and government (Charles & DeMaio, 1993; Crichton & Hsu, 1990; National Forum on Health, 1997). It is important to note that in Canada, there has been widespread support for an egalitarian approach to health care. This is in contrast to the United States, where preservation of the autonomy of individuals in the health care marketplace has tended to mitigate against universal health care coverage (Storch, 1988).

In fact, in a report from the National Forum on Health (1997) it was noted (contrary to widely held public beliefs) that health care costs in Canada have *decreased* from 10.3 percent of the GDP in 1992 to 9.5 percent in 1995. Further evidence for reduction in health care spending was reported in a health care study prepared for the Tommy Douglas Research Institute. This study showed a 1.1 percent decrease in health care spending between 1992 and 1997. The authors of this study note that "[t]his absolute decline is unprecedented" (Rachlis et al., 2000). Yet in the United States, the costs have increased from 14 percent of the GDP in 1992 to 14.5 percent in 1995 and have continued to rise.

In Canada in the late 1990s, the federal government and all ten provincial governments examined various options to maximize resource usage by focusing on restructuring, re-engineering, and/or decentralizing health care delivery systems and the more effective use of health care services and personnel (Barer & Stoddart, 1992; Barer, Welch, & Antioch, 1991; National Forum on Health, 1997). It has become clear that more health care does not necessarily mean better health for the population. There is a growing interest in moving to a health care model in which the broader determinants of health, such as social status and income, are central in the development of healthy public policy (Renaud, 1994). This interest is distinguished from traditional health care policy by being ecological in perspective, multidimensional in scope, and participatory in strategy (Milio, 1985; National Forum on Health, 1997).

Thus, all activities within the health care system are undergoing considerable scrutiny, and there is an emphasis on the need for all citizens to use resources in a responsible manner. There is an increasing emphasis on the development of research that focuses on the outcomes of health care and the impact of new technology on the health care system (Deber, 1992; Goodman, 1992; Hadorn, 1993; National Forum on Health, 1997). In 1990, Wennberg predicted that the use of outcome information might postpone the need for rationing health care services by determining which medical treatments are actually effective. At the same time, there is a growing recognition that not everything of significance that occurs in health care can be measured effectively (Mitchell, 1993). Others contend that, even if all the waste was eliminated within the health care system and the system organized in the most efficient manner, there would still be a gap between supply and demand (Roy, Williams, & Dickens, 1994).

PUBLIC VALUES

Although the tenets of medicare (universality, comprehensiveness, accessibility, portability, and a publicly administered health care system) are considered sacred by most Canadians,[3] these tenets are under siege. The reorganization of the health care system is rooted in the social ideology of each individual province. Decisions about allocation have been made primarily by governments, often in the form of cuts to programs, forcing rationing to occur at the meso level of health care agencies and institutions (Manga & Weller, 1991; Wilson, 1994, 1995). Moreover, some governments are examining methods (such as user fees, definitions of basic levels of care, and privatization of some health care services) that threaten to change the foundation upon which the Canadian health care system is built (National Forum on Health, 1997; Moorhouse, 1993). These changes point to a need for public discussion about resource allocation in health care to assure that the best decisions are made, that all societal voices are heard in the debate, and that the decisions are made in a democratic fashion (Starzomski, 1997).

Many hope that collaboration among stakeholders will ultimately improve the asymmetry in the relationship between provider and patient and result in the best possible health care for Canadians. Clearly, this dialogue must continue (Anderson & Rodney, 1999; Blue et al., 1999; Charles & DeMaio, 1993; National Forum on Health, 1997; Starzomski, 1997, 1998). Improved relationships have the potential to enhance the moral climate of health care agencies.

THE MORAL CLIMATE OF HEALTH CARE AGENCIES

As the above analysis of resource allocation has illustrated, this is a time of unrest in health care in Canada. Consequently, contextual issues in the delivery of health care — which have always been important — are now impossible to ignore for those involved in the planning, delivery, and receiving of health care. We wish to explore some of the implications in terms of the moral climate of health care agencies.

Agencies such as hospitals, long-term-care facilities, community centres, and research institutes are characterized by hierarchy, a complex division of labour, administrative positions based on technical expertise and knowledge, collective outputs, reliance upon rules and policies, and multiple institutional and staff relationships (Buchanan, 1996, pp. 419–420). Health care agencies have responsibility and accountability that transcend those of individual health care providers. This means that health care agencies have a role in the resolution and creation of ethical problems in health care.

For a number of years, sociological and nursing studies have portrayed a hierarchical caste system in health care agencies, particularly hospitals. This system creates centralized decision making, with resultant conflict and alienation for many health care providers, especially nurses (Anderson et al., 1997; Ashley, 1976; Campbell, 1987; Chambliss, 1996; Corley & Mauksch, 1988; Ericksen, Rodney, & Starzomski, 1995; Glaser & Strauss, 1965). Recent empirical work from a variety of disciplines has made it clear that one of the most problematic features of the moral climate of health care agencies is the fragmented communication between health care team members and departments. This fragmentation results in the inadequate involvement of patients, family, and providers (again, especially nurses) in treatment decisions (Corley, Selig, & Ferguson, 1993; Ericksen, Rodney, & Starzomski, 1995; Erlin & Frost, 1991; Rodney, 1989, 1994, 1997; Solomon et al., 1993; Street, 1992; Ventres et al., 1997; Olson, 1998). As indicated in the earlier discussion of clinical health ethics issues, problems with communication make it difficult for patients, families, and providers to negotiate crucial values-based decisions — for instance, whether to agree to a DNR order or whether to engage in genetic testing for Huntington's chorea. In this sense, the moral climate of health care agencies all too often exacerbates or even creates ethical conflicts.

Furthermore, there is evidence that the moral climate of health care agencies is worsening in today's era of resource allocation difficulties and subsequent cost constraints (see Chapter 6 in this book). Effective communication between patients, families, and providers requires time and trust, qualities that become much less accessible when hospital units are closed, programs are downsized, nursing workloads are excessive, care is offloaded on families in the community, and so on (Burgess, 1996; Dossetor & MacDonald, 1994; Rodney, 1997; Rodney & Varcoe, in press; Storch, 1996; Woodward et al., 1998; Wolf, 1994; Aiken, Clarke, & Sloane, 2000).

Traditional bioethics has not effectively addressed these kind of meso and **macro level** problems (Starzomski & Rodney, 1997). Such problems are "everyday" rather than "quandary" issues, and hence do not get the same kind of attention that clinical health ethics issues such as end-of-life treatment, transplantation/organ donation, and genetics/genetics testing do. However, everyday contextual issues are as significant as clinical issues, and, indeed, the latter cannot be adequately addressed without attention to the former. For example, the previous discussion of end-of-life issues pointed out that one of the findings of the Special Senate Committee on Euthanasia and Assisted Suicide (1995) and the Special Subcommittee update (2000) was that inadequate pain relief at the end of life has at least in part led to requests for euthanasia. Inadequate pain relief is related to excessive workloads for providers and interdisciplinary team conflict (Ericksen, Rodney, & Starzomski, 1995) — everyday problems that are commonplace in most health care agencies.

Finally, a serious contextual issue in the moral climate of health care agencies has to do with culture.[4] Health care agencies take their own culture for granted and tend to marginalize patients and families whose culture is not from mainstream biomedicine (Coward & Ratanakul, 1999; Weisz, 1990; Wolf, 1994). As Burgess explains:

> health care services and health care ethics have complex assumptions comparable to cultural background or religious traditions. The fact that the health care context and much of industrialized society share many of these assumptions makes them difficult to recognize. (1999, p. 159)

Consequently, the communication required for value-based decisions is often fraught with unshared assumptions and divergent meanings (Burgess et al., 1999). Aboriginal Canadians who are giving "informed" consent, for instance, may have an understanding of their illness and treatment options that is different from that of their more powerful health care providers (Kaufert & O'Neil, 1990). Given the importance of informed consent in health care delivery and health research, difficulties negotiating informed consent in cross-cultural contexts are of concern.

Being oblivious to their own culture also means that health care agencies tend to be oblivious to systematic inequities in the accessibility and delivery of health care (Blue et al., 1999; Stephenson, 1999). For example, immigrant women with a chronic illness such as diabetes who are employed in the lower echelons of the labour market may have difficulty in following the diet and blood glucose monitoring required to manage their disease, let alone in getting time off to attend appointments with their physicians (Anderson, Dyck, & Lynam, 1997). These kinds of problems pose significant challenges in terms of social justice (Anderson & Rodney, 1999; Watson, 1994). Some of the solutions are to be found through ethical critiques of health policy — two examples of which will be explored later in this chapter.

ADDRESSING HEALTH ETHICS ISSUES

Fortunately, there are a number of initiatives in health care ethics in Canada that have made significant inroads into (or are on the threshold of) resolving many of the clinical and contextual issues articulated here. These include the generation of theoretical and empirical work addressing the moral climate of health care agencies, the creation of structures and mechanisms to foster ethical decision making in practice, and the updating of professional codes of ethics.

Attending to the moral climate of health care agencies is a fairly new focus in ethics. A number of researchers and theorists claim that a better understanding is required of the morality of the complex organizational contexts within which ethics is enacted and within which professionals and providers, and patients and their family members, struggle to make ethical decisions (Hoffmaster, 1993; Jameton, 1990; Jennings, 1990; Liaschenko, 1993; Pellegrino, 1990; Reiser, 1994; Rodney, 1997; Storch, 1999; Webster & Baylis, 2000; Weisz, 1990; Winkler, 1993). Research related to the context of health care ethics is beginning to proliferate. For example, in the United States, an ethnographic study evaluating a form used by physicians to elicit patients' preferences about treatment provided important information about institutional policies and practices (Ventres et al., 1997). In a study cited earlier in this chapter's analysis of genetics and genetics testing, researchers tried to understand the interface of consent for genetics testing with family history and dynamics (Cox, McKellin, & Burgess, 1995). Another hopeful development toward change is the increased attention being accorded to organizational ethics in health care (see, for example, Blake, 1999; Weber, 2001; Persaud & Narine, 2000). This relatively recent phenomenon has the potential to influence the social organization of health care in significant and unprecedented ways.

The creation of structures and mechanisms to foster ethical decision making in practice have included (but are not limited to) the growth of ethics committees and the use of clinical ethics consultants. Ethics committees serve as an important resource for health care agencies in the areas of ethics education, case consultation, and policy formulation (Storch et al., 1990; Storch & Griener, 1992). Interestingly, all three authors[5] have noted that while the initial focus of ethics committees since their inception in the late 1970s was on difficult decision making at the **micro level**, a number of ethics committees are also beginning to grapple with meso-level decisions about the allocation of resources. Overall, ethics committees and ethics consultants seek to improve the moral climate of health care agencies.

An ethics consultant is:

> someone who has the knowledge, abilities, and attributes of character to facilitate...ethical discourse in case consultation on ethical issues in clinical care or clinical research, and in ethics consultation to ethics committees, to research ethics boards (institutional review boards), and to policy formulation committees. (Baylis, 1994, p. 28)

Thus, consultants — who may come from a variety of disciplinary backgrounds — serve as an important adjunct to committees (American Society for Bioethics and Humanities, 1998).

Codes of ethics have served as a long-standing mechanism to improve decision making in health care on matters of ethical concern. Codes of ethics set the standards by which the profession and the public can evaluate (and potentially discipline) individual members, and codes provide guidance for individual members about their own conduct. Codes also "inform the public about what they can expect from professional practitioners" (Du Gas, Esson, & Ronaldson, 1999, p. 115; Yeo, 1996, p. 3).

Most health care professionals have such codes, and most codes have been substantially revised in the past decade to maintain currency and relevance to the broadening field of health care ethics (Storch, 1992; Yeo, 1996; Baylis et al., 1999). For instance, The Canadian Code of Ethics for Registered Nurses was revised in 1997 on the basis of "the consequences of economic constraints; increasing use of technology in health care; and, changing ways of delivering nursing services, such as the move to care outside of the institutional setting" (Canadian Nurses' Association, 1997, p. 1; Du Gas, Esson, & Ronaldson, 1999, p. 115; see also Canadian Nurses' Association, 1998). Although codes of ethics cannot address all issues, nor provide complete guidance to address the complexity of issues at micro, meso, and macro levels, they do play a noteworthy role in providing a standard for ethical behaviour, and in facilitating greater sensitivity to ethical issues (Baylis et al., 1999).

ETHICS AND SOCIAL POLICY

Steps toward resolving many of the clinical and contextual issues articulated in this chapter require proactive responses in ethics and health and social policy. Thus, the interface of ethics and health and social policy is important, both in terms of generating policies to address ethical issues and in critiquing the ethical implications of existing policies (Malone, 1999).

As noted in an earlier section of this chapter, questions about the allocation of health resources are value laden and require policies that can facilitate meaningful public input. Furthermore, health promotion strategies (including nonsmoking policies and seat belt legislation), access to alternative therapies, mental health policy and legislation, and Aboriginal health policy are replete with ethics concerns. All health and social policy issues include the balancing of individual and collective rights, as well as ethical justifications for restrictive practices. Two examples of health policy (ethics and human reproduction, and ethics in research with human subjects) will be examined here to illustrate the breadth of ethics concerns raised by health policy issues.

ETHICS AND HUMAN REPRODUCTION

Less than 20 years ago, the range of ethical issues under a heading such as "ethics and human reproduction" were fairly circumscribed. One could expect such a discussion to include contraception, sterilization, and abortion; a modest discussion about the control of genetic quality made possible through prenatal diagnosis; sometimes a discussion about care in childbirth; and a hint of concern about the ethical implications of the new frontiers in reproductive technology, such as prenatal diagnoses and "test-tube" babies (Storch, 1982, pp. 129–137). In Catholic hospitals, in particular, there were long-standing committees (often named medical–moral committees) to deal with contraception, sterilization, and abortion in accord with Catholic doctrine. But these were not the only health agency committees concerned about intervention in human reproduction. Therapeutic abortion committees were also operative in most major hospitals as the only legal route to permissible abortion (under section 221 of the *Criminal Code*). By 1988, that law was ruled unconstitutional through a legal challenge (*R v. Morgentaler*), and section 221 was struck from the *Criminal Code*. It was considered as a violation of the *Canadian Charter of Rights and Freedoms* because it violated a woman's right to life and personal security (Keatings & Smith, 1995, p. 12). Thus, abortion became legalized in Canada.

From an ethics perspective, the dialogue about abortion and other issues related to human reproduction have often been framed by the language of rights, that is, the rights of the woman versus the rights of the fetus (Sherwin, 1995; Tong, 1997). It is argued that women, as autonomous beings, should be free to choose their own destiny. When that choice jeopardizes another beginning life (a fetus), differing values lead to moral and legal controversy. Apart from the controversy that continues to surround abortion, the matter of a woman's choice commands more newsworthy attention in contemporary cases in which pregnant women are found to be engaging in behaviour that has a strong potential to be detrimental to the well-being of the fetus. In such cases, should a fetus be seen as a child in need of protection? Should child welfare laws be invoked to compel a pregnant mother to have treatment? (Picard & Robertson, 1996, p. 78). In the Winnipeg case of Mrs. G., a young mother involved in sniffing glue, this matter was tested in the courts. It was determined that a woman could not be compelled to enter into treatment to protect the fetus because under Canadian law, a fetus is not a person until it has been born. Therefore, birth is viewed as the necessary condition for legal personhood, and until birth the pregnant woman and her unborn child are legally one (Windwick, 1997).

Whereas such matters and those of the nontherapeutic sterilization of mentally handicapped women dominated much of the ethics discussion for decades, the acceleration in the development of new reproductive technology has been breathtaking. Current reproductive ethics discussions focus on a plethora of issues, including ovulation enhancement, gamete intrafallopian transfer, ovum donation and reception, in vitro fertilization, sex selection, surrogacy,[6] cryo-banking, and a range of previously "unimagined" possibilities (Baylis et al., 1995b; Kluge & Lucock, 1991; Royal Commission on New Reproductive Technologies, 1993).

These developments raise clinical ethics issues about quality of life: for couples wishing to have children, for women who are taking extensive hormone therapy, selling their oocytes, or carrying a child for another couple; and for the children produced through the use of such technologies in human reproduction (Nisker, 1997; Tong, 1997). Central ethical concerns in the use of these technologies continue to be shaped in part by the language of rights; for example, the right of a child to know his or her origins, the right of couples to be parents, and so forth. For the most part, rights language tends to be limiting because it sets up a relationship of controversy. Many health care ethicists have found a focus on relationships to be a more helpful way to examine the ethics of human reproduction (Bergum, 1990; Sherwin, 1992, 1995; Tong, 1997). But apart from the clinical issues about quality of life that these newer reproductive technologies raise, they also raise serious matters of health policy.

McTeer (1995) suggests that there are few areas of modern life where the challenge to find a "balanced relationship" between law, the public good, and the life of the individual is as great. Because human reproduction and genetic technologies are complex, powerful, and progressing at a rapid pace, a moral consideration of the questions implied about the integrity and definition of the human person is critical. At issue as well is the rightful place of the law in the regulation and enforcement of the use of these technologies.

Perhaps because of the intimacy of human reproduction, medical specialists involved in enhancing reproductive capacity have tended to claim a greater degree of privacy and independence than have other practitioners. Such claims were evident in artificial insemination by donor programs, wherein donor secrecy is often an overriding principle. But when does public interest override claims by practitioners or patients to privacy? Should reproductive interventions through technology be considered simply as tools to assist individuals, otherwise unable to procreate, to have healthy babies? Or are there broader public concerns at stake here as well? Because prenatal and pre-implantation diagnoses make possible discrimination prior to birth, because genetic engineering and embryo research make it possible that legal status could be denied to human life, and because the integrity of society may be threatened by new reproductive technologies, legal safeguards to ensure safe use and development of these technologies can be seen as essential to security and well-being (McTeer, 1995, 1999; Nisker & Gore-Langton, 1995; Royal Commission on New Reproductive Technologies, 1993).

POLICY RESPONSES

The burgeoning new reproductive technologies, and the serious societal–ethical questions raised by the use or anticipated use of these means to alter human reproductive capacity, led the government of Canada to establish a Royal Commission on New Reproductive Technologies in 1989. This commission consisted of seven members, who, not unlike the subject that generated their development, encountered serious controversy in their work. Some commissioners viewed the concerns surrounding new reproductive technologies as problems of medical management, while others viewed the concerns as problems requiring value decisions (Kondro, 1992). In late 1993, the royal commission report was released (Royal Commission on New Reproductive Technologies, 1993). The general theme of the commission's recommendations was to "proceed with caution" in introducing these new reproductive technologies. Market forces were not to determine how these new reproductive technologies would be used, as has been the case in the United States. A permanent regulatory and licensing body was recommended to govern everything from sperm banks to in vitro fertilization to research involving human zygotes (Kondro, 1993).

The federal government has been slow to respond to the Commission's recommendations. Upon the release of the report, the health minister indicated that the government had no "immediate intention" of acting upon these recommendations without consulting with the provinces first. By July 1995, the minister declared a voluntary moratorium on applying nine reproductive technology procedures that she regarded as threatening to human dignity, presenting serious ethical, social, and health risks, and treating women as commodities. These technologies included sex selection; commercial surrogacy arrangements; buying and selling oocytes, sperm, or embryo; formation of animal–human gametes; retrieval of eggs from cadavers and fetuses for donation, fertilization, or research; creation of an artificial womb; germ-line genetic alteration; egg donation in exchange for in vitro fertilization (IVF) services; and human embryo cloning (Marleau, 1995).

CURRENT AND FUTURE CONCERNS

Unfortunately, in the absence of a definitive response by the federal government to regulate new reproductive technologies, the "voluntary" moratorium is having limited effect. In June 1999, for example, media stories abounded about the mishandling of new human reproductive technologies. Three sperm banks in the Toronto area were being closed while investigations proceeded to determine whether these clinics ignored standards of testing for disease prior to use of sperm. Other media stories surfaced about "mistakes" being made in the use of stored eggs or sperm. One reported case involved the birth of twins, one fair-skinned and the other darker-skinned, with a realization that the material used to create the pregnancies had been mixed with another couple's stored reproductive material. Surely the safety of women requesting sperm from these clinics and the safety of the offspring produced through use of such sperm should be a matter of grave public concern (Sherwin, 1995; Tong, 1997).

Even though the majority of fertility clinic services are not covered under health insurance in Canada, does that lack of coverage make the use of new reproductive technologies of less concern? One of the Canadian fertility clinics had on their Web site an animated ticking watch with the message: "We all face nature's biological clock. The...Centre wastes no time in meeting the challenges posed by the miracle of science and conception." Does this type of advertising of scientific possibility create need, or — of even greater concern — does it suggest that to be nonfertile is less than adequate in society or that human fulfillment comes only with "natural" parenthood? This, too, would seem to be a matter of public concern (Nisker, 1996; Nisker & Gore-Langton, 1995; Sherwin, 1995; Tong, 1997). The government's delay in taking action on the commission's recommendation to establish a permanent regulatory body appears to have been a costly delay.

One further new reproductive technology worthy of mention is the potential for human cloning. Arguments for and against human cloning are powerful and will continue to raise serious concerns about the human values involved, including genetic determinism, the interests of the child, the risks involved in cloning, the use of clones as donors, and the regulation of this technology (National Bioethics Advisory Commission, 1999).

Finally, market forces in new reproductive technologies appear to be thriving in the absence of regulation. Experts in new reproductive technology and the media continue to report that commercial surrogacy arrangements in Canada are occurring. Men and women continue to sell sperm and oocytes, the latter often "bartered" in exchange for infertility treatment. Surely, the supposedly egalitarian Canadian society should be distressed about the social justice implications of such arrangements (Nisker, 1996, 1997; Royal Commission on New Reproductive Technologies, 1993; Overall, 1995; Sherwin, 1995).

Not surprisingly, then, future concerns about new reproductive technologies are legion. For instance, the matter of health insurance coverage for the use of these technologies may well have to be a settled issue (i.e., health insurance would cover such procedures) in order to influence the regulation of this technology for the public good. Some ethicists have framed this issue as a matter of becoming a society compassionate enough to allow women and men a choice about parenthood. A second major concern is the potential inherent in the use of many of these technologies for denigrating people with defects. The control over the genetic transmission of defects through cell manipulation could well lead to further discrimination against those handicapped through genetic transmission. A third concern, as has been illustrated, is the commercialization of human reproduction, such as the buying and selling of eggs or of sperm, or the "renting" of wombs in surrogacy arrangements.[7] Such commercialization seems contrary to a respect for human personhood and human life. These are among the many matters necessitating policy directives. These directives will clearly not be easy to undertake, given diverse interests, values, and views about new reproductive technologies, not the least of which is the interest in scientific pursuit through research on human subjects and human tissue.

In May 2001, Minister of Health Alan Rock launched a review of draft legislation by presenting Proposals for Legislation Governing Assisted Human Reproduction (Health Canada, 2001) to the House of Commons Steering Committee on Health. This committee was asked to study the legislation, which would ban cloning and other unacceptable practices, regulate assisted reproduction, and address research in this area, and to report back to the Minister by January 2002. The two primary objectives of the proposed legislation were "...to ensure that Canadians using assisted human reproduction techniques can do so without compromising their health and safety...and to ensure that promising research related to assisted human reproduction takes place within a regulated environment" (Rock, 2001). While the majority of responses to these intents were supportive of the goals, Health Canada was criticized for its continued delay in regulating the area of human reproduction by yet further study.

Health Research Ethics: Protecting Human Subjects

Advances in medical science, in nursing science, and in the work of all health professionals involved in the delivery of health care have required that people participate in research studies to determine the effect of health care interventions. The most visible human research studies in health care are those involving the testing of pharmaceuticals, whether those studies encompass new drugs designed to treat cancer, to prevent malaria, to lower blood pressure, or to provide pain relief. Because much of what occurs in medical and health-related research involves the potential for significant risk to the people participating in the research study, many ethical concerns arise in such research. A principal cause for concern is the fact that for many of the interventions being tested, there may be no known benefit (i.e., no known therapeutic benefit) to the participant (commonly called the research subject), and there may be significant risk. The necessity to test interventions on human beings prior to introducing those interventions into standard practice often conflicts with the risks involved for human beings as subjects. In order to ensure that the researcher does as little harm as possible while carrying out such research, standards must be developed for research involving human subjects and mechanisms must be created to monitor the use of these standards.

PAST TO PRESENT

Concerns about the protection of human subjects involved in research studies is well founded. The history of abuses in health research became most apparent following World War II, when the reality of Nazi experimentation on prisoners in concentration camps became known. These abuses included starving inmates to study the physiology of nutrition, placing them in low-pressure chambers to determine the effects of rapid changes in altitude, infecting inmates with bacteria to study the course of disease, and exposing inmates to icy water or blizzards to test for revival after freezing (Pence, 1995; Brody, 1998). But these were not the only abuses of human subjects in research projects, and Germany is not the only country in which such inappropriate use of human subjects has occurred. Abuse in other countries has included injecting long-term-care patients with live cancer cells, injecting institutionalized mentally retarded children with hepatitis virus, and observing poor people of colour with syphilis to determine the effects of untreated syphilis long after effective treatment became available (Baylis et al., 1995c; Law Reform Commission of Canada, 1989). In Canada, the use of hallucinogenic drugs at the Allan Memorial Institute in Montreal for purposes of investigating brainwashing techniques is an example of the abuse of research subjects (Law Reform Commission of Canada, 1989). A common theme in most of these situations was that medical science had lost all ethical perspective and that the health professionals entrusted to provide therapeutic care for patients betrayed that trust by conscripting clients for research study without their consent.

As a result of these and other abuses of human subjects, codes of research ethics were developed by medical associations, government departments, nursing associations, and other groups. In Canada, the Medical Research Council took the lead in developing guidelines for the protection of human subjects in medical research. The various codes and guidelines (or standards) included several key protections:

1. Human subject research should be undertaken only if the potential benefits outweigh the potential risks.
2. A subject's involvement in research must be informed and voluntarily given.
3. Confidentiality cannot be breached without the subject's consent.
4. The research must be designed and conducted to yield fruitful results.
5. The subject must be protected from harm, and any harm must be minimized.
6. The subject must be free to withdraw from the experiment at any time (Medical Research Council, 1993).

INSTITUTIONAL STRUCTURES

In an attempt to establish mechanisms to deal with safeguarding human subjects and to operationalize ethical guidelines at the meso level, research ethics committees have been developed in universities and major health care agencies in Canada and the United States. In the United States, where this type of development was pioneered, these committees were called institutional review boards (IRBs). In Canada, these committees have been named research ethics boards (REBs). Their purpose is to review research proposals to determine if adequate provision has been made for the protection of human subjects involved in the research. Key elements of the ethics review are the assurance of the consent of the research subject and attention to privacy and confidentiality. Research relevance and research design are also considered fundamental to a sound ethics review, since poorly directed research or research with questionable methodology is unethical through the ineffective use of resources and the inappropriate involvement of human subjects.

To assist research ethics boards in their task, a Canadian organization called the National Council on Bioethics in Human Research (NCBHR) was created in 1989. Initially a "child" of the Medical Research Council (MRC), the Royal College of Physicians and Surgeons of Canada, and Health Canada, the NCBHR was designed to be an independent body for the education of REB members and for the monitoring of MRC-funded research involving human subjects. When the MRC, the Social Sciences and Humanities Research Council (SSHRC), and the Natural Sciences and Engineering Council (NSERC) chose to unite in developing one common code for research ethics in Canada, the National Council on Bioethics in Human Research (NCBHR) changed its name to become the National Council on Ethics in Human Research (NCEHR) to serve all constituencies. NCBHR (now NCEHR) has published numerous papers to provide more detailed guidance to researchers and research ethics boards, including one on research involving children and another designed to clarify the issue of consent in research (informed choice) (NCBHR, 1993, 1996).

The creation of the Tri-Council Policy Statement, Ethical Conduct for Research Involving Humans (1998), referred to as a common code above, was a major national endeavour. The admonition *respect for human dignity* is incorporated throughout the Tri-Council Policy Statement. For example, in section 9 of this statement, the importance of upholding fundamental values in research involving new reproductive technologies is highlighted, and respect for human dignity is stated as "a paramount consideration in evolving ethical, policy and social deliberations" (p. 9.1). Researchers and research ethics boards are reminded of their responsibility to be proactive in articulating the public interest in these issues, and to respect the developing legal and regulatory frameworks as well as policy developments. For example, reference is made to the *Report of the Royal Commission on New Reproductive Technologies* (1993). Thus, the statement directs researchers to obtain free and informed consent from individuals whose gametes are to be used for research purposes and prohibits the use of ova or sperm obtained through commercial transactions or exchange for services.

Under the 1998 Tri-Council Policy Statement (TCPS) (1998) requirements, REBs must consist of at least five members, and they must report to the highest level of authority in health agencies or universities. Expectations are also established in the statement for the REB's assessment of risk to the subject, the process for meetings and record keeping, the process for decision making, and the need for ongoing review.

Although the initiation and implementation of the TCPS has not been without some challenges, a committee called the Tri-Council Advisory Group (TCAG) was created as the TCPS was released to address areas of difficulty. The TCAG, made up of two representatives from each of the three granting councils plus two representatives from NCEHR, was charged with responding to concerns about the 'code' and revising sections of the TCPS as necessary. With the transition of the Medical Research Council of Canada to a new entity called the Canadian Institute for Health Research (CIHR), a new committee structure called the Standing Committee on Ethics, and a secretariat to support its work, was designed to promote health research ethics. This division within CIHR is mandated to ensure that research funded by CIHR meets the highest international standards of excellence and ethics, to ensure that funding is available to build capacity for ethics scholarship and training, and to recommend corporate ethics policy.

Meanwhile, the three research funding agencies (SSHRC, NSERC, and CIHR) have also collaborated to establish an Inter-Agency Panel on Ethics (IAPE). This enhanced committee, also supported by a secretariat, has been designed to support the continued development, evolution, interpretation, and implementation of the TCPS, and it replaces the TCAG. At the time of writing, these council-originated structures are in the process of development and distinctions between the mandates of all the new committees and secretariats are not entirely clear. Adding to some confusion in the research field are other new bodies recently created, such as the Canadian Biotechnology Advisory Committee (CBAC), as well as numerous other national groups. Meanwhile, the original organization formed to be arm's length from the source of funding, so as to remove conflict of interests in research ethics, namely, the National Council on Ethics in Human Research, continues to serve REBs in Canada, and continues to advocate for a separation of research funding from ethics oversight for human subjects (participants) (Storch, 2001).

FUTURE CHALLENGES

The structures noted above should be sufficient to ensure the ethical conduct of health research. However, situations that arise in health care and research agencies and in the media suggest that the conflicts inherent in the conduct of health research are not always successfully guided by the presence of such safeguards. In a Canadian case in the late 1990s, for example, Nancy Oliveri, a medical researcher at the Hospital for Sick Children in Toronto, took considerable risks in exposing a situation of purported harm to research subjects when she decided to "blow the whistle" during the trial of a drug that was apparently having unexpected side effects. Conflict between the research sponsor (a pharmaceutical company), hospital financing, and the researcher's concerns was at issue in this case, which emerged in the press in the fall of 1998 (Crelinston, 1999; Shuchman, 1999). Significantly, the corporatization of health research has come under scrutiny in this difficult case. It appears that corporate interests in research (including health research) rather than scientific merit have too often covertly driven research agendas and the dissemination of research findings (Demont, 1998).

In May 2000, the Law Commission of Canada released a report titled *The Governance of Health Research Involving Human Subjects (HRIHS)*, focusing on the ethical governance of research of HRIHS in Canada. The researchers in this study noted that the ethics of such research has three main objectives: promoting socially beneficial research, promoting respect for the dignity and rights of research subjects, and promoting the maintenance of trust between the research community and society as a whole. They concluded that there are significant gaps in the effectiveness and accountability of governance for HRIHS and recommended fostering a research ethics culture in which all involved in HRIHS recognized their role in human-research subject protection. Other recommendations included the greater independence of organizations established to monitor research with human subjects, including the National Council on Ethics in Human Research (NCEHR), and innovation in experimentation and research to fill gaps in knowledge of appropriate standards for performance-focused review (Law Commission, 2000, pp. v–xiv). Significant findings in this study were that Canadians likely know more about how animals fare in research than about how human subjects are being treated, and that too much of the focus of ethics review has centred on the bureaucratic process of approving consent forms, which is suggested to be a review with "tunnel vision." Broader concerns about the promotion of beneficial research, the protection of human subjects, and the generation of trust are considered to be critical to the future of human research ethics in Canada.

CONCLUSION

The significance and complexity of the clinical, contextual, and policy issues noted in this chapter cannot be overemphasized. Many of these issues challenge the most precious values of Canadian society. As Canada becomes increasingly multicultural, the task of arriving at shared social and ethical values becomes an enormous challenge. What is morally right and what is morally wrong has never been more clouded. One thing, however, is clear. In order to develop solutions to the ethical problems that face it, the health care system will require a partnership of members of the public, health care providers, and government. The solutions will only become apparent if they collaborate.

Although some ethical issues tend to continually "catch the headlines" in health care, taking ethics seriously often results in seeing problems where we previously saw none. Thus, even some of the more mundane everyday issues of health care, such as those involving greater attention to patient autonomy and patient choice, have become serious concerns. Attention to these issues, in turn, has led to a re-examination of the proper relationships between health professionals and patients, and to the structures in which health care is delivered. The less spectacular issues in health care remain troublesome as the needs of health professionals, health institutions, government funding formulas, and patients are often in conflict. The more spectacular issues of health care continue to be unsettled as beliefs about the sanctity of life, quality of life, and appropriate medical interventions elicit polarized value positions. And, as we have explained in this chapter, looming over *all* the issues are pressing questions about the equitable and effective allocation of health care resources.

Fortunately, attention to improved ethical decision making by all those involved in health care has never been greater. There have been tremendous strides made: in ethics education for health professionals, in ethics committees, in guidelines for ethical decision making, and in ethical standards and policies. It behooves all who have an interest in health care — providers, patients, families, communities, governments, and members of the public — to support such initiatives and to develop new and better ways to monitor and correct ethical violations, resolve ethical dilemmas, and relieve ethical distress. In the words of a health care ethicist:

> We want, as participants in [health care], to be able to notice our moral problems and to cope with them with sensitivity and integrity and to keep our health care institutions responsive to their moral goals." (Jameton, 1990, p. 450)

STUDY QUESTIONS

1. *What role has sociology played in our ability to understand, and ultimately improve, health ethics in Canada?*
2. *How would you define quality of life?*
3. *What is the difference between euthanasia and withholding or withdrawing treatment?*
4. *What are your opinions about the use of xenografts in transplantation?*
5. *What is the significance of the family in genetics and genetic testing?*
6. *Can you think of examples of problems in the allocation of resources that have worsened the moral climate of health care agencies?*
7. *What do you think of the morality of commercial surrogacy arrangements?*
8. *What do you think of corporate sponsorship of health research?*

GLOSSARY

assisted euthanasia (assisted suicide) Assisting a person in advancing his or her death at the request of that person.

advance directives (personal directives) A person's written wishes about life-sustaining treatment, meant to assist with decisions about withholding and withdrawing treatment.

futility Two components exist: *quantitative* futility, in which physicians conclude through an appeal to empirical data that they are not obligated to offer medical treatment to a patient; *qualitative* futility, in which physicians will not offer treatment because it will not result in a return to consciousness or the ability to leave a critical care hospital unit (Schneiderman, Jecker, & Jonsen, 1990; Taylor, 1995).

human genome project A project carried on worldwide in a number of research centres to coordinate scientific data in order to further understand the structure, function, and outcome of the hereditary instructions in the human genome.

low birth weight Birth weight of less than 2500 grams, or about 5.5 pounds.

macro-level approach A primary focus on large-scale social, political, economic, and cultural factors.

micro-level approach A primary focus on the interaction between patients and providers of services.

withholding and withdrawing treatment Reasoned clinical judgements identifying treatments that are or are not in the patient's best interest, determined on the basis of an assessment of the patient's personal, cultural, and spiritual values, as well as an assessment of the patient's prognosis, treatment options, and so forth (Moreno, 1999; Storch, 1999); withholding and withdrawing treatment used to be (misleadingly) called passive euthanasia.

RECOMMENDED READINGS

Baylis, F., Downie, J., Freedman, B., Hoffmaster, B., & Sherwin, S. (Eds.). (1995). *Health Ethics in Canada*. Toronto: Harcourt Brace. A carefully selected and wide range of classic and specifically Canadian articles that begins with a section on the nature and context of health care ethics and then turns to examine numerous areas of decision making in health care. Specific attention is directed to decisions at the beginning and end of life, including a series of articles about genetics, abortion, assisted reproductive technologies, withholding and withdrawing life-sustaining treatment, and euthanasia and assisted suicide.

Brody, B.A. (1998). *The ethics of biomedical research: An international perspective*. New York: Oxford University Press. An excellent resource on health research ethics, covering the range of research involving humans, from genetic research to clinical trials to research involving vulnerable populations; contains four valuable appendices on international research ethics policies, European transnational research ethics policies, U.S. research ethics policies, and research ethics policies in other countries.

Coward, H., & Ratanakul, P. (Eds.). (1999). *A cross-cultural dialogue on health care ethics*. Waterloo, ON: Wilfrid Laurier University Press. A collection of original articles by team members, devoted to culture, health, and illness; culture and health care ethics; ethical issues in the delivery of health care services; and cross-cultural dialogue in health policy; provides skillful analyses of complex multicultural issues and concerns in health care ethics.

Kluge, E.W. (Ed.). (1999). *Readings in biomedical ethics: A Canadian focus*. Scarborough, ON: Prentice-Hall Allyn and Bacon Canada. A book that begins with an examination of ethical theory and provides a useful listing of further readings, some annotated; places health as an ethical issue in context, and focuses as well on the patient and the health care professional, consent to health care, decisions about life and death, decisions about the beginning of life, and the genetic basis of human life.

Roy, D.J., Williams, J.R., & Dickens, B.M. (1994). *Bioethics in Canada*. Scarborough, ON: Prentice-Hall. Excellent coverage of the field of bioethics, including the history of bioethics, central issues and methods, the relationship of bioethics and law, and the Canadian health care system, including relationships between doctors, nurses, and patients.

REFERENCES

Aiken, L.H., Clarke, S.P., & Sloane, D.M. (2000). Hospital restructuring: Does it adversely affect care and outcomes? *Journal of Nursing Administration, 30*(10), 457–465.

American Society for Bioethics and Humanities. (1998). *Core competencies for health care ethics consultation*. Glenview, IL: Author.

Anderson, J.M., Dyck, I., & Lynam, J. (1997). Health care professionals and women speaking: Constraints in everyday life and the management of chronic illness. *Health, 1*(1), 57–80.

Anderson, J., & Rodney, P. (1999). Part IV [Health policy: A cross-cultural dialogue], Conclusion. In H. Coward & P. Ratanakul (Eds.), *A cross-cultural dialogue on health care ethics* (pp. 257–261). Waterloo, ON: Wilfrid Laurier University Press.

Ashley, J.A. (1976). *Hospitals, paternalism, and the role of the nurse*. New York: Teacher's College Press.

Bailey, L. (1990). Organ transplantation: A paradigm of medical progress. *Hastings Center Report*, *20*(1), 24–28.

Balk, R. (1990). Should transplantation be part of a health care system? *Canadian Medical Association Journal*, *36*, 1129–1132.

Barer, M., & Stoddart, G. (1992). *Toward integrated medical resource policies for Canada*. Report prepared for the Federal/Provincial/Territorial Conference of Deputy Ministers of Health. Manitoba: Manitoba Health.

Barer, M., Welch, P., & Antioch, L. (1991). Canadian/U.S. health care: Reflections on the HIAA's analysis. *Health Affairs*, *10*(3), 229–239.

Baylis, F.E. (1994). A profile of the health care ethics consultant. In F.E. Baylis (Ed.), *The health care ethics consultant* (pp. 25–44). Totowa, NJ: Humana Press.

Baylis, F., Downie, J., Freedman, B., Hoffmaster, B., & Sherwin, S. (Eds.). (1995a). *Health care ethics in Canada*. Toronto: Harcourt Brace.

Baylis, F., Downie, J., Freedman, B., Hoffmaster, B., & Sherwin, S. (1995b). Introduction [Assisted reproductive technologies]. In F. Baylis, J. Downie, B. Freedman, B. Hoffmaster, & S. Sherwin, *Health care ethics in Canada* (pp. 450–455). Toronto: Harcourt Brace.

Baylis, F., Downie, J., Freedman, B., Hoffmaster, B., & Sherwin, S. (1995c). Introduction [Research involving human subjects]. In F. Baylis, J. Downie, B. Freedman, B. Hoffmaster, & S. Sherwin, *Health care ethics in Canada* (pp. 320–325). Toronto: Harcourt Brace.

Baylis, J., Downie, B., Baylis, F., Downie, J., & Dewhirst, K. (1999). *Codes of ethics*. Toronto: Hospital for Sick Children.

Beardsley, T. (1996, March). Vital data: Trends in human genetics. *Scientific American*, 100–105.

Benjamin, C.M., Adam, S., Wiggins, S., Theilmann, J.L., Copely, T.T., Bloch, M., Squitieri, F., McKellin, W., Cox, S., Brown, S.A., Kremer, H.P.H., Burgess, M., Meshino, W., Summers, A., Macgregor, D., Buchanan, J., Greenberg, C., Carson, N., Ives, E., Frecker, M., Welsh, J.P., Fuller, A., Rosenblatt, D., Miller, S., Dufrasne, S., Roy, M., Andermann, E., Prevost, C., Khalifa, M., Girard, K., Taylor, S., Hunter, A., Goldsmith, C., Wehlan, D., Eisenberg, D., Soltan, H., Kane, J., Shokeir, M.H.K., Gibson, A., Cardwell, S., Bamforth, S., Grover, S., Suchowersky, O., Klimek, M., Garber, T., Gardner, H.A., MacLeod, P., & Hayden, M.R. (1994). Proceed with care: Direct predictive testing for Huntington Disease. *American Journal of Human Genetics*, *55*, 606–617.

Benjamin, M., & Curtis, J. (1992). *Ethics in nursing* (3rd ed.). New York: Oxford University Press.

Bergum, V. (1990, April). Abortion revisited: What can pregnancy tell us about abortion? *The Bioethics Bulletin*, pp. 3–5.

Bernabei, R., Gambassi, G., Lapane, K., Landi, F., Gatsonis, C., Dunlop, R., Lipsitz, L., Steel, K., & Mor, V. (1998). Management of pain in elderly patients with cancer. *JAMA*, *279*(23), 1877–1882.

Blake, D.C. (1999). Organizational ethics: Creating structural and cultural change in health-care organizations. *Journal of Clinical Ethics, 10*(3), 187–193.

Blondeau, D., Lavoie, M., Valois, P., Keyserlingk, E.W., Hébert, M., & Martineau, I. (2000). The attitude of Canadian nurses towards advance directives. *Nursing Ethics, 7*(5), 399–411.

Blue, A., Keyserlingk, T., Rodney, P., & Starzomski, R. (1999). A critical view of North American health policy. In H. Coward & P. Ratanakul (Eds.), *A cross-cultural dialogue on health care ethics* (pp. 215–225). Waterloo, ON: Wilfrid Laurier University Press.

Brody, B.A. (1998). *The ethics of biomedical research: An international perspective*. New York: Oxford University Press.

Brooks, J. (1993). The heart of the matter: Dalton Camp and his controversial transplant. *Canadian Medical Association Journal, 149*(7), 996–1002.

Browne, A. (2000). When patients demand too much. *Health Ethics Today, 11*(1), 2–3.

Buchanan, A. (1996). Toward a theory of the ethics of bureaucratic organizations. *Business Ethics Quarterly, 6*(4), 419–440.

Burgess, M. (1996). Health care reform: Whitewashing a conflict between health promotion and treating illness? In M. Stingl & D. Wilson (Eds.), *Efficiency vs equality: Health reform in Canada* (pp. 153–162). Halifax: Fernwood.

Burgess, M. (1999). Part III [Ethical issues in the delivery of health care services], Introduction. In H. Coward & P. Ratanakul (Eds.), *A cross-cultural dialogue on health care ethics* (pp. 157–159). Waterloo, ON: Wilfrid Laurier University Press.

Burgess, M., Rodney, P., Coward, H., Ratanakul, P., & Suwonnakote, K. (1999). Pediatric care: Judgements about best interests at the outset of life. In H. Coward & P. Ratanakul (Eds.), *A cross-cultural dialogue on health care ethics* (pp. 160–175). Waterloo, ON: Wilfrid Laurier University Press.

Callahan, D. (1990). *What kind of life: The limits to medical progress.* Toronto: Simon and Schuster.

Campbell, M.L. (1987). Productivity in Canadian nursing: Administering cuts. In D. Coburn, C. D'Arcy, G.M. Torrance, & P. New (Eds.), *Health and Canadian society: Sociological perspectives* (2nd ed., pp. 463–475). Toronto: Fitzhenry & Whiteside.

Canadian Nurses' Association. (1997). *Code of ethics for registered nurses.* Ottawa: Author.

Canadian Nurses' Association. (1998). *Everyday ethics: Putting the code into practice.* Ottawa: Author.

Chambliss, D.F. (1996). *Beyond caring: Hospitals, nurses, and the social organization of ethics.* Chicago: University of Chicago Press.

Charles, C., & DeMaio, S. (1993). Lay participation in health care decision making: A conceptual framework. *Journal of Health Politics, Policy and Law, 18*(4), 883–904.

Churchill, L.R. (1997). Bioethics in social context. In R.A. Carson & C.R. Burns (Eds.), *Philosophy of medicine and bioethics* (pp. 137–151). Dordrecht, Netherlands: Kluwer Academic.

Corley, M.C., Selig, P., & Ferguson, C. (1993). Critical care nurse participation in ethical and work decisions. *Critical Care Nurse, 13*(3), 120–128.

Coward, H., & Ratanakul, P. (Eds.). (1999). *A cross-cultural dialogue on health care ethics.* Waterloo, ON: Wilfrid Laurier University Press.

Cox, S., & McKellin, W. (1999). "There's this thing in our family": Predictive testing and the social construction of risk for Huntington Disease. In P. Conrad & J. Gabe (Eds.), *Sociological perspectives on the new genetics* (pp. 121–145). Oxford: Blackwell.

Cox, S., McKellin, W., & Burgess, M. (1995). The medical genetics patient: Individual or family? CSAA Annual Meetings, Montreal.

Crelinston, G. (1999). Adjudicating ethics in research: Independent review. *Canadian Medical Association Journal, 160*(3), 386–388.

Crichton, A., & Hsu, D. (1990). *Canada's health care system: Its funding and organization.* Ottawa: Canadian Hospital Association Press.

Deber, R. (1992). Translating technology assessment into policy: Conceptual choices and tough issues. *International Journal of Technology Assessment in Health Care, 8*(1), 131–137.

Degner, L.F., & Beaton, J.I. (1987). *Life and death decisions in health care.* New York: Hemisphere.

Demont, J. (1998, November 16). Pressure point: Federal researchers say drug companies push hard for approvals. *Maclean's, 111*(46), 70–72.

Dickens, B. (1988). The anencephalic organ donor and the law. *Transplantation/Implantation Today, 5*, 42–46.

Dickens, B. (1991). WHO guiding principles on human organ transplantation. *Transplantation/Implantation Today, 8*, 12–18.

Dossetor, J.B., & Cain, D.J. (Eds.). (1997). *A handbook of health ethics.* Edmonton: Bioethics Centre, University of Alberta.

Dossetor, J., & MacDonald, N. (1994). Ethics of palliative care in the context of limited resources: An essay on the need for attitudinal change. *Journal of Palliative Care, 10*(3), 39–42.

Douglas, R. (1993). *Unfinished business.* Auckland, NZ: Random House Press.

Du Gas, B.W., Esson, L., & Richardson, S.E. (with contribution from P. Rodney). (1999). The legal and ethical foundations of nursing practice. In *Nursing foundations: A Canadian perspective* (pp. 98–122). Scarborough, ON: Prentice-Hall.

Ericksen, J., Rodney, P., & Starzomski, R. (1995). When is it right to die? *Canadian Nurse, 91* (8), 29–34.

Erlen, J.A., & Frost, B. (1991). Nurses' perceptions of powerlessness in influencing ethical decisions. *Western Journal of Nursing Research, 13*, 397–407.

Evans, R.G. (1993, July/August). Health care reform: "The issue from hell." *Policy Options*, 35–41.

Evans, R.G., Barer, M.L., & Hertzman, C. (1991). The 20-year experiment: Accounting for, explaining, and evaluating health care cost containment in Canada and the United States. *Annual Review of Public Health, 12*, 481–518.

Evans, R.W. (1992). Need, demand, and supply in organ transplantation. *Transplantation Proceedings, 24*(5), 2152–2154.

Evans, R.W., Manninen, D., Dong, F., & McLynne, D. (1993). Is retransplantation cost effective? *Transplantation Proceedings, 25*(1), 1694–1696.

Fagerhaugh, S., Strauss, A., Suczek, B., & Weiner, C. (1980). The impact of technology on patients, providers, and care patterns. *Nursing Outlook, 28*(11), 666–672.

Federal–Provincial Advisory Committee on Health Services. (1996). *Organ and tissue distribution in Canada — A discussion document.* Ottawa: Health Canada.

Fox, R.C. (1990). The evolution of American bioethics: A sociological perspective. In G. Weisz (Ed.), *Social science perspectives on medical ethics* (pp. 201–217). Philadelphia: University of Pennsylvania Press.

Fox, R., & Swazey, J. (1992a). Leaving the field. *Hastings Center Report, 22*(5), 9–15.

Fox, R., & Swazey, J. (1992b). *Spare parts: Organ replacement in American society.* New York: Oxford University Press.

Glaser, B., & Strauss, A. (1965). *Awareness of dying.* Chicago: Aldine.

Goodman, C. (1992). It's time to rethink health care technology assessment. *International Journal of Technology Assessment in Health Care, 8*(2), 335–358.

Hadorn, D. (1993). *Outcomes management and resource allocation: How should quality of life be measured?* Health Policy Research Unit Discussion Paper Series. Vancouver: University of British Columbia (HPRU 93:7D).

Halsley-Lea, D., Jenkins, J., & Francomano, C. (1998). *Genetics in clinical practice: New directions for nursing and health care.* Toronto: Jones and Bartlett.

Hauptman, P., & O'Connor, K. (1997). Medical Progress: Procurement and allocation of solid organs for transplantation. *New England Journal of Medicine, 6*(336), 422–432.

Hayes, C. (1992). Genetic testing for Huntington's Disease: A family issue. *New England Journal of Medicine, 327*(20), 1449–1451.

Health Canada. (2001a). Guide to the proposals for legislation governing assisted human reproduction. May 2001.

Health Canada. (2001b). Proposals for legislation governing assisted human reproduction. May 2001.

Hoffman, E. (1994). The evolving genome project: Current and future impact. *American Journal of Human Genetics, 54*(1), 129–136.

Hoffmaster, B. (1990). Morality and the social sciences. In G. Weisz (Ed.), *Social science perspectives on medical ethics* (pp. 241–260). Philadelphia: University of Pennsylvania Press.

Hoffmaster, B. (1993). Can ethnography save the life of medical ethics? In E.R. Winkler & J.R. Coombs (Eds.), *Applied ethics: A reader* (pp. 366–389). Oxford: Blackwell.

Hunter, S. (2000). Determination of moral negligence in the context of the undermedication of pain by nurses. *Nursing Ethics, 7*(5), 379–391.

Jameton, A. (1990). Culture, morality, and ethics: Twirling the spindle. *Critical Care Nursing Clinics of North America, 2*(3), 443–451.

Jecker, N.S. (1991). Knowing when to stop: The limits of medicine. *Hastings Centre Report, 21*(3), 5–8.

Jennings, B. (1990). Ethics and ethnography in neonatal intensive care. In G. Weisz (Ed.), *Social science perspectives on medical ethics* (pp. 261–272). Philadelphia: University of Pennsylvania Press.

Jonsen, A.R. (1997). Introduction to the history of bioethics. In N.S. Jecker, A.R. Jonsen, & R.A. Pearlman (Eds.), *Bioethics: An introduction to the history, methods, and practice* (pp. 3–11). Boston: Jones and Bartlett.

Kaufert, J.M, & O'Neil, J.D. (1990). Biomedical rituals and informed consent: Native Canadians and the negotiation of clinical trust. In G. Weisz (Ed.), *Social science perspectives on medical ethics* (pp. 41–63). Philadelphia: University of Pennsylvania Press.

Kazim, E., Al-Rukaimi, H., Fernandez, S., Raizada, S., Mustafa, M., & Huda, N. (1992). Buying a kidney: The easy way out? *Transplantation Proceedings, 24*(5), 2112–2113.

Keatings, M., & Smith, O. (1995). *Ethical and legal issues in Canadian nursing.* Toronto: W.B. Saunders.

Kerr, A., Cunningham-Burley, S., & Amos, A. (1998). The new genetics and health: Mobilizing lay expertise. *Public Understanding of Science, 7,* 41–60.

Kessler, S. (1994). Invited editorial: Predictive testing for Huntington Disease: A psychologist's view. *American Journal of Medical Genetics, 54,* 161–166.

Kilner, J. (1990). *Who lives? Who dies? — Ethical criteria in patient selection.* New Haven, CT: Yale University Press.

Kjellstrand, C., & Dossetor, J. (1992). *Ethical problems in dialysis and transplantation.* Boston: Kluwer Academic.

Kluge, E. (1993). Age and organ transplantation. *Canadian Medical Association Journal, 149*(7), 1003.

Kluge, E. (Ed.). (1999). *Readings in biomedical ethics: A Canadian focus* (2nd ed.). Scarborough, ON: Prentice-Hall.

Kluge, E., & Lucock, C. (1991). *New human reproductive technologies.* Ottawa: Canadian Medical Association.

Kondro, W. (1992). Canada: Controversy over Royal Commission on new reproductive technologies. *The Lancet, 340*(14), 1214–1215.

Kondro, W. (1993). Proposed curbs on reproductive technology. *The Lancet, 340,* 1477–1478.

Kuhl, D.R. (1994). Ethical issues near the end of life: A physician's perspective on caring for persons with AIDS. *Journal of Palliative Care, 10*(3), 117–121.

Kuhl, D.R., & Wilensky, P. (1999). Decision making at the end of life: A model using an ethical grid and principles of group process. *Journal of Palliative Medicine, 2*(1), 75–86.

Laupacis, A., Feeny, D., Detsky, A., & Tugwell, P. (1992). How attractive does a new technology have to be to warrant adoption and utilization? Tentative guidelines for using clinical and economic evaluations. *Canadian Medical Association Journal, 146*(4), 473–481.

Laupacis, A., Keown, P., Pus, N., Kreuger, H., Ferguson, B., Wong, C., & Muirhead, N. (1996). A study of quality of life and cost-utility of renal transplantation. *Kidney International, 30,* 235–242.

Law Commission of Canada. (2000). The governance of health research involving human subjects (HRIHS). Ottawa: Author.

Law Reform Commission of Canada. (1983). *Report: Euthanasia, aiding suicide and cessation of treatment.* Ottawa: Author.

Law Reform Commission of Canada. (1989). *Biomedical experimentation involving human subjects.* Protection of Life Project. Working Paper 61. Ottawa: Author.

Lee, S., Penner, P., & Cox, M. (1991). Comparison of the attitudes of health care professionals and parents toward active treatment of very low birth weight infants. *Pediatrics, 88*(1), 110–114.

Liaschenko, J. (1993). Feminist ethics and cultural ethos: Revisiting a nursing debate. *Advances in Nursing Science, 15*(4), 71–81.

Lomas, J. (1996). Devolved authority in Canada: The new site of health care system conflict? In J. Dorland & S.M. Davis (Eds.), *How many roads?...Decentralization of health care in Canada* (pp. 25–34). Kingston, ON: Queen's School of Policy Studies.

Malone, R.E. (1999, May–June). Policy as product: Morality and metaphor in health policy discourse. *Hastings Centre Report,* 16–22.

Manga, P., & Weller, G. (1991). Health policy under conservative governments in Canada. In C. Altenstetter & S. Haywood (Eds.), *Comparative health policy and the new right: From rhetoric to reality.* New York: St. Martin's Press.

Martin, D. (1992). Fetal tissue transplantation research: A Canadian analysis. *Health Law in Canada, 13*(1), 132–141.

Marleau, D. (1995). Health minister calls for moratorium on applying nine reproductive technologies and practices in humans. *News Release.* Health Canada, July 27, 1995.

Mauksch, H.O. (1975). The organizational context of dying. In E. Kübler-Ross (Ed.), *Death: The final stage of growth* (pp. 7–24). Englewood Cliffs, NJ: Prentice-Hall.

McTeer, M. (1995). A role for law in matters of morality. *McGill Law Journal, 40*(4), 893–903.

McTeer, M. (1999). *Tough choices: Living and dying in the 21st century.* Toronto: Irwin Law.

Medical Research Council. (1993). *Guidelines on research involving human subjects.* Ottawa: Author.

Midgley, M. (2000). Biotechnology and monstrosity: Why we should pay attention to the "Yuk Factor." *Hastings Center Report, 30*(5), 7–15.

Milio, N. (1985). Healthy nations: Creating a new ecology of public policy for health. *Canadian Journal of Public Health, 76*(Suppl. 1), 79–87.

Mitchell, P.H. (1993). Perspectives on outcome-oriented care systems. *Nursing Administration Quarterly, 17*(3), 1–7.

Mohr, W.K., & Mahon, M.M. (1996). Dirty hands: The underside of marketplace health care. *Advances in Nursing Science, 19*(1), 28–37.

Molzahn, A. (1989). *Perceptions of patients, physicians, and nurses regarding the quality of life of individuals with end stage renal disease.* Unpublished doctoral dissertation. University of Alberta, Edmonton.

Molzahn, A. (1998). Quality of life: Definitions, measurement, and application to practice. In E. Banister (Ed.), *Focus on research: Mary Richmond lecture series* (pp. 55–69). Victoria: School of Nursing, University of Victoria.

Moorhouse, A. (1993). User fees: Fair cost containment or a tax on the sick? *Canadian Nurse, 89*(5), 21–24.

Moreno, J.D. (1995). *Arguing euthanasia.* New York: Touchstone

Murray, J. (1992). Human organ transplantation: Background and consequences. *Science, 256*, 1411–1416.

National Bioethics Advisory Commission. (1999). Executive summary: Cloning human beings. In J.D. Arras & B. Steinbock (Eds.), *Ethical issues in modern medicine* (5th ed., pp. 481–484). Mountain View, CA: Mayfield.

National Forum on Health. (1997). *Canada health action: Building on the Legacy (Volume 1&2).* Ottawa: National Forum on Health.

NCBHR. (1993). *Report on research involving children.* Ottawa: National Council on Bioethics in Human Research.

NCBHR. (1996). *Facilitating ethical research: Promoting informed choice.* Ottawa: National Council on Bioethics in Human Research.

Nicholson, R. (1996). This little pig went to market. *Hastings Center Report, 26*(4), 3.

Nisker, J.A. (1996). Rachel's ladders or how societal situation determines reproductive therapy. *Human Reproduction, 11*(6), 1162–1167.

Nisker, J.A. (1997). In quest of the perfect analogy for using in vitro fertilization patients as oocyte donors. *Women's Health Issues, 7*(4), 241–247.

Nisker, J.A. (2001). Chalcedonies. *CMAJ, 9*(1), 74–75.

Nisker, J.A., & Gore-Langton, R.E. (1995, March). Pre-implantation genetic diagnosis: A model of progress and concern. *Journal SOGC,* 247–262.

Olson, L. (1998). Hospital nurses' perceptions of the ethical climate of their work setting. *Image, 30*(4), 345–349.

Overall, C. (1995). Surrogate motherhood. In F. Baylis, J. Downie, B. Freedman, B. Hoffmaster, & S. Sherwin, *Health care ethics in Canada* (pp. 469–479). Toronto: Harcourt Brace. (Excerpt from C. Overall [1987], Surrogate motherhood. In M. Hanen & K. Nelson (Eds.), *Science, morality, and feminist theory.* Calgary: The University of Calgary Press).

Pellegrino, E.D. (1990). The medical profession as a moral community. *Bulletin of the New York Academy of Medicine, 66*(3), 221–232.

Pence, G.E. (1995). *Classic cases in medical ethics* (2nd. ed.). Toronto: McGraw-Hill Ryerson.

Persaud, D.D., & Narine, L. (2000). Organizational justice principles and large-scale change: The case of program management. *Healthcare Management Forum, 13*(4), 10–16.

Picard, E., & Robertson, G. (1996). *Legal liability of doctors and hospitals in Canada.* (3rd ed.). Scarborough: Carswell.

Rachlis, M., Evans, L.G., Lewis, P., & Barer, M.L. (2000). *Revitalizing medicare: Shared problems, public solutions.* Vancouver: Tommy Douglas Research Institute.

Reiser, S.J. (1994). The ethical life of health care organizations. *Hastings Center Report, 24*(6), 28–35.

Relman, A.S. (1980). The new medical industrial complex. *New England Journal of Medicine, 303*(17), 963–970.

Renaud, M. (1994). The future: Hygeia versus Panakeia? In R.G. Evans, M.L. Barer, & T.R. Marmor (Eds.), *Why are some people healthy and others not? The determinants of health of populations* (pp. 317–334). Hawthorne: Aldine deGruyter.

Rock, A. (2001). Rock launches review of draft legislation on assisted human reproduction to ban human cloning and regulate related research. *News Release 2001-44*, Health Canada, May 3, 2001.

Rodney, P. (1994). A nursing perspective on life-prolonging treatment. *Journal of Palliative Care, 10*(2), 40–44.

Rodney, P.A. (1997). *Towards connectedness and trust: Nurses' enactment of their moral agency within an organizational context.* Unpublished doctoral dissertation, University of British Columbia, Vancouver.

Rodney, P., & Starzomski, R. (1993). Constraints on the moral agency of nurses. *Canadian Nurse, 89*(9), 23–26.

Rodney, P., & Starzomski, R. (1994). Responding to ethical challenges. *Nursing BC, 26*(2), 10–13.

Rodney, P., & Varcoe, C. (in press). Toward ethical inquiry in the economic evaluation of nursing practice. *Canadian Journal of Nursing Research.*

Roy, D.J. (1994). Those days are long gone now. *Journal of Palliative Care, 10*(2), 4–6.

Roy, D., Williams, J., & Dickens, B. (1994). *Bioethics in Canada.* Scarborough, ON: Prentice-Hall.

Royal Commission on New Reproductive Technologies. (1993). *Proceed with care: Final report of the Royal Commission on new reproductive technologies.* Ottawa: Supply and Services.

Sadler, B. (1992). Presumed consent to organ transplantation: A different perspective. *Transplantation Proceedings, 24*(5), 2173–2174.

Saul, J.R. (1997). *Reflections of a Siamese twin: Canada at the end of the twentieth century.* Toronto: Penguin Books.

Sherwin, S. (1992). *No longer patient: Feminist ethics and health care.* Philadelphia: Temple University Press.

Sherwin, S. (1995). New reproductive technologies. In F. Baylis, J. Downie, B. Freedman, B. Hoffmaster, & S. Sherwin, *Health care ethics in Canada* (pp. 459–468). Toronto: Harcourt Brace. (From Sherwin, S. [1992]. *No longer patient: Feminist ethics and health care.* Philadelphia: Temple University Press).

Shuchman, M. (1999). Independent review adds to controversy at Sick Kids. *Canadian Medical Association Journal, 160*(3), 386–388.

Sieglar, M. (1992). Liver transplantation using living donors. *Transplantation Proceedings, 24*(5), 2223–2224.

Singer, P. (1992). Xenotransplantation and speciesism. *Transplantation Proceedings, 24*(2), 728–732.

Singer, P.A. (1994). Advance directives in palliative care. *Journal of Palliative Care, 10*(3), 111–116.

Sneiderman, B. (1994). The Rodriguez case: Where do we go from here — A multidimensional (6 layered) approach. *Health Law Journal, 2,* 1–38.

Sneiderman, B. (1997). The Latimer mercy killing case: A rumination on crime and punishment. *Health Law Journal, 5,* 1–26.

Sneiderman, L.J., Jecker, N.S., & Jonsen, A.R. (1990). Medical futility: Its meaning and ethical implications. *Annals of Internal Medicine, 112,* 949–954.

Solomon, M.Z., O'Donnell, L., Jennings, B., Guilfoy, V., Wolf, S.M., Nolan, K., Jackson, R., Koch-Weser, D., & Donnelley, S. (1993). Decisions near the end of life: Professional views on life-sustaining treatments. *American Journal of Public Health, 83*(1), 14–23.

Special Senate Committee on Euthanasia and Assisted Suicide. (1995). *Of life and death: Report of the special Senate Committee on euthanasia and assisted suicide.* Ottawa: Senate of Canada.

Spital, A. (1992). Unrelated living donors: Should they be used? *Transplantation Proceedings*, *24*(5), 2215–2217.

Spital, A. (1993). Living organ donation is still ethically acceptable. *Archives of Internal Medicine*, *153*(4), 529.

Standing Committee on Health. (1999). *Organ and tissue transplantation in Canada: Report of the Standing Committee on health*. Ottawa: House of Commons.

Starzomski, R. (1994). Ethical issues in palliative care: The case of dialysis and organ transplantation. *Journal of Palliative Care*, *10*(3), 27–33.

Starzomski, R. (1997). *Resource allocation for solid organ transplantation: Toward public and health care provider dialogue*. Unpublished doctoral dissertation, University of British Columbia, Vancouver.

Starzomski, R. (1998). Ethics in nephrology nursing. In J. Parker (Ed.), *Nephrology nursing: A comprehensive textbook* (pp. 83–109). Pitman, NJ: American Nephrology Nurses Association.

Starzomski, R., & Rodney, P. (1997). Nursing inquiry for the common good. In S.E. Thorne & V.E. Hayes (Eds.), *Nursing praxis: Knowledge and action* (pp. 219–236). Thousand Oaks, CA: Sage.

Stephenson, P. (1999). Expanding notions of culture for cross-cultural ethics in health and medicine. In H. Coward & P. Ratanakul (Eds.), *A cross-cultural dialogue on health care ethics* (pp. 68–91). Waterloo, ON: Wilfrid Laurier University Press.

Storch, J. (1982). *Patients' rights: Ethical and legal issues in health care and in nursing*. Toronto: McGraw-Hill Ryerson.

Storch, J. (1988). Major substantive ethical issues facing Canadian health care policy makers and implementers. *The Journal of Health Administration Education*, *6*(2), 263–271.

Storch, J.L. (1992). Ethical issues. In A.J. Baumgart & J. Larsen (Eds.), *Canadian nursing faces the future* (2nd ed., pp. 259–270). St. Louis, MO: Mosby Year Book.

Storch, J.L. (1996). Foundational values in Canadian health care. In M. Stingl & D. Wilson (Eds.), *Efficiency vs equality: Health reform in Canada* (pp. 21–26). Halifax: Fernwood.

Storch, J.L. (1998). Advancing our thinking about advanced directives: Ethics at the end of life. In E. Banister (Ed.), *Focus on research: Mary Richmond lecture series* (pp. 73–91). Victoria: School of Nursing, University of Victoria.

Storch, J.L. (1999). Ethical dimensions of leadership. In J.M. Hibberd & D.L. Smith (Eds.), *Nursing management in Canada* (2nd ed., pp. 351–367). Toronto: W.B. Saunders.

Storch, J.L. (in press). Current status of human participant protection in research in Canada. *Annals, RCPSC*.

Storch, J.L., Griener, G.G., Marshall, D.A., & Olineck, B.A. (1990, Winter). Ethics committees in Canadian hospitals: Report of a 1989 survey. *Healthcare Management Forum*, *3*, 3–8.

Storch, J.L., & Griener, G.G. (1992, Spring). Ethics committees in Canadian hospitals: Report of the 1990 pilot study. *Healthcare Management Forum*, *5*, 19–26.

Storch, J.L., & Meilicke, C.A. (1999). Political, social, and economic forces shaping the health care system. In J.M. Hibberd & D.L. Smith (Eds.), *Nursing management in Canada* (2nd ed., pp. 3–20). Toronto: W.B. Saunders.

Street, A.F. (1992). *Inside nursing: A critical ethnography of nursing practice*. Albany: State University of New York Press.

Subcommittee to update "Of Life and Death" of the Standing Committee on Social Affairs, Science and Technology. (2000). *Quality end-of-life care: The right of every Canadian*. Ottawa: Author.

Sudnow, D. (1967). *Passing on: The social organization of dying*. Englewood Cliffs, NJ: Prentice-Hall.

Taft, K., & Steward, G. (2000). *Clear answers: The economics and politics of for-profit medicine*. Edmonton: Duval.

Taylor, M.G. (1987). *Health insurance and Canadian public policy*. Montreal: McGill–Queen's University Press.

Taylor, C. (1995). Medical futility and nursing. *Image, 27*(4), 301–306.

Thorne, S. (1993). *Negotiating health care: The social context of chronic illness*. Newbury Park, CA: Sage.

Tilden, V.P., Tolle, S.W., Nelson, C.A., Thompson, M., & Eggman, S.C. (1999). Family decision making in foregoing life-extending treatments. *Journal of Family Nursing, 5*(4), 426–442.

Tong, R. (1997). *Feminist approaches to bioethics: Theoretical reflections and practical applications*. Boulder, CO: Westview Press.

Tri-Council Policy Statement. (1998). *Ethical conduct for research involving human subjects*. Ottawa: Supply and Services Canada.

Ventres, W., Nichter, M., Reed, R., & Frankel, R. (1997). Limitation of medical care: An ethnographic analysis. In N.S. Jecker, A.R. Jonsen, & R.A. Pearlman (Eds.), *Bioethics: An introduction to the history, methods, and practice* (pp. 218–231). Boston: Jones and Bartlett.

Warren, J. (1993). Financial incentive controversy continues. *Dialysis & Transplantation, 22*(3), 156–158.

Watson, S.D. (1994). Minority access and health reform: A civil right to health care. *Journal of Law, Medicine & Ethics, 22*, 127–137.

Weber, L.J. (2001). *Business ethics in health care: Beyond compliance*. Indiana University Press.

Webster, G.C., & Baylis, F.E. (2000). Moral residue. In S.B. Rubin & L. Zoloth (Eds.), *Margin of error: The ethics of mistakes in the practice of medicine* (pp. 217–230). Hagerstown, MD: University Publishing Group.

Weisz, G. (1990a). Introduction. In G. Weisz (Ed.), *Social science perspectives on medical ethics* (pp. 3–15). Philadelphia: University of Pennsylvania Press.

Weisz, G. (Ed.). (1990b). *Social science perspectives on medical ethics*. Philadelphia: University of Pennsylvania Press.

Wennberg, J. (1990). Outcomes research, cost containment, and the fear of health care rationing. *New England Journal of Medicine, 323*, 1202–1204.

Wexler, A. (1996). Genetic testing of families with hereditary diseases. *Journal of the American Medical Association, 276*(14), 1139–1140.

Wilson, D. (1994). Ethics and the crisis in health care organization. *Bioethics Bulletin, 6*(1), 5–7.

Wilson, D. (1995). The values that sustain the Canadian health-care system. *Humane Medicine, 11*(4), 178–179.

Wilson, D.M. (2000). End-of-life care preferences of Canadian senior citizens with caregiving experience. *Journal of Advanced Nursing, 31*(6), 1416–1421.

Wilson, D., Anderson, M., Dossetor, J., Lantz, H., & Lawrence, C. (1996). Advantages and disadvantages of Bill 35 — Personal care directives. *Health Law Review, 5*(1), 14–15.

Windwick, B.F. (1997). Recent Decisions: Winnipeg child and family services v. D.F.G, [1997] S.C.J. No. 96 (QL). *Health Law Review, 6*(2), 35–37.

Winkler, E.R. (1993). From Kantianism to contextualism: The rise and fall of the paradigm theory in bioethics. In E.R. Winkler & J.R. Coombs (Eds.), *Applied ethics: A reader* (pp. 343–365).

Wolf, S.M. (1994). Health care reform and the future of physician ethics. *Hastings Center Report*, 24(2), 28–41.

Wrobel, K. (1997). Cloning technology and the human species: Issues of compatibility. *Health Law Review*, 66(2), 3–13.

Yeo, M. (1996). Introduction. In M. Yeo & A. Moorhouse (Eds.), *Concepts and cases in nursing ethics* (2nd ed., pp. 1–26). Peterborough, ON: Broadview Press.

Yeo, M., & Moorhouse, A. (Eds.). (1996). *Concepts and cases in nursing ethics* (2nd ed.). Peterborough, ON: Broadview Press.

NOTES

1. For a comprehensive review of the contemporary debate about euthanasia in Canada, see Roy, Williams, and Dickens (1994), pp. 419–433.

2. The withholding and withdrawal of artificial feeding — particularly "tube feeding" — is an important contemporary issue here. A growing number of health care agencies (often after completing DNR policies) are working on policies to address artificial feeding and hydration.

3. Including the three authors of this chapter.

4. "Culture" here means more than ethnicity; it includes beliefs and values and is influenced by gender, race, and class. Understanding culture helps us to understand the meaning and significance of individual experience. *All* members of the health care system — not just patients and families — have culture (Coward & Ratanakul, 1999).

5. Each author is on one or more agency-based ethics committee(s), and serves as an ethics consultant.

6. Surrogacy involves a preconception arrangement whereby: a gestational mother is impregnated with the sperm of the man through a commissioning couple; or an embryo created by the egg and sperm of a commissioning couple is implanted in a gestational mother. Either may be a commercial arrangement whereby the commissioning couple pays fees to the gestational mother and/or a broker ($20 000 or more), or a noncommercial arrangement whereby no fees are involved, although the commissioning couple may agree to cover expenses (Royal Commission on New Reproductive Technologies, 1993, pp. 661–693).

7. Yet, in the field of organ donation, Western society has an almost universal abhorrence for buying and selling organs.

22

Personal and Structural Determinants
of Health and Illness:
Lifestyles and Life Chances

B. SINGH BOLARIA   University of Saskatchewan

ROSEMARY BOLARIA   Saskatchewan Institute on Prevention of Handicaps

INTRODUCTION

Lifestyles, healthy living, and health promotion have emerged as important areas of investigation in medical sociology. One of the issues that continues to receive considerable attention in the epidemiological, population health, and health promotion literature is the relative importance of the individual and structural determinants of health and illness. In this debate, a distinction is often made between societal factors that are beyond one's control and influence health, and individual behavioural factors, over which one presumably has control and can make healthy choices. In the former approach, the focus is on social-structural conditions, including economic and social inequality, that influence health status.

The latter approach focuses on overall aggregate patterns of health behaviour and health practices, such as smoking, alcohol consumption, exercise, and diet, which constitute lifestyles. It is assumed that lifestyles are matters of individual choice and that these choices have positive or negative health consequences. Within this framework, the responsibility for staying healthy is shifted to individuals. It is argued that since the major risk factors for ill health are at the personal discretion of individuals, there would be a considerable reduction in mortality if individuals focused on changing aspects of their lifestyles that are injurious to their health. On the other hand, the studies from a historical materialistic epidemiological perspective argue that the solution lies in changing the social, economic, and environmental conditions that produce illness and mortality.

This debate points to the significance of both the individual and the structural determinants in the health status of a population. It also points to the need to continue further investigation into the consumer behaviour and lifestyle choices the individuals make within the limits and constraints imposed upon them by the social and cultural environment and their material conditions, that is, their **life chances**. At a broader level, this constitutes the study of the relative importance of the role of structure (chances) and agency (choices) in shaping social behaviour in the structure–agency debate in the sociological literature. Structuralists give primacy to institutional factors, which both enable and constrain individuals to act, whereas agency refers to the ability of individuals to act and to choose their behaviour regardless of structural constraints (Cockerham, 2000).

Specific studies of health lifestyles and health behaviour would make significant contributions to the structure–agency debate. In addition, the sociological perspective broadens the scope of inquiry beyond individual psychology, to include the social, cultural, and normative context of people's lives and circumstances, which influence lifestyles and social behaviour. A consideration of the social and material conditions and of the circumstances of individuals' daily existence, as well as their coping responses to their circumstances and to societal forces beyond their control, is likely to provide a more complete picture of the persistence of certain behaviour patterns even when such behaviours have negative health consequences (Cockerham, 2000). The sociological perspective allows us to take into account social-structural factors in the discussion of lifestyles.

This chapter begins with a discussion of the reductionist orientation in medicine. It then considers conceptual and empirical issues and the relative importance of lifestyles and life chances in disease etiology and health. The chapter concludes with a discussion of the policy implications of individualist and structural perspectives concerning health promotion.

BACKGROUND TO REDUCTIONISM IN MEDICINE

To fully appreciate the current debate on personal and structural determinants, it is important to briefly consider the individualistic, biomedical, and reductionist orientations in medicine (Bolaria, 1994b, 1994c). The clinical paradigm, widely accepted in medical practice, defines health and illness in individual terms, independent of the social context in which they occur. This paradigm decontextualizes medical problems; individuals are "atomized" and decontextualized for treatment. This individual-centred concept of disease has led to an essentially curative orientation, whereby people can be made healthy by means of "technological fixes" (Renaud, 1975). Many diseases are viewed as malfunctions — technical defects in body machinery — and treatments are oriented toward restoring the "normal" functioning of the human body. The response to psychological disorders is often pharmacological, including the use of antidepressants, stimulants, and tranquilizers (for review, see Bolaria, 1994b). Although the clinical paradigm has received critical scrutiny, individualized etiology and treatment have a pervasive and continuing influence in medical practice (see, in particular, Doyal & Pennell, 1979; Waitzkin, 1983; Navarro, 1986). This orientation is also reflected in medical research. There has been a heavy emphasis on an individualized etiology of disease, rather than on social and environmental factors, such as occupational and environmental exposure to pollutants, chemicals, and other harmful agents (Waitzkin, 1983; Navarro, 1986; Firth, Brophy, & Keith, 1997).

This mechanistic-individualistic conception of disease, which engenders a disease-centred, high-technology orientation in medical practice and research, also largely absolves the economic and political systems of responsibility for disease, and denies the social foundations and **social causation** of disease. A similar reductionist approach has emerged that emphasizes individual lifestyle. In Canada in 1974, the publication of a federal policy paper gave prominent attention to health risks associated with individual lifestyles and consumption patterns (Lalonde, 1974). Lifestyle was also one of the foci of another official policy paper (Epp, 1986). Whereas the clinical model attributes disease to the malfunctioning of the human body, this reductionism introduces the idea that the causes of disease lie in individual lifestyles and behaviours. In the former case, the normal functions of the human body can be restored through "technological and chemical fixes," while in the latter, the solution lies primarily in changing individual behaviours and patterns of consumption. This approach, too, obscures the social nature of disease and fails to recognize the important relationships between social and material conditions and health and sickness. Both the biomedical-clinical paradigm and the individual lifestyle approach share a common orientation in disease etiology. With a focus on individuals, they tend to neglect the social context of individuals' lives and the social and material conditions that produce sickness and disease. **Social epidemiology** and the environmental approach to health are in conflict with the biological and individual orientation of the predominant paradigm.

LIFESTYLES AND LIFE CHANCES

In recent years, the study of lifestyles and the interplay and link between social-structural conditions and lifestyles and health behaviour has received considerable attention (Abel, 1991; Chaney, 1996; Bunton, Nettleton, & Burrows, 1995; William, 1995; Cockerham, 2000; Townsend, 1990). The growing body of literature addresses a wide range of theoretical and empirical questions as well as public health policy and health promotion issues.

An early discussion of lifestyles is found in Max Weber's work on social stratification, particularly in the distinction Weber makes between class and status (Weber, 1978; Garth & Mills, 1958). Class stratification, according to Weber, represents economic inequality, whereas status groups are distinguished by their specific lifestyles or style of life, which is manifested in their distinct consumption patterns. Status groups share similar lifestyles. As Weber (1978, p. 933) states: "One might thus say that classes are stratified according to their relations to the production and acquisition of goods; whereas status groups are stratified according to the principles of their consumption of goods as represented by special styles of life." Weber also recognized the importance of life chances in realizing specific lifestyles. Lifestyle choices, however, are not made in a vacuum; rather, these choices are influenced by life chances, which set the social parameters within which choices are realized. Life chances are structured by one's social situation. In short, lifestyle choices are constrained by life chances (Frohlich & Potvin, 1999; Cockerham, 2000). Yet the social context of lifestyles and the social-structural constraints within which lifestyle choices are made have often been ignored in the epidemiological and health promotion literature.

The term "lifestyle" is used to refer to certain individual behaviours such as smoking, drinking, and drug abuse, which are considered sources of illness (Frohlich & Potvin, 1999). In this context, health problems and health outcomes are linked to personal choices and lifestyles and behaviours that are presumably within individual discretion and control. Therefore, individual effort and responsibility are required to achieve and maintain health, and conversely individuals are blamed for their ill health and sickness. Thus, to be healthy, one has to "work at it"; otherwise one faces a risk of disease and premature death (Cockerham, 2000). This focus on individual responsibility for health and self-care is attributed to a number of factors, including the public recognition of the limitations of modern medicine in curing chronic diseases, state policies that emphasize personal responsibility for health, mass media attention, and educational campaigns by health professionals (Cockerham, 1998, 2000; Segall & Chappell, 2000).

Despite the current popularity of lifestyles in epidemiological studies and health promotion, this emphasis has received considerable criticism on conceptual, empirical, and ideological grounds. The term is used rather loosely (Abel, 1991), and it is often not clear whether it refers to discrete individual health practices or an aggregate of a number of discrete behaviours.

The tendency to treat lifestyles and health behaviour as matters of individual choice has received considerable criticism. Furthermore, the focus on individual lifestyles and self-imposed risks tends to downgrade the importance of social, economic, and environmental factors in the production of illness. Social-structural conditions in society can both enable and constrain individual lifestyle choices. In other words, lifestyles and life choices are influenced by life chances (Frohlich & Potvin, 1999; Cockerham, 1998, 2000). Cockerham states: "Health lifestyles are collective patterns of health-related behavior based on choices from options available to people according to their life chances. A person's life chances are determined by their socioeconomic status, age, gender, race, ethnicity, and other factors that impact on lifestyle choices" (1998, p. 85). Personal health practices and lifestyles are closely linked to social and economic life circumstances, and "lifestyle and health behaviours vary with one's position in a social hierarchy" (Frankish, Milligan, & Reid, 1998, p. 288).

That individual lifestyles are constrained by specific life solutions and social and material conditions is commonly recognized. The World Health Organization (WHO) conceptualizes lifestyle "as a way of life, a socio-cultural phenomenon arising from interactions between patterns of behaviour and specific life situations rather than individual decisions to avoid or accept certain health risks" (Dean, 1989, p. 137). Abel (1991, p. 901) defines health lifestyles as "patterns of health related behaviour, values, and attitudes adapted by groups of individuals in response to their social, cultural and economic environments." In short, individual choices are made in the context of specific life situations. Lifestyles are not simply matters of freedom of choice and individual decisions to choose between healthy and unhealthy practices, but are made in the specific context within which people live.

More importantly, as Berliner (1977, p. 119) has stated, "focussing on lifestyle serves only to reify the lifestyle as an entity apart from the social conditions from which it arises"; and "discussing changes in lifestyles without first discussing the changes in social conditions which give rise to them, without recognizing that lifestyle is derivative, is misleading and, in effect, is victim blaming." Health status and health outcomes are not just a matter of individual lifestyle and health behaviour but are closely linked to one's socioeconomic status and other social, economic, and environmental conditions (Frankish, Milligan, & Reid, 1998). In other words, there is a need to consider both the personal and the structural determinants of health and the combined impact of life circumstances and life choices (Segall & Chappell, 2000, pp. 82–86, 154; Gunning-Scheppers & Hagen, 1987; Blaxter, 1990; Frankish, Milligan, & Reid, 1998).

In Canada and elsewhere, socioeconomic status remains the most important link to health status. People who are advantaged in socioeconomic status are also advantaged in health status (Krieger & Fee, 1993, 1994; Link & Phelan, 2000; Mirowsky, Ross, & Reynolds, 2000; Hay, 1994; Ross & Roberts, 1999; Zong & Li, 1994; Tarasuk, 1994; Reading, 1997; see also Bolaria & Bolaria, 1994a, 1994b). The evidence of association between social class and longevity was provided several years ago by Antonovsky (1992, p. 28): "The inescapable conclusion is that class influences one's chances of staying alive." Based upon a review of numerous international studies, Wilkinson (1996, p. 3) concluded that "in the developed world, it is not the richest countries which have the best health but the most egalitarian." Cockerham (1998, p. 53) concludes: "The fact remains that people at the bottom of the society have the worst health of all, regardless of what country they live in, what type of insurance they have, and the level of health care they receive." Based upon their analysis of research findings, Krieger and Fee (1994, p. 28) state that "the poorest people have the worst health." The relationship between social class and health is attributed to the differential exposure to physical and social environments by members of different socioeconomic levels (Adler, 1995). Social inequality leads not only to differential exposure to health risks but also to unequal access to the social, economic, and other resources needed to deal with these risks. In short, **structured inequality** produces **inequality of conditions** and differential opportunity and life chances.

Other structural factors such as living and working conditions "are the most power-ful factors affecting health" (Millar & Hull, 1997, p. 148). Research in Canada on health status indicates the persistence of social variability in health status and that social fac-tors are "the most important determinants of health status" (Coburn & Eakin, 1993, p. 86). Denton and Walters (1999, p. 1229) also conclude that "these analyses suggest that the structural determinants of health play a greater role than the behavioural or lifestyle determinants in shaping the health status of Canadians." The Whitehall studies provide strong evidence of the association of health status and mortality with the social hierar-chy of British civil servants (Marmot et al., 1978, 1984, 1991): each group of civil ser-vants had worse health than the group above it in the hierarchy. What is also signifi-cant is that only a small portion of differences in coronary heart disease (CHD) mortal-ity could be explained by personal health habits and lifestyles such as cigarette smok-ing, physical activity, and blood pressure. Social hierarchy in the civil service appears to be an important gradient in differences in mortality among various grades.

Studies also show that those with higher socioeconomic status, particularly educa-tional level, have better health habits and lifestyles than those with lower socioeco-nomic status. For instance, those with higher educational achievement are more likely to engage in positive health behaviours such as exercising, moderate drinking, not smoking, avoiding obesity, and they are more likely to have preventive health checkups (Ross & Wu, 1995). Education enables people to have healthy lifestyles (Mirowsky & Ross, 1998). High educational achievement is key to gaining rewarding jobs with con-siderable control and autonomy over work and better income, and hence to a better position in the social hierarchy. These factors increase individuals' sense of control over their lives and provide motivation to live a healthy lifestyle (Mirowsky, Ross, & Reynolds, 2000). Based upon their review of extensive research, Mirowsky, Ross, & Reynolds draw the following conclusions:

First, higher social status protects and improves health. Second, the primary aspect of social status that improves health includes education, employment, autonomous and fulfilling work, and the absence of economic hardship. Third, those aspects of social status improve health by developing and reinforcing a sense of mastery and control and by encouraging and enabling a healthy lifestyle. (2000, p. 56)

Epidemiological data clearly demonstrates the differential health status of the population by socioeconomic status (Federal, Provincial and Territorial Advisory Committee on Population Health, 1999a, 1999b). The health gap between the rich and the poor continues to exist in Canada, where the principle of universality was a major impetus to the introduction of medicare in the 1960s. Upper-income Canadians live longer, healthier, and more disability-free lives on the average than do poor Canadians. This gap in health status is primarily due to the "debilitating conditions of life that poverty forces upon people" (National Council of Welfare, 1990, p. 6). Poor social and material conditions, such as poor housing, poor nutrition, poor neighbourhoods, and poor environment, contribute to high mortality in the low-income population. High mortality levels in poor neighbourhoods are well documented (Thomson, 1990; National Council of Welfare, 1990). Evidence indicates that the poorer the area, the shorter the life expectancy of both men and women. Data also show that children of parents in the poorest neighbourhoods have twice the infant mortality rates of children in the richest neighbourhoods. The high mortality, high disability, and low health status of Aboriginal people is associated with their poor environmental, economic, social, and living conditions (Borsellino, 1990; Mao et al., 1992). Other studies lend support to the general conclusion that low-income people have not only high mortality and morbidity, but also low utilization of health services (Driver, 1991; Wilkins et al., 1991). A report published by the federal minister of health revealed that "men in the upper income groups can expect 14 more disability-free years than men with a low income; in the case of women, the difference is eight years" (Epp, 1986, p. 398).

Low income and poverty forces upon people many debilitating conditions that produce poor health, shorter lives, high infant mortality, and other physical and mental health problems for the disadvantaged. Dependency on food banks further exacerbates these disadvantages (Bolaria, 1994a). The impact of environmental degradation also differs by socioeconomic status and race (Bolaria, 1991; Frideres, 1994). Aboriginal people are subject to more pollutants than is the general population because they frequently live in environmentally unsafe areas (Wotherspoon, 1994).

In summary, lifestyles are shaped by life chances. Yet the social and material context, which both enables and constrains chosen lifestyles, is often ignored. The focus on individuals and their life choices and lifestyles also obscures the social and material production of health and illness. The empirical reality is that socioeconomic inequalities produce social variability in health status.

TARGET INDIVIDUALS OR CONDITIONS

The level of analysis is crucial in any discussion of population health-promotion policies. If health problems are blamed on individuals and their lifestyles, then policies and programs need to target individuals and their harmful lifestyle behaviour. But if health problems are considered to be the product of social and material inequalities and conditions embodied in group-level characteristics, then the policies to improve population health need to target those inequalities and conditions (Taylor, 1989; Eakin et al., 1996; Matcha, 2000, p. 127). Individual-level solutions seem to be easier to implement than are social structural changes. Eakin and colleagues (1996, p. 161) comment: "Health related problems that are believed to reside in the individual are seen to be easier to address than those residing in such intangible and unyielding places as the environment, social interaction, economic systems, and social class." Within the individualistic framework, group-level characteristics (e.g., social class, race, and gender) related to health are "collapsed into handy individual risk factors that can be remedied by changing personal habits" (Conrad, 1987, p. 265).

Health promotion policies cannot be divorced from social and ideological contexts. Health promotion approaches and perspectives are embedded in prevailing ideologies, policies, and practices. The state is intimately involved in the health promotion movement. The individual-centred approach — individual etiology and individual solutions — has received considerable support and promotion in many Western countries (for review, see Bolaria, 1994c).

In times of economic constraint, when the situation becomes even more critical and the health-care crisis deepens, government programs promoting this type of individual emphasis gain dominance over others. An attempt is made "to shift the responsibility for disease back onto the worker, in this case through **victim-blaming epidemiology** and of individual solutions for the workers" (Berliner, 1977, p. 119). As Doyal and Pennell (1979, p. 296) put it: "Thus it is said that individuals are to blame for their own health problems and it is up to them to adopt a healthier lifestyle. The Victorian notion of 'undeserving poor' is being replaced by the equally inappropriate notion of 'the undeserving sick.'" This has strong implications for health care policy.

Health promotion strategies and educational campaigns are primarily oriented toward changing individuals and their lifestyles. These strategies continue to focus on lifestyle behavioural changes (Mechanic, 1999), and the emphasis remains at the individual level of lifestyles and behavioural changes. As McQueen (1989, p. 342) states:

> How else can one explain a public health rhetoric which argues that social conditions affect health outcomes and then, in turn, argues that the appropriate solution is to eat better, exercise more, drink less and give up smoking.

Relatively little attention is given to the transformation of the physical and social environment, of the health care system, or of public policy (McDowell, 1986). This response to crises in health care strengthens the **ideology of individualism**, emphasizes individual responsibility for one's social and economic position and health status, and masks the social production of inequality and social variability in health (Navarro, 1986). A focus on individuals displaces responsibility for health. For instance, a focus on workers' lifestyles diverts attention from unhealthy and unsafe work environments (Berliner, 1977). By promoting individual responsibility, this strategy distracts attention from the illness-generating economic and social environment. A popularization of this strategy, in the long run, would be instrumental in preparing the public to accept further reductions in health services, "to tighten their medical care belts" (Berliner, 1977, p. 116). It is likely to have adverse effects.

Healthy lifestyles, "wise living," and self-care, although positive choices, cannot substitute for professional health services when they are required (Waitzkin, 1983). Self-care is considered by many a "conservative idea that could strengthen arguments for the dismantling of the welfare state" (Kickbusch, 1989, p. 125). With regard to Epp's health promotion policy paper, McDowell (1986, p. 448) states: "Self-care and the assistance of neighbours are laudable, but are made here to sound like a cheap alternative to professional health care.... Epp is trying to reduce the demand for health services, rather than the need for them."

Therefore, the burden of health crises may be borne by individuals, to the extent that they are willing to accept the proposition that socially, economically, and politically caused conditions can be solved individually, either by medical intervention or by self-care and changes in lifestyle. This approach promotes a policy of "health education in prevention and clinical medicine in cure," rather than drawing attention to the organization of health-care delivery systems or to the nature, function, and composition of the health sector and the economic and political forces that influence the state of healthiness.

Health promotion policies have also been severely criticized when certain social groups are targeted. Analysis is extended from the individual to the collective way of life of a particular group; for instance, the health problems of minorities may be attributed to their cultural practices and beliefs rather than to their socioeconomic position and institutional racism (Douglas, 1995). Educative approaches are often based upon broad generalizations and stereotypes of cultural differences between mainstream and minority communities. Minority groups are often considered to have "special" health problems requiring "special" intervention. Well-intended, culturally sensitive approaches to health education and promotion only strengthen the cultural stereotypes, and in the process they often further marginalize these communities.

Another critique of health promotion comes from feminist groups: of educative programs based upon gender stereotypes that view caring and nurturing as "natural" to women and that target women as a homogeneous group (Daykin & Naidoo, 1995). Gender inequalities affect all women and constrain women's lives and opportunities. Women of colour and poor women are further disadvantaged. Such constraints and divisions need to be considered in health promotion; otherwise, "the current vogue for addressing women as consumers able to exercise personal choice over lifestyles and health care services is inappropriate, given the constraints on most women's lives" (Daykin & Naidoo, 1995, p. 69).

In some cases, health promotion policies penalize the most disadvantaged. For instance, poor women smokers are most affected by increases in tobacco and cigarette costs. Educational programs that target certain groups of women create negative self-images and self-blame. For instance, pregnant women, who are often the target of health education about smoking, drinking, and substance abuse, are made to feel guilty and responsible for their children's poor health outcomes (Burrows, Nettleton, & Bunton, 1995; Daykin & Naidoo, 1995). This has the effect of contributing to their marginalization, moral condemnation, and social stigmatization (Conrad, 1994). Nettleton and Bunton (1995, pp. 51–52) further elaborate on this point:

> Whilst the discourse of health promotion emphasizes the merits of providing people with knowledge and information so that they can make healthy choices, the structural critique

suggests that the notion of individual choice is a mythical one and draws attention to the fact that health promotion makes people feel responsible and culpable for their own health.

It is also pointed out that although the targets of health promotion are often disadvantaged groups, it is the structurally advantaged groups who benefit the most from lifestyle changes (Nettleton & Benton, 1995; Blaxter, 1990). Health promotion may further exacerbate the existing inequalities in health.

The focus on individuals and collectivities may also have the effect of extending medical surveillance, monitoring, and control to their bodies, lifestyles, and health behaviour, particularly for groups that are "problematized" (Conrad, 1987; Conrad & Walsh, 1992; Miller & Findlay, 1994; Nettleton & Bunton, 1995; O'Brien, 1995). The structural argument suggests that any attempt to prevent illness and promote health must consider the political economy that produces illness in the first place. Health promotion discourse that focuses on individuals fails to consider the social and material conditions of people's daily existence (Syme, 1994; Corin, 1994; McKinlay, 1993, 1994; Grace, 1991; Raphael & Bryant, 2000; Rutten, 1995). Resources that enhance participation in healthy lifestyles and promote a healthy existence are greater among the middle and upper classes (Cockerham, 1998; Blaxter, 1990). The argument advanced by structuralists is that the target of intervention should be the conditions that make people unhealthy and the societal conditions and forces that induce high-risk behaviours (Corin, 1994; Syme, 1994).

CONCLUSION

A growing body of literature on the determinants of health and illness addresses a wide range of theoretical and conceptual questions as well as public health policy and health promotion issues. Both the biomedical-clinical paradigm and individual lifestyle approach share a common reductionist orientation, and they tend to ignore the social context of individuals' lives and the social and material conditions that produce health and illness. The literature on lifestyles and life chances indicates that lifestyles are shaped by life chances. Social and material conditions both enable and constrain chosen lifestyles. A focus on lifestyles and self-imposed risks ignores the social basis of lifestyles and health and illness. The empirical reality is that socioeconomic inequalities produce social variability in health status.

The level of analysis also becomes crucial in public health policy. If the source of health problems is individual lifestyles, then programs and policies need to target individuals and their harmful lifestyles. On the other hand, if health problems are considered to be a product of social and material inequalities, then health promotion campaigns need to target the inequalities. Health promotion policies that primarily focus on changing individuals and their lifestyles are criticized on several grounds. A focus on individuals shifts the responsibility for health and illness onto them, and diverts attention from illness-generating conditions and a degraded environment. This also makes people feel responsible and guilty for their own health, producing negative self-images and self-blame.

A focus on individuals and collectivities often marginalizes and stigmatizes these individuals and groups. The primary structural argument suggests that the target of intervention must be the political economy that produces illness in the first place and induces high-risk behaviour.

Finally, a complete picture requires a consideration of both the personal and structural factors and a further investigation into the social behaviours and lifestyle choices of individuals within the structured constraints of their lives. The sociological perspective broadens the scope of inquiry to include the social, cultural, and normative contexts of people's lives, contexts that shape lifestyles and social behaviours. It enables researchers to understand the persistence of certain behaviour patterns, even when such behaviour has negative health consequences. The knowledge gained from specific studies of lifestyles would make a significant contribution to the structure–agency debate in sociology.

STUDY QUESTIONS

1. *Discuss the ideological and health policy implications of a focus on individual lifestyles and self-imposed risks.*
2. *Discuss the limitations of the persistence of the biomedical clinical paradigm in the understanding of health and illness.*
3. *How do biomedical lifestyle approaches obfuscate the significance of social-structural factors in the understanding of morbidity and mortality?*
4. *Briefly discuss the relationship between socioeconomic inequality and health status inequalities.*
5. *Discuss the evidence that people who are more socially advantaged also enjoy health advantages.*
6. *Discuss the statement that improving the health of vulnerable populations lies in altering the social-structural causes of inequalities in health and not in altering individual behaviour and lifestyles.*

GLOSSARY

ideology of individualism   The idea that individual qualities such as hard work, motivation, initiative, and intelligence determine one's station in life.

inequality of conditions   Differences in access to and the availability of material and social resources.

life chances   Opportunities to acquire material goods, services, and desirable living conditions.

lifestyles   The individual behaviours and consumption patterns associated with health and disease.

social causation   The social-structural factors and social conditions that produce different mortality and morbidity patterns in society.

social epidemiology   The social, economic, political, and cultural forces that shape patterns of disease and death in human populations.

structured inequality   An arrangement of social position whereby one's location in the social structure has important bearings on one's opportunities in life, or life chances.

victim-blaming epidemiology   A focus on individual health behaviours and lifestyles that places responsibility for illness on individuals and shifts the blame from a social causation of illness and disease to those who are ill and suffer.

RECOMMENDED READINGS

Blaxter, M. (1990). *Health and lifestyles*. London: Routledge. An important contribution to research on social class and lifestyles that examines important differences in lifestyles among social classes.

Bunton, R., Nettleton, S., & Burrows, R. (Eds.). (1995). *The sociology of health promotion*. London: Routledge. A general introduction to the basic literature on health promotion and a critical examination of consumption, lifestyle, and health risks.

Cockerham, W.C. (2000). The sociology of health behaviour and health lifestyles. In C.E. Bird, P. Conrad, & A.M. Fremont (Eds.), *Handbook of medical sociology* (5th ed., pp. 159–172). Upper Saddle River, NJ: Prentice-Hall. An examination of the current state of theory and research on health behaviour and health lifestyles; an excellent resource on these topics, with extensive references.

Federal, Provincial and Territorial Advisory Committee on Population Health. (1999). *Statistical report on the health of Canadians*. Ottawa: Minister of Public Works and Government Services Canada. An excellent report on the health status of Canadians, including a section on lifestyle behaviours such as smoking, drinking, physical activity, and dietary practices that is particularly relevant to the discussion in this chapter.

Federal, Provincial and Territorial Advisory Committee on Population Health. (1999). *Toward a healthy future: Second report on health of Canadians*. Ottawa: Minister of Public Works and Government Services Canada. Includes a section titled "Personal Health Practices," which examines trends in health practices of Canadians and the link between personal life choices and the socioeconomic environments in which people live.

Hay, D.I. (1994). Social status and health status: Does money buy health? In B.S. Bolaria & R. Bolaria (Eds.), *Racial minorities, medicine and health* (pp. 9–51). Halifax and Saskatoon: Fernwood Publishing and Social Research Unit. An extensive review of Canadian and international findings on the link between socioeconomic status and health status.

Ross, C.E., & Bird, C.E. (2000). Sex stratification and health lifestyle: Consequences for men's and women's perceived health. In W.C. Cockerham & M. Glasser (Eds.), *Readings in medical sociology* (2nd ed., pp. 91–111). Upper Saddle River, NJ: Prentice-Hall. An explanation of age-based gender differences in health through the examination of sex stratification, gender inequality in paid and unpaid work, the subjective experience of inequality, and sex differences in health lifestyles.

Subedi, J., & Gallagher, E.B. (Eds.). *Society, health and disease: Transcultural perspectives*. Upper Saddle River, NJ: Prentice-Hall. A cross-cultural reader on health attitudes and health behaviour that addresses the social production of health in the context of several countries, based on research from various disciplines.

REFERENCES

Abel, T. (1991). Measuring health lifestyles in a comparative analysis: Theoretical issues and empirical findings. *Social Science and Medicine, 32*(8), 899–908.

Adler, N.E. (1995). Are mind-body variables a central factor linking socioeconomic status and health? *Advances: The Journal of Mind-Body Health, 11*(3), 6–9.

Antonovsky, A. (1992). Social class, life expectancy and overall mortality. In E.G. Jaco (Ed.), *Patients, physicians and illness* (pp. 5–30). New York: Free Press.

Berliner, H.S. (1975). A large perspective on the Flexner report. *International Journal of Health Services, 5*, 573–592.

Berliner, H.S. (1977). Emerging ideologies in medicine. *Review of Radical Political Economics* 9(1), 116–124.

Blaxter, M. (1990). *Health and lifestyles.* London: Tavistock/Routledge.

Bolaria, B.S. (1991). Environment, work and illness. In B.S. Bolaria (Ed.), *Social issues and contradictions in Canadian society* (pp. 222–246). Toronto: Harcourt Brace Jovanovich.

Bolaria, B.S. (1994a). Income inequality, food banks and health. In B.S. Bolaria & H.D. Dickinson (Eds.), *Health, illness, and health care in Canada* (pp. 245–255). Toronto: Harcourt Brace.

Bolaria, B.S. (1994b). Sociology, medicine, health and illness: An overview. In B.S. Bolaria & H.D. Dickinson (Eds.), *Health, illness, and health care in Canada* (pp. 1–18). Toronto: Harcourt Brace.

Bolaria, B.S. (1994c). Lifestyles, material deprivation and health. In B.S. Bolaria & R. Bolaria (Eds.), *Racial minorities, medicine and health* (pp. 67–84). Halifax and Saskatoon: Fernwood Publishing and Social Research Unit.

Bolaria, B.S., & Bolaria, R. (Eds.). (1994a). *Racial minorities, medicine and health.* Halifax and Saskatoon: Fernwood Publishing and Social Research Unit.

Bolaria, B.S., & Bolaria, R. (Eds.). (1994b). *Women, medicine and health.* Halifax and Saskatoon: Fernwood Publishing and Social Research Unit.

Borsellino, M. (1990, March). Poor health care housing blamed for natives' high disability rate. *Medical Post, 27,* 20.

Brown, P. (2000). Environment and health. In C.E. Bird, P. Conrad, & A.M. Fremont (Eds.), *Handbook of medical sociology* (5th ed., pp. 143–158). Upper Saddle River, NJ: Prentice-Hall.

Bunton, R., Nettleton, S., & Burrows, R. (Eds.). (1995). *The sociology of health promotion: Critical analysis of consumption, lifestyle and risk.* London: Routledge.

Burrows, R., Nettleton, S., & Bunton, R. (1995). Sociology and health promotion. In R. Bunton, S. Nettleton, & R. Burrows (Eds.), *The sociology of health promotion: Critical analysis of consumption, lifestyle and risk* (pp. 1–9). London: Routledge.

Chaney, D. (1996). *Lifestyles.* London: Routledge.

Coburn, D., & Eakin, J. (1993). The sociology of health in Canada: First impressions. *Health and Canadian Society, 1,* 83–110.

Cockerham, W.C. (1997). Lifestyles, social class, demographic characteristics and health behavior. In D. Gochman (Ed.), *Handbook of health behavior research I: Personal and social determinants* (pp. 253–265). New York: Plenum Press.

Cockerham, W.C. (1998). *Medical sociology* (7th ed.). Upper Saddle River, NJ: Prentice-Hall.

Cockerham, W.C. (2000). The sociology of health behavior and health lifestyles. In C.E. Bird, P. Conrad, & A.M. Fremont (Eds.), *Handbook of medical sociology* (5th ed., pp. 159–172). Upper Saddle River, NJ: Prentice-Hall.

Cockerham, W.C., Rutten, A., & Abel, T. (1997). Conceptualizing contemporary health lifestyles: Moving beyond Weber. *Sociological Quarterly, 38,* 321–342.

Conrad, P. (1987). Wellness in the workplace: Potentials and pitfalls of worksite health promotion. *The Milbank Quarterly, 65*(2), 255–275.

Conrad, P. (1994). Wellness as a virtue: Morality and the pursuit of health. *Culture, Medicine and Society, 18,* 385–401.

Conrad, P., & Walsh, D.C. (1992). The new corporate health ethic: Lifestyle and the social control of work. *International Journal of Health Sciences, 22,* 89–111.

Corin, E. (1994). The social and cultural matrix of health and disease. In R.G. Evans, *Why are some people healthy and others not? The determinants of health in populations* (pp. 93–132). New York: Aldine deGruyter.

Crawford, R. (1977). You are dangerous to your health: The ideology and politics of victim blaming. *International Journal of Health Services, 7*(4), 663–680.

Daykin, N., & Naidoo, J. (1995). Feminist critiques of health promotion. In R. Bunton, S. Nettleton, & R. Burrows (Eds.), *The sociology of health promotion: Critical analysis of consumption, lifestyle and risk* (pp. 59–69). London: Routledge.

Dean, K. (1989). Self-care components of lifestyle: The importance of gender, attitudes and the social situation. *Social Science and Medicine, 29,* 137–152.

Denton, M., & Walters, V. (1999). Gender differences in structural and behavioral determinants of health: An analysis of the social production of health. *Social Science and Medicine, 48,* 1221–1235.

Douglas, J. (1995). Developing anti-racist health promotion strategies. In R. Bunton, S. Nettleton, & R. Burrows (Eds.), *The sociology of health promotion: Critical analysis of consumption, lifestyle and risk* (pp. 70–77). London: Routledge.

Doyal, L., & Pennell, I. (1979). *The political economy of health.* London: Pluto Press.

Driver, D. (1991, September 17). Poverty linked to higher risks of poor health, death. *Medical Post,* p. 81.

Eakin, J., Robertson, A., Poland, B., Coburn, D., & Edwards, R. (1996). Towards a critical social science perspective on health promotion research. *Health Promotion International, 11*(2), 157–165.

Epp, J. (1986). Achieving health for all: A framework for health promotion. *Canadian Journal of Public Health, 77*(6), 393–407.

Federal, Provincial and Territorial Advisory Committee on Population Health. (1999a). *Statistical report on the health of Canadians.* Ottawa: Minister of Public Works and Government Services Canada.

Federal, Provincial and Territorial Advisory Committee on Population Health. (1999b). *Toward a healthy future: Second report on the health of Canadians.* Ottawa: Minister of Public Works and Government Services Canada.

Firth, M., Brophy, J., & Keith, M. (1997). *Workplace roulette: Gambling with cancer.* Toronto: Between the Lines.

Frankish, C., Milligan, C., & Reid, C. (1998). A review of the relationship between active living and determinants of health. *Social Science and Medicine, 47,* 287–301.

Frideres, J.S. (1994). Racism and health: The case of the Native people. In B.S. Bolaria & H.D. Dickinson (Eds.), *Health, illness, and health care in Canada* (pp. 202–220). Toronto: Harcourt Brace.

Frohlich, K.L., & Potvin, L. (1999). Collective lifestyles as the target for health promotion. *Canadian Journal of Public Health, 90*(Suppl. 1), 511–514.

Garth, H.H., & Mills, C.W. (1958). *Max Weber: Essays in sociology.* New York: Galaxy.

Grace, V.M. (1991). The marketing of empowerment and the construction of the health consumer: A critique of health promotion. *International Journal of Health Services, 21*(2), 329–343.

Gunning-Scheppers, L., & Hagen, J. (1987). Avoidable burden of illness: How much prevention can contribute to health? *Social Science and Medicine, 24,* 945–951.

Harding, J. (1994). Environmental degradation and rising cancer rates: Exploring the links in Canada. In B.S. Bolaria & H.D. Dickinson (Eds.), *Health, illness, and health care in Canada* (pp. 649–667). Toronto: Harcourt Brace.

Hay, D.I. (1994). Social status and health status: Does money buy health? In B.S. Bolaria & R. Bolaria (Eds.), *Racial minorities, medicine and health* (pp. 9–52). Halifax and Saskatoon: Fernwood Publishing and Social Research Unit.

Kickbusch, I. (1989). Self-care in health promotion. *Social Science and Medicine, 29*(2), 125–130.

Krieger, N., & Fee, E. (1993). What's class got to do with it? The state of health data in the United States today. *Socialist Review, 23*(1), 59–82.

Krieger, N., & Fee, E. (1994). Social class: The missing link in U.S. health data. *International Journal of Health Services, 24*(1), 25–44.

Lalonde, M. (1974). *A new perspective on the health of Canadians*. Ottawa: Information Canada.

Link, B.G., & Phelan, J.C. (2000). Evaluating the fundamental cause explanation for social disparities in health. In C.E. Bird, P. Conrad, & A.M. Fremont (Eds.), *Handbook of medical sociology* (5th ed., pp. 33–46). Upper Saddle River, NJ: Prentice-Hall.

Mao, Y., Moloughney, B., Semenciw, R.M., & Morrison, H. (1992). Indian reserves and registered Indian mortality in Canada. *Canadian Journal of Public Health, 83*, 350–353.

Marmot, M., Rose, G., Shipley, M., & Hamilton, P. (1978). Employment grade and coronary heart disease in British civil servants. *Journal of Epidemiology and Community Health, 32*, 244–249.

Marmot, M., Shipley, M., & Rose, G. (1984). Inequalities in death — Specific explanations of a general pattern. *Lancet, 1*(83), 1003–1006.

Marmot, M., Smith, G.D., Stanfield, S., Patel, C., North, F., Head, J., White, I., Brunner, E., & Feeney, A. (1991). Health inequalities among British civil servants: The Whitehall II study. *Lancet, 337*(8754), 1387–1393.

Matcha, D.A. (2000). *Medical sociology*. Toronto: Allyn and Bacon.

McDowell, I. (1986). National strategies for health promotion. *Canadian Journal of Public Health, 77*(6), 448.

McKinlay, J.B. (1993). The promotion of health through planned sociopolitical change: Challenges for research and policy. *Social Science and Medicine, 36*(2), 109–117.

McKinlay, J.B. (1994). A case for refocussing upstream: The political economy of illness. In P. Conrad & R. Kern (Eds.), *The sociology of health and illness: Critical perspectives* (4th ed., pp. 509–523). New York: St. Martin's Press.

McQueen, D. (1989). Thoughts on the ideological origins of health promotion. *Health Promotion 4*(4), 339–342.

Mechanic, D. (1999). Issues in promoting health. *Social Science and Medicine, 48*, 711–718.

Millar, J., & Hull, C. (1997). Measuring human wellness. *Social Indicators Research, 40*, 147–158.

Miller, L., & Findlay, D. (1994). Through medical eyes: The medicalization of women's bodies and women's lives. In B.S. Bolaria & H.D. Dickinson (Eds.), *Health, illness, and health care in Canada* (pp. 276–306). Toronto: Harcourt Brace.

Mirowsky, J., & Ross, C.E. (1998). Education, personal control, lifestyle and health: A human capital hypothesis. *Research on Aging, 20*(4), 415–449.

Mirowsky, J., Ross, C.E., & Reynolds, J. (2000). Links between social status and health status. In C.E. Bird, P. Conrad, & A.M. Fremont (Eds.), *Handbook of medical sociology* (5th ed., pp. 47–67). Upper Saddle River, NJ: Prentice-Hall.

National Council of Welfare. (1990). *Health, health care and medicare*. Ottawa: Supply and Services Canada.

Navarro, V. (1986). *Crisis, health, and medicine*. New York: Tavistock.

Nettleton, S., & Bunton, R. (1995). Sociological critique of health promotion. In R. Bunton, S. Nettleton, & R. Burrows (Eds.), *The sociology of health promotion: Critical analysis of consumption, lifestyle and risk* (pp. 41–58). London: Routledge.

O'Brien, M. (1995). Health and lifestyle: A critical mess: Notes on the dedifferentiation of health. In R. Bunton, S. Nettleton, & R. Burrows (Eds.), *The sociology of health promotion: Critical analysis of consumption, lifestyle and risk* (pp. 191–205). London: Routledge.

Poland, B., Coburn, D., Robertson, A., & Eakin, J. (1998). Wealth, equity and health care: A critique of a population health perspective on the determinants of health. *Social Science and Medicine, 46*, 785–798.

Raphael, D., & Bryant, T. (2000). Putting the population into population health. *Canadian Journal of Public Health, 91*(1), 9–12.

Reading, R. (1997). Poverty and the health of children and adolescents. *Archives of Disease in Childhood, 76*, 463–467.

Renaud, M. (1975). On the structural constraints to state intervention in health. *International Journal of Health Services, 5*(4), 559–571.

Ross, C., & Wu, C.-L. (1995). The links between education and health. *American Sociological Review, 60*, 719–745.

Ross, C.E., & Bird, C.E. (1994). Sex stratification and health lifestyle: Consequences for men's and women's perceived health. *Journal of Health and Social Behaviour, 35*, 161–178.

Ross, D.P., & Roberts, P. (1999). *Income and child well-being: A new perspective on the poverty debate*. Ottawa: Canadian Council on Social Development.

Rutten, A. (1995). The implementation of health promotion: A new structural perspective. *Social Science and Medicine, 41*(12), 1627–1637.

Segall, A., & Chappell, N.L. (2000). *Health and health care in Canada*. Toronto: Prentice-Hall.

Syme, L. (1994, Fall). The social environment and health. *Daedalus*, 79–86.

Tarasuk, V. (1994). Poverty, homelessness and health. In B.S. Bolaria & R. Bolaria (Eds.), *Racial minorities, medicine and health* (pp. 53–66). Halifax and Saskatoon: Fernwood Publishing and Social Research Unit.

Taylor, R.C.R. (1989). The politics of prevention. In P. Brown (Ed.), *Perspectives in medical sociology* (pp. 368–388). Belmont, CA: Wadsworth.

Thomson, M. (1990, August). Association between mortality and poverty. *B.C. Medical Journal, 32*(8).

Townsend, P. (1990). Individual or social responsibility for premature death? Current controversies in the British debate about health. *International Journal of Health Services, 20*(3), 373–392.

Waitzkin, H. (1983). *The second sickness: Contradictions of capitalist health care*. New York: Free Press.

Weber, M. (1978). *Economy and society* (2 vols.). Ed. and trans. G.F. Roth & C. Wittick. Berkeley: University of California Press.

Wilkins, R., Adams, O., & Brancker, A. (1991). Changes in mortality by income in urban Canada from 1971–1986. *Health Reports, 1*, 137–174.

Wilkinson, R.G. (1996). *Unhealthy societies*. London: Routledge.

William, S.J. (1995). Theorizing, class, health, and lifestyles: Can Bourdieu help us? *Sociology of Health and Illness, 17*, 577–604.

Wotherspoon, T. (1994). Colonization, self-determination and the health of Canada's First Nation peoples. In B.S. Bolaria & R. Bolaria (Eds.), *Racial minorities, medicine and health* (pp. 247–267). Halifax and Saskatoon: Fernwood Publishing and Social Research Unit.

Zong, L., & Li, P.S. (1994). Different cultures or unequal life chances: A comparative analysis of race and health. In B.S. Bolaria & R. Bolaria (Eds.), *Racial minorities, medicine and health* (pp. 113–123). Halifax and Saskatoon: Fernwood Publishing and Social Research Unit.

23

Health Care Restructuring and Alternative Approaches to Health and Medicine

HERBERT C. NORTHCOTT   University of Alberta

INTRODUCTION

This chapter examines health care restructuring, paying particular attention to alternative approaches to health and medicine. First, health is defined, and the determinants of health are briefly discussed from both conventional and alternative points of view. Second, medicine, both conventional and alternative, is defined. Third, the conventional health care system is discussed and critiqued. Fourth, alternative approaches to health and health problems are discussed and critiqued. Fifth, the use of alternative health care is examined. Finally, health care restructuring is discussed, with particular emphasis on the emerging status and role of alternative health care therapies. This chapter contrasts conventional approaches to health and medicine with alternative approaches to health and medicine.

HEALTH AND HEALTH DETERMINANTS

This section presents a definition of health and a brief discussion of the determinants of health from the points of view of both conventional and alternative health care.

The World Health Organization's (WHO) 1947 definition of health continues to be widely accepted. The WHO defined **health** as "a state of complete physical, mental, and social well-being and not merely the absence of disease and infirmity" (Armstrong & Armstrong, 1996, pp. 13–14). This definition of health is comprehensive and holistic. Although it originates from within the conventional health care system, it is also consistent with the rhetoric of alternative health care, which tends to emphasize holistic definitions of health.

The WHO's definition of health contrasts health with "disease and infirmity." Health problems are described by a variety of terms. It has been suggested that a person may have a disease (an objective state), feel ill (a subjective state), and act sick (a behaviour) (Clarke, 1996, pp. 180–181). These three aspects of nonhealth do not necessarily go together. A person may feel ill and not act sick; another person may have a disease and not feel ill; and a third person may act sick and not have a disease. Conventional medicine tends to focus on disease and downplay the subjective and behavioural. Alternative health care claims to be more willing to treat all components — the objective, subjective, and behavioural aspects — of health problems.

Turning to the determinants of health, the WHO's comprehensive definition of healthful well-being implies that the determinants of health are wide-ranging, including biology, nutrition, clean air and water, housing, security, education, income, employment, lifestyles, social support, and health care. Thus, the health care system is only one of a number of determinants of health (Armstrong & Armstrong, 1996, pp. 13–14).

The strengths of the WHO's definition of health include a focus on health rather than on illness and disability, an emphasis on health promotion and disease prevention, and a holistic focus that recognizes the interconnectedness of body, mind, and society. Nevertheless, the WHO's definition of health can be criticized for being idealistic and for potentially medicalizing all aspects of human life (see Clarke, 1996, pp. 238–239). That is, the WHO's all-inclusive definition of health could justify the efforts of various experts who intervene in all aspects of our lives to advise, teach, treat, control, and profit from us, all in the name of health promotion.

Finally, despite the continuing appeal of the WHO's definition of health, the definition has not been taken all that seriously. Despite the holistic emphasis on the definition and determinants of health, most of these determinants have been neglected in practice (Armstrong & Armstrong, 1996) while attention has been primarily paid to illness and the development of an illness care system. One of the professed strengths of alternative health care is that it claims to focus more broadly on the determinants of health consistent with the WHO's conceptualization of health and its determinants.

MEDICINE AND THE HEALTH CARE SYSTEM

In popular usage, the term **medicine** often refers to a pharmacological remedy such as a "cough medicine." However, the term is also used more generically. For example, consider the following common usages: the practice of medicine, modern medicine, and medical professionals. Although the term is typically used to refer to conventional medicine, alternative health care is increasingly referred to as complementary medicine. Furthermore, the term "folk medicine" includes both the Aboriginal medicine man and the traditional medicines used by Native healers. In short, the term "medicine" includes all those persons (e.g., doctors, nurses, chiropractors, and Native healers), procedures (e.g., surgery, physiotherapy, acupuncture, and healing circles), and things (e.g., X-rays, drugs, and herbal remedies) committed to dealing with health problems and promoting health.

The term "health care system" is even broader. Besides medical practices and practitioners, the health care system includes institutions (e.g., hospitals, nursing homes, and educational facilities), mechanisms for payment (e.g., the health care insurance system), and aspects of government (e.g., relevant legislation and governmental departments of health). While contemporary usage often refers separately to the conventional health care system and to the alternative health care system, it is also recognized that the health care system is pluralistic, and the term can be thought of as incorporating both conventional and alternative medicine.

THE CONVENTIONAL HEALTH CARE SYSTEM

Various assumptions underlie different health care systems. **Conventional health care** is based on **allopathy**, which emphasizes curing disease by the use of surgery and drugs. There are alternative health care models, such as homeopathy and naturopathy, for example, which emphasize the stimulation of the natural healing powers of the body. Different assumptions about the causes and cures of illness lead to different health care systems.

The assumptions underlying conventional health care include the following: the determinants of illness are primarily biological, and therefore diagnosis relies heavily on objective data such as laboratory tests; the mind and body are largely separate; the body is like a machine made up of interrelated parts, and cure involves fixing the broken body part, often using a specialist's expertise; the goal of health care is to fix (cure) the body, and little attention need be paid to the psychosocial aspects of illness; medicine is scientific, implying that the subjective and metaphysical are largely irrelevant; and finally, doctors have expert knowledge and authority, which tends to minimize the knowledge, insight, and power of the layperson (Armstrong & Armstrong, 1996, pp. 19–23; see also Clarke, 1996, pp. 212–216, 228, 302). In summary, the assumptions underlying conventional health care largely overlook the society–mind–body connection and downplay the personal, subjective, psychosocial aspects of illness.

The person's "voice" is largely considered irrelevant because what is deemed important is what the body, not the person, "says" to the doctor. A person's illness is reduced to an isolated and dysfunctional body part, and control of the illness is taken by the medical professionals and the health care system. Although the sick person is depersonalized and disempowered, perhaps this is a small price to pay if one is quickly cured. However, for the chronically ill, for example, who are not quickly cured, the price is much greater.

Furthermore, Armstrong and Armstrong point out that the state-sanctioned monopoly enjoyed by conventional medicine has prevented the legitimization of alternative health care models (1996, pp. 24–27). They conclude: "Biological causes cannot be separated from social contexts, minds cannot be separated from bodies, and body parts cannot be separated from each other.... We need to integrate this knowledge into the restructuring of care to ensure that care delivery links body part and body part, mind and body, body and social context" (1996, p. 41).

The hospital plays a central role in conventional health care. Armstrong et al. (1994) studied hospital workers' perceptions of hospitals in Ontario during cutbacks in the early 1990s. Hospital workers indicated that funding cutbacks had resulted in fewer staff to deal with sicker patients. Shorter patient stays and home care meant that only the sickest patients were admitted to the hospital. At the same time, reduced staffing meant that patients received minimal care. "The increasing workloads, combined with reduced staff and a new business orientation, make it extremely difficult to provide a client-centred service that deals with the whole person in ways that ensure quality and help people get better, or at least live with dignity" (p. 57). The workers described care as hurried, assembly-line, impersonal, minimal, undignified, lacking in compassion, and generally unresponsive to the psychosocial needs of the patient. The workers described themselves as overloaded, harried, stressed, and demoralized.

Turning more specifically to the nurses who do much of the work of the hospital, Armstrong et al. quote nurses as saying: "each nurse has to work harder...there is little room for caring work.... You don't have time to talk to patients.... Nursing is fragmented into a series of discrete tasks; the work involves 'doing more things to people, not for people,' 'more machine tending than caring for people'" (1993, pp. 45–46; see also Growe, 1991).

In short, the conventional health care system tends to separate body from mind and from social context, to disempower the ill person, and to provide impersonal, fragmented care. In contrast, it is often claimed that **alternative health care** emphasizes holistic and personalized care that empowers the individual.

ALTERNATIVE APPROACHES TO HEALTH AND MEDICINE

There is considerable ambiguity in defining alternative therapies, partly because some alternative therapies, such as chiropractic, are now covered by health care insurance and partly because some alternative therapies, such as acupuncture, are offered by conventional practitioners, including medical doctors, and others, including herbal remedies, can be found in most pharmacies alongside conventional over-the-counter medicines.

Furthermore, despite a long-standing hostility between conventional and alternative practitioners and despite a rhetoric of exclusion, alternative and conventional therapies tend to be used concurrently by the public. Indeed, alternative health care is increasingly referred to as complementary health care, acknowledging that the two systems are not mutually exclusive (for a more complete discussion, see Northcott, 1994).

Alternative health care is not a single, unified system but a diverse plurality of therapies, which can be grouped into seven different categories:

1. medication, including homeopathy, naturopathy, and herbal remedies;
2. manipulation, including chiropractic, osteopathy, acupuncture, acupressure, and therapeutic massage;
3. devices that provide various treatments;
4. mind cures, such as meditation or visualization;
5. supernatural cures, often involving "magic";
6. folk medicine, such as traditional Native American or Ayurvedic (from India) health care systems; and
7. diagnostic techniques, such as iridology, which claims that the health of various parts of the body is evident in the iris of the eye.

Some of these alternative therapies are becoming increasingly conventional — chiropractic is one such example — and widely used, such as herbal remedies (for a more complete discussion, see Northcott, 1994).

There is evidence that the general public does not choose to use either conventional health care or alternative health care exclusively. Instead, people tend to seek care from both systems by, for example, purchasing both over-the-counter conventional and alternative medications. Furthermore, the public routinely visits conventional practitioners, such as medical doctors, and alternative practitioners, such as chiropractors.

The use of therapies tends to be pragmatic. If conventional therapy fails, people will try some alternative therapy or perhaps use both conventional and alternative therapies concurrently. Finally, the use of alternative health care tends to cut across all social categories and does not appear to be limited to a particular social class, age group, or sex (Northcott, 1994).

Alternative approaches to health and medicine tend to claim to be more **holistic** in treating the individual as a biological, psychological, and social whole, in contrast to allopathic medicine, which tends to reduce the individual's illness to a biological problem. Furthermore, alternative approaches to health and medicine tend to place a greater emphasis on health promotion than does conventional (allopathic) medicine. However, the history of medicine, both alternative and conventional, is filled with rhetoric that often falls short of reality. Although the alternative model of health employs a rhetoric of holism, this is not necessarily the case (Saks, 1997; see also Northcott, 1994).

The most widespread alternative health care modality is chiropractic. Furthermore, naturopaths are increasing in Canada and midwives are being increasingly legitimated (Clarke, 1996, p. 346). Finally, there is a substantial and growing interest in herbal remedies. These and other alternative health care occupations and therapies are discussed in the following sections.

Chiropractic

Chiropractic and allopathic medicine have had a long history of intense mutual animosity. Nevertheless, chiropractic has become increasingly legitimated. First of all, chiropractic is widely used by Canadians. Second, it enjoys state recognition in the form of provincial licensing legislation and coverage under provincial health care insurance and workers' compensation programs (Biggs, 1988; Clarke, 1996, pp. 346–350).

Chiropractic has evolved from an alternative health care system into a health care occupation that is increasingly being incorporated into the conventional health care system as a limited specialization focusing on neuromuscular problems, especially those involving the spine (Biggs, 1988; Coburn, 1998, pp. 339–340; Coburn & Biggs, 1987; Coulter, 1987). In this sense, chiropractic has been medicalized and professionalized to the point that it is no longer an alternative health care therapy. Rather, it has become one of the many health care professions that comprise conventional health care today.

The majority of chiropractors today are "mixers." Mixers do not hold to the earlier chiropractic dogma that virtually all illness originates in spinal "subluxations," misalignments of the spine that put pressure on the nerves radiating through the body. Mixers recognize multiple causes of disease and acknowledge the utility of a variety of therapeutic interventions. Some mixers provide naturopathic treatment such as nutritional, lifestyle, and exercise counselling, for example, in addition to spinal manipulation and other physical therapy.

Massage Therapy

Massage therapy "is an emerging health-care profession undergoing rapid expansion" (Hodgson, 1997, p. 242). Massage is increasingly prescribed by conventional health care practitioners as a supplementary treatment. It is regulated by legislation in British Columbia and Ontario and is covered under British Columbia's health care plan (Hodgson, 1997, pp. 242–245). Like chiropractic, massage has the potential to become a limited specialty within conventional medicine rather than an alternative health care modality.

Naturopathy

Naturopathy provides holistic health care based on the assumption that both health and illness are manifestations of the total individual. An individual's illness is considered to be unique to him or her. Healing involves the activation of the natural healing powers of the human body (Clarke, 1996, p. 351). Naturopathy emphasizes the healing power of nature and natural drugless therapeutic methods. Naturopaths are eclectic in the treatment modalities that they use. These include diet and nutrition treatments, lifestyle counselling, vitamins, herbal remedies, homeopathy, traditional Chinese medicine, hydrotherapy, acupuncture, manipulation, and physiotherapy (Crellin, Andersen, & Connor, 1997, pp. 139–141; Gort & Coburn, 1988; Boon, 1995, pp. 16–17).

Naturopathy has an uncertain future (Crellin, Andersen, & Connor, 1997, pp. 140–141). On the one hand, it is currently growing in Canada. Furthermore, naturopaths are licensed in British Columbia, Alberta, Saskatchewan, Manitoba, and Ontario and are partially covered under the British Columbia health insurance plan (Boon, 1997; Government of Alberta, 1999). On the other hand, Boon (1995) notes the considerable overlap between allopathic and naturopathic education in Canada. Furthermore, naturopathy's willingness to embrace a variety of treatment modalities, many of which are easily accepted by conventional medicine, may make it redundant. Finally, Boon notes that conventional allopathic medicine is moving "toward a paradigm of health care which more closely resembles the naturopathic paradigm, placing greater emphasis on the whole person and his or her environment" (1995, p. 37). In short, allopathic and naturopathic medicine appear to be converging. In time, it may no longer be appropriate to describe naturopathy as "alternative."

Homeopathy

Homeopathy is based on a philosophy opposite to that of allopathic medicine. Rather than viewing illness as a sign of disease to be cured by drugs and/or surgery (the allopathic model), homeopathy treats illness by administering natural remedies, mostly herbal, which produce symptoms similar to the illness symptoms. Minute dosages are used in the belief that "like cures like" by stimulating the body's natural healing powers (Clarke, 1996, p. 352). In contrast, allopathy is based on the assumption that opposites cure, that is, on the assumption that illness is cured by opposing it with drugs or surgery.

Homeopathy is not practised solely by homeopaths. Others using homeopathic remedies include some naturopaths, chiropractors, and conventional physicians. Furthermore, homeopathic remedies are increasingly available over the counter in pharmacies and health food stores (Crellin, Andersen, & Connor, 1997, p. 55).

Herbal Remedies

Herbal medicines are used not only by herbalists but also by homeopaths, chiropractors, naturopaths, Native healers, practitioners of traditional Chinese medicine, and others. Furthermore, herbal medicines are a significant component of self-care strategies and are often self-prescribed, purchased over the counter, and used not only as medicines for illness symptoms but also as nutritional supplements for the promotion of health (Crellin, Andersen, & Connor, 1997, pp. 184–186).

Herbal remedies have become a substantial and growing industry. Indeed, in 1998 *Time* magazine ran a cover story, "The Herbal Medicine Boom," noting that natural supplements were a $12 billion industry in the United States in 1997 and had a growth rate exceeding 10 percent a year (p. 47). Recently, major pharmaceutical companies and pharmacy chains have entered the business of herbal remedies. Concerns exist over unsubstantiated claims, quality control, safety, potentially negative side effects, and unwarranted usage.

Herbal remedies can be evaluated in the same way that conventional medicines are evaluated (Crellin, Andersen, & Connor, 1997, p. 187). However, the use of science to determine the active ingredients in herbal remedies and the use of scientific clinical trials to determine the efficacy of herbal remedies is a task that is neither easily nor quickly accomplished. When, or if, that task is accomplished, distinctions between alternative herbal remedies and conventional medicines will be meaningless. That is, alternative and conventional remedies will have converged to the point that they are indistinguishable.

In 1999, the federal government announced that it would spend $10 million over 3 years — $7 million for a new division of Health Canada to regulate natural (alternative) health products and $3 million for research. Furthermore, herbal medicines, including vitamins, minerals, herbal remedies, homeopathic remedies, and natural drugs, would be classified separately from foods (which cannot make health claims) and separately from drugs (which must be subjected to costly clinical trials) (Arab, 1999). Although this initiative does not put herbal remedies on exactly the same footing as prescription medicines, it does nevertheless introduce both state regulation and state-sponsored research designed to demonstrate the efficacy of herbal remedies. These steps encourage the convergence of conventional medicines and alternative herbal remedies.

Midwifery

According to Armstrong and Armstrong (1996, pp. 43–44), **midwifery** is an alternative practice to conventional medicine. Midwifery, these authors say, does not disempower the parents, does not take control of the birthing process (midwives assist the mother and "catch" rather than deliver babies), and is holistic in emphasizing the social and psychological along with the biological. Burtch (1994, p. 507) notes that midwifery rejects the notion that pregnancy is like a disease to be managed according to the medical model, using drugs, surgery when necessary, and physician control. Benoit (1998, p. 370) observes that midwifery claims a personal relationship between the midwife and the birth parents, which gives parents a greater voice and more control than do conventional birthing practices.

Midwifery has a long history. Since ancient times, women experienced and skilled in birthing techniques have been relied upon to assist women giving birth. However, over the past century and a half in Canada, the midwife has been replaced by the physician (Benoit, 1998, pp. 367–369; Coburn, 1998, p. 337; Clarke, 1996, pp. 356–357), and birthing has been medicalized and hospitalized. Today, there is a midwifery movement that is attempting to re-establish midwifery as a legitimate profession. In the early 1990s, midwives were legalized in Ontario, Alberta, and British Columbia (Burtch, 1994, p. 513).

The legitimization and professionalization of midwifery may be problematic for midwifery's claim to be an alternative health care modality (Benoit, 1998, pp. 370–373). Pressures to obtain expert knowledge and certification, desires to enhance income and to be funded under medicare, the desirability of group practice so that one can share "on-call" duties, and concerns about liability and litigation tend to push midwifery toward the medical model. Benoit (1998, p. 370) worries that the midwife may become simply another expert health care professional with a tendency to establish distance and take control from the client. In short, midwifery may become a limited specialty incorporated within the conventional health care system rather than an alternative to conventional health care.

Acupuncture

Acupuncture is a component of traditional Chinese medicine that is practised today by a variety of practitioners including conventional physicians. Crellin, Andersen, & Connor (1997, pp. 218–221) comment on the Westernization of acupuncture as it is incorporated into the conventional medical model.

Aboriginal Traditional Medicine

Aboriginal traditional medicine focuses on holistic healing using herbal remedies, listening and talking, and loving and accepting, all administered with humility, respect, and humour (Joe, 1997). Healing involves an emphasis on harmony with one's natural environment as well as with one's human community. Aboriginal traditional medicine is not antithetical to conventional medicine. Indeed, a patient in the hospital, for example, may be attended by both a conventional physician and a Native healer. The two systems of care involve different emphases that can be complementary rather than mutually exclusive. For more details on issues of Aboriginal health and healing, see Chapter 8 of this book.

THE USE OF ALTERNATIVE HEALTH CARE

In 1997, the Angus Reid Group conducted two telephone polls of adult Canadians. The first poll was done for the Fraser Institute, in Vancouver, and the second poll was done for CTV, a national television network.

The Fraser Institute–Angus Reid Group poll (Ramsay, Walker, & Alexander, 1999) surveyed 1500 randomly selected Canadians 18 years of age and older in May and June 1997. This poll found that 73 percent of Canadians had used at least one alternative therapy at some time in their lives. The alternative therapies were selected from a list of

22, including acupuncture, aromatherapy, biofeedback, chelation therapy, chiropractic, energy healing, folk remedies, herbal therapies, high-dose megavitamins, homeopathy, hypnosis, imagery techniques, lifestyle diet, massage, naturopathy, osteopathy, prayer, relaxation techniques, self-help groups, special diet programs, spiritual or religious healing by others, and yoga. The inclusion of diets, self-help groups, and prayer in the list of alternative therapies tends to increase the apparent usage of alternative health care, compared with more restrictive lists of alternative therapies.

According to the poll, chiropractic was the most common form of alternative medicine (used by 36 percent of adult Canadians at some time in their life), followed by relaxation techniques (23 percent), massage (23 percent), prayer (21 percent), herbal therapies (17 percent), special diet programs (12 percent), folk remedies (12 percent), acupuncture (12 percent), yoga (10 percent), homeopathy (8 percent), lifestyle diet (8 percent), and self-help groups (8 percent). Fifty percent of respondents reported using at least one alternative therapy in the previous 12 months, including prayer (18 percent), relaxation techniques (17 percent), chiropractic (13 percent), herbal therapies (12 percent), massage (12 percent), folk remedies (6 percent), lifestyle diet (5 percent), aromatherapy (5 percent), homeopathy (4 percent), and yoga (4 percent). Regarding funding, about 40 percent of Canadians said that alternative health care costs should be covered under provincial health care plans.

The CTV–Angus Reid Group poll (Angus Reid Group, 1997) surveyed 1200 randomly selected Canadians 18 years of age and older in August 1997. Respondents were asked if they had ever used any alternative medicines and practices, including acupuncture, homeopathy, herbology, macrobiotics, chiropractic, or any other therapies not usually prescribed by conventional doctors. The results of this poll are not directly comparable to those of the Fraser Institute poll because the questions used in the two surveys were not identical.

The CTV–Angus Reid Group poll found that 42 percent of Canadians said that they had used alternative health care at some time and that almost half of alternative health care users (19 percent of Canadians) said that they had started using alternative health care within the last 5 years. The most frequently used alternative health care options include chiropractic (used at some time by 25 percent of Canadians), herbology (10 percent), acupuncture (9 percent), and homeopathy (8 percent).

The majority of respondents (70 percent) in the CTV–Angus Reid Group poll said that provincial health care plans should cover the costs of alternative medicines and practices. In addition, a majority (66 percent) indicated that government should advocate the use of alternative medicines and practices to reduce the overall cost of health care. Finally, a majority (67 percent) felt that alternative medicines and practices should be regulated by government to ensure safety and efficacy.

The results of these two polls indicate that the use of alternative health care in Canada is widespread (see also Crellin, Andersen, & Connor, 1997, pp. 15–16) and that it cuts across all sectors of Canadian society — male and female, young and old, more educated and less educated, rich and poor, healthy and unhealthy. Whereas the alternative health care system is more likely to be used by individuals to prevent illness, both conventional and alternative systems are used for illness care. Generally, there is support for both systems, since users of alternative care tend also to be users of conventional care.

Health Care Restructuring and Alternative Health Care

It is often alleged that a primary weakness of alternative therapies is their claim of efficacy on the basis of personal anecdotes and testimonials rather than generalized, objective, rational, and scientific evidence. However, many conventional therapies themselves lack clear and consistent scientific evidence. Their efficacy may be assumed, and supporting scientific evidence may be partial or lacking. Furthermore, conventional therapies that are generally effective may not work for a particular individual. A particular individual may not respond to treatment, or might respond negatively, or suffer uncommon side effects. Although conventional medicine acknowledges the shortcomings of its science, and many clinicians will search for the best treatment modality for the individual patient, nevertheless, conventional medicine maintains its faith in the ultimate value of scientific generalizations.

It is often claimed that alternative health care is more likely to assume from the outset that the patient and his or her illness are unique and that treatment must be tailored to the individual. Nevertheless, like conventional therapists, alternative therapists also rely on generalizations about causes of illness and appropriate treatments. The generalizations used by alternative therapists are based on various assumptions about disease causation and cure.

The strength of most alternative therapies is said to be the personal emphasis on the whole individual, including the complex interplay of the unique biological, psychological, and sociological aspects of that individual in producing both illness and healing. Accordingly, alternative therapies tend to claim to offer personalized treatment focused on the whole individual and aimed at producing healing and wellness in the broadest sense.

Conventional medicine, on the other hand, is often criticized for overemphasizing objective and scientific biology and underemphasizing the subjective psychosocial aspects of the ill individual and therefore treating only the individual's disease and not the whole individual. Nevertheless, conventional medicine increasingly does acknowledge the complex interplay of biology, psychology, and sociology and its relevance for health care. Furthermore, conventional medicine is increasingly interested in wellness — in the total well-being of the individual (Crellin, Andersen, & Connor, 1997, p. 250).

In short, alternative and conventional health care may be becoming more similar. Both are increasingly concerned about demonstrating proof of their efficacy. Both are concerned about finding effective therapy for individual patients. And today both emphasize the holistic model, though sometimes more in word than deed, and both are concerned about promoting wellness in addition to treating illness.

Health care in Canada is becoming increasingly pluralistic. That is, health care consumers use both the conventional health care system and the more holistic alternative health care system. In addition, many conventional doctors feel that they offer holistic patient-centred care, in which they pay attention to the psychosocial needs of the ill person (Crellin, Andersen, & Connor, 1997, pp. 4, 250). Similarly, other conventional medical professions such as nursing tend to emphasize the holistic biopsychosocial model of individualized patient care (1997, pp. 250–251), although they may not always be able to put this model into practice as much as they would like.

Conventional medical practitioners themselves increasingly offer a variety of alternative therapies, including, for example, homeopathy, naturopathic remedies, herbal remedies, acupuncture, acupressure, massage, therapeutic touch, biofeedback, visualization and imaging, hypnosis, meditation, prayer, and faith (note that the long-recognized placebo effect acknowledges the power of the believing mind). In short, conventional medicine appears to be in the process of incorporating alternative perspectives and practices. Both conventional and alternative systems of care may be merging into one integrated, although pluralistic, health care system.

As for alternative medicine, the pursuit of legitimization, validation, and professionalization tends to lead to an emulation of and convergence with conventional medicine. Indeed, at times it is difficult to distinguish the conventional from the alternative. Some analysts prefer the term complementary medicine to alternative medicine. This implies that the relationship between the two has become close, even intertwined, rather than separate, distinct, and oppositional. The use of alternative therapies by conventional practitioners, the emulation of conventional medicine by alternative medicine, and the public's tendency to use both conventional and alternative medicine suggest that conventional and alternative health care are converging and combining. In short, the health care system today, broadly defined, incorporates to a degree both the conventional system and the alternative system.

In very general terms, this was also true in the past. The public has long had access to both conventional and alternative health care components. What is changing is the decline of the old hostilities and the inflammatory rhetoric, and the emergence of mutual tolerance and even acceptance. Furthermore, legislative changes in provinces such as Ontario and Alberta are increasingly recognizing alternative health care professions by bringing alternative and conventional health care practitioners under the same legislative umbrella.

In Ontario, the *Regulated Health Professions Act* of 1991 "regulates" 24 health professions, including chiropractors, midwives, and massage therapists (Crellin, Andersen, & Connor, 1997, pp. 3, 141). This legislation gives the included alternative health professions "the same legal organization and standing as the regular medical profession" (Crellin, Andersen, & Connor, 1997, p. 3). Naturopaths in Ontario have asked to be included under the *Regulated Professions Act* but continue to be licensed under the *Drugless Practitioners Act* of 1925 (Boon, 1997, pp. 173–174). The alternative medical professions are willing to accept increased regulation by the state in exchange for greater official recognition (Coburn, 1998, p. 340).

In Alberta, the *Health Professions Act* of 1999 (Government of Alberta, 1999) regulates 28 health professions, including acupuncturists, chiropractors, midwives, and naturopaths, along with the more conventional physicians, dentists, optometrists, pharmacists, nurses, and physical therapists. Ontario and Alberta appear to be taking the lead in creating this kind of umbrella legislation, which simultaneously recognizes the legitimacy of both conventional and alternative selected health care professions. It is important to note, however, that official recognition does not necessarily mean entitlement to funding under provincial health care insurance plans. Although the recognition of alternative health professions, in the form of provincial legislation, appears to be increasingly common, the funding of alternative health care treatment under provincial health care insurance plans is less common.

CONCLUSION

Conventional medicine has been very successful in the past two centuries. Conventional medicine has become dominant not only in terms of its ability to cure disease but also in its ability to control the "politics" of health care. As a consequence, alternative approaches to health care have typically been reviled and excluded.

Conventional medicine, however, has its limitations. As these limitations become increasingly apparent to health care consumers, alternative health care providers have found themselves in increasing demand. Indeed, the use of both conventional and alternative health care systems has become so common that analysts have begun to describe the alternative health care system as complementary rather than alternative.

Furthermore, the emerging health care system, including both conventional and alternative practices, is increasingly described as pluralistic. In this regard, legislative developments in Ontario and Alberta in the 1990s are instructive. Each of these provinces has enacted health professions legislation that recognizes a variety of health care professions, both conventional and alternative, under one statute.

In short, on the one hand, the conventional health care system is becoming less "conventional" as it becomes increasingly open to alternative practices. On the other hand, the alternative health care system is becoming less "alternative" as it emulates conventional health care in terms of professional education, scientific validation, and recognition under provincial legislation. Perhaps one of the most significant outcomes of health care restructuring in the late twentieth century will be an integrated, although pluralistic, system of health care in the early twenty-first century that combines both conventional and alternative practices.

STUDY QUESTIONS

1. *What is the World Health Organization's definition of health, and how is this definition reflected in conventional and alternative health care systems today?*
2. *Conventional and alternative health care systems may deal more or less effectively with different kinds of health problems. Discuss.*
3. *Discuss the assumptions underlying conventional and alternative health care and the consequences of these assumptions for patient care.*
4. *Discuss contemporary alternative health care therapies and comment on their relationship with conventional health care.*
5. *Discuss the legitimization of alternative health care therapies in terms of utilization, provincial legislation, and coverage under provincial health care insurance plans.*

GLOSSARY

acupuncture A treatment given by inserting needles under the skin.

allopathy A treatment using drugs and surgery to oppose disease.

alternative health care The wide range of health care practices and practitioners that are excluded from conventional health care.

chiropractic Treatment by manipulation of the bones, particularly the spine.

conventional health care The dominant system of health care.

health "A state of complete physical, mental, and social well-being and not merely the absence of disease and infirmity" (WHO, 1947).

holistic Treatment that emphasizes the whole person, including her or his biological, psychological, and social aspects.

homeopathy Treatment with minute doses of natural remedies that in larger quantities would produce the symptoms of the disease to be cured; it is believed that such treatment stimulates the body's natural healing powers.

medicine A substance used in treating disease, or, more broadly, all of those practices, persons, and things involved in treating disease and promoting health.

midwifery The practice of assisting in childbirth.

naturopathy Treatment with a variety of natural therapies.

RECOMMENDED READINGS

Angus Reid Group. (1997). *Use and dangers of alternative medicine and practices. Parts 1 and 2.* http://www.angusreid.com. A report of a survey of a randomly selected sample of 1200 Canadians, who were asked about their use of alternative health care and their attitudes to various health care issues such as governmental regulation and the promotion and funding of alternative health care.

Armstrong, P., & Armstrong, H. (1996*). Wasting away: The undermining of Canadian health care.* Don Mills, ON: Oxford University Press. A critical look at the conventional medical model, which, it is argued, fails to address many determinants of health. In addition, this book is critical of health care reform involving governmental cost-cutting, down-sizing, and privatization.

Crellin, J.K., Andersen, R.R., & Connor, J.T.H. (Eds.). (1997). *Alternative health care in Canada: Nineteenth- and twentieth-century perspectives.* Toronto: Canadian Scholars' Press. A collection of essays focusing on alternative health care in Canada; discussions cover the relationship of alternative and conventional health care and their development together over the past two centuries.

Pawluch, D., Cain, R., & Gillett, J. (1994). Ideology and alternative therapy use among people living with HIV/AIDS. *Health and Canadian Society, 2,* 63–84. A study of the use of alternative therapies by persons living with HIV/AIDS in Toronto in 1993 and of the individual users' rationales for using alternative therapies. The persons interviewed combined alternative and conventional therapies.

Ramsay, C., Walker, M., & Alexander, J. (1999). *Alternative medicine in Canada: Use and public attitudes.* Vancouver: Fraser Institute. A report of a survey of a randomly selected sample of 1500 Canadians who were asked about their health, their use of both conventional and alternative health care, and their attitudes to various health care issues.

REFERENCES

Angus Reid Group. (1997). *Use and dangers of alternative medicine and practices. Parts 1 and 2.* http://www.angusreid.com.

Arab, P. (1999, March 27). Ottawa puts $10 million toward herbal health: New office to oversee natural products. *Edmonton Journal,* p. A3.

Armstrong, P., & Armstrong, H. (1996*). Wasting away: The undermining of Canadian health care.* Don Mills, Ontario: Oxford University Press.

Armstrong, P., Choiniere, J., & Day, E. (1993*). Vital signs: Nursing in transition.* Toronto: Garamond.

Armstrong, P., Choiniere, J., Feldberg, G., & White, J. (1994). Voices from the ward: A study of the impact of cutbacks. In P. Armstrong, H. Armstrong, J. Choiniere, G. Feldberg, & J. White (Eds.), *Take care: Warning signals for Canada's health system* (pp. 53–94). Toronto: Garamond.

Benoit, C. (1998). Rediscovering appropriate care: Maternity traditions and contemporary issues in Canada. In D. Coburn, C. D'Arcy, & G. Torrance (Eds.), *Health and Canadian society: Sociological perspectives* (3rd ed., pp. 359-378). Toronto: University of Toronto Press.

Biggs, L. (1988). The professionalization of chiropractic in Canada: Its current status and future prospects. In B.S. Bolaria & H.D. Dickinson (Eds.), *Sociology of health care in Canada* (pp. 328–345). Toronto: Harcourt Brace.

Boon, H. (1995). The making of a naturopathic practitioner: The education of "alternative" practitioners in Canada. *Health and Canadian Society, 3,* 15–41.

Boon, H. (1997). Licensed naturopathic medicine in Canada today: A national profile. In J.K. Crellin, R.R. Andersen, & J.T.H. Connor (Eds.), *Alternative health care in Canada: Nineteenth- and twentieth-century perspectives* (pp. 172–182). Toronto: Canadian Scholars' Press.

Burtch, B.E. (1994). Promoting midwifery, prosecuting midwives: The state and the midwifery movement in Canada. In B.S. Bolaria & H.D. Dickinson (Eds.), *Health, illness, and health care in Canada* (2nd ed., pp. 504–523). Toronto: Harcourt Brace.

Clarke, J.N. (1996). *Health, illness, and medicine in Canada* (2nd ed.). Don Mills, ON: Oxford University Press.

Coburn, D. (1998). State authority, medical dominance, and trends in the regulation of the health professions: The Ontario case. In D. Coburn, C. D'Arcy, & G. Torrance (Eds.), *Health and Canadian society: Sociological perspectives* (3rd ed., pp. 332–346). Toronto: University of Toronto Press.

Coburn, D., & Biggs, C.L. (1987). Legitimation or medicalization? The case of chiropractic in Canada. In D. Coburn, C. D'Arcy, G. Torrance, & P. New (Eds.), *Health and Canadian society: Sociological perspectives* (2nd ed., pp. 366–384). Markham, ON: Fitzhenry & Whiteside.

Coulter, I.D. (1987). The chiropractic role: Marginal, supplemental or alternative health care? An empirical reconsideration. In D. Coburn, C. D'Arcy, G. Torrance, & P. New (Eds.), *Health and Canadian society: Sociological perspectives* (2nd ed., pp. 385–398). Markham, ON: Fitzhenry & Whiteside.

Crellin, J.K., Andersen, R.R., & Connor, J.T.H. (Eds.). (1997). *Alternative health care in Canada: Nineteenth- and twentieth-century perspectives.* Toronto: Canadian Scholars' Press.

Government of Alberta. (1999). *Health professions act.* Edmonton: Government of Alberta.

Gort, E.H., & Coburn, D. (1988). Naturopathy in Canada: Changing relationships to medicine, chiropractic and the state. *Social Science and Medicine, 26*(10), 1061–1072.

Growe, S.J. (1991). *Who cares: The crisis in Canadian nursing.* Toronto: McClelland & Stewart.

Hodgson, P. (1997). The practice of massage therapy in Canada. Standards in an emerging health care profession. In J.K. Crellin, R.R. Andersen, & J.T.H. Connor (Eds.), *Alternative health care in Canada: Nineteenth- and twentieth-century perspectives* (pp. 242–245). Toronto: Canadian Scholars' Press.

Joe, M. (1997). An address to the VIII International conference on traditional medicine and folklore. In J.K. Crellin, R.R. Andersen, & J.T.H. Connor (Eds.), *Alternative health care in Canada: Nineteenth- and twentieth-century perspectives* (pp. 206–212). Toronto: Canadian Scholars' Press.

Northcott, H.C. (1994). Alternative health care in Canada. In B.S. Bolaria & H.D. Dickinson (Eds.), *Health, illness, and health care in Canada* (2nd ed., pp. 487–503). Toronto: Harcourt Brace.

Ramsay, C., Walker, M., & Alexander, J. (1999). *Alternative medicine in Canada: Use and public attitudes.* Vancouver: Fraser Institute. http://www.fraserinstitute.ca.

Saks, M. (1997). Alternative therapies: Are they holistic? *Complementary Therapies in Nursing and Midwifery, 3,* 4–8.

The herbal medicine boom: It's great business, but is it good for what ails us? (1998, November 23). *Time,* pp. 46–59.

24

Multiculturalism, Ethnicity, Aging, and Health Care

K. VICTOR UJIMOTO University of Guelph

INTRODUCTION

Canadian immigration data over the past several decades reveal that more new immigrants are coming from Asia, Africa, and South America than from the traditional immigrant source-countries in Europe. Canada continues to be one of the few countries in which refugees are still accepted for humanitarian reasons during times of international conflicts. Refugees, such as those fleeing Kosovo (*The Globe and Mail,* 1999, p. A5), will continue to change the demographic composition of Canadian society.

The heterogeneous nature of Canadian society was recognized by the Canadian government in 1971, when it announced the policy on **multiculturalism**. The ***Multiculturalism Act*** was proclaimed in 1988, but even to this day multiculturalism is not well understood by Canadians. As Fleras and Elliott (1996, p. 324) have noted, the essence of multiculturalism cannot be captured in any simple definition. They suggest that distinctions must be made "between multiculturalism as a 'thing' or as a 'process' or as a 'condition.'" Thus, multiculturalism can be interpreted at different levels, as illustrated in Table 1.

In this chapter, the different interpretations or meanings attached to multiculturalism will be discussed in relation to our understanding of **ethnicity**, aging, and **health** care.

MULTICULTURALISM AS FACT

Multiculturalism as fact is essentially the same as Kallen's first statement on multiculturalism (1982, p. 51), which reflects the social reality of ethnic diversity in Canadian society. This reality is based on official Statistics Canada census data (1998, p. 4) shown in Table 2.

It will be noted in Table 2 that, with the exception of the Northwest Territories, the proportion of the population reporting single and multiple ethnic origins other than British, French, or Canadian was highest in Manitoba, followed by Saskatchewan and British Columbia. By itself, Table 2 does not inform us about the characteristics of the

TABLE 24.1 *Levels of Interpretation of Multiculturalism*

Multiculturalism as Fact	Multiculturalism as Ideology	Multiculturalism as Policy	Multiculturalism as Process
Empirical description of ethnic reality in Canada	Prescriptive statement of what ought to be —a set of ideas and ideals that extol the virtues of tolerance and diversity	Accommodating diversity through explicit state initiatives: (a) celebrating differences (1971–), (b) managing diversity (1981–), and (c) citizenship and belonging (1991–)	Manipulation by political sectors (multiculturalism means business) and minority sectors (culture + equality)

Source: Fleras and Elliott (1996, p. 326).
Reprinted with permission by Pearson Education Canada, Inc.

TABLE 24.2 *Proportion of Population by Ethnic Origin (Percent)*

	British Isles Only[1]	French Only[2]	Canadian	British Isles and/or French and/or Canadian[3]	Other and British Isles, French or Canadian[4]	Other Single and Multiple Origins[5]
Canada	17.1	9.5	18.7	10.2	16.1	28.5
Newfoundland	57.7	1.3	21.0	11.5	5.7	2.8
P.E.I.	42.8	6.4	13.0	24.8	9.6	3.4
Nova Scotia	33.0	4.3	19.2	18.9	16.5	8.1
New Brunswick	25.0	17.0	23.9	21.5	9.1	3.5
Quebec	3.0	29.3	37.7	9.6	5.4	14.9
Ontario	21.1	2.9	12.1	11.1	16.8	35.9
Manitoba	15.7	3.1	8.6	6.6	24.0	42.0
Saskatchewan	14.3	1.9	10.2	5.5	30.0	38.0
Alberta	16.5	1.8	12.8	7.4	27.4	34.1
British Columbia	21.5	1.3	9.7	8.1	23.2	36.2
Yukon Territory	17.1	2.3	15.0	9.2	28.4	28.2
Northwest Territories	9.5	1.4	6.9	4.4	16.7	61.1

1. British Isles includes single responses of English, Irish, Scottish, Welsh, or other British, as well as multiple British Isles only responses—that is, a combination of English, Irish, Scottish, Welsh, or other British.
2. French origins include single responses of French or Acadian, as well as multiple responses of French and Acadian.
3. British Isles and/or French and/or Canadian origins include multiple responses of any of the following: a British Isles origin (English, Irish, Scottish, Welsh, or other British), a French origin (French or Acadian), or Canadian. For example, "Scottish and Canadian," "Irish and Acadian," "English, Irish, French and Canadian," etc.
4. Other and British Isles, French or Canadian origins include multiple responses of at least one British Isles origin (English, Irish, Scottish, Welsh, or other British) and/or at least one French origin (French or Acadian) and/or Canadian, in combination with another ethnic origin.
5. Other single and multiple origins include single and multiple responses that do not include British Isles origins, French origins, or Canadian.

Source: Statistics Canada (1998, p. 4).

ethnic groups, except to note that their presence can no longer be ignored when addressing ethnicity and health care issues.

MULTICULTURALISM AS IDEOLOGY

Fleras and Elliott (1996, p. 326) note that "multiculturalism as an **ideology** refers to a normative statement of 'what ought to be.'" This is another way of stating what Kallen (1982, p. 251) previously noted as "the federal government policy designed to create national unity in ethnic diversity." Fleras and Elliott (1996, p. 325) provide several additional assumptions. First, it is assumed that "minority cultures can constitute living and lived-in realities that impart meaning and security to adherents at times of stress or social change." Another way of viewing this is to accept cultural differences as being compatible with national goals.

The second assumption noted by Fleras and Elliott (1996, p. 326) is that "multiculturalism does not downgrade diversity as contrary to the goals of national unity or socioeconomic progress." Thus, cultural diversity is accepted as an equal and integral aspect of the national ideology.

The third, and perhaps most important assumption to address, is "the open minded philosophy firmly grounded on the principles of tolerance and mutual respect" (Fleras & Elliott, 1996, p. 327). This statement should not be treated as a mere assumption, but as a worthwhile national educational goal. Such a goal will further enhance individual self-esteem by facilitating **ethnic identity** as an integral aspect of Canadian culture. As an educational objective, mutual respect can be enhanced while reducing **prejudice** and **discrimination**.

MULTICULTURALISM AS FEDERAL POLICY

Although multiculturalism as a federal policy has received much attention since the promulgation of the 1988 *Multiculturalism Act*, various government initiatives on ethnic relations can be traced back to the 1940s. A report prepared for Canadian Heritage (1966, p. 12) notes that the federal government sought ethnic support for the Canadian war effort in 1942. It must be noted, however, that such support over the years from some ethnic groups was not always welcome. For example, Japanese Canadians who had volunteered for the Boer War were rejected. Again, during World War I, Japanese Canadians were not able to enlist in the Canadian army, but in 1916 they received permission from Ottawa to commence military training and to organize the Japanese Volunteer Corps (Ujimoto, 1983, p. 133). Volunteering for army service at the outset of World War II was equally difficult for Japanese Canadians. The situation in 1999 appeared to be somewhat different. Kosovar Albanians were volunteering to join the Kosovo Liberation Army to fight Yugoslav forces in Kosovo (*The National Post,* 1999, A10).

Federal multiculturalism initiatives in the 1950s and 1960s emphasized naturalization and **citizenship** participation, and as Canadian Heritage (1996, p. 12) reports, government policies were meant to further recognize cultural diversity and national unity issues. The recognition of cultural diversity was based on the inadequate nature of the policy of **assimilation**. As Fleras and Elliott (1996, p. 330) have observed, the policy of multiculturalism has undergone many changes since its inception and continues to adjust to the changing realities of globalization. The transformations in the policy of multiculturalism can best be assessed as a social change process.

MULTICULTURALISM AS PROCESS

The changes in multiculturalism policies can be observed through the various programs administered by the Department of Multiculturalism and Citizenship over the years. In the 1970s, the major thrust of multicultural programs was to celebrate cultural diversity. This was most appropriate for the period, as many new immigrants retained their own language, customs, and ethnic identity. The government initiatives facilitated various ethnic groups to retain their **cultural heritage**, while at the same time it assisted immigrants to adjust and overcome cultural barriers in Canadian society. The celebration of multicultural festivals enabled ethnocultural groups to participate together and to create new meanings for Canadian citizenship through cultural diversity. A decade later, multiculturalism as a federal policy encouraged ethnocultural communities to articulate their own goals. The major task for the multiculturalism directorate was to create and manage the new institutions and changing social structures of Canadian society. The principle of equality naturally meant addressing issues of prejudice, discrimination, and **racism**. Various objectives were established to manage cultural diversity through race relations programs.

Canada became the first country to endow multiculturalism with legal authority, through the interpretation of the 1982 *Canadian Charter of Rights and Freedoms* (Fleras & Elliott, 1966, p. 333). The Canadian *Multiculturalism Act* of 1988 officially recognized the principles of institutional accommodation and promoted the cultural and racial diversity of Canadian society.

A final point to be observed in multiculturalism as a process is that the enhancement of multiculturalism is now an integral component of several federal laws, such as the Constitution, the *Canadian Charter of Rights and Freedoms*, and the *Canadian Citizenship Act*. The Canadian Race Relations Foundation was established in 1996. The institutional accommodation of various ethnocultural members in many government departments, such as Agriculture Canada, Environment Canada, Industry Canada, and Statistics Canada, is occurring gradually. The degree of institutional accommodation across Canada has yet to be established. A start in this direction can be made with a much better understanding of the ethnic diversity of Canadian society.

ETHNIC DIVERSITY IN CANADIAN SOCIETY

An important point to note with regard to the demographic changes that are occurring in Canada today is that social policy issues such as health care can no longer be considered from a single cultural perspective. As shown in Table 2, 17.1 percent of the total Canadian population reported their ancestry as British Isles only and 9.5 percent reported French-only ancestry. In contrast, 28.5 percent of the total population reported ethnic origins other than British, French, or Canadian. The so-called **visible minority population** across Canada is illustrated in Tables 3 and 4. In addition to noting the regional variations in the reported ethnic origins of Canadians, it is important also to note the considerable differences in the ethnic composition of a given metropolitan area (see Figure 1).

TABLE 24.3 *Visible Minority Population, by Province, 1996*

	Total Population	Total Visible Minority Population	Visible Minorities as % of Total Population	Geographic Distribution of Visible Minorities (%)
Canada	28 528 125	3 197 480	11.2	100.0
Newfoundland	547 155	3 815	0.7	0.1
Prince Edward Island	132 855	1 520	1.1	0.0
Nova Scotia	899 970	31 320	3.5	1.0
New Brunswick	729 625	7 995	1.1	0.3
Quebec	7 045 085	433 985	6.2	13.6
Ontario	10 642 790	1 682 045	15.8	52.6
Manitoba	1 100 295	77 355	7.0	2.4
Saskatchewan	976 615	26 945	2.8	0.8
Alberta	2 669 195	269 280	10.1	8.4
British Columbia	3 689 760	660 545	17.9	20.7
Yukon Territory	30 650	1 000	3.3	0.0
Northwest Territories	64 125	1 670	2.6	0.1

Source: Statistics Canada (1998, p. 6).

TABLE 24.4 *Visible Minority Population, by Ethnic Group, 1996*

	Number	Percent
Total visible minority population	3 197 480	100.0
Chinese	860 150	26.9
South Asian	670 585	21.0
Black	573 860	17.9
Arab/West Asian	244 665	7.7
Filipino	234 200	7.3
Latin American	176 975	5.5
Southeast Asian	172 765	5.4
Japanese	68 135	2.1
Korean	64 835	2.0
Visible minority, n.i.e.[1]	69 745	2.2
Multiple visible minority[2]	61 570	1.9

1. Includes Pacific Islanders and other visible minority groups.
2. Includes respondents who reported more than one visible minority group.
n.i.e. = not included elsewhere.

Source: Statistics Canada (1998, p. 5).

FIGURE 24.1

*Visible Minority Population as a
Percentage of Census Metropolitan
Area, 1996*

Source: Statistics Canada (1998, p. 6).

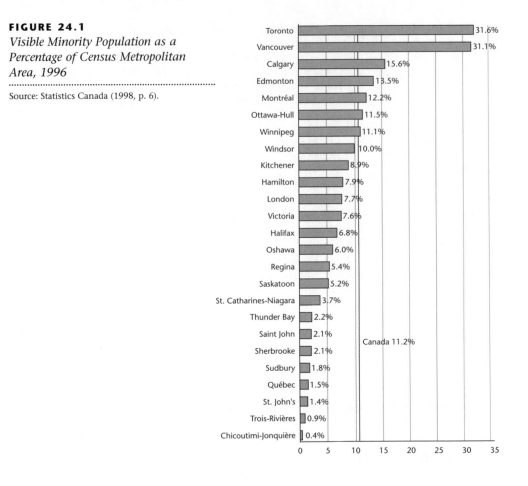

From Table 3, it can be observed that Ontario had 52.6 percent of Canada's visible minority population. This contrasts with the 37 percent of the national population residing in Ontario. Statistics Canada (1998, p. 7) reported that four out of five members of the visible minority population in Ontario lived in Toronto. The specific ethnic groups residing in the Toronto census metropolitan area are shown in Table 5, and those living in the Vancouver census metropolitan area are shown in Table 6.

With the exception of the Arab–West Asians and Japanese groups, the largest number of each of the visible minority groups lived in Toronto. Statistics Canada (1998, p. 7) reported that in 1996, British Columbia had the second-largest visible minority population in Canada after Ontario. The specific ethnic group composition is shown in Table 6; note that Chinese constitute nearly 50 percent of the visible minority population. This reflects the high levels of Asian immigration in recent years.

The third-largest visible minority population resided in Quebec. Table 7 shows the ethnic groups residing in Montreal; they represent 92 percent of the province's visible minority population, although Montreal itself had less than half (47 percent) of the total population of Quebec. In contrast to other census metropolitan areas, Blacks were

TABLE 24.5 *Visible Minority Population in the Toronto Census Metropolitan Area, 1996*

	Number	Percent
Total visible minority population	1 338 090	100.0
Chinese	335 185	25.0
South Asian	329 840	24.7
Black	274 935	20.5
Filipino	99 110	7.4
Arab/West Asian	72 160	5.4
Latin American	61 655	4.6
Southeast Asian	46 510	3.5
Korean	28 555	2.1
Japanese	17 050	1.3
Visible minority, n.i.e.[1]	45 655	3.4
Multiple visible minority[2]	27 435	2.1

1. Includes Pacific Islanders and other visible minority groups.
2. Includes respondents who reported more than one visible minority group.
n.i.e. = not included elsewhere.

Source: Statistics Canada (1998, p. 7).

TABLE 24.6 *Visible Minority Population in the Vancouver Census Metropolitan Area, 1996*

	Number	Percent
Total visible minority population	564 590	100.0
Chinese	279 040	49.4
South Asian	120 140	21.3
Filipino	40 710	7.2
Japanese	21 880	3.9
Southeast Asian	20 370	3.6
Arab/West Asian	18 155	3.2
Korean	17 080	3.0
Black	16 400	2.9
Latin American	13 830	2.4
Visible minority, n.i.e.[1]	6 775	1.2
Multiple visible minority[2]	10 210	1.8

1. Includes Pacific Islanders and other visible minority groups.
2. Includes respondents who reported more than one visible minority group.
n.i.e. = not included elsewhere.

Source: Statistics Canada (1998, p. 7).

TABLE 24.7 *Visible Minority Population in the Montreal Census Metropolitan Area, 1996*

	Number	Percent
Total visible minority population	401 425	100.0
Black	122 320	30.5
Arab/West Asian	73 950	18.4
Latin American	46 700	11.6
South Asian	46 165	11.5
Chinese	46 115	11.5
Southeast Asian	37 600	9.4
Filipino	14 385	3.6
Korean	3 500	0.9
Japanese	2 315	0.6
Visible minority, n.i.e.[1]	3 485	0.9
Multiple visible minority[2]	4 875	1.2

1. Includes Pacific Islanders and other visible minority groups.
2. Includes respondents who reported more than one visible minority group.
n.i.e. = not included elsewhere.

Source: Statistics Canada (1998, p. 8).

the largest visible minority population in Montreal. They were followed by the Arab–West Asian group.

A significant aspect of the data presented above is that more than two thirds (68 percent) of Canada's visible minority population were immigrants in 1996, and only 29 percent were Canadian born (Statistics Canada, 1998, p. 8). Thus, the most culturally sensitive and cost-effective health care policies and services should be developed to reflect the metropolitan ethnic composition rather than the province or region as a homogeneous whole. It is important to understand the cultural variations that exist today and will continue to exist in the foreseeable future due to immigration. With specific reference to health care and the well-being of ethnic minorities, this chapter addresses the following questions: What do we need to know about **ethnic culture** to understand the adjustment to aging by ethnic minorities? What do we need to know about attitudes toward aging for effective health care and social support? And what can be done to bridge the cultural gap in health care provision?

ETHNICITY AND AGING

Until very recently, the study of ethnic variations in the aging experience received very little attention in Canadian gerontological literature. Earlier studies that attempted to examine the relationship between ethnicity and aging failed to differentiate between the various meanings of ethnicity. One of the first attempts to give a conceptual clarification of what was usually meant by ethnicity is provided by Rosenthal (1986, p. 19). From an extensive review of the literature, she derived the following three conceptions of ethnicity: ethnicity as culture, especially immigrant culture; ethnicity as a determinant of social **inequality**; and ethnicity as synonymous with "traditional" ways of thinking and behaving. As indicated by Rosenthal, each of the above conceptions of ethnicity leads to a different model of aging of ethnic families because of different emphases. Therefore, she argues for an integrative approach in which connections or linkages between various conceptions of ethnicity can be drawn together in the study of ethnic families. This approach makes considerable sense, especially in the study of some ethnic families in which generational cohorts can be clearly identified; thus, different conceptions of ethnicity may be applied to each generation.

ETHNICITY AS CULTURE

The first conception of ethnicity as culture, particularly immigrant culture, takes on added significance if we reconsider the demographic changes taking place in Canadian society. It is a safe assumption that there will always be an immigrant or first generation of various ethnic groups in Canada. Therefore, the conception of ethnicity as immigrant culture requires a clear understanding of the various elements or components that constitute a given ethnic culture. Most definitions of culture include shared meanings (Gordon, 1964; Fry, 1980; Marshall, 1980; Hagedorn, 1986). As described by Hagedorn (1986, p. 36), meanings are usually shared through the various components of culture such as beliefs, norms, mores, values, and symbols.

An interesting point to be made in the definition of culture has been noted by Rosenthal (1986, p. 20): while some definitions of culture include both shared meanings and patterns of behaviour, others do not. For our purposes, however, the various components of culture, such as beliefs held, norms, mores, values, and symbols that constitute the shared meanings, are only important in influencing behavioural outcomes. The extent to which each component of culture will influence behaviour will depend on the degree of **institutional completeness**, a term developed by Breton (1964, p. 193) to describe the extent to which various social organizations are developed in an ethnic community. For example, depending on one's age at the time of emigration, beliefs held by the immigrant were most likely influenced by the earlier socialization processes. The traditional norms or rules of behaviour ingrained in the immigrant's mind may or may not be reinforced further, depending on the size, density, ethnic composition, and degree of institutional completeness of one's own ethnic community. Similarly, the enforcement of traditional mores and social interaction patterns based on a system of mutual obligations is also most likely to be influenced by the degree of institutional completeness.

Another important argument that is advanced by Rosenthal (1986, p. 20) is that a further distinction must be made between ethnic culture and immigrant culture. She argues that "if the conception of culture is limited to immigrant culture, then ethnic variability in family life should decrease over successive, new immigrant generations." While we have implied previously that immigrant culture is a "transplanted phenomenon," to use Rosenthal's term, and that its influence on behaviour will depend on the degree of institutional completeness, it must be underscored that ethnic cultural characteristics continue to exist, although in slightly modified forms. Some of these characteristics that impinge on the general health status and well-being of the elderly will be discussed later in further detail.

ETHNICITY AS INEQUALITY

Rosenthal's second conceptualization of ethnicity, as a determinant of inequality, (1986, p. 20) draws attention to the ways in which previous research has tended to equate ethnic group with minority group. While the main focus of current debate has been on the lack of distinction between social class and ethnicity (Holzberg, 1982) as key independent variables to account for variations in aging, there are nevertheless several key factors relevant to this discussion of ethnicity and inequality. Since there are several different forms of inequality in Canadian society, we must be extremely careful in selecting the particular form of inequality that we wish to address, not so much in terms of ethnicity, but with reference to our dependent variable, for example, health status and well-being of our elderly.

The most common form of inequality is economic inequality, the variations in one's income and other material resources. A key to understanding economic inequality with reference to ethnic groups is to understand the long history of exploitation, especially of the immigrant or first-generation ethnic group, and in many instances, that of institutional racism (Bolaria & Li, 1998). The adverse effects of institutional racism prevented equal access to many institutions and further increased economic inequality.

Another aspect of continued economic inequality that was deeply rooted in institutional racism was the eventual relegation of some ethnic groups to ethnic minority status. The concomitant effects of economic inequality, deprivation, lack of political power, minority status, and hence social inequality all contributed to the lack of the individual's sense of identity. The sense of who we are and how we relate to others depends on the position we occupy in the Canadian social structure. Another way of looking at this is to see which groups occupy dominant and subordinate positions in terms of influence and decision making. The numerical size of the group, where it is located, its role in the economy, its level of education, and its occupational position all tend to influence not only the identity of the ethnic group members, but also the attitudes of the dominant groups toward the minority group. Attitudes in turn govern social relationships and the degree to which meaningful social interaction can take place. The development of one's ethnic identity and the strengths of this identity in relation to the extent of external or societal constraints is a complex issue that requires further investigation.

Ethnicity: Traditional versus Modern

The third conception of ethnicity advanced by Rosenthal (1986, p. 20) as being synonymous with "traditional" as opposed to the "modern" ways of thinking and behaving is based on several assumptions and misconceptions. As in the first conceptualization of ethnicity as culture, particularly immigrant culture, there is an implicit assumption that the traditional forms of family life and social discourse are retained and that ethnic culture does not change. Thus, there is a very strong tendency for researchers to overidealize the ethnic family. Cultural change and generational differences in cultural retention have been subordinated or neglected altogether. This tendency to both generalize and idealize the ethnic family in traditional family typology stems partly from the inclination to equate ethnic group with minority group, and this latter labelling implies that the ethnic group is a relative newcomer to Canadian society. This implication is often based on a lack of appreciation of the history of the ethnic group concerned, which in many instances goes back several generations in Canada. By conveniently disregarding the history and social experiences of ethnic groups in Canadian society and by failing to differentiate between various ethnic groups, it is possible to dichotomize ethnicity in terms of the traditional and modern orientations.

While the limitations of conceptualizing ethnicity in terms of the traditional and modern typology may be fairly obvious, the influence of traditional roles and values is still extremely important to our understanding of the variations in aging, health care, and mental health. Furthermore, a simple definition of ethnicity will no longer suffice; we must draw upon several different conceptions of ethnicity to capture the dynamics of the aging process as it relates to the health status and general well-being of the elderly. However, before proceeding to examine the relationship between the various components of ethnicity and the social aspects of aging as they relate to health, a brief overview is provided of what is meant by health, health care, and mental health.

AGING AND HEALTH

The well-being of the individual becomes a primary concern, especially when one approaches retirement age. A crucial variable in assessing individual well-being, regardless of one's age, is health. What is meant by health? Shanas and Maddox (1985, p. 701) note that health in the aged is usually defined in terms of the presence or absence of disease, or in terms of how well the aged are able to function. The determination of one's health in terms of the presence or absence of disease is usually considered to be an objective assessment because it is based on medical examinations and laboratory tests to confirm the medical diagnosis. However, Shanas and Maddox (1985, p. 701) note that a truly objective measure of health is difficult to achieve and that the administration of a laboratory test to measure health varies from time to time. They provide, as an example, physiological measures such as blood pressure readings and glucose levels.

An alternative way to define health among the elderly, suggested by Shanas and Maddox (1985, p. 701), is based on how well the elderly are able to function in terms of day-to-day activities. They argue that the various things that the elderly can do, or think that they can do, are useful indicators not only of their health, but of the kinds of health services they may require. This functional approach to the assessment of one's health is of particular importance, especially with respect to ethnic minorities, because it assumes that "both the individual and the physicians may have relevant and possibly conflicting information about health status" (Shanas & Maddox, 1985, p. 701). Such conflicting information may easily occur as a result of different perspectives or different cultural perceptions of a given health condition. For example, symptoms such as a headache may be attributed to a particular disease by an elderly ethnic person, while this same symptom may be completely disregarded by the doctor as a sign of old age. Such a problem in the interpretation of the symptom may be doubly troublesome because various ethnic groups have different levels of pain threshold (Hayashida, 1984).

Although both the medical and functional models of health evaluation may provide an overall assessment of the elderly person, caution must be exercised if such health assessment are used to decide whether or not the elderly patient should be placed in a given institution. The time and location of the initial health evaluation may be extremely critical in terms of the assessment outcome. Shanas and Maddox (1985, p. 702) report that "different service settings, for example, institutions or mental health clinics attract elderly patients with differing assessment profiles." In this regard, it is of interest to examine a few studies that have compared the functional health evaluation of the elderly in different settings.

One such study that compared the self-assessment of health with objective measures of health is a study by Fillenbaum (1979, p. 45), which compared these two measures by utilizing a sample of older persons who resided in the community and in institutions. The objective measures of health were based on an OARS (Older American Resources and Services) questionnaire, which provided an assessment of the various levels of functioning. Some of the selected items employed by Fillenbaum (1979, p. 46) were as follows:

1. the number of health-related problems reported in the previous month;
2. the number of different types of medication taken during the previous month; and
3. the number of different illnesses and disabilities currently affecting the respondent.

Objective measures were compared against the responses to the following subjective questions:

1. How would you rate your health at the present time — excellent (4), good (3), fair (2), or poor (1)?
2. How concerned do you feel about your health troubles — not concerned (4), mildly concerned (3), moderately concerned (2), or very concerned (1)?
3. How much do your health troubles stand in the way of your doing the things you want to do — not at all (3), a little (some) (2), or a great deal (1)?

For the elderly residents of the community, it was found that the self-assessment or subjective evaluations of health reflected the actual state of health as assessed by the objective measures. This probably derives from the fact that elderly persons who are able to function independently in the community are also in better health and have a higher degree of self-esteem and life satisfaction than those who are institutionalized. Indeed, this is indicated in the Fillenbaum study, which indicated that for the elderly in institutional settings, the self-evaluations of health were not consistent with the objective measures of health. Fillenbaum (1979, p. 50) concludes that "it is possible that the objective measures used — number of health problems, medicines, illness — may not be appropriate where the institutionalized are concerned, or may have a different meaning in institutions."

While these results of the Fillenbaum study may be both time and location specific, the results from an earlier longitudinal study by Maddox and Douglass (1973, p. 87), which compared the medical and self-assessments of the elderly over a 15-year period, indicated persistent positive congruency for the two types of health assessment. Of interest is their finding that whenever there was a difference in the physician's and the self-assessment of health, the tendency was for the individual to overestimate, rather than underestimate, his or her own health. Maddox and Douglass (1973, p. 92) noted the substantial stability over time in both the self-assessments and physician's health ratings; however, the self-assessed health rating showed slightly more stability. Their unexpected finding was "the tendency for self health rating to be a better predictor of future physician's ratings than the reverse." Maddox and Douglass (1973, p. 92) conclude that although their data did not provide a conclusive pattern to confirm or refute the commonly reported findings regarding the two types of health assessment, their data demonstrated that "self-assessment of health is not random but is persistently and positively related to objective evaluations of health status."

An excellent overview of the literature on the health status of the elderly from several different perspectives, as well as from several different levels of function, is provided by Shanas and Maddox (1985, p. 703), who draw attention to the growing acceptance and merging of the medical and functional models of health assessment, especially by those in geriatrics. To underscore this latter observation, they quote the following from the World Health Organization:

> It is now accepted by the medical profession that morbidity should be measured not only in terms of the extent of the pathological process but also in terms of the impairment of the function in the person affected by a pathological condition.... Functional diagnosis is one of the most important elements that has been introduced in geriatrics. In this approach a distinction is made between an impairment and a disability caused by a pathological condition. (1985, p. 703)

The utility in employing both models of health assessment becomes evident when we consider the distinction made between an impairment and a disability. From the World Health Organization report, Shanas and Maddox (1985, p. 703) note that impairment is "a physiological or psychological abnormality that does not interfere with the normal life activities of the individual." They further note that disability is "a condition that results in partial or total limitation of the normal activities of the individual." It is important to keep these distinctions in mind when considering the health status of aged ethnic minorities. Some types of impairment may eventually result in disability.

While the physiological or physical aspects of aging are important considerations in terms of the functional capabilities of the elderly, it is also important to examine the effects of aging on one's mental health. In order to study the psychological aspects of aging, it is necessary to have an understanding of exactly what is meant by mental health. The World Health Organization (WHO) defines mental health as:

> a state in which a person demonstrates his competence to think, feel and (inter)act in ways that demonstrate his ability to deal effectively with the challenges of life. The mentally healthy person is accepting of himself, able to give as well as receive in relationships and, having realistically evaluated his assets and liabilities, has an appropriate level of self-confidence, making decisions based on sound judgement and accepting responsibility for his actions. (D'Arcy, 1987, p. 425)

There are several key components in this definition that merit our attention, particularly with reference to ethnicity and health. One such component concerns the individual's ability to think. As noted earlier in the discussion on ethnicity and traditional ways of thinking, misunderstandings can occur if the traditional cultural backgrounds of ethnic groups are not understood. Social behaviour as outward manifestations of the thinking process may often be interpreted as "bizarre" when it may be considered "normal" in one's own cultural group. Another important component noted in the World Health Organization's definition of mental health is the ability to deal effectively with various day-to-day situations in life. As noted elsewhere by Ujimoto (1987a, p. 131), there is accumulating evidence that coping plays a central role in reducing stress-related illnesses and in promoting good health. The coping strategies utilized by the elderly who have different sociodemographic characteristics are particularly relevant to the study of aging and health because constant psychosocial adjustments must be made throughout one's life. Therefore, an understanding of the cultural context in which these adjustments occur is very important.

The final component of the WHO's definition of mental health to be discussed here concerns the types of social relationships that can realistically occur, given the limited assets and resources of the elderly. The study of social relationships in terms of the cultural context in which they occur requires an understanding of the social exchange mechanisms of the particular group. For example, in the case of the elderly *issei* (immigrant or first-generation Japanese Canadian) and *nisei* (second-generation or Canadian born), it has been observed by Kobata (1979, p. 100), Nishio and Sugiman (1983, p. 19), and Ujimoto (1987a, p. 116) that traditional Japanese values influence generational relationships. Intergenerational relationships based on a system of mutual and moral obligations, as well as on social customs, may be applicable only to certain groups, and at the same time, there may be less importance placed on them by subsequent generations. Social relationships based on concepts such as filial piety and familial dependency in old age are other factors that may intervene in social relationships, depending on the ethnic group.

From our brief discussion of the three components crucial to the definition of mental health provided by the WHO, it can be hypothesized that the negative effects of daily-life situations will have a more severe impact on the mental health of recent immigrants to Canadian society than on subsequent generations. The recent arrivals to Canada are the ones who will experience the greatest changes in mental health because of value conflicts and other adjustment difficulties to their new environment. Support for this observation is provided by Kuo and Tsai (1986, p. 133) who have documented that "an excessive amount of social stress among immigrants — resulting from social isolation, cultural conflicts, poor social integration and assimilation, role changes and identity crises, low socioeconomic status, and racial discrimination — has led to a high prevalence of ill health and psychological impairment among them." The plethora of factors that impinge on one's mental health are extremely difficult to disentangle. As Chappell, Strain, and Blandford (1986, p. 37) have noted, "changes in mental health as we age are less straightforward. Mental health encompasses numerous aspects, including cognitive, psychological and emotional functioning. It is known to be related to both physiological conditions and social environments." At present, the social environment of aged ethnic minority groups is a relatively unexplored area of study.

ETHNICITY, AGING, AND HEALTH

There are several Canadian publications on aging and health, including Simmons-Tropea and Osborn (1987, p. 424), D'Arcy (1987, p. 424), Connidis (1987, p. 451),

Marshall (1987, p. 473), Chappell (1987, p. 489), Schwenger (1987, p. 505), and Shapiro and Roos (1987, p. 520). These studies do not, however, consider the cultural variations in Canadian society and their implications for the future health care provisions of aging ethnic minorities. Since this is an important area of study, it is beginning to receive more attention. As noted by Chappell, Strain, and Blandford (1986, p. 30), "the relevance of subculture (ethnic, minority, and racial) for the elderly population and, in particular, for the provision of health care is an under-researched area in gerontology. Even though conceptually and theoretically it has been argued that subcultural cohesiveness is likely to result in more social support for its elderly members, this has not been established empirically."

One study that examined the relationship between aging and health as interpreted through culture is the study by Rempel and Havens (1986), who identified the differential perceptions of health of older persons based on twelve ethnic groups in Manitoba. The Rempel and Havens data analysis indicates that ethnicity and education affect health perception (1986, p. 18). They note that the Asians and Northern Europeans have the highest positive rating of their own health and the Middle Eastern and Eastern Europeans the poorest health. Because of the small sample size for each of the ethnic groups represented in the sample, caution must be exercised in interpreting the data. The study is nevertheless useful in suggesting several new avenues for future research.

An area of study in health behaviour that is rapidly gaining attention concerns stress and coping behaviour. One study that examines the relevance of ethnicity in relation to stress and coping, particularly with reference to the minority elderly, is the study by Wong and Reker (1985, p. 29). In their comparative study of elderly Chinese and Anglos, Wong and Reker were interested in determining how the Chinese and Anglos differed in their coping behaviour. The three categories of coping strategies that they examined were as follows:

1. Internal strategies are one's own instrumental efforts.
2. External strategies include various forms of dependence on others to reduce stress.
3. Palliative strategies are ways of coping that make one feel better without solving the problem.

Analysis of the Wong and Reker (1985, p. 33) data revealed the presence of several stress-producing health problems. In addition to arthritis or rheumatism, eye problems, and other health disorders, other stressful factors that influenced the well-being of the elderly included in-law problems, loss of a spouse, worries about the family, and economic problems. On the basis of their data analysis, Wong and Reker concluded that the "Chinese did not report having more problems, but they perceived their problems, especially the general problem of aging, as more serious than Anglos." The authors note that in addition to the normal biological constraints of aging, there are other compounding factors associated with the minority status of the Chinese aged, such as a "language barrier, lack of information, and fear of racial discrimination."

In terms of coping strategies, Wong and Reker (1985, p. 33) found that the Chinese relied more on external and palliative strategies than did the Anglos. Although the Chinese relied more on external help, the source of the outside help was primarily family members and relatives. The Chinese also tended to reminisce and seek refuge in the past rather than attempting to solve a given stress situation, except in coping with health-related problems. Wong and Reker suggest that "Chinese elderly not only experience more stress, but possess less adequate coping resources." Since the aged Chinese sample was all first-generation or immigrant Chinese, while the Anglos were either born in Canada or were long-time residents, the results are not too surprising. However, they do point out the concerns, and health care policies should not be based on the common assumption that the aged are homogeneous.

A national study of aging Asian Canadians by Ujimoto et al. (1993, p. 229) reported data on health satisfaction by Chinese, Japanese, and Korean Canadian elderly. These data are shown in Table 8.

Generally, a high proportion of respondents were satisfied with their health. The Chinese respondents appeared to be the most satisfied, followed by the Japanese, but the Japanese elderly tended to have the highest mixed feelings about their health, compared with the Chinese and Korean elderly. Of those respondents who were dissatisfied with their present status, the Koreans were the most dissatisfied.

The relatively high percentage of Korean elderly who are dissatisfied with their own self-assessment of health appears to be in contrast to earlier studies that indicated that Koreans were well adjusted. In a study by Kim and Berry (1986) that assessed the mental health of Korean immigrants who resided in Toronto, it was found that the Koreans scored low on the Cawte Stress Scale and also on the Mann Marginality Scale when compared with other groups undergoing acculturation in Canada. Kim (1987) argued that these findings are consistent with several other studies. He noted that several factors may account for the successful adaptation of Korean immigrants. First, since Koreans were voluntary migrants, their mental health status would be better than that of others, such as refugees. Second, Kim noted that the Koreans have developed better coping skills to deal with stressful life events. A third factor is that the Canadian government selection criteria are such that only the highly educated and those with occupational skills are chosen to immigrate. Finally, the relatively high degree of established Korean community institutions and the policy of multiculturalism both encourage Korean immigrants to retain their cultural identity. How, then, can we account for the relatively high degree of dissatisfaction reported by the Korean elderly?

In terms of the possible contradiction between our data and the previously reported findings, caution must be exercised in interpreting and comparing the data. By using the standard stress and marginality instruments, it is conceivable that fairly consistent

TABLE 24.8 *Health Satisfaction of Aged Asian Canadians, by Ethnic Group (Percent) (n = 774)*

Health Satisfaction	Chinese	Japanese	Korean
Dissatisfied	15.7	10.2	21.9
Mixed	8.1	20.1	10.1
Satisfied	76.2	69.7	68.0
	100.0 (223)	100.0 (373)	100.0 (178)

Source: Based on data in Ujimoto et al. (1993, p. 229).

results can be obtained. However, from the Korean health professionals, a much different picture emerges. Kim's (1987) intensive interviews with medical and social support staff revealed that Koreans tended to internalize their problems, thus making it difficult for health care personnel to assess the real problems.

Kim (1987) reported that Koreans do not want to admit they are sick or to show any signs of weakness and that they tend to somatize their illnesses because of the stigma attached to psychological illnesses. Korean doctors reported to Kim that many of the Korean illnesses are psychological and stem from loneliness, depression, and anxiety. These, in turn, further aggravate the existing somatic problems. These illness characteristics and behaviours are not limited to the Korean elderly, but are very often manifested by other Asian Canadian elderly, particularly the first generation. Indeed, Liu (1986) noted that "somatization is culturally sanctioned in Chinese society, it is an adaptive coping response that allows the person to escape stigmatization." Table 9 indicates that the highest degree of self-reported health dissatisfaction is by the first generation and the most satisfied are the second generation and *kika-nisei.*

Further insight regarding the relatively high percentage of Korean elderly reporting dissatisfaction with their health can be obtained from time-budget data. Koreans as a group are extremely devoted to long hours of hard work. More time devoted to work means less time for family and leisure activities, and eventually, this will have an impact on one's health. Kim (1987) reported that about half of the Korean households in Toronto operate a small business. Many of them are open from 14 to 16 hours per day; a few are open 24 hours per day.

Gender differences in self-reported health satisfaction are shown in Table 10. Note that both Chinese and Korean elderly women report a higher degree of dissatisfaction with their health than do the Japanese elderly women. While Japanese men and women expressed similar degrees of mixed feelings, both Chinese and Korean elderly men reported higher degrees of health satisfaction.

The dissatisfaction expressed by the elderly Korean and Chinese women may stem from the fact that both Chinese and Korean women immigrated to Canada as "captive immigrants," a term used by Kim to describe Korean parents or grandparents who came to Canada because of their sense of responsibility toward their family. In a Korean household that operates a small business or has dual income earners, the baby-sitting role is most often provided by the parents or grandparents. This appears to be the only role given to the elderly Koreans, thus compounding their sense of anxiety and depression. Such a limited role does not provide the elderly with the opportunity to become fully integrated

TABLE 24.9 *Health Satisfaction by Generation (Percent) (n = 774)*

Health Satisfaction	First Generation	Second Generation	Kika-Nisei
Dissatisfied	16.3	8.0	3.6
Mixed	13.8	16.8	14.3
Satisfied	69.9	75.2	82.1
	100.0 (621)	100.0 (125)	100.0 (28)

Source: Bolaria and Dickinson (1996, p. 412).

TABLE 24.10 *Health Satisfaction by Ethnic Group and Gender (Percent) (n = 774)*

Health Satisfaction	Chinese		Japanese		Korean	
	M	**F**	**M**	**F**	**M**	**F**
Dissatisfied	9.2	20.8	11.4	8.6	12.8	29.0
Mixed	6.1	9.6	19.9	20.4	9.0	11.0
Satisfied	84.7	69.6	68.7	71.0	78.2	60.0
	100.9 (98)	100.0 (125)	100.0 (211)	100.0 (162)	100.0 (78)	100.0 (100)

Source: Bolaria and Dickinson (1996, p. 413).

into Canadian society. Kim (1987) noted that Korean elderly are totally dependent on their children or grandchildren and that "they do not have the cognitive and social skills to participate in the larger society and their adjustment is limited to the ethnic pockets."

CULTURAL FACTORS AND AGING

One of the key cultural variables that requires examination is the degree of obligation, as perceived by the children toward their parents. The concept of filial piety has its roots in Confucianism and involves several types of obligations. According to Osako and Liu (1986, p. 130), the child must obey his or her parents, support them in old age, and succeed in his or her career to bring honour to parents and ancestors. What happens then, when children do not fulfill the filial roles as expected by their parents? As a partial response to this question, it is suggested that intergenerational conflict is one possible outcome, and in those situations where conflict appears to be minimized, it is the parents who internalize their feelings and suffer the consequences in silence. This tends to be the case more for elderly immigrants who arrived recently than for those immigrants who have become acculturated to Canadian societal norms.

Table 11 illustrates the variations in response to the question, "What aspect of your cultural heritage do you feel has enabled you to grow old successfully?" It can be seen from Table 11 that 25.5 percent of the Korean elderly indicated filial piety as the key cultural variable for successful aging. This contrasts with the Chinese and Japanese elderly respondents, of whom 12.2 percent and 7.1 percent respectively indicated filial piety. The Korean elderly also indicated that pride in their cultural heritage was important. It should be observed, however, that Koreans are the most recent immigrants to Canada among the Asian elderly studied here. This means that most of the socialization had taken place in Korea, and thus it can be argued that there is a relatively strong attachment to traditional Korean values. The Chinese tend to fall between the Korean and the Japanese responses.

From Table 11, it can be seen that an extremely high percentage of Japanese elderly indicated that discipline and perseverance were important cultural factors that contributed to their successful aging. The Japanese term ***gaman*** was most frequently cited. According to Kobata (1979), *gaman* is literally translated as "self-control." The outward

TABLE 24.11 *Cultural Factors Considered Important for Successful Aging, by Ethnic Group (Percent) (n = 632)*

Cultural Factors	Chinese	Japanese	Korean
Discipline	0.6	18.4	1.9
Patience, tolerance	3.3	20.1	2.5
Filial piety	12.2	7.1	25.5
Group loyalty	1.7	2.7	1.9
Sense of duty	3.3	3.7	3.8
Thriftiness	1.7	1.0	—
Moral obligations	0.6	3.4	8.3
Emphasis on education	17.7	3.1	5.3
Pride in culture, tradition	24.6	8.2	10.8
Honesty, courtesy, manners	—	10.6	0.6
Religious teachings	2.8	2.7	3.8
Traditional family emphasis	1.7	3.7	—
Fatalism	2.2	0.3	—
Deferred gratification	—	1.4	0.6
Martial and traditional arts	—	2.0	—
Modesty	0.6	2.4	—
Self-reliance	6.6	2.4	0.6
Optimism	7.7	—	—
Nothing in particular	12.7	6.8	34.4
	100.0 (181)	100.0 (294)	100.0 (157)

Source: Bolaria and Dickinson (1996, p. 414).

manifestation of this is the tendency to suppress emotions, whether positive or negative. In traditional Japanese society, *gaman* was considered virtuous, and Kobata argues that "the tendency to suffer in silence with a great deal of forbearance provides some insights into the nature of the family as the source of dealing with problems rather than the outside service providers." It is not surprising, therefore, to note in Table 8 that Japanese elderly have the highest percentage of mixed feelings regarding their own evaluation of health. Both dissatisfaction and satisfaction appear to be suppressed, in comparison with the Korean and Chinese elderly.

Associated with the concept of *gaman* or self-control is **enryo**. According to Kobata, "the norm of *enryo* includes, but is not limited to, reserve, reticence, self-effacement, deference, humility, hesitation, and denigration of one's self and possessions." Because of the plethora of terms that can be associated with *enryo*, it is extremely difficult to assess the well-being of the Japanese elderly. As Kobata notes, "the concept had its origins in the cultural norm of knowing one's position in relation to another when interacting with the others perceived as 'inferior' or 'superior' to oneself." Thus, in interactions with authority figures, such as doctors, the Japanese elderly very often do not volunteer their true feelings.

How can researchers differentiate empirically whether it is *gaman* or *enryo* or both that are operating in order to account for the lack of interaction? This is an extremely crucial aspect to understand if health care providers are to provide effective care. Our data revealed that 15.7 percent of the Japanese elderly respondents and 6.1 percent of the Korean respondents indicated that *enryo* or reserve was a negative aspect of their culture that affected their well-being. This is particularly true in health care settings in which those who are able to complain the loudest very often receive the most care.

More and more research on various aspects of aging and health are being reported in the literature. However, future studies will have to examine the influence of ethnicity on aging and health in greater detail. As reported by Ujimoto (1987a, p. 117), difficulties with language and the inability of aged immigrants to express their innermost feelings erect formidable barriers that prevent easy access to the available social, economic, and health support services. Whether it is the lack of health services available in one's own language, or the cultural and psychological barriers that prevent ethnic minorities from using various services, the net result is the underutilization of health services and facilities by ethnic minorities.

IMMIGRANT ADAPTATION AND COPING

Much of the cultural diversity of Canadian society is due to the continuing inflow of new immigrants. The well-being of newcomers to Canada will obviously depend to a considerable extent on the processes of adaptation to Canadian society. Interest in the role of ethnicity in adaptation and health is a relatively recent development (Rosenthal, 1986; Wong & Reker, 1985; Wong & Ujimoto, 1998). Although there is a paucity of data and very little theoretical development in this area, one model that may be useful is the resource-congruence model of adaptation (R-C Model) developed by Wong (1993).

The R-C Model shown in Figure 2 takes into account cultural factors and examines individual resources and deficits as well. The R-C Model is an extension of the cognitive-relational model developed by Lazarus and Folkman (1984), which states that "stress is experienced only when the demands of the environment are appraised by the person as

FIGURE 24.2
Schematic Presentation of the Resource-Congruence Model of Effective Coping

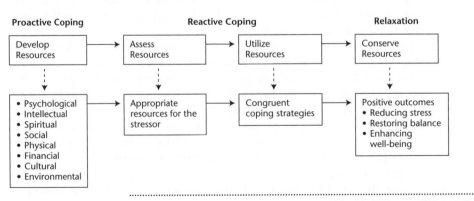

Source: Wong and Ujimoto (1998, p. 174).

exceeding his or her resources" (Wong & Ujimoto, 1998, p. 171). Wong (1993) argues that stressful situations do not always stem from person–environment interactions, but may also originate from a person's inner conflicts. Thus, the cultural component is recognized as an integral aspect of the stress producing processes.

It will be noted in Figure 2 that the key resources necessary for effective coping or adaptation to a new environment are the psychological resources to maintain one's self-confidence and the emotional stability to endure pain and other hardships that create stress. Kobasa (1979) emphasized three personality characteristics that enabled people to cope with stress: the belief that they can control or influence their life events, the ability to feel deeply involved and committed in life activities that minimize feelings of alienation, and the optimistic anticipation of change as a challenge.

Social resources are also important in buffering stress. Such resources include social relationships, practical and moral support, and a system of reciprocal exchanges in both material and nonmaterial goods, based on traditional obligations. Social systems based on mutual obligations are very common in Asian cultures. As Wong and Ujimoto (1998, p. 174) have noted, "problem solving skills include the ability to search for information, to identify difficulties, and to generate appropriate acts to manage life crises." Both social and personal resources are crucial for the maintenance of good emotional health.

The various resources noted in Figure 2 should be considered when examining the relationship between ethnicity, health, and well-being, especially in late life. However, one of the major barriers in our understanding of ethnicity and health is the common assumption that all people follow rather similar life-course trajectories. Generally, it is assumed that most people have received at least a high school education and that the more fortunate ones had access to postsecondary education. From this starting point, it is further assumed that employment was secured until retirement, and that one's retirement years may be either blessed or cursed, depending on how well one has been able to prepare for retirement. Obviously, such a scenario does not apply to many new immigrants to Canadian society. Therefore, it is important to take into account one's life trajectories when examining health and well-being in late life.

LIFE-COURSE TRAJECTORIES

Although gerontological theories and research methodologies appear to treat sample populations as being relatively homogeneous, the demographic diversity of Canada's urban areas has already been noted. One way to obtain a better understanding of this diverse population is to examine some of the key variables that characterize them over time. From this data, it should be possible to draw a picture that reveals one's life-course events as a path or trajectory. Gotlib and Wheaton (1997, p. 2) provide the following definition of a trajectory:

> A trajectory is the stable component of a direction toward a life destination and is characterized by a given probability of occurrence. A trajectory refers to the tendency to persistence in life-course patterns, but not necessarily as defined by an unchanging probability of a life outcome. Rather, a trajectory can be defined by a linearly increasing probability over time, by a nonlinearly decreasing probability, or by other combinations of these probabilities.

An example of a nonlinear **life-course trajectory** is illustrated in Figure 3. The horizontal axis represents the life course and the vertical axis the probability of life destinations or outcomes. Examples of life outcomes are such events as high school graduation, marriage, employment, having children, and job mobility over time.

Gotlib and Wheaton (1997, p. 2) note that "to define or think of a trajectory in the life course, we must have in mind some endpoint to which it is leading — in essence, a criterion that reflects a long-term impact of something that occurred earlier in life." As an example, Wheaton and Gotlib consider the long-term impacts of earlier life stressors on later mental health. Similarly, for the purposes of this chapter, one can consider the well-being of the aged in late life, however defined, as the endpoint of the life-course trajectory.

The life-course trajectory is shaped by various events in one's life from the time of early childhood. Furthermore, the role of membership or assignment to a particular ethnic group will also have some influence on one's access to education, employment, place of residence, status mobility, and privilege. Gordon (1964, p. 27) describes an ethnic group as "any group which is defined or set off by race, religion, or national origin or some combination of these categories...all of these categories have a common social–psychological referent, in that all of them serve to create, through historical circumstances, a sense of peoplehood for groups." One's identification with an ethnic group is usually expressed through one's ethnicity at both the subjective and objective levels.

The subjective approach to ethnicity defines it as a process by which individuals identify themselves as being different from others because of particular ways of thinking and behaving, based on traditional values and roles. The objective approach to ethnicity is based on physical characteristics or attributes. Both the subjective and objective aspects of ethnicity may be cause for cross-cultural misunderstanding and, in some extreme cases, open conflict. Ethnicity can affect one's choice of friendship, social support groups, family life, financial transactions, living conditions, personal health, and life expectations, all of which in turn affect life-course trajectories. In other words, ethnicity can influence the amount or degree of social resources available to the individual.

ETHNICITY, GENDER INEQUALITY, AND HEALTH

In addition to the ethnic differences in Canada's population, another significant factor to consider is gender differences that persist over time and have an effect on health. Gee and Kimball (1987, p. 9) and several other gerontologists have criticized the various gerontological perspectives or theories in the literature, noting that none were based on women's experiences. They argue that while stage theory may be applied to either sex, the various stages experienced over the life-course by women are obviously quite different from those by men. Again, with regard to Figure 3 and the life-course trajectory, we can expect to observe both ethnic and gender differences in the life-course trajectory if those variables are included in the discourse. Figure 4 illustrates how such a trajectory might look. The initial slope of the trajectory is not as steep and will be offset by a series of setbacks, as indicated by a slight "dip" in the curve.

The feminist approach to aging takes into account the everyday experiences of women. As noted earlier, the inequality that exists over the life-course will have an adverse effect on the well-being of older women. Human Resources Development Canada

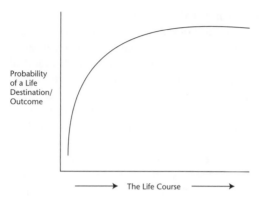

FIGURE 24.3
Nonlinear Life-Course Trajectory

Source: Adapted from Gotlib and Wheaton (1997, p. 3).

(1997, p. 15) reports that "more than half of senior unattached women have low incomes, compared with less than a third of their male counterparts." Inequalities that have persisted over time are most often a result of differences in employment opportunities, job security, and wage–salary differentials.

For women who had elected to stay at home to raise their families, the burdens of household and family responsibilities are further compounded by difficulties that stem from lost employment opportunities and associated benefits. The loss of full-time employment forces more women into nonstandard or contract and part-time work. Such part-time or contract work seldom provides benefits such as medical and dental insurance, paid vacation leave, and retirement pension benefits. Thus, gender inequality has compounding effects on one's late life.

Human Resources Development Canada (1997, p. i) reports that two thirds of non-standard workers in Canada are female and that one third are male. As Evans (1998, p. 47) notes, the "disadvantageous relationship between gender and employment accumulates over a lifetime to produce low pensions." Evans further notes that "women are more likely to be poor than men, and the phrase 'the **feminization of poverty**' was coined to capture this vulnerability."

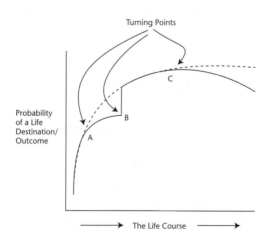

FIGURE 24.4
Life-Course Trajectory Offset by Ethnic and Gender Differences

Source: Adapted from Gotlib and Wheaton (1997, p. 3).

Studies on gender inequality must also recognize the heterogeneity among women. Specifically, there is a paucity of literature on women of colour and health. With reference to caregiving, George (1998, p. 69) observes that "the absence of scholarly interest in how caring affects the lives of women of colour can be attributed to both practical and theoretical issues." At the practical level, George notes that it was necessary to address the more immediate problems of settlement and adaptation needs of immigrant women. Thus, at the theoretical level, theories of immigrant adaptation and ethnic identity received far greater attention than the long-term effects on immigrant health.

From this brief description of gender inequality, it can be seen that the status and position of older women can vary according to the cultural, social, economic, and political contexts in which daily life experiences occur. Because of differences in the adaptation process due to ethnicity, race, social class, and gender, the life-course trajectory will also vary. For ethnic minorities, it remains to be seen if the relative disadvantages of early childhood and adulthood can be compensated for in later life. A good start in the search for an answer to this issue is to secure both quantitative and qualitative health data that can be analyzed according to age, gender, and ethnicity. Research of this magnitude must go beyond the boundary of a single discipline.

CONCLUSION

This chapter noted the relationship between multiculturalism, ethnicity, gender inequality, and their possible influences on health in later life. Studies to date have not attempted to consider all of these variables in a coherent theoretical framework, as suggested by Wong (1993) in his resource-congruence model of adaptation. The original model was developed further (Wong & Ujimoto, 1998, p. 174) to include additional factors such as personal, psychological, and social resources that may considerably affect everyday life.

In order to better understand the impact of cultural diversity and the prevalent attitudes and behaviours from a health care perspective, it was argued that an understanding of what is meant by ethnicity is crucial. While ethnicity can be viewed in several ways, as noted by Rosenthal (1986, p. 19) — such as ethnicity being synonymous with "traditional" ways of thinking and behaving — it was emphasized that the systemic or integrative approach, which draws upon the different conceptions of ethnicity, is necessary to understand the dynamics of life trajectories as they relate to health status and general well-being in late life.

The sharing of emotional and symbolic support by the patient with his or her family is an important consideration, particularly with reference to the East Asian ethnic groups such as Chinese, Korean, and Japanese Canadians. One way in which cultural misunderstandings may be reduced is to enable health care professionals to recognize the nonverbal aspects of communication in health care. This requires a greater sensitivity to the cultural dimensions of the ways in which illnesses are viewed in different ethnic groups. In this regard, an excellent start has been made in Ontario by the Multicultural Health Coalition, which was established in 1983 to "promote culturally relevant and appropriate programs, services and materials." Through a series of seminars, workshops, and publications, health professionals and educators are gradually being made aware of the health beliefs of over 100 ethnocultural groups currently residing in the greater Toronto area.

Significant developments in addressing the concerns of various ethnocultural communities have also taken place in Ontario. In 1988, the Ministry of Health of Ontario (1990, p. 2) established an Advisory Committee on Multicultural Health. The committee's terms of reference were as follows:

1. to advise the minister of health on means of facilitating access to health care by all ethnocultural communities across Canada;
2. to encourage communications with ethnocultural groups across the province to receive and share information on how to achieve more culturally sensitive health-service delivery;
3. to work in co-operation with the Ontario Advisory Council on Multiculturalism and Citizenship on issues of mutual concern as they relate to health and health care in Ontario; and
4. to recommend specific actions or initiatives to the Ministry of Health that might be incorporated into existing and new health programs and services so that they may be more responsive to the needs of ethnocultural groups.

Since its establishment, the Advisory Committee on Multicultural Health has developed a number of important initiatives. It has developed the multicultural health implementation strategy, which provides a set of guidelines to develop culturally sensitive health programs. The advisory committee was instrumental in making available 600 additional nursing home beds to meet the needs of the ethnocultural communities. Other areas in which the advisory committee is currently active are cultural interpretation programs, ethnocultural health information services in Ontario, and the development of a framework to support the access of ethnocultural groups to various health and social services.

This chapter has noted only some of the major issues related to cultural misunderstanding that may affect the well-being and health of ethnic minorities and the provision of health care. Differences in mental health, stress, and coping strategies were discussed with reference to only a few ethnic groups. Further research in this area, particularly with reference to the health and aging of ethnic minorities, is still urgently required.

STUDY QUESTIONS

1. *What are some of the factors that account for the changing demographic profile of Canadian society?*
2. *What are some of the ways in which ethnicity can be defined?*
3. *Why is it important to consider the history of ethnic groups in Canada in order to understand the aging process from a life-span development perspective?*
4. *In what ways do traditional roles and values influence health care behaviour?*
5. *What are the three key components in the definition of mental health?*
6. *Why is it important to consider gender inequalities over the life span in determining health outcomes?*

GLOSSARY

assimilation The process by which one cultural group, usually a minority group, is absorbed by the dominant group.

citizenship A status of rights, privileges, and responsibilities conferred on a person who owes allegiance to a country.

cultural heritage A system of rules, meanings, knowledge, artifacts, and symbols transmitted from generation to generation.

discrimination The behavioural aspects of prejudice that deny equal treatment or equal opportunity to people because of race, gender, ethnicity, religion, or disability.

enryo The norm that includes reserve, reticence, self-effacement, deference, humility, hesitation, and denigration of one's self and possessions.

ethnic culture Various shared meanings, norms, mores, and values that characterize a particular ethnic group. Such shared meanings are often based on a common language, symbols, and traditional customs and practices.

ethnic identity The distinguishing characteristic or personality of an individual that identifies a person as part of a particular ethnic group.

ethnicity Both the subjective sense of belonging to a particular ethnic group based on one's origins or parentage, traditional values, and beliefs, and the objective aspects as manifested in attitudes and behaviour that reflect those values and beliefs.

feminization of poverty The correlation between poverty and women.

gaman Self-control, or the tendency to suppress emotions, whether positive or negative.

health The presence or absence of disease, or an indication of how well one is able to function in day-to-day activities.

ideology A set of beliefs that explains how society operates.

inequality A condition or quality of being unequal or uneven; a condition of disparity in opportunity, power, pay, prestige, and privilege.

institutional completeness The extent to which everyday transactions can be accommodated in one's own language, customs, and other modes of behaviour.

life-course trajectory The stable component of a direction toward a life destination.

multiculturalism The cultural and racial diversity of Canadian society, reflected in different ways: as an empirical fact, as an ideology, as a policy, or as a dynamic process that is continuously changing.

Multiculturalism Act A statute passed by the Canadian government in 1988 to recognize and promote the understanding that multiculturalism reflects the cultural and racial diversity of Canadian society.

prejudice A set of prejudgements derived from generalizations about others, often inaccurate and misleading.

racism An organized set of beliefs based on the supposed superiority of one racial group over another; the notion of superiority is based on a combination of prejudice, discrimination, and the perception of social power and privilege in society.

visible minority population Persons, other than Aboriginal peoples, who are non-Caucasian in race and non-white in colour.

RECOMMENDED READINGS

Chappell, N., Strain, L.A., & Blandford, A.A. (1986). *Aging and health care: A social perspective.* Toronto: Holt, Rinehart & Winston. A study of health status and informal networks of care from family and friends and an assessment of the formal care systems provided by community health and social services. These topics are examined from historical, societal, and demographic perspectives.

Helman, C.G. (1997). *Culture, health and illness: An introduction for health professionals* (3rd ed.). Oxford: Butterworth Heinemann. An introduction to the latest developments in medical anthropology. Topics covered include gender cultures, pain and culture, culture and pharmacology, and the cultural aspects of stress, for a cross-cultural comparative perspective on various problems of health and illness in different parts of the world.

Lee, C.L., & Zane, N.W.S. (1998). *Handbook of Asian American psychology.* Thousand Oaks, CA: Sage. A comprehensive overview of contemporary research on Asian Americans, and to a lesser extent, on Asian Canadians, that provide a critical examination of construct validity, ethnic identity, family socialization, the role of women, the status of children, youth, and the elderly, and Asian American mental health problems.

Markides, K.Y., & Miranda, M.R. (Eds.). (1997). *Minorities, aging, and health.* Thousand Oaks, CA: Sage. A summary of the current knowledge on the health of the minority elderly. Although the subjects addressed are American minorities, the health care needs of minority populations appear to be quite similar to those needs experienced by ethnic minorities in Canada.

Naylor, C.D. (1992). *Canadian health care and the state: A century of evolution.* Montreal & Kingston: McGill–Queen's University Press. A social history of health care that examines "the modern origins, institutional manifestations, and the effects of state involvement in the health care field."

REFERENCES

American Association of Retired Persons. (1989). *Empowerment of minority elderly.* Conference and Roundtable Discussions. Washington: Author.

American Association of Retired Persons. (1990). *Aging and old age in diverse populations.* Research papers presented at Minority Affairs Initiative Empowerment Conferences. Washington: Author.

Bolaria, B.S., & Dickinson, H.D. (Eds.). (1996). *Health, illness, and health care in Canada* (2nd ed.). Toronto: Harcourt Brace.

Bolaria, B.S., & Li, P. (Eds.). (1998). *Racial oppression in Canada.* Toronto: Garamond Press.

Breton, R. (1964). Institutional completeness of ethnic communities and the personal relations of immigrants. *American Journal of Sociology, 70,* 193–205.

Canadian Heritage. (1996). *Strategic evaluation of multicultural programs.* Ottawa: Department of Canadian Heritage, Corporate Review Branch.

Canadian Public Health Association. (1988). *Ethnicity and aging.* Ottawa: Author.

Chappell, N. (1987). Canadian income and heath-care policy: Implications for the elderly. In V.W. Marshall (Ed.), *Aging in Canada* (pp. 489–504). Markham, ON: Fitzhenry & Whiteside.

Chappell, N., Strain, L.A., & Blandford, A.A. (1986). *Aging and health care.* Toronto: Holt, Rinehart & Winston.

City of Toronto, Department of Public Health. (1991). *Health inequalities in the city of Toronto: Summary report.* Toronto: Author.

Connidis, I. (1987). Life in older age: The view from the top. In V.W. Marshall (Ed.), *Aging in Canada* (pp. 451–472). Markham, ON: Fitzhenry & Whiteside.

D'Arcy, C. (1987). Aging and mental health. In V.W. Marshall (Ed.), *Aging in Canada* (pp. 424–450). Markham, ON: Fitzhenry & Whiteside.

Driedger, L., & Chappell, N. (1987). *Aging and ethnicity: Toward an interface.* Toronto: Butterworths.

Economic Council of Canada. (1987). *Aging with limited health resources*. Proceedings of a Colloquium on Health Care. Ottawa: Supply and Services Canada.

Employment and Immigration Canada. (1986). *Immigration statistics*. Ottawa: Minister of Supply and Services.

Evans, P.M. (1998). Gender, poverty, and women's caring. In C. Baines, P. Evans, & S. Neysmith (Eds.), *Women's caring: Feminist perspectives on social welfare* (pp. 47–68). Toronto: Oxford University Press.

Fillenbaum, G.G. (1979). Social context and self-assessments of health among the elderly. *Journal of Health and Social Behavior, 20*(1), 45–51.

Fleras, A., & Elliott, J.L. (1996). *Unequal relations: An introduction to race, ethnic and aboriginal dynamics in Canada* (2nd ed.). Scarborough, ON: Prentice-Hall.

Fry, C.L. (1980). *Aging in culture and society*. Brooklyn: J.F. Bergin.

Gee, E., & Kimball, M. (1987). *Women and aging*. Toronto: Butterworths.

George, U. (1998). Caring and women of colour: Living the intersecting oppressions of race, class, and gender. In C. Baines, P. Evans, & S. Neysmith (Eds.), *Women's caring: Feminist perspectives on social welfare* (pp. 69–83). Toronto: Oxford University Press.

Gordon, M.M. (1964). *Assimilation in American life*. New York: Oxford University Press.

Gotlib, I.H., & Wheaton, B. (1997). *Stress and adversity over the life course: Trajectories and turning points*. Cambridge: Cambridge University Press.

Hagedorn, R. (1986). *Sociology*. Toronto: Holt, Rinehart & Winston.

Hayashida, C. (1984). Extending the medical center to a multi-ethnic aging population with long-term care needs. Paper presented at the 37th Annual Scientific Meeting, Gerontological Society of America, San Antonio.

Health and Welfare Canada. (1988). *After the door has been opened. Report on the Canadian task force on mental health issues affecting immigrants and refugees*. Ottawa: Author.

Holzberg, C.S. (1982). Ethnicity and aging: Anthropological perspectives on more than just the minority elderly. *Gerontologist, 22*, 249–257.

Human Resources Development Canada. (1997). *Gender-based analysis backgrounder*. Ottawa: Women's Bureau, Strategic Policy Branch, Human Resources Development Canada.

It's illegal for Canadians to fight against Canada. (1999, April 28). *The National Post*, p. A10.

Kallen, E. (1982, Spring). Multiculturalism: Ideology, policy, and reality. *Journal of Canadian Studies, 1*, 51–63.

Kendall, P.R.W. (1989a). *The Native Canadian community*. Toronto: City of Toronto, Department of Public Health, Health Promotion and Advocacy Section.

Kendall, P.R.W. (1989b). *The Chinese community in Toronto*. Toronto: City of Toronto, Department of Public Health, Health Promotion and Advocacy Section.

Kendall, P.R.W. (1989c). *The Italian Canadian community*. Toronto: City of Toronto, Department of Public Health, Health Promotion and Advocacy Section.

Kendall, P.R.W. (1989d). *The Greek Canadian community*. Toronto: City of Toronto, Department of Public Health, Health Promotions and Advocacy Section.

Kendall, P.R.W. (1989e). *The Caribbean community in Toronto*. Toronto: City of Toronto, Department of Public Health, Health Promotion and Advocacy Section.

Kendall, P.R.W. (1989f). *The Sri Lankan Tamil community in Toronto*. Toronto: City of Toronto, Department of Public Health, Health Promotion and Advocacy Section.

Kim, U. (1987). Illness behavior patterns of Korean immigrants in Toronto: What are the hidden costs? In K.V. Ujimoto & J. Naidoo (Eds.), *Asian Canadians: Contemporary issues* (pp. 194–219). Guelph: University of Guelph.

Kim, U., & Berry, J. (1986). Predictors of acculturative stress: Korean immigrants in Toronto, Canada. In L.H. Ekstrand (Ed.), *Ethnic minorities and immigrants in cross cultural perspectives* (pp. 159–179). Lisse: Swets & Zeitlinger.

Kobasa, S.C. (1979). Stressful life events, personality and health: An inquiry into hardiness. *Journal of Personality and Social Psychology, 37,* 1–11.

Kobata, F. (1979). The influence of culture on family relations: The Asian American experience. In P. Ragan (Ed.), *Aging parents* (pp. 94–106). Los Angeles: University of Southern California.

Kuo, W.H., & Tsai, Y. (1986, June). Social networking, hardiness and immigrant's mental health. *Journal of Health and Social Behaviour, 27,* 133–149.

Kurzeja, P.L., Koh, T.H., & Liu, W.T. (1986). Ethnic attitudes of Asian American elderly. *Research on Aging, 8*(1), 110–127.

Lam, L. (1982). The Chinese-Canadian families of Toronto in the 1970s. *International Journal of Sociology of the Family, 12,* 11–32.

Lazarus, R.S., & Folkman, S. (1984). Stress, appraisal and coping. New York: Springer.

Liu, W.T. (1986). Health services for Asian elderly. *Research on Aging, 8*(1), 156–175.

Liu, W.T. (1989). Culture and social support. *Research on Aging, 8*(1), 156–175.

Lock, M. (1979). Scars of experience: The art of moxibustion in Japanese medicine and society. *Culture, Medicine and Psychiatry, 2,* 151–175.

Maddox, G.L., & Douglass, E.B. (1973). Self-assessment of health. A longitudinal study of elderly subjects. *Journal of Health and Social Behavior, 14,* 87–93.

Markides, K.S. (1989). *Aging and health: Perspectives on gender, race, ethnicity, and class.* Newbury Park, CA: Sage.

Marshall, V.W. (1980). *Last chapters: A sociology of aging and dying.* Monterey, CA: Brooks/Cole.

Marshall, V.W. (1987). The health of very old people as a concern of their children. In V.W. Marshall (Ed.), *Aging in Canada* (pp. 473–485). Markham, ON: Fitzhenry & Whiteside.

Ministry of Health of Ontario. (1990). *Report of minister of health's advisory committee on multicultural health.* Toronto: Author.

Ministry of Health of Ontario. (1991). *Guidelines to promote cultural/racial sensitivity and awareness in health care programs and services.* Toronto: Author.

Moon, S.G. (1982). Adjustment patterns among Koreans in Canada. In C. Yunshik, T.H. Kwon, & P.J. Donaldson (Eds.), *Society in transition with special reference to Korea.* Seoul: Seoul National University Press.

Nishio, H., & Sugiman, P. (1983). Socialization and cultural duality among aging Japanese Canadians. *Canadian Ethnic Studies, 15*(3), 17–35.

Ontario Advisory Council on Senior Citizens. (1988–89). *Aging together: An exploration of attitudes towards aging in a multicultural Ontario.* Toronto: Author.

Osako, M.M., & Liu, W.T. (1986). Intergenerational relations and the aged among Japanese Americans. *Research on Aging, 8*(1), 128–155.

Refugee airlift to Canada revived. (1999, May 1). *The Globe and Mail,* p. A1.

Rempel, J.D., & Havens, B. (1986). Aged health experiences as interpreted through culture. Paper presented at the Canadian Sociology and Anthropology Association Annual Meeting, Winnipeg.

Rosenthal, C. (1986). Family support in later life. Does ethnicity make a difference? *Gerontologist, 26*(1), 19–24.

Schwenger, C.W. (1987). Formal health care for the elderly in Canada. In V.W. Marshall (Ed.), *Aging in Canada* (pp. 505–519). Markham, ON: Fitzhenry & Whiteside.

Shanas, E., & Maddox, G.L. (1985). Health, health resources, and the utilization of care. In R. Binstock & E. Shanas (Eds.), *Handbook of aging and the social sciences* (pp. 696–726). New York: Van Nostrand Reinhold.

Shapiro, E., & Roos, N.P. (1987). Predictors, patterns and consequences of nursing-home use in one Canadian province. In V.W. Marshall (Ed.), *Aging in Canada* (pp. 520–537). Markham, ON: Fitzhenry & Whiteside.

Simmons-Tropea, D., & Osborn, R. (1987). Disease, survival and death: The health status of Canada's elderly. In V.W. Marshall (Ed.), *Aging in Canada* (pp. 329–423). Markham, ON: Fitzhenry & Whiteside.

Statistics Canada. (1984). *The elderly in Canada*. Ottawa: Minister of Supply and Services Canada.

Statistics Canada. (1998, February 17). *The Daily*. Ottawa: Author (cat. no. 11-001E).

Statistics Canada and Department of the Secretary of State of Canada. (1986). *Report of the Canadian health and disability survey 1983–1984*. Ottawa: Minister of Supply and Services Canada.

Ujimoto, K.V. (1983). Institutional controls and their impact on Japanese Canadian social relations. In P.S. Li & B.S. Bolaria (Eds.), *Racial minorities in multicultural Canada* (pp. 121–147). Toronto: Garamond Press.

Ujimoto, K.V. (1987a). The ethnic dimension of aging in Canada. In V.W. Marshall (Ed.), *Aging in Canada* (pp. 11–137). Markham, ON: Fitzhenry & Whiteside.

Ujimoto, K.V. (1987b). Organizational activities, cultural factors, and well-being of aged Japanese Canadians. In D.E. Gelfand & C. Barresi (Eds.), *Ethnicity and aging: New perspectives* (pp. 186–204). Beverly Hills, CA: Sage.

Ujimoto, K.V. (1990a). Time-budget methodology for research on aging. *Social Indicators, 23,* 381–393.

Ujimoto, K.V. (1990b, March 8). Health care issues for an aging multicultural society: A role for information technology. Paper presented to the House of Commons Standing Committee on Health and Welfare, Social Affairs, Seniors and the Status of Women. In *Minutes of proceedings and evidence of the standing committee on health and welfare, social affairs, seniors and the status of women*, Issue No. 18. Ottawa: House of Commons.

Ujimoto, K.V., Nishio, H., Wong, P.T.P., & Lam, L. (1993). Cultural factors affecting self-assessment of health satisfaction of Asian-Canadian elderly. In R. Masi, K.A. Mcleod, & L. Mensah (Eds.), *Multicultural health and culture: Exploring the relationship* (p. 229). Toronto: Multicultural Health Coalition.

U.S. Department of Health and Human Services. (1985). *Report of the secretary's task force on black and minority health*. Washington: Author.

Verma, R., Chan, K.B., & Lam, L. (1980). The Chinese-Canadian family: A socio-economic profile. In K. Ishwaran (Ed.), *Canadian families: Ethnic variations* (pp. 138–156). Scarborough, ON: McGraw-Hill Ryerson.

Wong, P.T.P. (1993). Effective management of stress: The resource-congruence model. *Stress Medicine, 9,* 51–60.

Wong, P.T.P., & Reker, G.T. (1985). Stress, coping, and well-being in Anglo and Chinese elderly. *Canadian Journal on Aging, 4,* 29–37.

Wong, P.T.P., & Sproule, C.F. (1984). Attributional analysis of locus of control and the Trent Attribution Profile (TAP). In H.M. Lefourt (Ed.), *Research with the locus of control construct*. Vol. 3. *Limitations and extension* (pp. 309–306). New York: Academic Press.

Wong, P.T.P., & Ujimoto, K.V. (1998). The elderly: Their stress, coping, and mental health. In L.C. Lee & N.W.S. Zane (Eds.), *Handbook of Asian American psychology* (pp. 165–209). Thousand Oaks, CA: Sage.

Yu, E.S.H. (1986). Health of the Chinese elderly in America. *Research on Aging, 8*(1), 84–109.

PART 8

Sociology, Health, Illness, and the Health Care System

25

Sociology, Health, Illness, and the Health Care System: Current Issues and Future Prospects

HARLEY D. DICKINSON AND B. SINGH BOLARIA University of Saskatchewan

INTRODUCTION

When it was established after World War II, medicare had the goal of increasing overall population health status. This was to be accomplished by eliminating financial barriers to necessary medical care and hospital services. Access to these benefits is still considered important for achieving increased population health status. It is, however, no longer seen as sufficient. The determinants of health–health promotion policy framework currently in place understands population health status to be a result of the interaction of numerous factors, including, but not limited to, access to necessary medical and hospital care (Evans, Barer, & Marmor, 1994; Hamilton & Bhatti, 1996).

The determinants of health–health promotion policy framework was first articulated in a federal government discussion paper released in 1974 (Epp, 1986; Lalonde, 1974). In that document, four broad determinants of population health status were identified: human genetics, lifestyles, the social and physical environments, and the health care system. These factors interact to determine population health status. Intervention in these areas, in the form of health promotion initiatives, is considered the means of achieving the goal of health for all. This chapter identifies a number of issues and areas for sociological research related to the determinants of health framework.

HUMAN GENETICS

The human genome project is a development that will have profound medical and social consequences. Its general objective is to identify and locate, or map, all human genes and their functions. This project began in the United States in the late 1980s and was originally sponsored by the National Institutes of Health and the Department of Energy (Department of Energy & National Institutes of Health, 1996; Kevles, 1993). Since then, it has become a massive international collaborative effort, involving many nations, including Canada. The first genes to be mapped were those associated with various abnormalities. It was recently announced, however, that the initial mapping is complete, ahead of schedule.

The application of this knowledge, in the form of biotechnology, will alter our understanding of the potentials and limitations of human existence, and as a result will alter many of our social institutions. The most critical debate has focused on agricultural biotechnology and its implications for environmental and food health and safety issues (see Chapter 16 in this book; Ammann, 1999; Buttel, 1998; Ho, 1998; Krimsky & Wrubel, 1996). Concerns about the social, legal, and ethical consequences of human experimentation with genetic therapies, human cloning, xenotransplantation, and the creation of designer babies, for example, also have been raised (Bullard, 1987; Came, 1999; Chisolm, 1999; Geddes, 1999; Robinson, 1994; Sonneborn, 1973).

These possibilities have the aura of science fiction. A more immediate concern, however, is the likely impact of medical biotechnology on the nature, organization, and costs of health care. Most research and development in biotechnology is driven by private, for-profit corporations. Massive investments have been made, with the expectation of similar returns. Most biotechnological innovation results in patentable therapeutic products or processes that offer significant profits through their extensive use in hospital-based systems of medical care (Yoxen, 1981, p. 110).

Biotechnology is likely to have significant consequences not only for health, but also for the patterns and costs of health care services. It is not certain what consequences await the publicly funded Canadian health care system, which is under pressure from the for-profit medical biotechnology industry. It is clear, however, that these therapeutic technologies will be accompanied by demands for their use. Someone will have to pay for them. Whether a publicly funded health care system like Canada's can pay, or will pay, is an open question. If it is decided that medicare should pay for these new biotechnological therapies, they could become a kind of black hole, absorbing ever-growing proportions of the gross national product.

In the current political and fiscal climate, this scenario seems unlikely. More likely is the situation in which some of the new biotechnologies will be covered by medicare and some will not. This opens the door to an extension of the two-tiered health care system and all its accompanying inequities, which medicare was intended to eliminate in the first place.

Some elements of this dilemma are characteristic of the new reproductive technologies. The new reproductive technologies are concerned with the creation of human embryos. As such, they can be understood, at least in part, as a component of medical biotechnology. As Burstyn (1993, p. 64) states, the new reproductive techniques are "handmaids to the genetic technologies, for without them the human embryo would not be open to judgment and available for genetic manipulation."

Many people question whether childlessness is a medical condition and whether the new reproductive technologies are medically necessary treatments. If one takes a negative position on these issues, it follows that the substantial costs associated with these technologies should not be covered by medicare. If this is the case, then only those who can afford to purchase these services will have access to them. If one answers in the affirmative to the questions "Are these necessary medical services?" and "Should medicare pay?" then one has an equitable but increasingly expensive health care system.

Despite the real promise of these two bodies of knowledge and associated technologies — coming together to bring babies to the childless and to prevent unnecessary suffering by identifying genetic defects and preventing them through therapeutic abortion or other techniques — many see a darker horizon on this new frontier of human knowledge. Specifically, concerns have been expressed about the possibility that the new reproductive technologies and the new genetics might give rise to a new eugenics movement.

The original eugenics movement developed in the nineteenth century in an effort to apply the principles of plant and animal breeding to human populations. Eugenicists thought that various aspects of modern social life and government policy were contributing to the social and racial degeneration of society by encouraging the breeding of socially undesirable elements and discouraging breeding among those with socially desirable characteristics. Eugenicists proposed to correct this "problem," either by encouraging those with desirable qualities — usually the white, middle, and upper classes — to bear more children, or by discouraging or preventing those who were deemed to be dysgenic from bearing or raising children. These two interrelated objectives are known as positive and negative eugenics respectively.

Negative eugenics was predominant. In its most brutal manifestation, it took the form of genocide and other attempts to exterminate "problem" populations in Nazi Germany. Although the Nazi atrocities in the name of eugenics and science are often explained away as a historical aberration that could not happen again, eugenics policies involving compulsory sterilization, especially of those considered mentally ill and "feebleminded," were enacted throughout much of the Western world, including some Canadian provinces (McLaren, 1990). It is increasingly being argued that although the brutality of the Nazi application of genetic and medical science to its subject populations was exceptional in its magnitude, it was not absolutely aberrant, but rather an extreme example of the application of normal science. If this is so, critics warn, it could happen again.

In the past, programs of positive eugenics were much more limited than were those of negative eugenics, largely due to lack of knowledge and technical ability. The promise, and threat, of the new genetics in combination with the new reproductive technologies is that it is now possible to selectively produce embryos through such technologies as pharmaceutically induced ovulation, sperm and egg manipulation, surgical insemination, Petri dish insemination, embryo transfer, embryo banking, and so on (Burstyn, 1993, p. 64). Critics warn that these new technologies have the potential of enabling a new eugenics movement, one that could be more effective in achieving its goals of social development and racial purity than was previously possible.

Even if concerns about the possibility of a new eugenics movement are dismissed, a host of ethical, social, and legal issues arise regarding the potential of these new technologies to enable human reproduction in ways that were not possible before. The institutions of society have not been developed and are not equipped to solve the problems that this new knowledge and these new technologies may generate. The magnitude of the potential consequences of the further development and application of this knowledge resulted in the establishment in Canada of a Royal Commission on the New Reproductive Technologies. The commission was surrounded by conflict and controversy from its inception, and the release of its report intensified the debate. It is clear that this area requires further study.

LIFESTYLES

Lifestyles are also considered important factors in increasing or decreasing health risks and health status. The decisions that individuals make concerning diet, exercise, sexual behaviour, drinking habits, tobacco use, and so on are important factors affecting a person's health. Considerable resources have been directed toward trying to persuade people to maximize healthy choices and minimize unhealthy ones. The public has been exposed to a barrage of information on safe sex, drinking and driving, smoking, exercise and diet, and a multitude of other behaviours thought to have health consequences. At the same time, it has been bombarded by messages from commercial interests intent on persuading it to consume a plethora of dangerous and potentially health- and environment-destroying products such as automobiles, high-fat fast foods, alcohol, and tobacco, to name just a few. It has been suggested that these economically motivated "manufacturers of illness" are largely responsible for many of the unhealthy habits that are the object of recent health promotion campaigns (McKinlay, 1981).

Although the messages of the purveyors of healthy lifestyles are self-evidently true, it has been pointed out that such an approach to the issues of health and illness tends to individualize the problems and the solutions. Many people are unable to choose healthy lifestyles because of the social, economic, and political structures that constrain their opportunities and shape their conditions of existence. Thus, entreaties to choose healthy lifestyles seem to fall on deaf ears. This often results in the assessment of people who persist in unhealthy lifestyles as stupid or self-destructive or both. Such people are considered to be personally responsible for their own poor health.

Victim-blaming of this sort is often used to justify rationing access to publicly financed health care services. If individuals insist on living unhealthy lives, goes the argument, they should not expect taxpayers to pick up the bill for their health care services. In the context of vigorous efforts to reduce health care costs, attacks like these on the principle of universality may gain increased support. Research into public attitudes concerning such issues is both timely and important.

SOCIAL AND PHYSICAL ENVIRONMENTS

The issue of lifestyles, as is suggested above, must be placed in the context of both the social and the physical environments within which individuals live. This is one of the primary insights of sociology. An important — arguably the most important — aspect of the social environment is the economy, including the nature and organization of work (see Chapter 17 of this book).

On the other hand, in these times of globalization and capital restructuring, the health effects of unemployment and underemployment are increasingly important. Also relevant to the economic component of the social environment is the manufacture and marketing of various products. This point is clearly made in relation to revelations about the distribution and use of blood tainted with the HIV virus.

The relationship between the social environment, the physical environment, and health also promises to be an area of increasing importance. Current economic and military practices have the potential to result in ecological disasters of unprecedented proportions. The disposal of nuclear wastes, clear-cut logging, oil spills, and other forms of environmental pollution may have profound consequences for human morbidity and mortality patterns. Indeed, some people predict that unless there are major changes to the ways we are using and abusing the physical environment, it may become incapable of sustaining life.

HEALTH CARE SYSTEM

Another area of research for medical sociologists, and an area of social life that is seen as directly affecting health, is the nature and organization of the health care system itself. Although many health care professionals are at least partly motivated by altruism and a genuine desire to help others, they are also at least partly motivated by professional self-interest, including control over the terms and conditions of their work and the form and level of their remuneration.

It is becoming increasingly clear that a potential conflict of interest exists between health care service providers and consumers. A growing patient–consumer rights movement that is willing and able to develop effective advocacy organizations and to use various legal channels to pursue its interests is resulting in substantial changes in relations between health care providers and consumers. Increased numbers of malpractice suits and widespread concerns about sexual misconduct are indicative of some of these changes.

There is also an obvious tension between health care providers and payers over the costs of health care services. In Canada, the main payer is the government. Recently, though, an increasing proportion of health care costs are being paid for privately, either through private insurance or directly out-of-pocket. To put it simply, those who pay are interested in controlling costs, whereas those who provide services, particularly physicians on a fee-for-service remuneration system, are not.

This tension has contributed to the massive restructuring of the health care system that began in the 1980s and continued through the 1990s into the present. The determinants of health–health promotion policy framework that is being developed and applied across the country has the objective of reducing and reallocating health care resources. What this will ultimately mean for the health care system is unknown, although there is mounting pressure from several sources for the abandonment of the principles of universality and comprehensiveness.

Moves in that direction have already been taken in a number of provinces, in the form of caps or restrictions placed on the number and types of health care services that individuals can receive under medicare. This, of course, is a form of rationing of health care services. Those who have employer-provided health care insurance, or who can afford private insurance, or who can pay directly for health care services, will exercise those advantages. Those most negatively affected by the erosion of universality are the poor. As we have seen, poverty and ill health go hand in hand. Consequently, rationing health care services in order to cut costs has the effect of reducing access to necessary services for those with the greatest need.

Moves to ration health care services as a way of managing the fiscal crisis of the state are also related to various efforts to privatize health care provision. Proponents of privatization were very vocal in the 1980s and 1990s, claiming that government-operated and -financed services of any kind were inherently inefficient, compared with those owned and operated on a private, for-profit basis. There is no evidence that this is true. In fact, the evidence with regard to health care appears to show the opposite.

This has not muted the call for privatization. Recently, particularly in Alberta and Ontario, privatization has reached the top of the political agenda (Health Edition on Line, 2001). However, it is still the case that for many Canadians, medicare and the principles upon which it is founded are considered to be definitive of the Canadian identity — something that distinguishes Canadians from, and makes them better than, Americans.

Given the still high levels of emotional and political support for medicare, most proposals for change are presented as improvements to existing arrangements or reforms necessitated by fiscal exigencies. Such is the case in Alberta. Despite the stated intentions, however, the consequences are the same: the erosion of the health care system as we know it. Whether the new system that emerges in the wake of the reform efforts now underway will be better or worse than what we have remains to be seen. Research into these issues is much needed.

Sociologists should also undertake research into the relationships between the health care system, current health care reform, and the broader society. Canadians have been told so often, by so many people, that government deficits and mounting debts have created a situation that requires drastic cost cutting and sacrifice by all, that many people accept these as self-evident truths. It is worthwhile to critically examine these "truths."

The fact that over $72 billion per year is spent on health care, although staggering, is not proof in itself that *too much* is being spent, or that costs are out of control. There is no way that one can determine if too much or too little is being spent simply by looking at absolute dollar amounts. Those decisions are moral and political in nature; they are not purely technical or accounting decisions. Thus, to say that too much is being spent on health care means that one thinks those funds should be spent on something else, and often by someone else. Proponents of tax cuts make the argument that governments should leave as much money as possible in the hands of individuals so that they have the freedom of choice to purchase the goods and services, including health care services, that they need or want in the marketplace. Although some people will agree for ideological reasons that too much is being spent on health care, often the principal proponents of an idea have real political or economic interests at stake.

Concerning the idea that too much is being spent on health care and that privatization will solve the fiscal crisis, it is apparent that many political and economic advantages exist for the main advocates of that policy: private insurance companies, the pharmaceutical industry, other health sector businesses, pro-business political parties and governments, and many service providers. Similarly, it is apparent that there are few tangible benefits for most health care consumers, other than the rather vague promise of increased freedom of choice.

Whether defenders of medicare, and the principles upon which it stands, can successfully organize and mobilize to protect and extend the availability of effective and appropriate health care services remains to be seen. Success in this regard depends in part on the availability of information and knowledge. Under the current system, health care providers have privileged access if not an outright monopoly of information. For some time, this knowledge imbalance has been under attack from health care consumers and third-party health care purchasers, including both governments and private insurance companies.

The new information technologies have the potential to alter the flow of information and hence the balance of power in the health care system. Whether these changes will result in a more democratic health care system, in which more people have more information, or an increasingly bureaucratized health care system, in which private- or public-sector system managers control service providers and consumers, is still an open question. The outcome will be determined, in part, by organizational and decision making structures and procedures. Currently, subprovincial, regional governance, and service delivery systems are being developed across the country.

The regionalization of health care policy making and service delivery is the most significant structural change in health care since the introduction of medicare. Regionalization is a highly complex and contradictory process. The implications of regionalization for medicare and the achievement of improved population health status require research and evaluation.

CONCLUSION

As has been seen throughout this book, and as we have tried to summarize in this short chapter, sociology can make contributions to an understanding of the nature and social distribution of health, illness, injury, and death, as well as to an understanding of both the internal and external forces shaping the health care system. Although a number of specific objectives underpin any individual piece of research, the ultimate goal is to contribute to the improvement of the health status of the population and to improve the efficiency and effectiveness of our health care system.

Achieving these goals often entails challenging powerful vested interests and established patterns of thinking and practice. This fact places limits on the pace and extent of reform efforts. Just as socioeconomic structures are implicated in morbidity and mortality patterns and are powerful influences on the form and content of the health care system, so too those same forces influence the extent and effectiveness of reform. It is now apparent, for example, that inequalities of health status cannot be eliminated simply by removing barriers to access to health care services. So long as class, gender, race, and other structural forms of inequality persist, there will continue to be inequalities in health status. It is in this sense that health and illness are political, economic, moral, and cultural phenomena as well as medical problems. By theorizing and analyzing the linkages between the broad determinants of health, including the biological base of the human species, lifestyles, the social and physical environments, and the health care system itself, medical sociologists can make important contributions to health, health care, and sociology.

REFERENCES

Ammann, K. (1999). Environmental benefits of biotechnology: Viewpoints on biotechnology. Center for International Development, Harvard University, Boston, August 15.

Bullard, L. (1987). Killing us softly: Towards a feminist analysis of genetic engineering. In P. Spallone & D.L. Steinberg (Eds.), *Made to order: The myth of reproductive and genetic progress*. Toronto: Pergamon Press.

Burstyn, V. (1993, June). Breeding discontent. *Saturday Night,* 15–17 and 62–67.

Buttel, F. (1998). Assessing the environmental implications of agricultural biotechnologies: A sociological perspective. *National Agricultural Biotechnology Council (NABC), Report, 10,* 45–57.

Came, B. (1999, December 6). Under the microscope. *Maclean's,* p. 62.

Chisolm, P. (1999, December 6). Under the microscope. *Maclean's,* pp. 58–60.

Department of Energy & National Institutes of Health. (1996). *Understanding our genetic inheritance. The US human genome project: The first five years, 1991–1995.* Washington, DC: Author.

Epp, J. (1986). *Achieving health for all: A framework for health promotion.* Ottawa: Health Canada.

Evans, R.G., Barer, M.L., & Marmor, T.R. (Eds.). (1994). *Why are some people healthy and others not? The determinants of health of populations.* New York: Aldine deGruyter.

Geddes, J. (1999, December 6). Under the microscope. *Maclean's,* pp. 53–56.

Grace, E.S. (1997). *Biotechnology unzipped: Promises and reality.* Toronto: Trifolium Books.

Hamilton, N., & Bhatti, T. (1996). *Population health promotion: An integrated model of population health and health promotion.* Ottawa: Health Canada.

Health Edition on Line. (2001, February 23). Miscellany. http://www.healthedition.com/home.cfm.

Ho, M.-W. (1998). *Genetic engineering — Dream or nightmare? The brave new world of bad science and big business.* Bath, UK: Gateway Books.

Kevles, D.J. (1993, Spring). Is the past prologue? Eugenics and the human genome project. *Contention, 2*(3), 21–37.

Krimsky, S., & Wrubel, R. (1996). *Agricultural biotechnology and the environment.* Chicago: University of Illinois Press.

Lalonde, M. (1974). *A new perspective on the health of Canadians: A working document.* Ottawa: Health Canada.

McKinlay, J.B. (1981). A case for refocusing upstream: The political economy of illness. In P. Conrad & R. Kerns (Eds.), *The sociology of health and illness: Critical perspectives* (pp. 613–633). New York: St. Martin's Press.

McLaren, A. (1990). *Our own master race: Eugenics in Canada, 1885–1945.* Toronto: McClelland & Stewart.

Robinson, L. (1994). The ethics of gene research. *Canadian Medical Association Journal, 150*(5), 721–727.

Sonneborn, T. (1973). Ethical issues arising from the possible uses of genetic knowledge. In B. Hilton, D. Callahan, M. Harns, P. Condliffe, & B. Berkley (Eds.), *Ethical issues in human genetics* (pp. 1–6). New York: Plenum Press.

Yoxen, E. (1981). Life as a productive force: Capitalizing the science and technology of molecular biology. In L. Levidow & B. Young (Eds.), *Science, technology and the labour process: Marxist studies.* Vol. 1 (pp. 66-122). London: CSE Books.

INDEX

Note: A page number appearing in bold type refers to a glossary definition of the term.